Organic Reactions

Organic Reactions

VOLUME III

JOHN WILEY & SONS, INC.

New York London Sydney

ELEVENTH PRINTING, AUGUST, 1967

PRINTED IN THE UNITED STATES OF AMERICA

PREFACE TO THE SERIES

In the course of nearly every program of research in organic chemistry the investigator finds it necessary to use several of the better-known synthetic reactions. To discover the optimum conditions for the application of even the most familiar one to a compound not previously subjected to the reaction often requires an extensive search of the literature; even then a series of experiments may be necessary. When the results of the investigation are published, the synthesis, which may have required months of work, is usually described without comment. The background of knowledge and experience gained in the literature search and experimentation is thus lost to those who subsequently have occasion to apply the general method. The student of preparative organic chemistry faces similar difficulties. The textbooks and laboratory manuals furnish numerous examples of the application of various syntheses, but only rarely do they convey an accurate conception of the scope and usefulness of the processes.

For many years American organic chemists have discussed these problems. The plan of compiling critical discussions of the more important reactions thus was evolved. The volumes of *Organic Reactions* are collections of about twelve chapters, each devoted to a single reaction, or a definite phase of a reaction, of wide applicability. The authors have had experience with the processes surveyed. The subjects are presented from the preparative viewpoint, and particular attention is given to limitations, interfering influences, effects of structure, and the selection of experimental techniques. Each chapter includes several detailed procedures illustrating the significant modifications of the method. Most of these procedures have been found satisfactory by the author or one of the editors, but unlike those in *Organic Syntheses* they have not been subjected to careful testing in two or more laboratories. When all known examples of the reaction are not mentioned in the text, tables are given to list compounds which have been prepared by or subjected to the reaction. Every effort has been made to include in the tables all such compounds and references; however, because of the very nature of the reactions discussed and their frequent use as one of the several steps of syntheses in which not all of the intermediates have been isolated, some instances may well have been missed.

Nevertheless, the investigator will be able to use the tables and their accompanying bibliographies in place of most or all of the literature search so often required.

Because of the systematic arrangement of the material in the chapters and the entries in the tables, users of the books will be able to find information desired by reference to the table of contents of the appropriate chapter. In the interest of economy the entries in the indices have been kept to a minimum, and, in particular, the compounds listed in the tables are not repeated in the indices.

The success of this publication, which will appear periodically in volumes of about twelve chapters, depends upon the cooperation of organic chemists and their willingness to devote time and effort to the preparation of the chapters. They have manifested their interest already by the almost unanimous acceptance of invitations to contribute to the work. The editors will welcome their continued interest and their suggestions for improvements in *Organic Reactions*.

CONTENTS

SUBJECTS OF PREVIOUS VOLUMES

CHAPTER 1

THE ALKYLATION OF AROMATIC COMPOUNDS BY THE FRIEDEL-CRAFTS METHOD

CHARLES C. PRICE

University of Illinois

CONTENTS

INTRODUCTION

Since the discovery by Friedel and Crafts [1] that aluminum chloride catalyzes the condensation of alkyl and acyl halides with various aromatic compounds to effect substitution of an alkyl or acyl group for one or more hydrogen atoms of the aromatic compound, this reaction has been greatly extended in scope with respect to alkylating or acylating agents and catalysts. The use of aluminum chloride as a catalyst for such condensations has been considered in detail by Thomas,[2] and certain aspects of the reaction have been treated in an earlier volume of this series.[3] The present discussion is limited to the direct introduction of alkyl, cycloalkyl, or aralkyl residues containing no functional groups into various aromatic compounds under the influence of such catalysts as $AlCl_3$, $FeCl_3$, $SbCl_5$, BF_3, $ZnCl_2$, $TiCl_4$, HF, H_2SO_4, H_3PO_4, and P_2O_5. The alkylating agents include olefins, highly strained cycloparaffins, polyalkylbenzenes, alkyl halides, alcohols, ethers, and esters of organic and inorganic acids. The aromatic compound may be a hydrocarbon, an aryl chloride or bromide, a mono- or poly-hydric phenol or its ether, an aromatic amine, an aldehyde, an acid, a quinone, or certain derivatives of heterocyclic aromatic compounds such as furfural or thiophene.

The Friedel-Crafts process is frequently the most useful method for the introduction of an alkyl group. The reaction is capable of many practical applications, and a large number of patents have appeared on the preparation of alkyl derivatives of various aromatic compounds such as xylene,[4] naphthalene, and phenols. Patents have covered the utilization of such alkylating agents as the olefins derived from cracking, the mixtures prepared by chlorination of petroleum fractions,[5] and various naturally occurring waxy esters.[6] The most important application is the synthesis of ethylbenzene from ethylene and benzene.

SCOPE AND LIMITATIONS

Activity of Catalysts. Very little work has been done on the direct comparison of the relative efficacy of the catalysts used in the Friedel-

[1] Friedel and Crafts, *Compt. rend.*, **84**, 1392, 1450 (1877).

[2] Thomas, "Anhydrous Aluminum Chloride in Organic Chemistry," American Chemical Society Monograph 87, Reinhold Publishing Corp., New York, N. Y., 1941.

[3] (*a*) Blatt, *Organic Reactions*, I, "The Fries Rearrangement"; (*b*) Fuson, *ibid.*, "Chloromethylation of Aromatic Compounds."

[4] Akt.-Ges. f. Anilinf., Ger. pat., 184,230 [*Chem. Zentr.*, II, 366 (1907)].

[5] Thomas (to Sharples Solvents Corp.), U. S. pat., 2,072,061 [*C. A.*, **31,** 2613 (1937)]. Wiggins, Hunter, and Nash. *J. Inst. Petroleum*, **26,** 129 (1940).

[6] Robinson (to National Aniline and Chemical Co.), U. S. pat., 2,061,593 [*C. A.*, **31,** 785 (1937)].

Crafts reaction. The catalytic activity for various metal chlorides in the condensation of toluene with acetyl chloride [7] is in the order $AlCl_3 > SbCl_5 > FeCl_3 > TeCl_2 > SnCl_4 > TiCl_4 > TeCl_4 > BiCl_3 > ZnCl_2$. The effect of catalysts for the Friedel-Crafts reaction in promoting the racemization of α-phenylethyl chloride,[8] which should parallel their effect in catalyzing alkylation,[9] is in the order $SbCl_5 > SnCl_4 > TiCl_4 > BCl_3 > ZnCl_2 > HgCl_2$.

$$\begin{matrix} C_6H_5 \\ \quad\diagdown \\ \qquad CHCl \\ \quad\diagup \\ CH_3 \end{matrix} + MCl_x \rightleftarrows \begin{matrix} C_6H_5 \\ \quad\diagdown \\ \qquad CH^+[MCl_{x+1}]^- \\ \quad\diagup \\ CH_3 \end{matrix}$$

Hydrogen chloride, lithium chloride, and tetramethylammonium chloride are ineffective as catalysts for both racemization and alkylation.

No direct comparison of the acidic catalysts has been made, although the order appears to be $HF > H_2SO_4 > P_2O_5 > H_3PO_4$. In general, a direct comparison of the metal halides with the acids is limited by the fact that the activity varies to some extent with the alkylating agent selected. Sulfuric and phosphoric acids are usually more effective for olefins or alcohols than for alkyl halides. For example, allyl chloride and allyl alcohol condense principally at the double bond in the presence of sulfuric acid,[10] whereas in the presence of boron fluoride,[11] ferric chloride,[12] or zinc chloride [12] these substances react chiefly to form the allyl derivative. Aluminum chloride causes condensation at both functional groups.[12]

It is of interest to note that in several instances the effect of a catalyst such as aluminum chloride or boron fluoride is enhanced by the presence of an acidic "assistant." Alkylation by olefins with aluminum chloride as a catalyst is favored by the presence of anhydrous hydrogen chloride,[13] and the condensation of primary alcohols with benzene using boron fluoride is possible only with the aid of an assistant such as phosphoric anhydride, benzenesulfonic acid, or sulfuric acid.[14] It has been found also that chlorides of tin, silicon, or titanium increase the catalytic activity of aluminum chloride, whereas ferric chloride decreases the

[7] Dermer, Wilson, Johnson, and Dermer, *J. Am. Chem. Soc.*, **63,** 2881 (1941).

[8] Bodendorf and Bohme, *Ann.*, **516,** 1 (1935).

[9] Price, *Chem. Revs.*, **29,** 37 (1941).

[10] Truffault, *Compt. rend.*, **202,** 1286 (1936); see also Niederl, Smith, and McGreal, *J. Am. Chem. Soc.*, **53,** 3390 (1931); Smith and Niederl, *ibid.*, **55,** 4151 (1933).

[11] McKenna and Sowa, *J. Am. Chem. Soc.*, **59,** 470 (1937).

[12] Ninetzescu and Isacescu, *Ber.*, **66,** 1100 (1933).

[13] Berry and Reid, *J. Am. Chem. Soc.*, **49,** 3142 (1927).

[14] Toussaint and Hennion, *J. Am. Chem. Soc.*, **62,** 1145 (1940).

activity.[15] Limited amounts of water frequently increase the effectiveness of boron fluoride or hydrogen fluoride.

Alkylating Agents. The ease of alkylation by means of a reagent RX is dependent not only on the nature of X but also on the structure of the group R. Structural factors in the alkyl group promoting the polarization of RX in the sense R^+X^- facilitate alkylation.[16]

$$RX + Cat \rightarrow R^+(X \cdot Cat)^-$$

$$R^+ + C_6H_6 \rightarrow \left[C_6H_6R^+ \right] \rightarrow C_6H_5R + H^+$$

Thus, with halides, alcohols, ethers, and esters, alkylation proceeds most readily for tertiary or benzyl types, less readily for secondary types, still less readily for primary types, and least readily for methyl.[17] It is therefore generally necessary to use increasingly vigorous catalysts or conditions to introduce the alkyl groups in the above sequence. For example, reactive halides like benzyl chloride will react with benzene in the presence of traces of such a weak catalyst as zinc chloride, whereas an inert halide like methyl chloride requires a considerable quantity of a powerful catalyst such as aluminum chloride.

The relative reactivity of the alkyl halides is also conditioned by the halogen atom. For aluminum chloride-catalyzed alkylations with either *n*-butyl or *t*-butyl halides,[18] the order of activity is F > Cl > Br > I.[19] This same order of reactivity has been found for hydrogen fluoride-catalyzed alkylation of benzene with cyclohexyl and *s*-octyl halides.[20] The order of reactivity of the halides is thus the reverse of the normal order.

Of the wide variety of alkylating agents which have been reported, the alkyl halides, olefins, and alcohols are by far the most useful. Aluminum chloride is an effective catalyst for all three classes. With halides and olefins, it is required in only catalytic amounts; but with alcohols con-

[15] Ott and Brugger, *Z. Elektrochem.*, **46,** 105 (1940).

[16] For reviews summarizing the evidence on the mechanism of the Friedel-Crafts reaction see Calloway, *Chem. Revs.*, **17,** 327 (1935); Nightingale, *ibid.*, **25,** 329 (1939); Price, *ibid.*, **29,** 37 (1941).

[17] This same order of activity holds for the ease of migration and displacement of alkyl groups already attached to the aromatic nucleus.

[18] Calloway, *J. Am. Chem. Soc.*, **59,** 1474 (1937).

[19] Calloway (see reference 18) made the interesting observation that the ease of acylation with acyl halides is in the reverse order.

[20] Simons and Bassler, *J. Am. Chem. Soc.*, **63,** 880 (1941).

siderably larger quantities are necessary because of the reaction of the aluminum chloride with the alcohol. (See the article by Norris and Sturgis cited on p. 8, reference 30.)

$$
\begin{array}{ccc}
C_2H_5OH + AlCl_3 & \longrightarrow & C_2H_5OH \cdot AlCl_3 \\
 & & \downarrow \\
C_2H_5Cl + AlOCl & \xleftarrow{\text{Heat}} & C_2H_5OAlCl_2 + HCl
\end{array}
$$

Although boron fluoride or hydrogen fluoride will catalyze alkylation by means of alkyl halides, these catalysts are much more effective and useful with olefins or alcohols. Reactions carried out with either of these catalysts are distinguished by the lack of colored and resinous by-products which so generally accompany the use of aluminum chloride.

Ethers and esters have not been widely applied in syntheses by the Friedel-Crafts reaction, chiefly because they offer no particular advantage over the alcohols. In fact, with esters of organic acids and aluminum chloride as catalyst, a disadvantage is the simultaneous acylation which may occur. However, the synthesis of toluene in 60% yield from benzene, methyl sulfate, and aluminum chloride represents the most successful procedure for the monomethylation of benzene (see p. 22).

The use of cyclopropane as an alkylating agent has yielded *n*-propylbenzene in 65% yield (see references 26 and 36 on p. 8), but other syntheses, such as the preparation from *n*-propyl alcohol in 52% yield (see references 26 and 27, p. 8), are probably of more practical application.

$$C_6H_6 + \underset{\text{(cyclo-}CH_2CH_2CH_2)}{} \rightarrow C_6H_5CH_2CH_2CH_3$$

Aromatic Compounds. One characteristic feature of alkylation by the Friedel-Crafts procedure is that alkyl substituents in the aromatic ring markedly increase the ease of alkylation. Thus, there is a general tendency for the formation of considerable amounts of polyalkyl derivatives.

An interesting observation in this connection is that the structure of the alkyl group is an important factor regulating the maximum number of alkyl groups which can be introduced into the benzene ring by the Friedel-Crafts method. (See reference 36, p. 8.) Although all six of the hydrogen atoms of benzene can be replaced by methyl, ethyl, or *n*-propyl groups, only four can be replaced by isopropyl groups, and, although three have been replaced by *t*-butyl groups, the usual and principal product in this instance is the *p*-di-*t*-butyl derivative.

$$C_6(C_2H_5)_6 \qquad 1,2,4,5\text{-}C_6H_2[CH(CH_3)_2]_4 \qquad p\text{-}C_6H_4[C(CH_3)_3]_2$$

The effect of a hydroxyl or an alkoxyl group on the ease of alkylation is complex. In some instances, the effect appears to be an activation. For example, although nitrobenzene has not been alkylated, *o*-nitroanisole has been converted into the isopropyl derivative in good yield.

$$CH_3O\text{-}C_6H_4\text{-}NO_2\,(o) + (CH_3)_2CHOH \xrightarrow{HF} CH_3O(O_2N)C_6H_3CH(CH_3)_2 \quad (84\%)$$

The normal activating influence of the hydroxyl or alkoxyl group is counterbalanced by the tendency for the catalyst to coördinate with the oxygen atom.

$$C_6H_5\text{—}\ddot{O}(CH_3): + BF_3 \rightarrow C_6H_5\text{—}\overset{(+)}{O}(CH_3)\rightarrow \overset{(-)}{BF_3}$$

This process not only decreases the activity of the catalyst but also tends to nullify the activating effect of the oxygen atom. This general effect is still more pronounced for aromatic amines, so that alkylation of these substances has found only very limited application.

Rearrangements of Alkyl Groups. One factor involved in alkylation by the Friedel-Crafts method which has led to many conflicting and erroneous reports in the literature is the tendency for rearrangements of the alkyl group to occur during alkylation. The exact nature of the influence involved in these rearrangements is still not entirely clear. In general, the tendency of the rearrangements is in the direction: primary → secondary → tertiary. Usually the rearrangements involve only the migration of hydrogen atoms in the alkyl group rather than a rearrangement of the carbon skeleton.

The first observation of such a rearrangement was made by Gustavson [21] only a year after the announcement of the Friedel-Crafts reaction. He found that *n*-propyl and isopropyl bromides react with

[21] Gustavson, *Ber.*, **11**, 1251 (1878).

benzene in the presence of aluminum chloride to form the same substance, isopropylbenzene (cumene). The discovery that *n*-propyl bromide is isomerized to isopropyl bromide in the presence of aluminum chloride offers an explanation for this observation.[22]

$$\left.\begin{array}{l} C_6H_6 + n\text{-}C_3H_7Br \\ C_6H_6 + iso\text{-}C_3H_7Br \end{array}\right\rangle \xrightarrow{AlCl_3} iso\text{-}C_3H_7C_6H_5$$

$$n\text{-}C_3H_7Br \xrightarrow{AlCl_3} iso\text{-}C_3H_7Br$$

Since such rearrangements may be represented as occurring by intermediate formation of an olefin, it has been suggested that olefins are involved as intermediates in the alkylations.[11, 23]

$$n\text{-}C_3H_7Br \xrightarrow{AlCl_3} [C_3H_6] \xrightarrow[AlCl_3]{C_6H_6} iso\text{-}C_3H_7C_6H_5$$

$$[C_3H_6] \xrightarrow{HBr} iso\text{-}C_3H_7Br$$

The general theory of molecular rearrangements as outlined by Whitmore [23a] offers an alternative explanation of the isomerizations of alkyl groups during alkylation.[9]

$$CH_3CH_2CH_2Cl + AlCl_3 \rightleftarrows CH_3CH_2CH_2^+ AlCl_4^- \updownarrow (CH_3)_2CH^+$$

$$C_6H_6 + \overset{+}{C}H(CH_3)_2 \rightarrow [C_6H_6^{+}\text{—}CH(CH_3)_2] \rightarrow C_6H_5\text{—}CH(CH_3)_2 + H^+$$

It is by no means necessary to suppose that an olefin is formed as an intermediate in all alkylations. For example, benzyl alcohol and benzhydrol are particularly effective alkylating agents, but the intermediate formation of an olefin is impossible. Furthermore, under many conditions alkylation may proceed without rearrangement. It has been found that *n*-propyl chloride *in the cold* will react with benzene in the presence

[22] Kekulé and Schrotter, *Bull. soc. chim.*, [2] **34**, 485 (1879).
[23] McKenna and Sowa, *J. Am. Chem. Soc.*, **59**, 1204 (1937).
[23a] Whitmore, *J. Am. Chem. Soc.*, **54**, 3274 (1932).

of aluminum chloride to give chiefly *n*-propylbenzene whereas at higher temperatures the product is chiefly isopropylbenzene.[24, 25, 26]

The catalyst may also influence the fate of the alkyl group. Normal alcohols, for example, usually alkylate without rearrangement in the presence of aluminum chloride,[26, 27, 28] but rearrangement does occur when sulfuric acid [26, 29] or boron fluoride [11, 14] is used as a catalyst.

Under vigorous conditions changes even more extensive than isomerization of the alkyl group can occur. Although benzene is alkylated normally in good yield with *t*-butyl alcohol and aluminum chloride at 30°, the products at 80–95° are toluene, ethylbenzene, and isopropylbenzene.[30] Alkylation with 2,4,4- or 2,3,3-trimethyl-2-pentanol can proceed to yield both normal and degraded alkylation products, the extent of degradation increasing with temperature.[31] The alkylation of methyl 2-furoate proceeds normally at the active 5-position, but the alkylation of methyl 5-bromo-2-furoate at the inactive 4-position proceeds with degradation of all alkyl groups with more than four carbon atoms to give the 4-*t*-butyl derivative in every case.[32, 33] Treatment of paraffin hydrocarbons with benzene in the presence of aluminum chloride leads to the formation of various alkylbenzenes by degradation of the paraffin, a reaction which has been termed "destructive alkylation." [34]

Orientation in Alkylation. An additional factor complicating the usefulness of Friedel-Crafts alkylations is the orientation involved in the introduction of more than one alkyl group.[35, 36] It was discovered at an early date that alkylation with aluminum chloride and alkyl halides yields considerable proportions of *m*-dialkylbenzenes, as well as the expected *o*- and *p*-isomers. The relative extent of normal and abnormal orientation has been found to be a function of the conditions of alkylation. In general, the more vigorous the conditions with respect to the activity of the catalyst or the alkylating agent or the severity of the time and temperature factors, the greater is the tendency for the forma-

[24] Heise, *Ber.*, **24,** 768 (1891).

[25] Konowalow, *J. Russ. Phys.-Chem. Soc.*, **27,** 457 (1895).

[26] Ipatieff, Pines, and Schmerling, *J. Org. Chem.*, **5,** 253 (1940).

[27] Tsukervanik and Vikhrova, *J. Gen. Chem. U.S.S.R.*, **7,** 632 (1937) [*C. A.*, **31,** 5779 (1937)].

[28] Bowden, *J. Am. Chem. Soc.*, **60,** 645 (1938).

[29] Meyer and Bernhauer, *Monatsh.*, **53** and **54,** 721 (1929).

[30] Norris and Sturgis, *J. Am. Chem. Soc.*, **61,** 1413 (1939).

[31] Huston, Guile, Sculati, and Wasson, *J. Org. Chem.*, **6,** 252 (1941).

[32] Gilman and Burtner, *J. Am. Chem. Soc.*, **57,** 909 (1935).

[33] Gilman and Turck, *J. Am. Chem. Soc.*, **61,** 473 (1939).

[34] Grosse, Mavity, and Ipatieff, *J. Org. Chem.*, **3,** 137 (1938).

[35] See Ingold, Lapworth, Rothstein, and Ward, *J. Chem. Soc.*, **1931,** 1959; Bird and Ingold, *ibid.*, **1938,** 918.

[36] Grosse and Ipatieff, *J. Org. Chem.*, **2,** 447 (1937).

tion of the abnormal *m*-derivatives. Thus, alkylation catalyzed by aluminum chloride, the most active catalyst, leads to large proportions of *m*-dialkylbenzenes, particularly with large amounts of catalyst at high temperatures or for long reaction times. Alkylations catalyzed with boron fluoride, sulfuric acid, ferric chloride, and most other catalysts yield chiefly the normal *p*-dialkylbenzenes.

CH_3 + RX —$AlCl_3$→ CH_3, R (meta); —$FeCl_3$→ CH_3, R (para)

CH_3 + ROH —HF or BF_3→ CH_3, R (para)

Naphthalene likewise yields two dialkyl derivatives; the principal dialkylation product from the reaction of naphthalene and cyclohexanol or cyclohexene with aluminum chloride as the catalyst has been shown to be 2,6-dicyclohexylnaphthalene,[36a] but from cyclohexanol and boron fluoride, 1,4-dicyclohexylnaphthalene is obtained.[36b]

Naphthalene + $C_6H_{11}OH$ —$AlCl_3$→ 2,6-(C_6H_{11})$_2$-naphthalene; —BF_3→ 1,4-(C_6H_{11})$_2$-naphthalene

A similar situation obtains in the trialkylation of benzene, the 1,2,4-trialkyl derivative being formed only under mild conditions, the 1,3,5-isomer under more vigorous conditions.[37] It has been shown that the 1,2,4-trialkyl derivatives will, in many instances, rearrange to the 1,3,5-isomer under the influence of aluminum chloride.[38, 39, 40, 41, 42]

36a Price and Tomisek, *J. Am. Chem. Soc.*, **65**, 439 (1943).
36b Price, Shafer, Huber, and Bernstein, *J. Org. Chem.*, **7**, 517 (1942).
37 Norris and Rubinstein, *J. Am. Chem. Soc.*, **61**, 1163 (1939).
38 Baddeley and Kenner, *J. Chem. Soc.*, **1935**, 303.
39 Nightingale and Smith, *J. Am. Chem. Soc.*, **61**, 101 (1939).
40 Smith and Perry, *J. Am. Chem. Soc.*, **61**, 1411 (1939).
41 Nightingale and Carton, *J. Am. Chem. Soc.*, **62**, 280 (1940).
42 Nightingale, Taylor, and Smelser, *J. Am. Chem. Soc.*, **63**, 258 (1941).

Even in the alkylation of phenols and aromatic halides similar effects on orientation have been observed. Thus, the ethylation of phenol with ethanol and aluminum chloride yields the *o*- and *p*-derivatives,[43] whereas with ethyl ether as the alkylating agent at a higher temperature 3,5-diethylphenol [44] is obtained. Alkylation of chlorobenzene with ethanol and aluminum chloride at 80–90° yields *p*-chloroethylbenzene,[45] but with ethylene at 100°, the principal product is the *m*-isomer.[46]

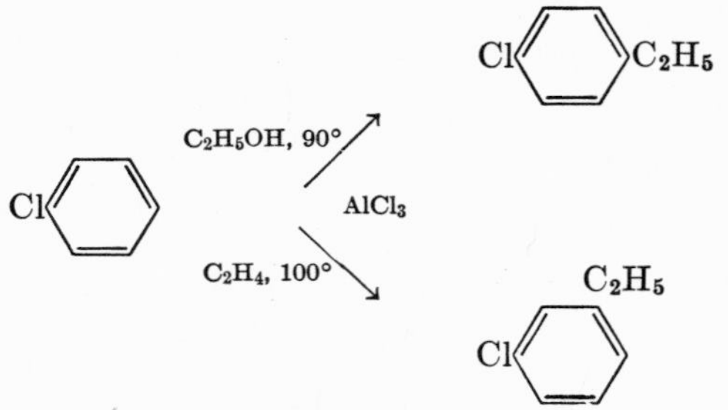

C_2H_5OH, 90°; $AlCl_3$; C_2H_4, 100°

Since alkylation by the Friedel-Crafts reaction has been demonstrated to be a reversible reaction,[47, 48, 49] it has been suggested that the various anomalous orientations can be explained on this basis. Jacobsen [50] was the first of many [38, 51, 52, 53] to point out that normal alkylation to form the 1,2,4-trialkyl derivative, followed by loss of the alkyl group in the 1-position, might account for the anomalous formation of *m*-dialkyl derivatives.

Identification. The many possibilities for the formation of isomeric or anomalous products due to rearrangement, unusual orientation, or degradation of alkyl groups during the Friedel-Crafts reaction, coupled with the fact that the products are usually liquids, difficult to separate and identify, frequently necessitate particular care in establishing the structure and the purity of the products.[54] The most effective method

[43] Tsukervanik and Nazarova, *J. Gen. Chem. U.S.S.R.*, **7,** 623 (1937) [*C. A.* **31,** 5778 (1937)].

[44] Jannasch and Rathjen, *Ber.*, **32,** 2391 (1899).

[45] Tsukervanik, *J. Gen. Chem. U.S.S.R.*, **8,** 1512 (1938) [*C. A.*, **33,** 4587 (1939)].

[46] Istrati, *Ann. chim.*, [6] **6,** 395 (1885).

[47] Boedtker, *Bull. soc. chim.*, [3] **35,** 834 (1906).

[48] Boedtker and Halse, *Bull. soc. chim.*, [4] **19,** 447 (1916).

[49] Woodward, Borcherdt, and Fuson, *J. Am. Chem. Soc.*, **56,** 2103 (1934).

[50] Jacobsen, *Ber.*, **18,** 342 (1885).

[51] Anschütz, *Ann.*, **235,** 177 (1886); Moyle and Smith, *J. Org. Chem.*, **2,** 114 (1937).

[52] Schorger, *J. Am. Chem. Soc.*, **39,** 2671 (1917).

[53] Price and Ciskowski, *J. Am. Chem. Soc.*, **60,** 2499 (1938).

[54] See Marvel and Himel, *J. Am. Chem. Soc.*, **62,** 1550 (1940), who found that the aluminum chloride-catalyzed condensation of cyclohexyl chloride with bromobenzene yielded a mixture of all three bromocyclohexylbenzenes.

of establishing the orientation of the alkyl groups is oxidation to the corresponding aromatic acids. This is sometimes difficult for the tertiary groups, particularly *t*-butyl; for example, the oxidation of *p*-di-*t*-butylbenzene with chromic acid yields 2,5-di-*t*-butylbenzoquinone as the principal product.[55]

$$p\text{-}(CH_3)_3C\text{-}C_6H_4\text{-}C(CH_3)_3 \xrightarrow{CrO_3} 2,5\text{-}[(CH_3)_3C]_2C_6H_2O_2 \text{ and } p\text{-}(CH_3)_3C\text{-}C_6H_4\text{-}COCH_3$$

The structure of the side chain may be established by a synthesis that leaves no doubt about the structure of the product. Alkylbenzenes containing primary alkyl groups may be prepared by Clemmensen reduction of an aryl alkyl ketone,[39, 56] and those containing secondary groups by reaction of an aryl alkyl ketone with a Grignard reagent followed by dehydration and reduction.[57] A primary alkyl group attached to a benzene ring can be distinguished from a secondary or tertiary group by bromination in the presence of aluminum bromide; all hydrogen atoms and secondary or tertiary alkyl groups attached to a benzene ring are replaced by bromine under these conditions, whereas primary alkyl groups are not affected.[58]

$$iso\text{-}C_3H_7C_6H_5 \xrightarrow[AlBr_3]{6Br_2} C_6Br_6 + iso\text{-}C_3H_7Br + 5HBr$$

$$n\text{-}C_3H_7C_6H_5 \xrightarrow[AlBr_3]{5Br_2} n\text{-}C_3H_7C_6Br_5 + 5HBr$$

Identification of alkylated benzenes can be accomplished to some degree by the physical properties, more definitely by preparation of a solid derivative such as a sulfonamide,[29, 59, 60] a diacetamino derivative,[60a] or a picrate.[53, 59]

[55] Boedtker, *Bull. soc. chim.*, [3] **31,** 969 (1904).

[56] Gilman and Turck, *J. Am. Chem. Soc.*, **61,** 478 (1939); Martin, *Organic Reactions*, **I,** "The Clemmensen Reduction."

[57] Klages, *Ber.*, **35,** 3509 (1902).

[58] Bodroux, *Ann. chim.*, [10] **11,** 511 (1929); Hennion, *J. Am. Chem. Soc.*, **66,** 1801 (1944).

[59] Shriner and Fuson, "Identification of Organic Compounds," John Wiley & Sons, New York, 2nd ed., 1940.

[60] Huntress and Autenrieth, *J. Am. Chem. Soc.*, **63,** 3446 (1941).

[60a] Ipatieff and Schmerling, *J. Am. Chem. Soc.*, **59,** 1056 (1937); **60,** 1476 (1938); see also reference 42.

Related Reactions. Many compounds containing more than one carbon-halogen or carbon-oxygen bond, although beyond the scope of this chapter (see p. 4), undergo stepwise reaction with aromatic compounds to form, as intermediates, alkylating agents of the type under consideration. For example, methylene chloride reacts with benzene in the presence of aluminum chloride to yield diphenylmethane, presumably through the intermediate formation of benzyl chloride.[36] Other examples are noted in the following equations.

$$C_6H_6 + CH_2Cl_2 \xrightarrow{AlCl_3} [C_6H_5CH_2Cl] \xrightarrow[AlCl_3]{C_6H_6} (C_6H_5)_2CH_2$$

$$C_6H_6 + CH_2O \xrightarrow{AlCl_3} [C_6H_5CH_2OH] \xrightarrow[AlCl_3]{C_6H_6} (C_6H_5)_2CH_2$$

$$2C_6H_6 + CHCl_3 \xrightarrow{AlCl_3} [(C_6H_5)_2CHCl] \xrightarrow[AlCl_3]{C_6H_6} (C_6H_5)_3CH$$

$$C_6H_6 + C_6H_5CHO \xrightarrow{AlCl_3} [(C_6H_5)_2CHOH] \xrightarrow[AlCl_3]{C_6H_6} (C_6H_5)_3CH \; ^{61}$$

$$C_6H_6 + CH_2ClCH_2Cl \xrightarrow{AlCl_3} [C_6H_5CH_2CH_2Cl] \xrightarrow[AlCl_3]{C_6H_6} C_6H_5CH_2CH_2C_6H_5$$

$$C_6H_6 + \underset{\diagdown\,O\,\diagup}{CH_2{-}{-}CH_2} \xrightarrow{AlCl_3} [C_6H_5CH_2CH_2OH] \xrightarrow[AlCl_3]{C_6H_6} C_6H_5CH_2CH_2C_6H_5 \; ^{61,62}$$

The reactions of aldehydes and ketones with phenols have been investigated extensively.

If the two groups in a molecule capable of condensing with the aromatic ring are properly situated, the reaction may yield a cyclic product, a process which has been termed "cyclialkylation." [63]

$$C_6H_6 + (CH_3)_2CCl{-}CH_2{-}CH_2{-}CCl(CH_3)_2 \text{ or } \underset{\text{(2,2,5,5-tetramethyltetrahydrofuran)}}{(CH_3)_2C{-}CH_2{-}CH_2{-}C(CH_3)_2{-}O} \xrightarrow{AlCl_3} C_6H_4\langle C(CH_3)_2CH_2CH_2C(CH_3)_2 \rangle$$

The condensations of halides, alcohols, and unsaturated compounds containing a variety of other functional groups have been carried out

[61] Schaarschmidt, Hermann, and Szemzo, *Ber.*, **58**, 1914 (1925).

[62] Theimer, *Abstracts*, Division of Organic Chemistry, 99th Meeting of the American Chemical Society, Cincinnati, Ohio, April, 1940, p. 42. Matui, *J. Soc. Chem. Ind. Japan*, **44**, No. 2, 88 (1941).

[63] Bruson and Kroeger, *J. Am. Chem. Soc.*, **62**, 36 (1940).

successfully. Thus, nitrobenzyl alcohols and halides [64] condense in the normal manner, and the addition of a variety of aromatic compounds to the double bonds in unsaturated ketones such as benzalacetophenone [49] or unsaturated acids such as cinnamic [65] or oleic acids [66] has been reported.

Limitations. Two important factors which govern the application of the Friedel-Crafts reaction are the activity of the aromatic compound and the activity of the alkylating agent and catalyst. Thus if the alkylating agent and catalyst are very reactive and the aromatic substrate is relatively inert, extensive degradation [30, 31, 32, 33] or polymerization [67] of the alkylating agent may occur. If the aromatic substrate is very reactive toward the catalyst and the alkylating agent is relatively inert, decomposition of the aromatic compound may take precedence over alkylation. For example, naphthalene reacts in the presence of aluminum chloride to form binaphthyls [68] and tetralin is degraded to

$$2C_{10}H_8 \xrightarrow{AlCl_3} H_2 + (C_{10}H_7)_2$$

benzene and a mixture of octahydroanthracene and octahydrophenanthrene through the intermediate formation of β-(4-phenylbutyl)-tetralin.[69]

$$\text{tetralin} + \text{tetralin} \xrightarrow{AlCl_3} C_6H_5CH_2CH_2CH_2CH_2\text{-tetralin}$$

$$\xrightarrow{AlCl_3} \text{benzene} + \text{octahydroanthracene} + \text{octahydrophenanthrene}$$

Methylation of naphthalene and tetralin therefore can be accomplished only in very poor yields. Similarly such reactive heterocyclic aromatic substances as furan and thiophene have not been alkylated successfully by the Friedel-Crafts method. Deactivation of the furan nucleus by the carboxyl group of furoic acid, however, makes alkylation by the Friedel-Crafts procedure feasible and useful (see Table XV, p. 76).

[64] Staedel, *Ann.*, **283,** 157 (1895).
[65] Liebermann and Hartmann, *Ber.*, **25,** 957 (1892).
[66] Stirton and Peterson, *Ind. Eng. Chem.*, **31,** 856 (1939).
[67] Truffault, *Compt. rend.*, **202,** 1286 (1936).
[68] Homer, *J. Chem. Soc.*, **91,** 1108 (1907).
[69] Barbot, *Bull. soc. chim.*, [4] **47,** 1314 (1930).

The alkylation of anisole under the vigorous conditions necessary to introduce an isopropyl group (aluminum chloride at 120–140°) leads to extensive demethylation.[43] Alkylation of phenol under many condi-

$$C_6H_5OCH_3 + C_3H_7OH \xrightarrow[140°]{AlCl_3} C_3H_7C_6H_4OCH_3 \quad \text{and} \quad C_3H_7C_6H_4OH$$

tions may produce ethers as well as nuclear alkylation products.[91] Both

$$C_6H_5OH + C_3H_6 \rightarrow C_3H_7C_6H_4OH, \; C_6H_5OC_3H_7 \quad \text{and} \quad C_3H_7C_6H_4OC_3H_7$$

formation and splitting of ethers seems to be minimized by the use of hydrogen fluoride as the catalyst for alkylation of phenol or its ethers.

Aluminum chloride has been used as a catalyst for the alkylation of phenols or of acids, but it should be noted that these reagents frequently react vigorously to yield aluminum salts of the phenols or acids. For this reason boron fluoride, hydrogen fluoride, and sulfuric acid generally have been used as catalysts for alkylation of such substances.

$$C_6H_5OH + AlCl_3 \rightarrow C_6H_5OAlCl_2 + HCl$$

$$ArCO_2H + AlCl_3 \rightarrow ArCO_2AlCl_2 + HCl$$

The reaction of bromo compounds is complicated by the possibility of migration of the aromatically bound bromine atom in the presence of aluminum chloride.[54, 70] Thus appreciable quantities of *p*-dibromobenzene are produced in aluminum chloride-catalyzed alkylations of bromobenzene.

$$C_6H_5Br + RCl \xrightarrow{AlCl_3} RC_6H_4Br \quad \text{and} \quad p\text{-}C_6H_4Br_2$$

Recently, alkylation of a few aromatic aldehydes and acids has also been accomplished successfully.[32, 71] Nitrobenzene is not alkylated under Friedel-Crafts conditions; it is converted slowly to *o*- and *p*-chloroaniline in the presence of isobutyl chloride and aluminum chloride.[72]

Other Methods of Alkylation. A useful method for the preparation of certain alkylated phenols is that devised by Claisen [73] and extended by a number of investigators.[74, 75, 76, 77] The nuclear alkylation of phenols is accomplished by treating the sodium phenoxide with an active halide of

[70] Copisarow, *J. Chem. Soc.*, **119,** 442 (1921).

[71] Calcott, Tinker, and Weinmayr, *J. Am. Chem. Soc.*, **61,** 1010 (1939).

[72] Gilman, Burtner, Calloway, and Turck, *J. Am. Chem. Soc.*, **57,** 907 (1935).

[73] Claisen, *Ann.*, **442,** 220 (1925); *Ber.*, **58,** 275 (1925); **59,** 2344 (1926).

[74] Schorigin, *Ber.*, **58,** 2033 (1925); **59,** 2506 (1926); Busch, *Z. angew. Chem.*, **38,** 1145 (1925); *Ber.*, **60,** 2243 (1927); van Alphen, *Rec. trav. chim.*, **46,** 287, 799 (1927).

[75] Huston and Houk, *J. Am. Chem. Soc.*, **54,** 1506 (1932).

[76] Huston and Lewis, *J. Am. Chem. Soc.*, **53,** 2379 (1931).

[77] Huston, Swartout, and Wardwell, *J. Am. Chem. Soc.*, **52,** 4484 (1930).

the allyl or benzyl type (or even *t*-butyl chloride [78]) in an inert solvent such as toluene. The alkylation of phenols by this procedure supplements the Friedel-Crafts method since the products by the Claisen method are practically always the *o*-isomers whereas Friedel-Crafts alkylation usually yields the *p*-isomer.[73, 75, 76, 77] Another method for the preparation of alkylated phenols, also due to Claisen, is the rearrangement of phenyl ethers, a reaction which is considered in detail in another chapter.[78a]

One or two useful indirect methods have been reported for the introduction of methyl groups. Nuclear methylation of phenols has been accomplished by the condensation of phenols with formaldehyde and secondary amines,[79] followed by hydrogenation of the intermediate benzylamine.[79a]

$$ArOH + CH_2O + R_2NH \rightarrow R_2NCH_2ArOH \xrightarrow{(H)} R_2NH + CH_3ArOH$$

A successful preparation of 1,2,3-trimethylbenzene (not available by the Friedel-Crafts method) has been accomplished by use of the Tiffeneau rearrangement which occurs during the reaction of benzyl-type Grignard reagents with formaldehyde.[80]

$$CH_3C_6H_4CH_2MgX + CH_2O \rightarrow CH_3C_6H_3(CH_3)CH_2OH \xrightarrow{(H)} CH_3C_6H_3(CH_3)CH_3$$

A number of polyalkylbenzene derivatives not directly available by the Friedel-Crafts procedure may be prepared by application of the Jacobsen rearrangement.[80a]

The alkylation of aromatic nitro compounds and of quinones has been accomplished by means of the radicals liberated by the decomposition of tetravalent lead salts of organic acids or of acyl peroxides, or by the electrolysis of sodium salts of organic acids.[80b]

$$CH_3C_6H_2(NO_2)_3 \xrightarrow[(CH_3CO_2)_2]{Pb(OCOCH_3)_4 \text{ or}} (CH_3)_2C_6H(NO_2)_3$$

[78] Lewis, *J. Am. Chem. Soc.*, **83**, 329 (1903).

[78a] Tarbell, *Organic Reactions*, **II**, "The Claisen Rearrangement."

[79] Blicke, *Organic Reactions*, **I**, "The Mannich Reaction."

[79a] Caldwell and Thompson, *J. Am. Chem. Soc.*, **61**, 2345 (1939).

[80] Smith and Spillane, *J. Am. Chem. Soc.*, **62**, 2643 (1940).

[80a] Smith, *Organic Reactions*, **I**, "The Jacobsen Reaction."

[80b] Fieser and Chang, *J. Am. Chem. Soc.*, **64**, 2043 (1942); Fieser, Clapp, and Daudt, *ibid.*, 2052; Fieser and Oxford, *ibid.*, 2060.

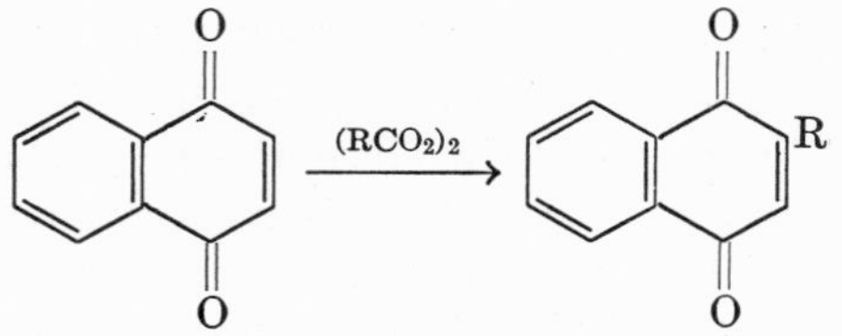

$$\xrightarrow{(RCO_2)_2}$$

EXPERIMENTAL DIRECTIONS [81]

Selection of Experimental Conditions. An examination of the tables will suggest the most favorable experimental conditions for many particular alkylations. A few generalizations are evident. Owing to the activation of the aromatic nucleus by the alkyl group, maximum conversion to the monoalkyl derivative is favored by the presence of a large excess of the aromatic compound. To increase further the overall conversion to the monoalkyl derivative, the polyalkylated material from one run may be recovered and added to the next. Because of mobility of the alkyl groups, some are removed to another aromatic nucleus by this process. The polyalkylated material thus actually may serve as the alkylating agent.[48]

Orientation in di- or trialkylation may be regulated by controlling the vigor of the reaction. Relatively mild catalysts, such as boron fluoride (with an alcohol), hydrogen fluoride (with an olefin), or ferric chloride (with an alkyl halide), may lead almost exclusively to *p*-dialkylation or 1,2,4-trialkylation. Under more vigorous conditions, as with excess aluminum chloride at elevated temperatures, the *m*-dialkyl or *sym*-trialkyl derivative predominates.

The quantity of catalyst necessary may vary considerably. Only catalytic amounts of aluminum chloride are required when olefins or alkyl halides are the alkylating agents. With alcohols or their derivatives, much larger amounts of catalyst are required, owing to inactivation by reaction with the alcohol or with the water formed during the reaction. With hydrogen fluoride it is universal practice to use a large excess of catalyst, so much so that it is actually the solvent medium for the reaction.

1. *sym-Triethylbenzene.*[82] A 5-l. three-necked flask surrounded by a

[81] Since an excellent preparation utilizing sulfuric acid, that of cyclohexylbenzene from cyclohexene and benzene, has been described in detail in *Organic Syntheses* (*Coll. Vol,* **2,** 151, John Wiley & Sons, New York, 1943), no experimental directions illustrating the technique employed with this useful catalyst have been included in this section.

[82] This is essentially the procedure of Norris and Rubinstein (reference 37). Norris and Ingraham [*J. Am. Chem. Soc.,* **60,** 1421 (1938)] have prepared the same compound in 65–70% yield with ethanol as the alkylating agent. In this case, a considerably larger ratio of aluminum chloride is required.

tub of ice-salt mixture is fitted with (1) an efficient stirrer sealed with a mercury seal or a tight-fitting piece of rubber pressure tubing lubricated with mineral oil (*not* glycerol), (2) a long reflux condenser with a glass outlet tube leading to a hood or an efficient apparatus for absorbing hydrogen halide, (3) a thermometer well (containing ethanol), and (4) a 500-cc. separatory funnel.

Four pounds [83] (1815 g., 6.8 moles) of anhydrous aluminum chloride is added to the flask and is moistened with 750–1000 cc. of dry ethyl bromide. The stirrer is started, and, when the temperature reaches −10°, addition of dry benzene (530 g., 604 cc., 6.8 moles) through the separatory funnel is carried out at such a rate that the temperature stays below −5° (about two and a quarter hours is necessary). The rapid current of hydrogen halide evolved carries some of the ethyl bromide out through the condenser.

After the benzene has been added the remainder of a total of 2425 g. (1695 cc., 21.8 moles) of ethyl bromide is added over a period of about one and a quarter hours. The ice is then removed from the cooling bath and stirring is continued overnight while the mixture gradually warms to room temperature. The bath is then removed and stirring is continued for another twenty-four hours, when evolution of hydrogen halide has ceased.

The reaction mixture is poured into a large separatory funnel from which it is added, in a fine stream and with vigorous stirring, to 10 kg. of ice and 300 cc. of concentrated hydrochloric acid in a large crock. This operation should be performed in a good hood. When hydrolysis is complete, the major portion of the lower water layer is removed by siphoning and the reaction mixture is filtered to remove a black solid which impedes separation of the layers during washing. The organic layer is then separated and washed with dilute hydrochloric acid, twice with water, with 5% aqueous sodium hydroxide, and twice with water. After drying over calcium chloride, the product is distilled through an efficient fractionating column. The triethylbenzene (943–962 g., 86–87%) boils at 72.5–75°/3 mm. or 215–216°/760 mm.; n_D^{20} 1.4955–1.4968.[84]

2. *t-Butylbenzene.*[85] A mixture of 105 g. (1.35 moles) of benzene and

[83] This preparation may be run as efficiently on a much smaller scale, if desired.

[84] Norris and Ingraham (reference 82) give directions for further purification of the *sym*-triethylbenzene by means of sulfonation; b.p. 214.8° (755.1 mm.); $n_D^{18.1}$ 1.4956.

[85] These directions are those of Nightingale, Taylor, and Smelser (reference 42). A smaller yield (50–55%) is obtained with aluminum chloride as a catalyst (Fieser, "Experiments in Organic Chemistry," 2nd ed., D. C. Heath and Co., New York, 1941, p. 179). The same situation holds for *t*-butyl alcohol, ferric chloride giving better yields than aluminum chloride [Potts and Dodson, *J. Am. Chem. Soc.*, **61,** 2553 (1939)].

12 g. (0.07 mole) of anhydrous ferric chloride (in a flask fitted with a condenser and a trap to absorb hydrogen chloride [85a]) is cooled to 10°, and 25 g. (0.27 mole) of *t*-butyl chloride is added. As the mixture is slowly warmed to about 25°, evolution of hydrogen chloride proceeds smoothly. When the evolution of hydrogen chloride ceases, the reaction mixture is washed with dilute hydrochloric acid and with water, dried, and fractionally distilled. The *t*-butylbenzene (29 g., 80%) boils at 167–170°.

3. *β-Cyclohexylnaphthalene.*[86] Boron fluoride [87] is passed through an empty 250-cc. suction filter flask (as a safety trap) and is then bubbled through a suspension of 50 g. (0.39 mole) of naphthalene in 40 cc. (38 g., 0.47 mole) of cyclohexanol in a 500-cc. flask at room temperature [87a] until two liquid layers separate in the reaction mixture (fifteen to thirty minutes).[88]

The reaction flask is fitted with an outlet tube [89] leading to the top of a vertical meter-long glass tube through which a stream of water is passed; this apparatus serves to absorb the excess boron fluoride.

After standing for about an hour, the reaction mixture is separated and the upper layer washed [90] with dilute alkali and with water. After drying, the mixture is fractionally distilled under diminished pressure in a modified Claisen flask, 52 g. (63%) of β-cyclohexylnaphthalene (b.p. 190–195°/15 mm.; n_D^{20} 1.5973; d_{25}^{25} 1.020) is obtained. The product may be characterized by preparation of the picrate,[59] m.p. 100°.[53, 58]

4. *2,4,6-Triisopropylphenol.*[91] About 800 g. of liquid hydrogen

[85a] *Org. Syntheses, Coll. Vol.* **2**, 4, John Wiley & Sons, New York, 1943.

[86] These directions are based on the general procedure described by McKenna and Sowa (reference 11) for benzene and adapted to naphthalene by Price and Ciskowski (reference 53). It is useful for alkylation by means of secondary, tertiary, and benzyl-type alcohols. Toussaint and Hennion (reference 14) have found that by addition of an "assistant," such as phosphoric anhydride or benzenesulfonic acid, the procedure may be extended to many primary alcohols.

[87] Cylinders of the compressed gas can be purchased from the Harshaw Chemical Co., Cleveland, Ohio.

[87a] If the reaction mixture is cooled to 0°, the boron fluoride dissolves without reacting until finally the reaction occurs with nearly explosive violence.

[88] Glass apparatus is satisfactory although it has been found that, after repeated use, Pyrex flasks used for the condensation become appreciably etched.

[89] As much as possible of the tubing for handling boron fluoride should be glass, since rubber soon hardens on contact with the gas.

[90] Occasionally, naphthalene may crystallize during the washing. If so, it should be separated by filtration.

[91] These are the directions of Calcott, Tinker, and Weinmayr (reference 71). Hydrogen fluoride appears to be particularly suitable for nuclear alkylation of phenols and amines, since there was no detectable alkylation of the hydroxyl or amino group, a side reaction which occurs to an appreciable extent with such catalysts as aluminum chloride (see reference 43) and boron fluoride [Sowa, Hinton, and Nieuwland, *J. Am. Chem. Soc.*, **54**, 3694 (1932)].

fluoride [92] is placed in a 2- to 3-l. copper, stainless steel, or nickel vessel (such as a beaker made of the metal) which is thoroughly cooled with an ice or ice-salt bath. The reaction vessel should be fitted with a cover perforated for a mechanical stirrer, a thermometer well, and an opening for the addition of reagents. The reaction mixture is kept below 8° while a solution of 140 g. (1.49 moles) of phenol in 515 cc. (405 g., 6.75 moles) of isopropyl alcohol is added from a separatory funnel over a period of three hours. The reaction mixture is then allowed to stand in a hood at room temperature for sixteen hours, after which time it is poured onto a large excess of ice (in a Pyrex beaker). Benzene is added; the organic layer is separated and washed with water, with dilute sodium bicarbonate, and again with water. The mixture is then dried and, after evaporation of the benzene, distilled under diminished pressure. 2,4,6-Triisopropylphenol (310 g., 95%) boils at 125°/7 mm.

TABULATION OF EXPERIMENTAL RESULTS

The summary of experimental results of the alkylation of various aromatic compounds has been divided into tables on the basis of the aromatic compound alkylated. These tables summarize the reagents and catalysts used for the various alkylations and, when available, such details as moles of reactants, solvent, temperature, time of reaction, products, and yields.

In each table the alkylations have been arranged in order according to the increasing number of carbon atoms in the alkyl group. These groups are further subdivided in order on the basis of decreasing number of hydrogen atoms; thus, examples of the introduction of the allyl group follow those of the propyl, and examples of the introduction of the cyclohexyl group follow those of the hexyl. For the introduction of any particular alkyl group, the arrangement is based on the alkylating agent. Hydrocarbons, such as olefins, are first, then alkyl halides, followed by alcohols and finally alcohol derivatives, such as ethers and esters of organic and inorganic acids.

[92] Since hydrogen fluoride boils at 20°, the liquid can be very readily withdrawn from *cooled* inverted cylinders with a length of copper tubing leading from the valve of the cylinder to a copper beaker or flask immersed in an ice bath. If the liquid is kept cold (10° or below), it can be handled quite easily. The reactions should be carried out in a hood, however, and all handling of the liquid should be done with long, heavy rubber gloves as a precaution against accidental contact with the liquid.

TABLE I

Reaction of Benzene with Aluminum Chloride

Moles of Benzene	Catalyst (moles)	Temperature, ° C.	Time	Products (% Yield)	Reference *
10	$AlCl_3$ (0.6)	125	24 hr.	Ethylbenzene (1.6%), biphenyl (0.8%)	200, 163
—	$AlCl_3$—HCl (—)	Warm	—	Methylphenylcyclopentane, diphenylcyclohexane (m.p. 170°)	181
25	$AlBr_3$ (3)	20	20 weeks	Phenylcyclohexane (21 g.), biphenyl (1.5 g.), diphenylcyclohexane (2.0 g.)	335

* References 93–350 appear on pp. 78–82.

TABLE II

ALKYLATION OF BENZENE

Moles of Benzene	Alkylating Agent (moles)	Catalyst (moles)	Temperature, °C.	Time, hours (unless noted otherwise)	Products (% Yield)	Reference *
1	Methyl chloride (—)	$AlCl_3$ (0.3)	80	—	Toluene, xylenes, trimethylbenzenes, durene, penta- and hexa-methylbenzenes	164
0.5	Methyl bromide (0.5)	$AlCl_3$ (0.1)	100	—	Xylene (plus toluene)	164
0.4	Methyl bromide (1.2)	$AlCl_3$ (0.8)	−40	—	1,2,4-Trimethylbenzene (50%)	37
—	Methyl iodide	I_2 (trace)	250	4–8	Toluene	277
6	Methyl alcohol (1)	$AlCl_3$ (2)	90–95	9	Toluene (21%)	30
0.25	Methyl chloroformate (0.1)	$AlCl_3$ (0.1)	0–80	1	Toluene (20%), *m*-xylene (20%)	231
1	Methyl formate (3)	$AlCl_3$ (5)	25–95	–	Mesitylene (46%)	261
8	Methyl sulfate (0.25)	$AlCl_3$ (0.36)	25–70	2	Toluene (60%)	214
5	Ethylene (10)	$AlCl_3$ (0.4)	70–90	48–72	Ethylbenzene (34%, 60%), diethylbenzenes (20%), triethylbenzenes (10%)	107, 252
0.8	Ethylene (—)	$AlCl_3$ (0.5)	80	3–4	*sym*-Triethylbenzene (70%)	167, 252, 141
10	Ethylene (18.8)	P_2O_5 (0.3)	250	—	Ethylbenzene (18.4%), diethylbenzenes (40%), triethylbenzenes (20%), hexaethylbenzene (3%)	244, 67
—	Ethylene (—)	H_3PO_4 (—)	300	12	Ethylbenzene, diethylbenzenes, triethylbenzenes	204, 67

2	Ethylene (—)	H_2SO_4 (1) (—) BF_3 † (0.15)	10–20	—	Ethylbenzene (5%)	341
3	Ethylene (0.9)	BF_3—H_2O (0.25)	20–25	8	Ethylbenzene (60%)	199
—	Ethylene (—)	$AlCl_3$ (—)	—	—	Hexaethylbenzene (56–59%)	222
8	Polyethylbenzenes (ca. 1)	$AlCl_3$ (0.1)	80	5	Ethylbenzene (80%)	274, 48
—	Ethyl chloride	$AlCl_3$ (—)	—	—	Hexaethylbenzene (43%)	95, 334
—	Ethyl chloride	$AlCl_3$ (—)	—	—	*sym*- and *asym*-Triethylbenzenes	219
13	Ethyl chloride (1.5)	$AlCl_3$ (0.1)	100	—	Ethylbenzene (50%)	290
1	Ethyl chloride (3)	$AlCl_3$ (2)	25–50	24	*sym*-Triethylbenzene (85%)	37
6	Ethyl chloride (1)	$Al(Hg)_x$ (0.1)	25	18	Ethylbenzene (76%)	347
11.3	Ethyl chloride (28)	$AlCl_3$ (1.5)	70–75	12	1,3,5- and 1,2,4-Triethylbenzene (67%, 6 : 1)	312
11.3	Ethyl chloride (35)	$AlCl_3$ (1.5)	70–75	12	1,2,4,5- and 1,2,3,5-Tetraethylbenzene (52%, 1 : 1), pentaethylbenzene (14%)	312
11.3	Ethyl chloride (40)	$AlCl_3$ (1.5)	75–80	16	1,2,4,5- and 1,2,3,5-Tetraethylbenzene (13%, 1 : 1), pentaethylbenzene (39%), hexaethylbenzene (15%)	312
1	Ethyl bromide (3)	$AlCl_3$ (2)	0–25	24	*sym*-Triethylbenzene (85–90%)	37
1	Ethyl bromide (1)	$AlCl_3$ (0.1)	25	48–72	Ethylbenzene (33%)	293
25	Ethyl bromide (10)	$AlCl_3$ (1.1)	7–25	—	Ethylbenzene (52%), polyethylbenzenes (ca. 15%)	274
65	Ethyl bromide (4.4)	$AlCl_3$ (0.8)	80	—	Ethylbenzene (83%)	119
8	Ethyl bromide (2)	Al—HCl (0.1)	25–80	48–2	Ethylbenzene (70%)	275
8	Ethyl bromide (2)	Al—$HgCl_2$ (0.2)	0–25	3–48	Ethylbenzene (53%)	275
—	Ethyl bromide (—)	$AlCl_3$ (—)	—	—	*m*- and *p*-Diethylbenzenes	96, 161, 329

* References 93–350 appear on pp. 78–82.
† When the BF_3 is omitted, no alkylation occurs (198, 341).

TABLE II—*Continued*

ALKYLATION OF BENZENE

Moles of Benzene	Alkylating Agent (moles)	Catalyst (moles)	Temperature, ° C.	Time, hours (unless noted otherwise)	Products (% Yield)	Reference *
—	Ethyl bromide (—)	$AlCl_3$ (—)	100	—	1,2,3,4-Tetraethylbenzene, † hexaethylbenzene	166
—	Ethyl bromide (—)	$AlCl_3$ (—)	Cold	—	1,2,4,5-Tetraethylbenzene, † 1,2,3,4-tetraethylbenzene, pentaethylbenzene	211
1.3	Ethyl iodide (0.5)	$AlCl_3$ or AlI_3 (—)	—	—	Ethylbenzene, polyethylbenzenes	164
0.1	Ethanol (0.1)	$ZnCl_2$ (0.15)	300	—	Ethylbenzene (poor yield)	171
1.6	Ethanol (0.3)	$AlCl_3$ (0.6)	120–130	10	Ethylbenzene (49%), *m*-diethylbenzene, diethylbiphenyl, and diethylterphenyl	27, 30
0.4	Ethanol (1.0)	$AlCl_3$ (1.5)	80	3	*sym*-Triethylbenzene (65–70%)	82
—	Ethyl ether (—)	$AlCl_3$ (—)	—	—	Hexaethylbenzene (50%)	212
3.0	Ethyl ether (0.5)	$AlCl_3$ (1.0)	25–120	48	Ethylbenzene (36%)	30
2	Ethyl ether (1)	BF_3 (1)	150	3	Ethylbenzene (25%), *p*-diethylbenzene (20%)	264
4	Ethyl ether (1)	$ZnCl_2$ (1)	180	12	Ethylbenzene	108
2	Ethyl formate (0.45)	$AlCl_3$ (0.67)	80	5	Ethylbenzene (63%), diethylbenzene (13%)	234
1	Ethyl formate (1)	BF_3 (1)	—	—	Ethylbenzene (6%)	23

1	Ethyl formate (3)	$AlCl_3$ (5)	0–95	—	*sym*-Triethylbenzene (50%)	261
—	Ethyl chloroformate (—)	$AlCl_3$ (—)	Cold	—	Ethylbenzene, polyethylbenzene	164, 279
0.3	Ethyl chloroformate (0.2)	$AlCl_3$ (0.1)	0–80	—	*p*-Diethylbenzene (40%)	231
8	Ethyl carbonate (0.5)	$AlCl_3$ (0.72)	25–70	30	Ethylbenzene (56%)	214
2	Ethyl acetate (0.45)	$AlCl_3$ (0.67)	80	5	Ethylbenzene (45%), *p*-ethylacetophenone (23%)	217, 234, 261
3	Ethyl acetate (0.25)	$AlCl_3$ (0.3)	80	1	Ethylbenzene (60%)	28
—	Ethyl acetate (—)	$AlCl_3$ (—)	0–25	25	Ethylbenzene (12–18.5%), *m*-diethylbenzene (30–50%), triethylbenzene (8–18%)	261
—	Ethyl chloroacetate (—)	$AlCl_3$ (—)	80	—	Ethylbenzene	164, 279
8	Ethyl sulfate (0.5)	$AlCl_3$ (0.72)	0–70	2	Ethylbenzene (71%)	214
3	Ethyl sulfate (0.125)	$AlCl_3$ (0.3)	80	1	Ethylbenzene (80%)	28
2	Ethyl *p*-toluenesulfonate (0.15)	$AlCl_3$ (0.2)	80	2	Ethylbenzene (64%)	139
8	Ethyl orthosilicate (0.25)	$AlCl_3$ (0.72)	25–70	20	Ethylbenzene (53%)	214
2.3	Cyclopropane (1)	$AlCl_3$—HCl (0.06)	0–5	5	*n*-Propylbenzene (65%)	26, 36
1	Cyclopropane (1)	$AlCl_3$—HCl (0.06)	25–30	3	*n*-Propylbenzene (30%), di-*n*-propylbenzene (20%)	36 36
1.1	Cyclopropane (0.4)	H_2SO_4 (0.4)	2	1	*n*-Propylbenzene (10%)	206
1.1	Cyclopropane (0.6)	H_2SO_4 (80%) (3.0)	65	5	Cumene (58%)	26
—	Cyclopropane (—)	HF (—)	0	—	*n*-Propylbenzene (42%), dipropylbenzene (20%)	307
—	Propylene (—)	HF (—)	0	—	Cumene (84%)	71, 303
5	Propylene (23)	HF (25)	20	24	1,2,4,5-Tetraisopropylbenzene (77%)	71
—	Propylene (—)	$FeCl_3$ (0.3)	25	—	Cumene (91%)	272
1	Propylene (0.75)	$AlCl_3$ (0.1)	80	—	Cumene (40%), *m*-di- and *sym*-triisopropylbenzenes	13

* References 93–350 appear on pp. 78–82.
† Products isolated through treatment with concentrated sulfuric acid, suggesting possibility of a Jacobsen rearrangement (211).

TABLE II—*Continued*

ALKYLATION OF BENZENE

Moles of Benzene	Alkylating Agent (moles)	Catalyst (moles)	Temperature, °C.	Time, hours (unless noted otherwise)	Products (% Yield)	Reference *
—	Propylene (—)	P_2O_5—H_3PO_4 (—)	80	—	Cumene	67
10	Propylene (7)	H_2SO_4 (96%) (3)	10	2	Cumene (78%), *p*-diisopropylbenzenes (18%)	198
2	Propylene (3)	H_2SO_4 (96%) (1.5)	10	2	Cumene (32%), *p*-diisopropylbenzene (33%), triisopropylbenzene (12%), 1,2,4,5-tetraisopropylbenzene (2%)	198
—	Propylene (—)	H_2SO_4 (96%) (—)	—	—	1,2,4,5-Tetraisopropylbenzene (35%)	222
2	Propylene (1.5)	H_2SO_4(1)	4	2	Cumene (35%), *p*-diisopropylbenzene (18%)	341
2	Propylene (1.5)	H_2SO_4 (1) (—) BF_3 (0.15)	4	2	Cumene (50%), *p*-diisopropylbenzene (30%), 1,2,4-triisopropylbenzene	341, 310
9.0	Polyisopropylbenzenes (65 g.)	$AlCl_3$ (0.1)	80	6	Cumene (65 g.)	48
13	Cymene (0.75)	$AlCl_3$ (0.03)	80	10	Toluene (80%), cumene (85–90%)	48
2	*n*-Propyl chloride (1)	$AlCl_3$ (0.08)	−6	5	*n*- and Isopropylbenzenes (41%; 3 : 2)	26
2	*n*-Propyl chloride (1)	$AlCl_3$ (0.08)	35	5	*n*- and Isopropylbenzenes (48%; 2 : 3)	26
6	*n*-Propyl chloride (1)	$Al(Hg)_x$ (0.1)	25	18	*n*- and Isopropylbenzenes (67%; 1 : 3)	347
1	*n*-Propyl chloride (3)	$AlCl_3$ (1)	−10	—	*sym*-Triisopropylbenzene † (90%)	180
0.7	*n*-Propyl bromide (0.4)	$AlCl_3$ (0.07)	−2	5	*n*-Propylbenzene (30%)	24
—	*n*-Propyl bromide (—)	$AlCl_3$ (—)	Below 0	—	*n*-Propylbenzene (30%)	25

—	*n*-Propyl bromide (—)	HF (—)	80	—	Isopropylbenzene (42%), *n*-propylbenzene (6%)	304
1.0	*n*-Propyl bromide (0.5)	$AlBr_3$ (—)	—	—	Cumene (30%)	21
—	*n*-Propyl alcohol (—)	H_2SO_4 (80%) (—)	65	—	Cumene (45%), *p*-diisopropylbenzene, 1,2,4-triisopropylbenzene	26, 29
1.6	*n*-Propyl alcohol (0.5)	$AlCl_3$ (0.7)	110	10	*n*-Propylbenzene (52%), *m*-di-*n*-propylbenzene (37%)	26, 27
1	*n*-Propyl alcohol (1)	BF_3 (1)	60	9	Cumene (20%), *p*-diisopropylbenzene (20%)	11
2	*n*-Propyl alcohol (0.5)	BF_3—P_2O_5 (0.5)	80	3	Cumene (60%), *p*-diisopropylbenzene (13%)	14
1	*n*-Propyl formate (1)	BF_3 (0.8)	—	—	Cumene (30%), *p*-diisopropylbenzene (30%)	23
3	*n*-I ropyl formate (0.25)	$AlCl_3$ (0.2)	25–60	8	*n*-Propylbenzene (60%)	28
2	*n*-Propyl acetate (0.45)	$AlCl_3$ (0.67)	80	5	Propylbenzene (32%), *p*-propylacetophenone	234
1	*n*-Propyl sulfate (1)	BF_3 (0.1)	—	—	Cumene (40%), *p*-diisopropylbenzene (25%)	23
3	*n*-Propyl sulfite (0.125)	$AlCl_3$ (0.2)	25–60	8	*n*-Propylbenzene (66%)	28
—	Isopropyl chloride (—)	$AlCl_3$ (—)	—	—	Cumene, *m*- and *o*-diisopropylbenzenes	300, 323
4	Isopropyl chloride (1)	Al—HCl (0.1)	25	18	Cumene (66%)	275
6	Isopropyl chloride (1)	$Al(Hg)_x$ (0.1)	25	18	Cumene (83%)	347
1	Isopropyl chloride (3)	$AlCl_3$ (1)	−10	—	*sym*-Triisopropylbenzene (90%) †	180
0.01	Isopropyl chloride (0.12)	$AlCl_3$ (0.01)	25	—	1,2,4,5-Tetraisopropylbenzene (10%)	334
—	Isopropyl bromide (—)	$AlBr_3$ (—)	—	—	Cumene	21
0.7	Isopropyl alcohol (0.7)	H_2SO_4 (80%) (6)	65	3–4	Cumene (65%)	29

* References 93–350 appear on pp. 78–82.
† Proceeds through the formation of an intermediate crystalline complex, $Al_2Cl_6 \cdot 2C_{15}H_{24} \cdot HCl$ (180).

TABLE II—*Continued*

ALKYLATION OF BENZENE

Moles of Benzene	Alkylating Agent (moles)	Catalyst (moles)	Temperature, °C.	Time, hours (unless noted otherwise)	Products (% Yield)	Reference *
2–5	Isopropyl alcohol (1.0)	$AlCl_3$ (0.5)	30	24	Cumene (25%)	30, 195
7.5	Isopropyl alcohol (15)	H_2SO_4 (80%) (65)	65	5	Cumene (8%), *p*-diisopropylbenzene (22%) 1,2,4-triisopropylbenzene (8%), 1,2,4,5-tetraisopropylbenzene	29, 218
1	Isopropyl alcohol (1)	BF_3 (0.7)	25	12	Cumene (20%), *p*-diisopropylbenzene (20%)	11
2	Isopropyl alcohol (0.5)	BF_3—P_2O_5 (0.5)	80	—	Cumene (40%), *p*-diisopropylbenzene (20%)	14
7	Isopropyl alcohol (1)	HF (—)	—	—	Cumene (22%), *p*-diisopropylbenzene (14%), 1,2,3-triisopropylbenzene (26%), 1,2,4,5-tetraisopropylbenzene (28%)	306
2	Isopropyl ether (1)	BF_3 (—)	—	—	Cumene (25%), *p*-diisopropylbenzene (20%)	264
7	Isopropyl ether (1)	HF (—)	—	—	Cumene (26%), *p*-diisopropylbenzene (24%), 1,2,4-triisopropylbenzene (25%), 1,2,4,5-tetraisopropylbenzene (8%)	306
2	Isopropyl phenyl ether (1)	BF_3 (—)	—	—	Cumene (25%), *p*-diisopropylbenzene (10%)	264

1	Isopropyl acetate (1)	BF_3 (1)	—	—	Cumene (15%), *p*-diisopropylbenzene (10%)	23
1	Isopropyl acetate (1)	BF_3 (1)	—	—	Cumene (15%), *p*-diisopropylbenzene (10%)	23
3	Isopropyl acetate (0.25)	$AlCl_3$ (0.3)	80	1	Cumene (68%)	28
—	Isopropyl acetate (—)	HF (—)	80	—	Cumene (53%), acetophenone, *p*-isopropylacetophenone	309
1	Isopropyl trichloroacetate (1)	BF_3 (0.3)	—	—	Cumene (30%), *p*-diisopropylbenzene (25%)	23
8	Isopropyl sulfate (0.5)	$AlCl_3$ (0.72)	0–70	2	Cumene (44%)	214
1	Isopropyl sulfate (1)	BF_3 (0.05)	—	—	Cumene (35%), *p*-diisopropylbenzene (25%)	23
2	Allyl chloride (0.7)	$AlCl_3$ (0.15)	—	—	*n*-Propylbenzene † (50%?)	12, 339, 340
—	Allyl chloride (—)	$AlCl_3$ (—)	—	—	Isopropylbenzene,† 1,2-diphenylpropane	302, 340
3	Allyl chloride (0.6)	$FeCl_3$ or $ZnCl_2$ (0.1)	25	—	2′-Chloro-*n*-propylbenzene (30%), 1,2-diphenylpropane	12
—	Allyl chloride (—)	H_2SO_4 (—)	—	—	2′-Chloroisopropylbenzene	67
1	Allyl alcohol (1)	BF_3 (—)	—	—	Allylbenzene (8%)	11
—	Allyl alcohol (—)	HF (—)	—	—	Allylbenzene (11–20%), 1,2-diphenylpropane (8–12%)	305
3	Trimethylene bromide (0.45)	$AlCl_3$ (0.25)	60–100	—	*n*-Propylbenzene (35%) 1,3-diphenylpropane (20%)	125
—	Isopropylidene chloride (—)	$AlCl_3$ (—)	—	—	Isopropylbenzene	302
—	1-Butene (—)	H_2SO_4 (96%) (—)	—	—	*s*-Butylbenzene, *p*-di-*s*-butylbenzene	198
—	Isobutylene (—)	P_2O_5 (—)	200–240	2	*t*-Butylbenzene (50%), *p*-di-*t*-butylbenzene (15%)	244

* References 93–350 appear on pp. 78–82.

† Bodroux (125) found that 1,2-diphenylpropane decomposed under the influence of aluminum chloride, yielding a mixture of *n*- and isopropylbenzenes.

TABLE II—*Continued*

ALKYLATION OF BENZENE

Moles of Benzene	Alkylating Agent (moles)	Catalyst (moles)	Temperature, °C.	Time, hours (unless noted otherwise)	Products (% Yield)	Reference *
2	Isobutylene (2.5)	H_2SO_4 (96%) (1.5)	15	1.2	*t*-Butylbenzene (7%), *p*-di-*t*-butylbenzene (77%), tri-*t*-butylbenzene (8%)	198, 222
—	Isobutylene (—)	HF (—)	0	—	*t*-Butylbenzene (44%), *p*-di-*t*-butylbenzene (41%)	303
—	Isobutylene (—)	$FeCl_3$ (0.3)	25	—	*t*-Butylbenzene (89%)	272
0.1	*n*-Butyl fluoride (0.1)	$AlCl_3$ (0.1)	—	—	*t*-Butylbenzene (10%)	18
4	*n*-Butyl chloride (0.8)	$AlCl_3$ (0.6)	0	48	*s*-Butylbenzene (50%)	287
8	*n*-Butyl chloride (1.6)	Al—$HgCl_2$ (0.3)	0	48	*n*- and *s*-Butylbenzenes (62%)	151
6	*n*-Butyl chloride (0.5)	Al—$HgCl_2$ (0.1)	80	—	*s*-Butylbenzene (80%)	151
6	*n*-Butyl chloride (1)	$Al(Hg)_x$ (0.1)	25	18	*s*-Butylbenzene (36%), *n*-butylbenzene	347
—	*n*-Butyl alcohol (—)	H_2SO_4 (80%) (—)	70	—	*s*-Butylbenzene, *p*-di-*s*-butylbenzene	29
1	*n*-Butyl alcohol (1)	BF_3 (1)	60	9	*s*-Butylbenzene (35%), *p*-di-*s*-butylbenzene (25%)	11
2	*n*-Butyl alcohol (0.5)	BF_3—P_2O_5 (0.5)	80	—	*s*-Butylbenzene (75%), *p*-di-*s*-butylbenzene (5–10%)	14
1	*n*-Butyl formate (1)	BF_3 (1)	80	5	*s*-Butylbenzene (30%), *p*-di-*s*-butylbenzene (30%)	23
3	*n*-Butyl formate (0.25)	$AlCl_3$ (0.3)	40–75	6	*s*-Butylbenzene (73%)	28
—	*n*-Butyl acetate (—)	HF (—)	80	—	*s*-Butylbenzene (60%)	309
2	*n*-Butyl acetate (0.45)	$AlCl_3$ (0.67)	80	5	Butylbenzene (32%), *p*-butylacetophenone (9%)	234

3	*n*-Butyl propionate (0.25)	$AlCl_3$ (0.3)	40–75	6	*s*-Butylbenzene (92%)	28
3	*n*-Butyl isobutyrate (0.25)	$AlCl_3$ (0.3)	40–75	6	*s*-Butylbenzene (73%)	28
3	*n*-Butyl valerate (0.25)	$AlCl_3$ (0.3)	40–75	6	*s*-Butylbenzene (85%)	28
3	*n*-Butyl 2-ethylvalerate (0.25)	$AlCl_3$ (0.3)	40–75	6	*s*-Butylbenzene (78%)	28
3	*n*-Butyl benzoate (0.25)	$AlCl_3$ (0.3)	40–75	6	*s*-Butylbenzene (80%)	28
3	*n*-Butyl stearate (0.25)	$AlCl_3$ (0.3)	40–75	6	*s*-Butylbenzene (40%)	28
3	*n*-Butyl oxalate (0.125)	$AlCl_3$ (0.3)	80	1	*s*-Butylbenzene (55%)	28
3	*n*-Butyl sulfite (0.125)	$AlCl_3$ (0.3)	80	1	*s*-Butylbenzene (41%)	28
2.67	*n*-Butyl sulfate (0.17)	$AlCl_3$ (0.24)	0–30	20	Butylbenzene (44%)	214
27	*n*-Butyl chlorosulfonate (3)	$AlCl_3$ (6)	0–5	3	*s*-Butylbenzene (19%), *m*-di-*s*-butylbenzene (27%), chlorobenzene (11%)	111
1	*n*-Butyl phosphate (1)	BF_3 (1)	—	—	*s*-Butylbenzene (8%), *p*-di-*s*-butyl benzene (20%)	23
8	*s*-Butyl chloride (0.9)	Al—$HgCl_2$ (0.15)	0	—	*s*-Butylbenzene (82%)	151
6	*s*-Butyl chloride (1)	$Al(Hg)_x$ (0.1)	25	18	*t*-Butylbenzene (60%)	347
—	*s*-Butyl alcohol (—)	H_2SO_4 (80%) (—)	70	—	*s*-Butylbenzene, *p*-di-*s*-butylbenzene	29
2–5	*s*-Butyl alcohol (1.0)	$AlCl_3$ (0.5)	30	24	*s*-Butylbenzene (25, 60%)	195, 273
1	*s*-Butyl alcohol (1)	BF_3 (0.7)	25	12	*s*-Butylbenzene (25, 50%), *p*-di-*s*-butylbenzene (20%, 12%)	11, 14, 273
2	*s*-Butyl alcohol (0.5)	BF_3—P_2O_5 (0.5)	—	—	*s*-Butylbenzene (45%), *p*-di-*s*-butyl benzene (13%)	14
2	*d*-*s*-Butyl alcohol (0.32)	$AlCl_3$ (0.3)	0–25	12	*dl*-*s*-Butylbenzene (50%)	273
1.3	*d*-*s*-Butyl alcohol (0.32)	BF_3 (0.2)	25	18	*l*-*s*-Butylbenzene (48%) (99.5% racemized)	273, 351
0.75	*l*-*s*-Butyl alcohol (0.16)	H_3PO_4 (0.78)	70	2	*d*-*s*-Butylbenzene (12%)	351
0.75	*l*-*s*-Butyl alcohol (0.16)	H_2SO_4 (0.18)	50	3	*d*-*s*-Butylbenzene (37%), di-*s*-butylbenzene (40%)	351
0.75	*l*-*s*-Butyl alcohol (0.16)	BF_3	20	12	*d*-*s*-Butylbenzene (51%)	351
0.75	*d*-*s*-Butyl alcohol (0.16)	HF (1.62)	16	5	*l*-*s*-Butylbenzene (30%), di-*s*-butylbenzene (27%)	351

* References 93–350 appear on pp. 78–82.

TABLE II—*Continued*

ALKYLATION OF BENZENE

Moles of Benzene	Alkylating Agent (moles)	Catalyst (moles)	Temperature, °C.	Time, hours (unless noted otherwise)	Products (% Yield)	Reference *
1	*s*-Butyl formate (1)	BF_3 (1)	—	—	*s*-Butylbenzene (20%), *p*-di-*s*-butylbenzene (15%)	23
1	*s*-Butyl acetate (1)	BF_3 (0.9)	—	—	*s*-Butylbenzene (25%), *p*-di-*s*-butylbenzene (15%)	23
—	*s*-Butyl isobutyrate (—)	HF (—)	80	—	*s*-Butylbenzene (56%)	309
—	Isobutyl chloride (0.5)	$AlCl_3$ (—)	—	—	*t*-Butylbenzene † (55%)	25, 175
12	Isobutyl chloride (3.3)	$AlCl_3$ (2.2)	0	48	*t*-Butylbenzene † (60%)	287
8	Isobutyl chloride (1.1)	$AlCl_3$ (0.7)	4	48	*t*-Butylbenzene † (70%) *p*-di-*t*-butylbenzene and tri-*t*-butylbenzene, m.p. 128°	295
0.08	Isobutyl alcohol (0.1)	$ZnCl_2$ (0.15)	260–270	48–72	*iso*- and *t*-Butylbenzenes	171, 296
13	Isobutyl alcohol (2)	H_2SO_4—SO_3(30%) (1 kg.)	0	0.7–0.8	*t*-Butylbenzene (50%), *p*-di-*t*-butylbenzene (40%)	326
0.2	Isobutyl alcohol (0.2)	H_2SO_4 (70%–80%) (5)	70	4	*t*-Butylbenzene (70%), *p*-di-*t*-butylbenzene	29
1	Isobutyl alcohol (1)	BF_3 (0.7)	—	—	*t*-Butylbenzene (12%), *p*-di-*t*-butylbenzene (10%)	11
1	Isobutyl formate (1)	BF_3 (1)	—	—	*t*-Butylbenzene (25%), *p*-di-*t*-butylbenzene (30%)	23

—	Isobutyl chloroformate (—)	$AlCl_3$ (—)	0	—	*t*-Butylbenzene	231
—	Isobutyl chloroformate (—)	$AlCl_3$ (—)	Warm	—	*p*-Di-*t*-butylbenzene (28%), tri-*t*-butylbenzene (15%) (m.p. 128°)	231
3	Isobutyl acetate (0.25)	$AlCl_3$ (0.2)	25–60	8	*t*-Butylbenzene (33%)	28
2	*t*-Butyl chloride (0.6)	$AlCl_3$ (0.4)	0	48	*t*-Butylbenzene (60%)	287
—	*t*-Butyl chloride (—)	HF (—)	0	—	*t*-Butylbenzene (10%), *p*-di-*t*-butylbenzene (60%)	304
1.3	*t*-Butyl chloride (0.3)	$FeCl_3$ (0.08)	25	—	*t*-Butylbenzene (80%)	42
6	*t*-Butyl chloride (1)	$Al(Hg)_x$ (0.1)	25	18	*t*-Butylbenzene (75%)	347
—	*t*-Butyl alcohol (—)	H_2SO_4 (70–80%) (—)	70	—	*t*-Butylbenzene, *p*-di-*t*-butylbenzene	29
2–5	*t*-Butyl alcohol (1.0)	$AlCl_3$ (0.5)	30	24	*t*-Butylbenzene (67%, 84%)	30, 195
—	*t*-Butyl alcohol (—)	$AlCl_3$ (—)	80–95	8	Toluene, ethylbenzene, cumene	30
1	*t*-Butyl alcohol (1)	BF_3 (0.3)	25	12	*t*-Butylbenzene (25%), di-*t*-butylbenzene (25%)	11
—	*t*-Butyl alcohol (—)	HF (—)	—	—	*t*-Butylbenzene (40%), *p*-di-*t*-butylbenzene (50%)	306
5	*t*-Butyl alcohol (1)	$FeCl_3$ (1)	25	—	*t*-Butylbenzene (82%)	85
—	*t*-Butyl acetate (—)	HF (—)	80	16	*t*-Butylbenzene (72%), acetophenone	309
1.63	2,2,4-Trimethylpentane (1.40)	$AlCl_3$—HCl (0.07)	25–50	4	*t*-Butylbenzene (35%), di-*t*-butylbenzenes (25%), isobutane (70%)	176
0.7	2,2,4-Trimethylpentane (0.5)	H_3PO_4 (0.15)	450	6	*t*-Butylbenzene (20%)	201
0.5	2,2,3-Trimethylpentane (0.25)	$AlCl_3$—HCl (0.03)	80–90	11	*t*-Butylbenzene (15%)	34
0.7	*p*-Di-*t*-butylbenzene (0.025)	$AlCl_3$ (0.002)	—	—	*t*-Butylbenzene (90%)	48
6	*p*-Di-*t*-butylbenzene (0.25)	$FeCl_3$ (0.2)	83	4	*t*-Butylbenzene (85%)	197

* References 93–350 appear on pp. 78–82.

† Boedtker (128) has reported that *t*-butylbenzene prepared from isobutyl chloride may be contaminated with *iso*- and *s*-butylbenzenes.

TABLE II—*Continued*

ALKYLATION OF BENZENE

Moles of Benzene	Alkylating Agent (moles)	Catalyst (moles)	Temperature, °C.	Time, hours (unless noted otherwise)	Products (% Yield)	Reference *
2	*p*-Di-*t*-butyl benzene (0.5)	H_2SO_4 (1.5)	50	5	*t*-Butylbenzene (31%), *p*-*t*-butylbenzenesulfonic acid (25%)	197
2	*p*-Di-*t*-butyl benzene (0.5)	H_3PO_4 (2)	300	6	*t*-Butylbenzene (23%)	197
3.0	Poly-*t*-butyl benzenes (22 g.)	$AlCl_3$ (0.03)	—	—	*t*-Butylbenzene (5 g.)	48
2	*p*-*t*-Butyl phenol (0.5)	$AlCl_3$ (0.67)	80	8	*t*-Butylbenzene, phenol	311
2	2-*p*-Hydroxyphenyl-2,4,4-trimethylpentane (0.5)	$AlCl_3$ (0.67)	25	12 days	*t*-Butylbenzene (50%)	311
2	2-*p*-Hydroxyphenyl-2,4,4-trimethylpentane (0.5)	$AlCl_3$ (0.67)	80	8	*t*-Butylbenzene (70%)	311
2	Isobutylene bromide (0.35)	$AlCl_3$ (0.15)	0–100	1.5	Isobutylbenzene (25%), 1,2-diphenyl-2-methylpropane (30%)	126
1.3	*n*-Pentane (0.7)	$AlCl_3$—HCl (0.06)	175	8	Toluene (10%), ethylbenzene (25%)	34
1.3	Isopentane (0.7)	$AlCl_3$—HCl (0.06)	175	8	Toluene (10%), ethylbenzene (25%)	34
0.4	1-Pentene (0.3)	H_2SO_4 (96%) (0.6)	5	1.2	2- and 3-Phenylpentanes (65%; ca. 3 : 2)	26
—	2-Pentene (—)	HF (—)	0	—	*s*-Amylbenzenes (47%)	303
5	3-Methyl-1-butene (3)	H_2SO_4 (96%) (1.8)	5	2	*t*-Amylbenzene (20%), di-*t*-amylbenzene (56%)	205
0.5	3-Methyl-1-butene (0.25)	$AlCl_3$—HCl (0.08)	5	1.7	3-Methyl-2-phenylbutane (12%)	26

5	Trimethylethylene (3)	H_2SO_4 (96%) (1.8)	5	2	*t*-Amylbenzene (18%), di-*t*-amylbenzene (50%)	205
—	Trimethylethylene (—)	HF (—)	0	—	*t*-Amylbenzene (21%), *p*-di-*t*-amylbenzene (60%)	303
2.3	Amylene (0.7)	$AlCl_3$ (0.2)	80	—	*t*-Amylbenzene (20%)	149
—	Amylene (—)	H_2SO_4 (—)	—	—	Amyl-, di-, and tri-amylbenzenes	198
1.2	Methylcyclobutane (0.4)	H_2SO_4 (0.9)	2	2.5	*t*-Amylbenzene (2%)	206
0.3	Methylcyclobutane (0.15)	$AlCl_3$—HCl (0.01)	25	22	Amylbenzenes (25% isoamylbenzene + isomers)	36
1.5	Cyclopentane (0.7)	$AlCl_3$—HCl (0.07)	150	8	Amylbenzenes, cyclopentylbenzene (8%)	36
0.5	*n*-Amyl alcohol (0.3)	H_2SO_4 (80%) (7)	70	6	2- and 3-Phenylpentanes (60%; ca. 3 : 2)	26
4	*n*-Amyl alcohol (0.5)	BF_3—P_2O_5 (0.5)	80	—	*s*-Amylbenzene (85%)	14
2	*n*-Amyl ether (1)	BF_3 (—)	150	3	*s*-Amylbenzene (20%)	264
—	Isoamyl chloride (—)	$AlCl_3$ (—)	—	—	*t*-Amylbenzene	164
5	Isoamyl chloride (1.6)	$AlCl_3$ (1.4)	0	48	*t*-Amylbenzene (20%)	287
—	Isoamyl chloride (—)	$AlCl_3$ (—)	0 or 80	—	Isoamylbenzene, 2-phenyl-3-methylbutane, *t*-amylbenzene	228
—	Isoamyl chloride (—)	$AlCl_3$ (—)	—	—	*t*-Amylbenzene (70%)	170
—	Isoamyl bromide (—)	$AlCl_3$ (—)	—	—	*t*-Amylbenzene	98
0.8	Isoamyl alcohol (0.8)	H_2SO_4 (80%) (6)	65	5	*t*-Amylbenzene (36%)	26
2	Isoamyl ether (1)	BF_3 (—)	150	3	*t*-Amylbenzene (10%)	264
7.5	*act*-Amyl chloride (αD = 0.11°) (2)	$AlCl_3$ (0.4)	—	—	*t*-Amylbenzene, diamylbenzene	101
2–5	2-Pentanol (1.0)	$AlCl_3$ (0.5)	30	24	2-Phenylpentane (25%)	195
2–5	3-Methyl-2-butanol (1.0)	$AlCl_3$ (0.5)	30	24	3-Methyl-2-phenylbutane (25%)	195
2	*t*-Amyl chloride (0.2)	$AlCl_3$ (0.1)	0	—	*t*-Amylbenzene (40%)	149, 287

* References 93–350 appear on pp. 78–82.

TABLE II—*Continued*

ALKYLATION OF BENZENE

Moles of Benzene	Alkylating Agent (moles)	Catalyst (moles)	Temperature, °C.	Time, hours (unless noted otherwise)	Products (% Yield)	Reference *
—	*t*-Amyl chloride (—)	HF (—)	0	—	*t*-Amylbenzene (42%), *p*-di-*t*-amylbenzene (22%)	304
—	*t*-Amyl bromide (—)	$AlCl_3$ (—)	—	—	*t*-Amylbenzene	98
7	*t*-Amyl alcohol (1)	HF (—)	—	—	*t*-Amylbenzene (40%), di-*t*-amylbenzene (50%)	306
0.2	Neopentyl chloride (0.15)	$AlCl_3$ (0.04)	0	—	2-Methyl-3-phenylbutane (24%)	270
0.25	Neopentyl alcohol (0.25)	H_2SO_4 (80%) (3)	65	6	*t*-Amylbenzene (30%)	270
1.0	Neopentyl alcohol (0.25)	$AlCl_3$ (0.33)	80	8	Neopentylbenzene (9%)	270
6	*p*-Di-*t*-amylbenzene (0.25)	$FeCl_3$ (0.25)	80	5	*t*-Amylbenzene (70%)	197
2	*p*-*t*-Amylphenol (0.5)	$AlCl_3$ (0.67)	25	12 days	*t*-Amylbenzene, phenol	311
—	Cyclopentyl chloride (—)	$AlCl_3$ (—)	15	3	Cyclopentylbenzene (47%)	349
1.3	Cyclobutylcarbinol (0.3)	$AlCl_3$ (0.2)	25	24	Benzylcyclobutane † (29%)	194
1.3	Cyclobutylcarbinol (0.3)	$AlCl_3$ (0.2)	75–80	—	Benzylcyclobutane † (21%)	194
0.6	*n*-Hexane (0.6)	H_3PO_4 (0.2)	450	10	Cumene (15%), butylbenzene (10%)	201
1.2	*n*-Hexane (0.6)	$AlCl_3$—HCl (0.06)	175	8	Toluene (10%), ethylbenzene (25%)	334
1	1-Hexene (1)	H_2SO_4 (0.1)	25	—	2-Phenylhexane (50%)	134
1	3-Hexene (0.66)	HF (—)	—	—	3-Phenylhexane (59%)	315
1	3-Hexene (0.66)	$H_3BO_2F_2$ (—)	—	—	3-Phenylhexane (24%)	315
1	3-Hexene (0.05)	H_2SO_4 (—)	—	—	3-Phenylhexane (50%)	315

1	3-Hexene (3.0)	HF (—)	—	—	*p*-Dihexylbenzene (41%)	315
10	2-Chloro-2-methylpentane (1)	$AlCl_3$ (0.2)	—	—	2-Phenyl-2-methylpentane (50%)	291
—	2-Methyl-2-pentanol (—)	$AlCl_3$ (—)	—	—	2-Phenyl-2-methylpentane (50%)	195
10	3-Chloro-3-methylpentane (1)	$AlCl_3$ (0.2)	—	—	3-Phenyl-3-methylpentane	291
—	3-Methyl-2-pentanol (—)	$AlCl_3$ (—)	—	—	3-Phenyl-3-methylpentane	195
—	2,3-Dimethyl-2-butanol (—)	$AlCl_3$ (—)	—	—	2,3-Dimethyl-2-phenylbutane	195
4	Cyclohexene (4)	$AlCl_3$ (0.4)	25–55	—	Cyclohexylbenzene (10%)	13
(Excess)	Cyclohexene (1)	H_2SO_4 (1)	—	0.5	Cyclohexylbenzene (70%), *p*-dicyclohexylbenzene (25%)	67, 81, 350
4.5	Cyclohexene (1.5)	$AlCl_3$ (0.45)	25	3	Cyclohexylbenzene (70%), diphenylcyclohexane (m.p. 169–170°)	58, 350
—	Cyclohexene (—)	HF (—)	0	—	Cyclohexylbenzene (62%)	303
1.3	Cyclohexyl chloride (0.4)	$AlCl_3$ (0.05)	5–25	—	Cyclohexylbenzene (50–60%), *m*-dicyclohexylbenzene and *p*-diphenylcyclohexane	232, 246
0.7	Cyclohexanol (0.6)	H_2SO_4 (80%) (6)	70	—	Cyclohexylbenzene (50%), dicyclohexylbenzene	29
1.0	Cyclohexanol (0.4)	$AlCl_3$ (0.25)	80	2	Cyclohexylbenzene (62%), *p*- and *m*-dicyclohexylbenzenes, *sym*-tricyclohexylbenzene	320
1	Cyclohexanol (1)	BF_3 (0.7)	—	—	Cyclohexylbenzene (35%), *p*-dicyclohexylbenzene (25%)	11
1	Cyclohexyl acetate (1)	BF_3 (0.3)	—	—	Cyclohexylbenzene (25%), *p*-dicyclohexylbenzene (12%)	23
1.7	Cyclopentylcarbinol (0.4)	$AlCl_3$ (0.2)	75–80	—	Benzylcyclopentane † (45%)	194
10	3-Chloro-2-methylhexane (1)	$AlCl_3$ (0.2)	—	—	3-Methyl-3-phenylhexane (40%)	182
10	3-Chloro-3-ethylpentane (1)	$AlCl_3$ (0.2)	—	—	3-Ethyl-3-phenylpentane	291

* References 93–350 appear on pp. 78–82.
† No proof was offered that rearrangement of the alkyl group had not occurred.

TABLE II—*Continued*

ALKYLATION OF BENZENE

Moles of Benzene	Alkylating Agent (moles)	Catalyst (moles)	Temperature, °C.	Time, hours (unless noted otherwise)	Products (% Yield)	Reference *
10	2,4-Dimethyl-2-chloropentane (1)	$AlCl_3$ (0.2)	—	—	2,4-Dimethyl-2-phenylpentane	291
1.3	1,1-Dichloroheptane (0.1)	$AlCl_3$ (0.1)	40–50	4	*n*-Heptylbenzene, 1,1-diphenylheptane (3 : 1)	100, 230
2.6	1,1-Dichloroheptane (0.3)	$AlCl_3$ (0.05)	25–30	48	*n*-Heptylbenzene, 1,1-diphenylheptane (1 : 2.5)	100, 230
2.5	3-Methylcyclohexene (0.7)	$AlCl_3$ (0.25)	25	3	Methylphenylcyclohexane (33%), di-(methylcyclohexyl)-benzene	58
—	3-Methylcyclohexyl chloride (—)	$AlCl_3$ (—)	—	—	3-Methyl-1-phenylcyclohexane	233
1.6	Cyclohexylcarbinol (0.3)	$AlCl_3$ (0.2)	75–80	—	Benzylcyclohexane † (7%)	194
0.5	Benzyl chloride (0.08)	$ZnCl_2$ (0.8)	80	12	Diphenylmethane (30%)	164
0.8	Benzyl chloride (0.25)	Zn (0.4)	80	3	Diphenylmethane (15%) toluene	164, 343
0.8	Benzyl chloride (0.2)	Ti (0.1)	90	10	Diphenylmethane (30%)	297
0.5	Benzyl chloride (0.08)	$AlCl_3$ (0.04)	—	—	Diphenylmethane (45%)	164
0.9	Benzyl chloride (0.8)	$AlCl_3$ (0.15)	7	—	Diphenylmethane (80%), *p*- and *o*-dibenzylbenzene	274
4.5	Benzyl chloride (0.4)	Al—HCl (0.1)	25	18	Diphenylmethane (63%)	275

4.5	Benzyl chloride (0.4)	Al—$HgCl_2$ (0.1)	0 25	3–48	Diphenylmethane (60%)	275
0.7	Benzyl chloride (0.25)	$Al(Hg)_x$ (0.5 g.)	100	—	Diphenylmethane (35%)	190
—	Benzyl chloride (—)	$SnCl_4$ (—)	—	—	Diphenylmethane (35%)	346
3	Benzyl chloride (0.1)	Ag_2SO_4 or $CH_2(SO_3Ag)_2$ (0.05)	80	4	Diphenylmethane (50%)	292
4	Benzyl chloride (0.2)	$TlCl_3$ (0.1)	80	—	Diphenylmethane, *p*- and *m*-dibenzylbenzene	217
2	Benzyl chloride (0.2)	$TiCl_4$ (0.15)	80	—	Diphenylmethane (40%) *p*- and *m*-dibenzylbenzene (8%, and 9%, resp.)	316
—	Benzyl chloride (—)	HF (—)	—	—	Diphenylmethane (56%)	305
2	Benzyl chloride (0.5)	$NaCl\cdot AlCl_3$ (0.15)	15–20	2	Diphenylmethane (50%)	263
0.5	Benzyl chloride (0.1)	TeO_2 (0.06)	80	72	Diphenylmethane (40%)	158
9	Benzyl alcohol (—)	HF (—)	—	—	Diphenylmethane (65–70%)	306
—	Benzyl alcohol (—)	H_2SO_4—HOAc (—)	Cold	—	Diphenylmethane	250
2	Benzyl alcohol (0.15)	P_2O_5 (0.2)	25	48	Diphenylmethane (30%)	258
2	Benzyl alcohol (0.15)	$AlCl_3$ (0.1)	25	48	Diphenylmethane (50%)	258
2.5	Benzyl alcohol (0.5)	$AlCl_3$ (0.3)	30–35	120	Diphenylmethane (55%), *p*- and *o*-dibenzylbenzenes, anthracene	192
0.3	Benzyl alcohol (0.2)	H_2SO_4 (70%) (4)	40	3	Diphenylmethane (40–50%), *p*-dibenzylbenzene	29
1	Benzyl alcohol (1)	BF_3 (0.7)	—	—	Diphenylmethane (15%), *p*-dibenzylbenzene (20%)	11
—	Benzyl methyl ether (—)	$SnCl_4$ (—)	—	—	Diphenylmethane	346
4	Benzyl methyl ether (0.2)	$TlCl_3$ (0.1)	80	—	Diphenylmethane, *p*- and *m*-dibenzylbenzene	217
—	Benzyl ethyl ether (0.15)	P_2O_5 (0.15)	80	—	Diphenylmethane (40%)	251, 258

* References 93–350 appear on pp. 78–82.
† No proof was offered that rearrangement of the alkyl group had not occurred.

TABLE II—*Continued*

ALKYLATION OF BENZENE

Moles of Benzene	Alkylating Agent (moles)	Catalyst (moles)	Temperature, ° C.	Time, hours (unless noted otherwise)	Products (% Yield)	Reference *
2	Benzyl ethyl ether (0.4)	$SnCl_4$ (0.2)	—	—	Diphenylmethane (25%), *p*- and *m*-dibenzylbenzenes	346
0.7	Benzyl ethyl ether (0.4)	$AlCl_3$ (0.3)	45	—	Diphenylmethane (15%)	192, 217
4	Benzyl ethyl ether (0.5)	$TiCl_4$ (0.25)	—	—	Diphenylmethane (55%), *p*- and *m*-dibenzylbenzenes (25%)	316
2	Benzyl ethyl ether (1)	BF_3 (—)	—	—	Diphenylmethane (20%)	264
4	Benzyl *n*-propyl ether (1)	BF_3 (0.5)	80–90	2	Diphenylmethane (33%)	255
3.3	Benzyl *n*-propyl ether (1)	BF_3 (1)	80–90	2	Diphenylmethane (46%), cumene (11%)	255
—	Benzyl isoamyl ether (—)	$SnCl_4$ (—)	—	—	Diphenylmethane	346
2	Benzyl ether (1)	BF_3 (—)	—	—	Diphenylmethane (15%), dibenzylbenzenes (20%), etc.	264
—	Benzyl ether (—)	HF (—)	—	—	Diphenylmethane (65–70%)	306
—	Benzyl acetate (—)	HF (—)	80	—	Diphenylmethane (75%)	309
—	Benzyl benzoate (—)	$SnCl_4$ (—)	—	—	Diphenylmethane, *p*-dibenzylbenzene	346
—	Benzyl benzoate (—)	$AlCl_3$ (—)	—	—	Diphenylmethane, *p*-dibenzylbenzene	217
—	Octene (—)	H_2SO_4 (—)	—	—	Octyl- and dioctyl-benzene	198
8	*n*-Octyl alcohol (1)	BF_3—P_2O_5 (1)	80	—	*s*-Octylbenzene (79%)	14
2.5	2-Methyl-2-heptanol (0.5)	$AlCl_3$ (0.25)	25	—	2-Methyl-2-phenylheptane (24)	31

10	4-Chloro-4-methylheptane (1)	$AlCl_3$ (0.2)	—	—	4-Methyl-4-phenylheptane (70%)	182
2.5	2,3-Dimethyl-2-hexanol (0.5)	$AlCl_3$ (0.25)	10	—	2,3-Dimethyl-2-phenylhexane (20%)	31
2.5	2,4-Dimethyl-2-hexanol (0.5)	$AlCl_3$ (0.25)	25	—	2,4-Dimethyl-2-phenylhexane (25%)	31
10	2-Chloro-2,5-dimethylhexane (1)	$AlCl_3$ (0.2)	—	—	2,5-Dimethyl-2-phenylhexane	182
10	3-Chloro-3-ethylhexane (1)	$AlCl_3$ (0.2)	—	—	3-Ethyl-3-phenylhexane (50%)	182
2.5	3-Ethyl-2-methyl-2-pentanol (0.5)	$AlCl_3$ (0.25)	10	—	3-Ethyl-2-methyl-2-phenylpentane (18%)	31
2.5	2,3,3-Trimethyl-2-pentanol (0.5)	$AlCl_3$ (0.25)	−15	—	2,3,3-Trimethyl-2-phenylpentane (4%), *t*-butylbenzene (9%)	31
2.5	2,4,4-Trimethyl-2-pentanol (0.5)	$AlCl_3$ (0.25)	−15	—	2,4,4-Trimethyl-2-phenylpentane (22%), *t*-butylbenzene (18%)	31
2.5	2,4,4-Trimethyl-2-pentanol (0.5)	$AlCl_3$ (0.25)	10	—	2,4,4-Trimethyl-2-phenylpentane (10%), *t*-butylbenzene (42%)	31
4	Styrene (0.25)	$AlCl_3$ (0.01)	25	—	1,1-Diphenylethane (5%) (mainly polystyrene)	259, 288
4	β-Phenylethyl chloride (0.25)	$AlCl_3$ (0.02)	25	45	1,2-Diphenylethane (85%)	259
—	α-Phenylethyl bromide (—)	Zn (—)	—	—	1,1-Diphenylethane	276
5	α-Phenylethyl alcohol (1)	$AlCl_3$ (0.5)	10	8 days	1,1-Diphenylethane (65%), ethylbenzene (4%), diphenylmethane	193
0.4	*m*-Xylyl chloride (4)	$AlCl_3$ (0.02)	80	0.1–0.2	*m*-Benzyltoluene (55%)	294
0.4	*m*-Xylyl chloride (4)	$AlCl_3$ (0.02)	Cold	6	*m*-Benzyltoluene (45%)	294
—	*o*-Xylyl chloride (—)	Zn (—)	—	—	*o*-Benzyltoluene	110
—	Nonene (—)	H_2SO_4 (—)	—	—	Nonyl- and dinonyl-benzenes	198
10	4-Chloro-4-ethylheptane (1)	$AlCl_3$ (0.2)	—	—	4-Ethyl-4-phenylheptane (75%)	181
10	3-Chloro-3,6-dimethylheptane (1)	$AlCl_3$ (0.2)	—	—	3,6-Dimethyl-3-phenylheptane (50%)	182

* References 93–350 appear on pp. 78–82.

TABLE II—*Continued*

ALKYLATION OF BENZENE

Moles of Benzene	Alkylating Agent (moles)	Catalyst (moles)	Temperature, °C.	Time, hours (unless noted otherwise)	Products (% Yield)	Reference *
10	3-Chloro-3-ethyl-5-methylhexane (1)	$AlCl_3$ (0.2)	—	—	3-Ethyl-5-methyl-3-phenylhexane (45%)	181
5	α-Phenylpropanol (1)	$AlCl_3$ (0.5)	10	12 days	1,1-Diphenylpropane (40%), *n*-propylbenzene (12%), diphenylmethane (4%)	193
—	Allylbenzene (—)	HF (—)	—	—	1,2-Diphenylpropane (63%)	305
10	4-Chloro-4-*n*-propylheptane (1)	$AlCl_3$ (0.2)	—	—	4-Phenyl-4-*n*-propylheptane (45%) (plus didecylbenzene)	182
10	4-Chloro-2,4,6-trimethylheptane (1)	$AlCl_3$ (0.2)	—	—	2,4,6-Trimethyl-4-phenylheptane (65%)	182
1.2	Menthene (0.3)	$AlCl_3$ (0.15)	25	3	Menthylbenzene (22%)	58
—	Menthyl chloride (—)	$AlCl_3$ (—)	—	—	Menthylbenzene	25
10	4-Chloro-4-*n*-propyl-2-methylheptane (1)	$AlCl_3$ (0.2)	—	—	2-Methyl-4-phenyl-4-*n*-propylheptane (50%)	182
—	5-Phenyl-1-chloropentane (—)	$AlCl_3$ (—)	—	—	Cyclopentylbenzene, 1,5-diphenylpentane	132
—	Dodecene (—)	H_2SO_4 (—)	—	—	Dodecyl- and didodecylbenzenes	198
4	*n*-Dodecyl alcohol (0.5)	BF_3—P_2O_5 (0.5)	80	—	*s*-Dodecylbenzene (33%)	14

2	*n*-Dodecyl alcohol (0.5)	BF_3—$C_6H_5SO_3H$ (0.5)	80	—	*s*-Dodecylbenzene (45%)	14
10	5-Chloro-2,5,8-trimethylnonane (1)	$AlCl_3$ (0.2)	—	—	2,5,8-Trimethyl-5-phenylnonane (70%)	182
1.1	1-Phenylcyclohexene (0.25)	$AlCl_3$ (0.1)	25	3	Diphenylcyclohexane (20%)	58
10	5-Chloro-2,8-dimethyl-5-ethylnonane (1)	$AlCl_3$ (0.2)	—	—	5-Ethyl-2,8-dimethyl-5-phenylnonane (60%)	182
—	Benzhydryl chloride (0.1)	$AlCl_3$ (—)	50	—	Diphenylmethane (35%), triphenylmethane (2%), triphenylmethyl chloride (30%)	130
0.7	Benzhydrol (0.02)	P_2O_5 (0.05)	0	48	Triphenylmethane (70%)	258
5	Benzhydrol (1)	$AlCl_3$ (1)	10	72	Triphenylmethane (70%), diphenylmethane (1%)	193
0.7	Benzhydryl ether (0.01)	P_2O_5 (0.04)	0	48	Triphenylmethane (60%)	258
0.7	Benzhydryl acetate (0.03)	H_2SO_4—HOAc (0.02)	0	48	Triphenylmethane (40%)	251
0.5	9-Chlorofluorene (0.03)	$AlCl_3$ (0.1)	80	3	9-Phenylfluorene	333
—	9-Hydroxyfluorene (0.06)	P_2O_5 (0.1)	140–150	5	9-Phenylfluorene	185
10	5-Chloro-2,8-dimethyl-5-*n*-propylnonane	$AlCl_3$ (0.2)	—	—	2,8-Dimethyl-5-phenyl-5-*n*-propylnonane (80%)	182
—	*p*-Methylbenzhydrol (—)	P_2O_5 (—)	130–150	2–3	Diphenyl-*p*-tolylmethane	156
10	5-Chloro-2,8-dimethyl-5-isobutylnonane (1)	$AlCl_3$ (0.2)	—	—	5-Isobutyl-2,8-dimethyl-5-phenylnonane	182
—	Di-*p*-xylylcarbinol (—)	P_2O_5 (—)	140	4	2,5,2′,5′-Tetramethyltriphenylmethane	146
—	*n*-Octadecyl bromide (—)	$AlCl_3$ (—)	—	—	*n*-Octadecylbenzene (50%)	56

* References 93–350 appear on pp. 78–82.

TABLE III

Alkylation of Halogenated Benzene Derivatives

Aromatic Compound (moles)	Alkylating Agent (moles)	Catalyst (moles)	Temperature, ° C.	Time, hours	Products (% Yield)	Reference *
Chlorobenzene (5)	Ethylene (—)	$AlCl_3$ (1)	100	—	*o*-, *m*-, and *p*-Chloroethylbenzenes (2 : 3 : 1), chlorodiethylbenzenes, etc.	46
Chlorobenzene (5)	Ethyl bromide (2)	$AlCl_3$ (0.1)	100	—	*p*-Chloroethylbenzene	290
Chlorobenzene (1)	Ethyl alcohol (0.6)	$AlCl_3$ (1)	80–90	2–3	*p*-Chloroethylbenzene (40%)	45
Chlorobenzene (1)	Isopropyl alcohol (—)	H_2SO_4 (80%) (—)	70	—	*p*-Chlorocumene (75%)	29
Chlorobenzene (1)	Isopropyl alcohol (1)	$AlCl_3$ (1)	80–90	2–3	*p*-Chlorocumene (62%)	45
Chlorobenzene (1)	*s*-Butyl alcohol (0.5)	$AlCl_3$ (0.4)	80–90	2–3	*p*-*s*-Butylchlorobenzene (50%)	45
Chlorobenzene (1.4)	Isobutyl alcohol (1.0)	$AlCl_3$ (1.5)	80–90	2–3	*p*-*t*-Butylchlorobenzene (30%)	45
Chlorobenzene (1)	*t*-Butyl alcohol (0.5)	$AlCl_3$ (0.2)	80–90	2–3	*p*-*t*-Butylchlorobenzene (65%)	45
Chlorobenzene (3.5)	Isoamyl chloride (0.6)	$AlCl_3$ (0.1)	100	—	*p*-*t*-Amylchlorobenzene	170
Chlorobenzene (1)	Isoamyl alcohol (0.5)	$AlCl_3$ (0.6)	80–90	2–3	*p*-*t*-Amylchlorobenzene (35%)	45
Chlorobenzene (1)	*t*-Amyl alcohol (0.5)	$AlCl_3$ (0.2)	80–90	2–3	*p*- and *m*-*t*-Amylchlorobenzene (50%)	45
Chlorobenzene (1)	3-Hexene (0.66)	HF (—)	—	—	2-(*p*-Chlorophenyl)hexane (25%)	315
Chlorobenzene (1.5)	Cyclohexyl chloride (0.5)	$AlCl_3$ (0.1)	25	—	*p*-Cyclohexylchlorobenzene (70%)	246
o-Dichlorobenzene (0.7)	Methyl chloride (—)	$AlCl_3$ (0.2)	100	12	Hexamethylbenzene, trichloromesitylene	165, 165
Bromobenzene (2.5)	Ethyl bromide (2)	$AlCl_3$ (0.1)	100	—	*o*-, and *p*-Bromoethylbenzenes	290
Bromobenzene (1)	Ethyl bromide (2)	$AlCl_3$ (2)	0–25	24	*sym*-Triethylbenzene, *p*-dibromobenzene	348
Bromobenzene (15)	Isoamyl chloride (1)	$AlCl_3$ (0.2)	25	48–72	*p*-*t*-Amylbromobenzene	170
Bromobenzene (7.5)	Cyclohexyl chloride (2.5)	$AlCl_3$ (0.6)	25	12	*o*-, *m*-, and *p*-Cyclohexylbromobenzene (65%), *p*-dibromobenzene	54, 135, 246

* References 93–350 appear on pp. 78–82.

TABLE IV

ALKYLATION OF TOLUENE

Moles of Toluene	Alkylating Agent (moles)	Catalyst (moles)	Temperature, °C.	Time, hours	Products (% Yield)	Reference *
30	Methyl chloride (—)	$AlCl_3$ (10)	80	—	*m*-Xylene and *p*-xylene (20 : 1), pseudocumene and mesitylene (5 : 1), durene and isodurene	94
60	Methyl chloride (—)	$AlCl_3$ (20)	80	—	*o*-Xylene and *m*- and *p*-xylenes), pseudocumene, mesitylene	50,† 209
3.5	Methyl chloride (—)	$AlCl_3$ (0.55)	93–95	—	Durene (30%)	117
1.5	Methyl chloride (0.4)	$AlCl_3$ (1.5)	0	2	*o*-, *m*- and *p*-Xylenes (5 : 3 : 2)	37
1.5	Methyl chloride (0.4)	$AlCl_3$ (1.5)	100	0.1	*m*- and *o*-Xylenes (50 : 1)	37
1.9	Methyl bromide (0.6)	$AlCl_3$ (0.9)	0	1	*o*-, *m*- and *p*-Xylenes (2 : 1 : 1)	37
1.9	Methyl bromide (0.6)	$AlCl_3$ (0.9)	95	—	*m*-, *p*- and *o*-Xylenes (10 : 1 : 1)	37
2.5	Methyl alcohol (1)	$AlCl_3$ (2)	100	3	Mesitylene (53%)	30, 82
0.2	Methyl chloroformate (0.2)	$AlCl_3$ (0.15)	80	0.25	*p*-Xylene, pseudocumene	231
0.6	Ethylene (—)	$AlCl_3$ (0.5)	80–90	3–4	3,5-Diethyltoluene (good yield)	167
3	Ethylene (3)	$AlCl_3$ (0.2)	80	—	Ethyltoluene (35%)	13
0.5	Ethyl bromide (1.0)	$AlCl_3$ (1.0)	−10	18	3,5-Diethyltoluene (78%)	37
0.9	Ethanol (0.5)	$AlCl_3$ (0.75)	140	8	*m*- and *p*-Ethyltoluene (74%), diethyltoluene (20%)	27
0.25	Ethyl chloroformate (0.2)	$AlCl_3$ (0.1)	25–80	—	3,4-Diethyltoluene (35%)	231
7	Propylene (2)	$AlCl_3$ (0.5)	80	—	*p*-Cymene (50%)	13
9.4	Propylene (16.6)	P_2O_5 (0.3)	150	—	*p*-Cymene (50%)	244
—	Propylene (—)	H_2SO_4 (—)	15	—	*p*-Cymene (50%)	198, 310
0.9	Propyl alcohol (0.5)	$AlCl_3$ (0.7)	125	4	*m*- and *p*-Propyltoluene (85%), dipropyltoluenes (10%)	27
—	Isopropyl chloride (—)	$AlCl_3$ (—)	—	—	*m*-Cymene	301, 302
5	Isopropyl iodide (0.6)	$AlCl_3$ (0.3)	80–100	—	*m*-Cymene (75%)	215

* References 93–350 appear on pp. 78–82.

† Jacobsen [reference 50, p. 342 (footnote 1)] points out that the aluminum chloride-catalyzed decomposition of pseudocumene (I) to *m*-xylene (II) suggests that (I) is an intermediate in the formation of II by the methylation of toluene, as reported by Ador and Rilliet (94).

TABLE IV—*Continued*

ALKYLATION OF TOLUENE

Moles of Toluene	Alkylating Agent (moles)	Catalyst (moles)	Temperature, °C.	Time, hours	Products (% Yield)	Reference *
0.4	Isopropyl alcohol (0.4)	H_2SO_4 (80%) (5)	70	—	*p*-Cymene (35%), diisopropyltoluene	29, 218
0.9	2,2,4-Trimethylpentane (0.6)	$AlCl_3$—HCl (0.04)	80–90	8	*m*-*t*-Butyltoluene (34%)	177
4.35	Diisobutylene (2)	HF (5)	0–5	20	*p*-*t*-Butyltoluene (77%), di-*t*-butyltoluene (19%)	71
1.4	*n*-Butyl chloride (0.25)	$AlCl_3$ (0.1)	0	5	*m*- and *p*-*s*-Butyltoluenes (75 : 25, 46%)	298
0.05	*n*-Butyl alcohol (0.08)	$ZnCl_2$ (0.15)	300	24	Butyltoluene	171
54	*n*-Butyl chlorosulfonate (6)	$AlCl_3$ (12)	0	3	*m*-*s*-Butyltoluene (32%), *p*-*s*-butyltoluene (20%), *o*-chlorotoluene (22%), *p*-chlorotoluene (6%)	111
—	*s*-Butyl alcohol (—)	H_2SO_4 (80%) (—)	70	—	*p*-*s*-Butyltoluene	29
1	Isobutyl chloride (1)	$FeCl_3$ (—)	—	—	*p*-*t*-Butyltoluene (30%)	121
—	Isobutyl chloride (—)	$AlCl_3$ (—)	—	—	*m*- and *p*-*t*-Butyltoluenes	227
11	Isobutyl alcohol (3.3)	H_2SO_4—SO_3 (25%) (1 kg.)	25	0.7–0.8	*p*-*t*-Butyltoluene (60%)	326
0.05	Isobutyl alcohol (0.05)	$ZnCl_2$ (0.15)	300	24	Butyltoluene	171
—	Isobutyl alcohol (—)	H_2SO_4 (80%) (—)	70	—	*p*-*t*-Butyltoluene	29
—	Isobutyl chloroformate (—)	$AlCl_3$ (—)	—	—	*p*-*t*-Butyltoluene (25%)	231
1	*t*-Butyl chloride (1)	$FeCl_3$ (—)	—	—	*p*-*t*-Butyltoluene (50%)	121
—	*t*-Butyl chloride (—)	$AlCl_3$ (—)	0–100	—	*m*-*t*-Butyltoluene, *t*-butylbenzene and 3,5-dimethyl-*t*-butylbenzene	114
1.4	*t*-Butyl chloride (0.25)	$AlCl_3$ (0.1)	0	5	*m*- and *p*-*t*-Butyltoluene (62 : 38,† 46%)	298
1.4	*t*-Butyl chloride (0.25)	$FeCl_3$ or $AlCl_3$—$C_6H_5NO_2$ (0.1)	0	5	*m*- and *p*-*t*-Butyltoluene (67 : 33,† 70–75%)	298
—	*t*-Butyl chloride (—)	HF (—)	0	—	*p*-*t*-Butyltoluene (75%)	304
5.5	Amylene (3)	$AlCl_3$ (0.2)	25–100	—	*m*-*t*-Amyltoluene (45%)	150

—	*act*-Amyl chloride (—)	$AlCl_3$ (—)	—	—	*m*-*t*-Amyltoluene	150
—	Isoamyl chloride (—)	$AlCl_3$ (—)	—	—	*m*-*t*-Amyltoluene	150
—	Amyl chloroformate (—)	$AlCl_3$ (—)	—	—	*p*-Amyltoluene (30%)	231
1.0	3-Hexene (0.66)	HF (—)	—	—	3-(*p*-Tolyl)-hexane (63%)	315
5	Cyclohexene (1.5)	$AlCl_3$ (0.45)	25	3	Cyclohexyltoluene (40%)	58
—	Cyclohexene (—)	HF (—)	0	—	*p*-Cyclohexyltoluene (74%)	20
—	Cyclohexyl fluoride‡ (—)	HF (—) or BF_3	0	—	*p*-Cyclohexyltoluene (76%)	20, 351
—	Cyclohexyl chloride‡ (—)	HF (—)	—	—	*p*-Cyclohexyltoluene (8%)	20
—	Cyclohexyl chloride (—)	$AlCl_3$ (—)	—	—	*m*- and *p*-Cyclohexyltoluene	233
2	Cyclohexanol (0.75)	$AlCl_3$ (0.6)	80	2	*m*- and *p*-Cyclohexyltoluene (72%), 3,5-dicyclohexyltoluene (18%)	320
—	Cyclohexanol (—)	HF (—)	—	—	*p*-Cyclohexyltoluene (45%)	20
—	Benzyl chloride (—)	$AlCl_3$ (—)	—	—	Benzyltoluene, dibenzyltoluene, 2,7-dimethylanthracene	164
—	Benzyl chloride (0.1)	$Al(Hg)_x$ (0.02)	—	—	Benzyltoluene, dimethylanthracene	190
—	Benzyl chloride (0.2)	Ti (0.1)	90	10	*p*-Benzyltoluene (35%), 2,4-dibenzyltoluene (30%)	297
2.5	Benzyl chloride (3)	Zn (—)	100	—	*o*- and *p*-Benzyltoluenes (total yield—45%)	344
—	Benzyl ethyl ether (—)	P_2O_5 (—)	—	—	*p*-Benzyltoluene	251
1	Benzyl alcohol (0.4)	H_2SO_4 (70%) (15)	40	—	*p*-Benzyltoluene, anthracene	29
—	1-Octene (—)	HF (—)	—	—	*p*-Octyltoluene (73%)	20
—	2-Fluorooctane § (—)	HF (—)	—	—	*p*-Octyltoluene (13%)	20
—	2-Octanol (—)	HF (—)	—	—	*p*-Octyltoluene (42%)	20
5	Styrene (0.4)	H_2SO_4 (—)	—	—	1-Phenyl-1-tolylethane (65%)	229
—	α-Phenylethyl bromide (—)	Zn (—)	—	—	1-Phenyl-1-*p*-tolylethane	109
—	Bornyl chloride (—)	$AlCl_3$ (—)	10–40	—	*m*- and *p*-Bornyltoluene	213
—	Benzhydrol (—)	P_2O_5 (—)	—	—	Diphenyl-*p*-tolylmethane	156
—	Benzhydrol (—)	$SnCl_4$ (—)	—	—	Diphenyl-*p*-tolylmethane	122
—	9-Hydroxyfluorene (—)	P_2O_5 (—)	110	—	9-*p*-Tolylfluorene (good yield)	185

* References 93–350 appear on pp. 78–82.

† The ratio of isomers was determined by sulfonation with concentrated sulfuric acid. Since Ipatieff and Corson (197) have demonstrated that a *t*-butyl group will migrate under these conditions, this proof cannot be considered entirely adequate.

‡ Cyclohexyl bromide and iodide failed to react under these conditions (20, 351).

§ 2-Chloro- and 2-bromo-octane failed to react under similar conditions (20).

TABLE V

ALKYLATION OF VARIOUS ALKYLBENZENES

Aromatic Compound (moles)	Alkylating Agent (moles)	Catalyst (moles)	Temperature, °C.	Time, hours	Products (% Yield)	Reference*
o-Chlorotoluene (0.2)	*t*-Butyl alcohol (0.25)	$AlCl_3$ (0.1)	80–90	2–3	2-Chloro-*x*-*t*-butyltoluene (45%)	45
Ethylbenzene (3)	*n*-Propyl bromide (4)	$AlCl_3$ (0.4)	25	192	*m*- and *p*-Ethylisopropylbenzenes (10% each)	118
Ethylbenzene (2)	*t*-Butyl chloride (0.45)	$FeCl_3$ (0.03)	−10	48	Ethyl-*t*-butylbenzene (100%)	114
Ethylbenzene (—)	*t*-Butyl chloride (—)	$AlCl_3$ (CS_2) (—)	−10	—	Ethyl-*t*-butylbenzene (low yield), *t*-butylbenzene, *t*-butyltoluene, etc.	114
Ethylbenzene (2)	Benzyl chloride (25)	Zn (—)	—	—	*p*-Ethyldiphenylmethane (35%)	330
Ethylbenzene (—)	α-Phenylethylbromide (—)	Zn (—)	—	—	1-Phenyl-1-*p*-ethylphenylethane	276
o-Xylene (—)	Methylchloride (—)	$AlCl_3$ (—)	80	—	Pseudocumene	209, 284
o-Xylene (—)	Benzyl alcohol (—)	H_2SO_4 (70%) (—)	40	—	3,4-Dimethyldiphenylmethane, 1-methylanthracene	29
o-Xylene (0.4)	Styrene (0.15)	H_2SO_4 (0.2)	Cold	—	1-Phenyl-1-*o*-xylylethane (70%)	229
o-Xylene (—)	3-Chloro-1-phenylpropane (—)	$AlCl_3$ (—)	—	—	1-Phenyl-3-*o*-xylylpropane (60%)	133
o-Xylene (—)	Benzhydrol (—)	P_2O_5 (—)	140	4	3,4-Dimethyltriphenylmethane	188
m-Xylene (—)	Methyl chloride (—)	$AlCl_3$ (—)	80	—	Pseudocumene and mesitylene (4 : 1)	209, 284
m-Xylene (2)	Methyl chloride (1.8)	$AlCl_3$ (4)	100	1	Mesitylene (65%)	37
m-Xylene (30)	Methyl chloride (—)	$AlCl_3$ (7.5)	80–90	100	Tetramethylbenzenes (50%), durene, (15%), pentamethylbenzene (18%), hexamethylbenzene	265
m-Xylene (—)	Methyl iodide (—)	I_2 (trace)	250	4–8	Pseudocumene and mesitylene	277
m-Xylene (0.3)	Ethylene (—)	$AlCl_3$ (0.2)	—	1.5	5-Ethyl-1,3-dimethylbenzene (50%)	167
m-Xylene (2)	Ethyl bromide (2)	$AlCl_3$ (0.4)	40	48	5-Ethyl-1,3-dimethylbenzene, 4-ethyl-1,3-dimethylbenzene (total yield—35%)	318
m-Xylene (1)	Ethyl bromide (1)	$AlCl_3$ (2)	0	—	5-Ethyl-1,3-dimethylbenzene † (45%)	37
m-Xylene (—)	Ethyl chloroformate	$AlCl_3$ (—)	—	—	5-Ethyl-1,3-dimethylbenzene (25%)	231
m-Xylene (1)	Cyclopropane (0.5)	$AlCl_3$ (0.03)	0–15	—	4-*n*-Propyl-*m*-xylene (40%)	41

m-Xylene (1)	Cyclopropane (0.5)	$FeCl_3$ (0.06)	—	—	4-*n*-Propyl-*m*-xylene (19%)	41
m-Xylene (0.5)	*n*-Propyl chloride (0.3)	$AlCl_3$ (0.1)	25	4	5-Isopropyl-*m*-xylene (46%)	41
m-Xylene (1)	*n*-Propyl formate (0.3)	$AlCl_3$ (—)	25–60	—	5-Isopropyl-*m*-xylene (50%)	41
m-Xylene (0.5)	Isopropyl chloride (0.3)	$AlCl_3$ (0.1)	25	4	5-Isopropyl-*m*-xylene (48%)	41
m-Xylene (3)	Isopropyl alcohol (0.6)	H_2SO_4 (80%) (8)	75	16	4-Isopropyl-*m*-xylene (75%)	41
m-Xylene (1.3)	*n*-Butyl chloride (0.5)	$AlCl_3$ (0.2)	0	5	5-*s*-Butyl-*m*-xylene (50%)	39
m-Xylene (3)	*s*-Butyl alcohol (0.6)	H_2SO_4 (80%) (9)	25	16	4-*s*-Butyl-*m*-xylene (50%)	39
m-Xylene (—)	Isobutyl bromide (—)	$AlCl_3$ (—)	100	—	3,5-Dimethyl-*t*-butylbenzene	114
m-Xylene (1)	Isobutyl alcohol (1)	H_2SO_4 (5)	45	1	3,5-Dimethyl-*t*-butylbenzene	260
m-Xylene (1)	*t*-Butyl chloride (1)	$AlCl_3$ (0.4)	100	—	5-*t*-Butyl-*m*-xylene ‡ (23–26%)	40
m-Xylene (1.3)	*t*-Butyl chloride (0.5)	$AlCl_3$ (0.2)	25	—	5-*t*-Butyl-*m*-xylene ‡ (50%)	39
m-Xylene (1.6)	*t*-Butyl alcohol (1.2)	HF (25)	0	18	*t*-Butyl-*m*-xylene (94%)	71
m-Xylene (1.75)	*t*-Butyl alcohol (0.3)	$AlCl_3$ (0.9)	0	5	5-*t*-Butyl-*m*-xylene (89%)	30
m-Xylene (3)	*t*-Butyl alcohol (0.6)	H_2SO_4 (80%) (9)	25	16	4-*t*-Butyl-*m*-xylene (48%)	39
m-Xylene (1)	3-Hexene (0.75)	HF (—)	—	—	Hexylxylenes (80%)	315
m-Xylene (1)	3-Bromohexane (1)	$AlCl_3$ (—)	—	—	3-(*m*-Xylyl)-hexane (27%)	315
m-Xylene (1)	3-Hexyl ether (0.18)	HF (—)	—	—	3-(*m*-Xylyl)-hexane (61%)	315
m-Xylene (4)	Cyclohexene (1.5)	$AlCl_3$ (0.45)	25	3	5-Cyclohexyl-*m*-xylene (56%)	58
m-Xylene (0.5)	Cyclohexyl bromide (0.3)	$FeCl_3$ (0.02)	20–50	3	5-Cyclohexyl-*m*-xylene (75%)	113
m-Xylene (0.5)	3-Ethyl-α-pentene (0.2)	$AlCl_3$—HCl (0.004)	25–50	3	3-Ethyl-3-(3,5-dimethylphenyl)pentane (50%)	113
m-Xylene (—)	Benzyl chloride (—)	Zn (—)	—	—	2,4-Dimethyldiphenylmethane	345
m-Xylene (—)	Benzyl alcohol (—)	H_2SO_4 (70%) (—)	40	—	2,4-Dimethyldiphenylmethane, 2-methylanthracene	29
m-Xylene (5)	Styrene (0.3)	H_2SO_4 (0.5)	Cold	—	1-Phenyl-1-*m*-xylylethane (65%)	229
m-Xylene (—)	Benzhydrol (—)	P_2O_5 (—)	140	4	2,4-Dimethyltriphenylmethane	188
p-Xylene (—)	Methyl chloride (—)	$AlCl_3$ (—)	80	—	Pseudocumene (pure)	209, 284
p-Xylene (0.5)	Ethyl bromide (0.5)	$AlCl_3$ (CS_2) (0.1)	—	24	2-Ethyl-1,4-dimethylbenzene (25%)	124
p-Xylene (—)	Ethyl chloroformate (—)	$AlCl_3$ (—)	25–80	—	2-Ethyl-1,4-dimethylbenzene (40%)	231
p-Xylene (2)	Cyclohexene (0.7)	$AlCl_3$ (0.2)	25	3	2-Cyclohexyl-*p*-xylene (33%), dicyclohexyl-*p*-xylene (5%)	58

* References 93–350 appear on pp. 78–82.
† See the original literature (37, 262) for certain discrepancies concerning the derivatives of this hydrocarbon.
‡ The hydrocarbon was also formed by treating the 4-isomer with aluminum chloride (40).

TABLE V—*Continued*

ALKYLATION OF VARIOUS ALKYLBENZENES

Aromatic Compound (moles)	Alkylating Agent (moles)	Catalyst (moles)	Temperature, °C.	Time, hours	Products (% Yield)	Reference*
p-Xylene (—)	3-Methylcyclohexene (—)	$AlCl_3$ (—)	25	3	2-(Methylcyclohexyl)-*p*-xylene (19%)	58
p-Xylene (—)	Benzyl chloride (—)	Zn (—)	—	—	2,5-Dimethyldiphenylmethane	345
p-Xylene (—)	Benzyl alcohol (—)	H_2SO_4 (70%) (—)	40	—	2,5-Dimethyldiphenylmethane, 2-methylanthracene	29
p-Xylene (—)	Styrene (—)	H_2SO_4 (—)	Cold	—	1-Phenyl-1-*p*-xylylethane	229
p-Xylene (—)	Benzhydrol (—)	P_2O_5 (—)	140	4	2,5-Dimethyltriphenylmethane	187
p-Xylene (—)	2,5-Dimethylbenzhydrol (—)	P_2O_5 (—)	140	4	2,5,2′,5′-Tetramethyltriphenylmethane (50–60%)	146
p-Xylene (0.3)	2-Methyl-5-isopropylbenzhydrol (0.1)	P_2O_5 (0.1)	140	5	2,2′5′-Trimethyl-5-isopropyltriphenylmethane (35%)	146
n-Propylbenzene (0.4)	*n*-Propylbenzene (0.4)	$AlCl_3$ (—)	100	6	*m*- and *p*-Di-*n*-propylbenzenes (50%)	24
Cumene (1)	Propylene (1.97)	$AlCl_3$ (0.1)	80	—	1,3,5- and 1,2,4-Triisopropylbenzenes (60%, 3 : 1), *m*- and *p*-diisopropylbenzenes, (2 : 1)	13

Cumene (—)	Isobutyl chloride (—)	$AlCl_3$ (—)	25	—	*t*-Butylbenzene, *p*-di-*t*-butylbenzene, isopropyl chloride	47
Pseudocumene (—)	Methyl chloride (—)	$AlCl_3$ (—)	80	—	Durene	209
Pseudocumene (—)	Methyl chloride (—)	$AlCl_3$ (—)	100–110	—	Penta- and hexa-methylbenzene	210
Pseudocumene † (1)	Methyl iodide (1)	$AlCl_3$ (0.8)	45	120	Durene and isodurene (total yield, 80–85%)	138
Pseudocumene (—)	Styrene (0.5)	H_2SO_4 (—)	Cold	—	1-Phenyl-1-pseudocumylethane (75%)	229
Mesitylene (—)	Methyl chloride (—)	$AlCl_3$ (—)	80	—	Isodurene	209
Mesitylene (—)	Methyl chloride (—)	$AlCl_3$ (—)	100–110	—	Penta- and hexa-methylbenzene	210
Mesitylene † (1)	Methyl iodide (1)	$AlCl_3$ (0.8)	45	120	Isodurene and durene (total yield, 80–85%)	138
Mesitylene † (2)	Cyclohexene (0.6)	$AlCl_3$ (0.2)			Cyclohexylmesitylene (21%)	58
Mesitylene (1)	Benzyl chloride (0.2)	$AlCl_3$ (0.01)	25 100	3 —	Benzylmesitylene (good yield), dibenzylmesitylene	241, 242
Mesitylene (—)	Benzyl chloride (—)	*p*-Cymene (—)	(Boiling)	60	Benzylmesitylene	259
Durene † (0.08)	Benzyl chloride (0.07)	$AlCl_3$ (trace)	45	12	Benzyldurene	117
p-Cymene (—)	*p*-Cymene (—)	$AlCl_3$ (—)	—	—	3,5-Triisopropyltoluene	52
p-Cymene (1)	Cyclohexene (0.2)	$AlCl_3$ (0.1)	25	3	Cyclohexyl-*p*-cymene (46%), dicyclohexyltoluene (30%)	58
Amylbenzene (1)	*act*-Amyl chloride (1)	$AlCl_3$ (0.1)	—	—	Diamylbenzene	101
Di-*n*-propylbenzene (0.01)	*n*-Propyl chloride (0.6)	$AlCl_3$ (0.005)	25	45	Hexa-*n*-propylbenzene (10%)	334

* References 93–350 appear on pp. 78–82.
† In carbon disulfide.

TABLE VI

Alkylation of Tetralin

Moles of Tetralin	Alkylating Agent (moles)	Catalyst (moles)	Temperature, ° C.	Time	Products (% Yield)	Reference *
3	Methyl bromide (0.8)	$AlBr_3$ (0.05)	140–150	48 hours	β-Methylnaphthalene (14%), benzene, octahydroanthracene, octahydrophenanthrene †	69
—	Ethylene (—)	H_3PO_4 (—)	300	—	Ethyltetralin, etc.	204
15	Ethyl bromide (5)	$AlCl_3$ (0.5)	80	—	β-Ethyltetralin (3%)	129
6	Ethyl bromide (3)	$AlBr_3$ (0.15)	110–120	20 hours	β-Ethyltetralin (28–35%), β-(δ-phenylbutyl)-tetralin	69
1	Propylene (5.3)	HF (23)	5–15	20 hours	Isopropyltetralins	71
5	*n*-Propyl chloride (1.3)	$AlCl_3$ (0.15)	25–80	15 days	β-Isopropyltetralin (10%)	129
3	Isopropyl bromide (1)	$AlBr_3$ (0.05)	120–130	40 hours	β-Isopropyltetralin (37%)	69
4	*t*-Butyl chloride (1)	$AlCl_3$ (0.08)	50	—	β-*t*-Butyltetralin (20%)	129
2.3	*t*-Butyl bromide (1)	$AlBr_3$ (0.3)	—	—	β-*t*-Butyltetralin (70%)	69
4	*t*-Amyl chloride (1)	$AlCl_3$ (0.08)	25	48–72 hours	β-*t*-Amyltetralin (20%), α-*t*-amyltetralin (8%)	129
—	Cyclopentene (—)	$AlCl_3$ (—)	—	—	Cyclopentyltetralin, dicyclopentyltetralin	271
1.7	Cyclohexene (0.5)	$AlCl_3$ (0.15)	25	3 hours	β-Cyclohexyltetralin (40%)	58

* References 93–350 appear on pp. 78–82.
† Tetralin reacts with aluminum chloride alone, yielding benzene, octahydroanthracene, and octahydrophenanthrene (69, 129); see p. 13.

TABLE VII

Alkylation of Naphthalene

Moles of Naphthalene	Alkylating Agent (moles)	Catalyst (moles)	Solvent	Temperature, °C.	Time, hours	Products (% Yield)	Reference*
—	Methylene chloride (—)	$AlCl_3$ (—)	—	—	—	β-Methylnaphthalene	127
—	Methyl chloride (—)	$AlCl_3$ (—)	CS_2	25	16	β-Methylnaphthalene (11%)	319
—	Methyl bromide (—)	$AlCl_3$ (—)	CS_2	25	16	α- and β-Methylnaphthalenes (ca. 4% each)	319
0.5	Methyl iodide (0.6)	$AlCl_3$ (0.6)	CS_2	25	16	α- and β-Methylnaphthalenes (5%)	319
—	Ethylene bromide (—)	$AlCl_3$ (—)	—	Warm	—	α- and β-Methylnaphthalenes	281
7.1	Ethylene (17.2)	P_2O_5 (0.5)	—	250	—	Ethyl- and diethyl-naphthalenes	244
—	Ethylene (—)	H_3PO_4 (—)	—	300	14	Ethyl- and diethyl-naphthalenes	204
4	Diethylbenzene (—)	$AlCl_3$ (0.4)	—	80	5	β-Ethylnaphthalene (30%)	252
—	Ethyl chloride (—)	$AlCl_3$ (—)	—	—	—	β-Ethylnaphthalene	245
—	Ethyl bromide (—)	$AlCl_3$ (—)	—	—	—	β-Ethylnaphthalene	136
1.6	Ethyl iodide (1.3)	$AlCl_3$ (0.2)	—	Warm	—	β-Ethylnaphthalene	281
—	Propylene (—)	H_3PO_4 (—)	—	200	14	Isopropylnaphthalene, etc.	204
—	Propylene (—)	H_2SO_4 (—)	CCl_4	Cold	—	Isopropylnaphthalene, etc.	198, 310
1	Propylene (5.8)	HF (25)	—	0–72	24	Tetraisopropylnaphthalene (m.p. 125°, 98%)	71
3	*n*-Propyl bromide (1.8)	$AlCl_3$ (0.2)	—	Warm	4–5	β-Isopropylnaphthalene or β-*n*-propylnaphthalene	280, 281, 184
3	Isopropyl bromide (2)	$AlCl_3$ (0.3)	—	80	6	β-Isopropylnaphthalene (60%)	184
†0.5	Isopropyl alcohol (0.75)	H_2SO_4 (80%) (6)	—	80	3	α- and β-Isopropyl- 1,6-, 2,6-, and 2,7-di-, tri-, and tetra-isopropylnaphthalenes	29
—	Isopropyl alcohol (—)	H_2SO_4 (96%) (—)	—	40–45	—	Diisopropylnaphthalene (m.p. 38°), tetraisopropylnaphthalene	29

* References 93–350 appear on pp. 78–82.

† Since the naphthalene is first transformed to α-naphthalenesulfonic acid, the latter may be used as the starting material.

TABLE VII—*Continued*

ALKYLATION OF NAPHTHALENE

Moles of Naphthalene	Alkylating Agent (moles)	Catalyst (moles)	Solvent	Temperature, °C.	Time, hours	Products (% Yield)	Reference *
0.5	Isopropyl alcohol (0.5)	$AlCl_3$ (0.35)	Ligroin	90	4	β-Isopropylnaphthalene (33%), diisopropylnaphthalenes (15%), triisopropylnaphthalenes (11%)	322
0.4	Isopropyl alcohol (0.6)	BF_3 (—)	—	25	—	β-Isopropylnaphthalene (35%)	53
0.4	Isopropyl alcohol (1.6)	BF_3 (—)	—	25	—	Triisopropylnaphthalenes (57%)	53
0.25	*n*-Butyl alcohol (0.25)	$AlCl_3$ (0.33)	Ligroin	—	—	α-Butylnaphthalene (40%)	268
1.2	Isobutyl chloride (0.6)	$AlCl_3$ (0.1)	—	Warm	—	β-*t*-Butylnaphthalene (plus di-*t*-butylnaphthalenes)	116, 331
—	Isobutyl alcohol (—)	H_2SO_4 (80%) (—)	—	70	—	Di-*t*-butylnaphthalene (m.p. 142°)	29
0.2	Isobutyl alcohol (0.25)	$AlCl_3$ (0.03)	—	—	—	β-(and α)-*t*-Butylnaphthalenes, di-*t*-butylnaphthalenes	268
0.2	*s*-Butyl alcohol (0.25)	$AlCl_3$ (0.3)	Ligroin	90	5	α-*s*-Butylnaphthalene (20%), di-*s*-butylnaphthalenes (35%)	322
1	*t*-Butyl chloride (2)	$AlCl_3$ (0.01)	—	25→80	—	Di-*t*-butylnaphthalenes (m.p. 82° † and 146°, good yield)	178
2.6	*t*-Butyl chloride (2.7)	$AlCl_3$ (0.08)	—	50–60	2	β-*t*-Butylnaphthalene (30%), di-*t*-butylnaphthalenes (30%)	154
—	*t*-Butyl chloride (—)	HF (—)	CCl_4	0	—	*t*-Butylnaphthalene (46%), di-*t*-butylnaphthalene (m.p. 81°†, 28%), di-*t*-butylnaphthalene (m.p. 148°, 8%)	304
0.2	*t*-Butyl alcohol (0.25)	$AlCl_3$ (0.12)	Ligroin	90	3	β-(and α)-*t*-Butylnaphthalene (21%), di-*t*-butylnaphthalene (37%, m.p. 132°)	322
0.4	*t*-Butyl alcohol (1.0)	BF_3 (—)	—	25	—	β-*t*-Butylnaphthalene (62%), di-*t*-butylnaphthalenes (5%, m.p. 80° and 145°)	53

1	*t*-Butyl alcohol (3)	HF (25)	—	0–5	24	Di-*t*-butylnaphthalene (m.p. 143°, 76%)	71
2.6	Isoamyl chloride (4)	$AlCl_3$ (0.2)	—	—	—	β-Amylnaphthalene	281
—	Isoamyl alcohol (—)	$AlCl_3$ (—)	—	—	—	β-*t*-Amylnaphthalene (62%)	268
0.2	*t*-Amyl alcohol (0.25)	$AlCl_3$ (0.12)	Ligroin	90	2	α- and β-*t*-Amylnaphthalenes (34%), di-*t*-amylnaphthalenes (20%)	322
—	Cyclopentene (—)	$AlCl_3$ (—)	—	—	—	Cyclopentyl-, di-, tri- and tetra-cyclopentylnaphthalene	271
1	3-Hexene (1)	HF (—)	—	—	—	3-Naphthylhexane (30%)	315
3.5	Cyclohexene (1)	$AlCl_3$ (0.3)	CS_2	25	3	α- and β-Cyclohexylnaphthalenes (19%)	58
1.8	Cyclohexene (0.5)	$AlCl_3$ (0.15)	—	80	18	β-Cyclohexylnaphthalene (30%), 2,-6-dicyclohexylnaphthalene	58, 36*a*
0.4	Cyclohexene (0.6)	BF_3 (—)	—	25	24	β-Cyclohexylnaphthalene (35%)	53
0.4	Cyclohexanol (0.45)	BF_3 (—)	—	25	—	β-Cyclohexylnaphthalene (63%), 1,-4-dicyclohexylnaphthalene (9%)	53, 36*b*
1.3	Benzyl chloride (0.6)	$AlCl_3$ (0.05)	—	80	0.1–0.2	α-Benzylnaphthalene	281, 327
1.3	Benzyl chloride (0.6)	$AlCl_3$ (0.05)	—	150	1	β-Benzylnaphthalene	281, 327
1.3	Benzyl chloride (0.6)	$ZnCl_2$ (0.25)	—	150	1.5	α-Benzylnaphthalene	253, 281, 327
—	Benzyl chloride (—)	— (—)	—	Boiling	3	α-Benzylnaphthalene	259
—	Benzyl chloride (0.2)	Ti (0.1)	—	90	10	α-Benzylnaphthalene (25%), β-benzylnaphthalene	297
0.4	Benzyl alcohol (0.45)	BF_3 (—)	—	25	—	α-Benzylnaphthalene (28%), β-benzylnaphthalene (2%), dibenzylnaphthalenes (15%), tribenzylnaphthalenes (20%)	53
—	Benzyl ethyl ether (—)	P_2O_5 (—)	—	—	—	α-Benzylnaphthalene	251
2	Benzyl *n*-propyl ether (1)	BF_3 (0.5)	—	—	—	α-Benzylnaphthalene (48%)	255
1	Benzhydrol (0.5)	P_2O_5 (1)	—	140–145	4–5	α-Benzhydrylnaphthalene	235
—	Benzhydrol (—)	H_2SO_4 (—)	—	—	—	α-Benzhydrylnaphthalene	186

* References 93–350 appear on pp. 78–82.

† This material has been shown to be a molecular compound of one mole of the di-*t*-butylnaphthalene, m.p. 146°, and two moles of an isomer, m.p. 103° (36*b*).

TABLE VIII

Alkylation of Miscellaneous Polynuclear Aromatic Compounds

Aromatic Compound (moles)	Alkylating Agent (moles)	Catalyst (moles)	Solvent	Temperature, °C.	Time, hours	Products (% Yield)	Reference *
1-Chloronaphthalene (0.5)	Isopropyl alcohol (0.5)	$AlCl_3$ (0.5)	—	80–90	2–3	1-Chloro-*x*-isopropylnaphthalene (45%)	45
1-Chloronaphthalene (0.8)	*t*-Amyl alcohol (0.5)	$AlCl_3$ (0.2)	—	80–90	2–3	*x*-*t*-Amyl-1-chloronaphthalene (60%)	45
α-Nitronaphthalene (1.25)	Isopropyl ether (1.2)	HF (23)	—	0 → 20	20	Isopropyl-1-nitronaphthalene (10%), diisopropyl-1-nitronaphthalene (82%)	71
α-Naphthalenesulfonic acid (—)	Isopropyl alcohol (—)	H_2SO_4 (80%) (—)	—	80	—	1- and 2-Isopropyl-,1,6-, 2,6-, and 2,7-di-, tri-, and tetra-isopropyl-naphthalenes	29
β-Naphthalenesulfonic acid (0.5)	Isopropyl alcohol (3)	H_2SO_4 (96%) (1.3)	—	120	12	1,6-Diisopropyl-3-naphthalenesulfonic acid	29
β-Naphthalenesulfonic acid (0.5)	Isopropyl alcohol (1.5)	HF (24)	—	0 → 20	20	Polyisopropyl-2-naphthalenesulfonic acid	71
β-Methylnaphthalene (0.6)	Cyclopropane (0.5)	$ZnCl_2$—HCl (0.02)	—	30–35	4	Propyl-β-methylnaphthalene (15%)	36
Biphenyl (—)	Methyl chloride (—)	$AlCl_3$ (—)	—	100	—	*m*-Methylbiphenyl, dimethylbiphenyl, *p*- and *m*-terphenyl	93
Biphenyl (2)	Methyl sulfate (5)	$AlCl_3$ (2.88)	*o*-Dichlorobenzene	42	10	*m*- and *p*-Methylbiphenyl (25%), dimethylbiphenyls (20%)	147
Biphenyl (—)	Ethylene (—)	$AlCl_3$ (—)					
Biphenyl (10)	Ethyl chloride (6)	$AlCl_3$ (5)	—	100	—	*m*-Ethylbiphenyl, diethylbiphenyl, *p*- and *m*-terphenyl	93
Biphenyl (—)	Ethyl bromide (—)	$AlCl_3$ (—)					

Biphenyl (2)	Ethyl sulfate (3)	$AlCl_3$ (2.25)	*o*-Dichlorobenzene	5 → 25	14	*m*- and *p*-Ethylbiphenyl (20%), diethylbiphenyls (40%)	147
Biphenyl (0.8)	2,2,4-Trimethylpentane (0.4)	$AlCl_3$—HCl (0.04)	—	80–90	8	*p*-*t*-Butylbiphenyl (35%)	177
Biphenyl (0.7)	Cyclohexene (0.3)	$AlCl_3$ (0.1)	CS_2	25	3	*p*-Cyclohexylbiphenyl (40%), dicyclohexylbiphenyl (m.p. 205–206°)	58
Biphenyl (—)	Benzyl chloride (—)	Zn (—)	—	100	—	*p*-Benzylbiphenyl (50%)	173
Biphenyl (—)	Benzyl chloride (—)	— (—)	—	Boiling	3	*p*-Benzylbiphenyl	259
Biphenyl (—)	Benzyl chloride (0.2)	Ti (0.1)	—	90	10	*p*-Benzylbiphenyl (25%)	297
Diphenylmethane (1)	Cyclohexene (0.5)	$AlCl_3$ (0.15)	CS_2	25	3	*p*-Cyclohexyldiphenylmethane (27%), *p*-benzylbiphenyl (3%)	58
Diphenylmethane (—)	3-Methylcyclohexene (—)	$AlCl_3$ (—)	—	25	3	Methylcyclohexyldiphenylmethane	58
Dibenzyl (0.6)	Cyclohexene (0.4)	$AlCl_3$ (0.1)	CS_2	25	3	Cyclohexyldibenzyl (30%) (2 isomers)	58
Acenaphthene (1)	3-Hexanol (1.17)	$ZnCl_2$ (—)	—	180	—	3-Acenaphthylhexane (32%)	315
Acenaphthene (0.3)	Benzyl chloride (0.3)	$ZnCl_2$ (0.5)	—	125 → 180	2	3-Benzylacenaphthene (30%)	143, 144
Acenaphthene (—)	Benzyl chloride (0.2)	Ti (0.1)	—	90	—	3-Benzylacenaphthene (42%) (plus 2-benzylacenaphthene)	297
Fluorene (—)	Propylene (—)	H_3PO_4 (—)	—	200	11	Isopropylfluorene (25%)	204
Fluorene (0.06)	Benzyl chloride (—)	Zn (—)	—	125	—	2-Benzylfluorene (5%)	160, 173
Anthracene (1.5)	Isopropyl ether (3)	HF (55)	—	10	3	Diisopropylanthracenes (80%)	71
Anthracene (1)	3-Hexene (0.66)	$AlCl_3$ (—)	—	—	—	Di-*s*-hexylanthracene (20%)	315
Anthracene (0.27)	3-Bromohexane (0.25)	HF (2.5)	—	120–125	20	Di-*s*-hexylanthracene (20%)	71
Anthracene (0.6)	Benzyl chloride (1.2)	Zn (0.15)	CS_2	45	—	9,10-Dibenzylanthracene (35%)	239
Phenanthrene (0.75)	*t*-Butyl alcohol (1.65)	HF (21)	—	15–20	18	*t*-Butylphenanthrenes (60%)	71
Phenanthrene (—)	Benzyl chloride (—)	Zn (—)	—	125	—	9-Benzylphenanthrene †	142, 173

* References 93–350 appear on pp. 78–82.

† This product, m.p. 155–156°, was found by Goldschmiedt (173) to yield phenanthrenequinone on chromic acid oxidation. Willgerodt and Albert (336) have prepared a benzylphenanthrene melting at 91–92° which they believe to be the 9-isomer, but Bachmann [*J. Am. Chem. Soc.*, **56,** 1363 (1934)] supports Goldschmiedt.

TABLE IX

ALKYLATION OF PHENOL

Moles of Phenol	Alkylating Agent (moles)	Catalyst (moles)	Solvent	Temperature, °C.	Time, hours	Products (% Yield)	Reference*
—	Methyl alcohol (—)	Al_2O_3 (—)	—	440	—	*o*-Cresol, anisole	203
1	Ethylene (1)	H_3PO_4 (0.3)	—	225	16	*o*- and *p*-Ethylphenol (35%), diethylphenol (25%), phenetole, ethylphenetole	207
—	Ethanol (—)	$ZnCl_2$ (—)]	—	180	—	*p*-Ethylphenol and isomers, and *p*-ethylphenetole	99, 119, 148
—	Ethanol (—)	$AlCl_3$ (—)	—	120–140	6	Diethylphenol (36%), *o*- and *p*-ethylphenols (24%)	43
3	Ethyl ether (4)	$AlCl_3$ (9)	—	145	—	3,5-Diethylphenol	44
—	Ethyl chloroformate (—)	$FeCl_3$ (—)	—	—	—	*p*-Ethylphenol (poor yield)	247
1.5	Propylene (6.75)	HF (41)	—	$5 \rightarrow 25$	20	2,4,6-Triisopropylphenol (95%)	71
1	Propylene (0.5)	BF_3 (0.08)	Benzene	0	2	*o*-(?)-Isopropylphenol (41%), isopropyl phenyl ether (54%)	91
1	Propylene (2)	BF_3 (0.08)	Benzene	15	2	*o* - (?) - Isopropylphenyl isopropyl ether (41%)	91
1	Propylene (1)	BF_3 (0.05)	—	20	2	2,4-Diisopropylphenyl isopropyl ether (30%)	91
1	Propylene (excess)	BF_3 (0.05)	—	30–40	—	2,4,6-Triisopropylphenyl isopropyl ether (92%)	91

1	*n*-Propyl alcohol (2)	Al_2O_3 (0.1)	—	400	12	*o*-Propylphenol, *n*-propylphenyl ether, *n*-propyl *o*-propylphenyl ether	202
—	*n*-Propyl alcohol (—)	$AlCl_3$ (—)	—	120–140	6	*o*- and *p*-Propylphenols (73%)	43
1	*n*-Propyl alcohol (1)	BF_3 (0.3)	—	115–160	1	*o*-Isopropylphenol (28%), *p*-isopropylphenol (20%), 2,4-diisopropylphenyl isopropyl ether (11%)	314
1	Isopropyl alcohol (1)	BF_3 (0.3)	—	115–160	1	*o*-Isopropylphenol (32%), *p*-isopropylphenol (16%), 2,4-diisopropylphenyl isopropyl ether (13%)	314
—	Isopropyl alcohol (—)	$AlCl_3$ (—)	—	110–120	6	*p*- and *o*-Isopropylphenols (52%), *p*-isopropylphenyl isopropyl ether (23%)	43
5	Allyl iodide (3)	Zn-Al (—)	—	Warm	—	*n*-Propylphenol	162
—	Isobutylene (—)	$AlCl_3$ (—)	—	—	—	*p*-*t*-Butylphenol (60–75%)	208
—	Diisobutylene (—)	H_2SO_4 (—)	—	—	—	*t*-Butylphenol	256
1	Diisobutylene (0.5)	$AlCl_3$ (1.3)	—	80	6	*p*-*t*-Butylphenol (67%), *p*-*t*-octylphenol (14%)	313
1	*p*-*t*-Octylphenol (1)	$AlCl_3$ (2)	—	80	10	*p*-*t*-Butylphenol (75%)	313
0.2	*n*-Butyl chloride (0.2)	$AlCl_3$ (0.2)	—	110	4	*p*-*n*-Butylphenol (35%), *p*-*n*-butylphenyl butyl ether (20%)	321
—	*n*-Butyl alcohol (—)	$AlCl_3$ (—)	—	140	6	Butylphenol (72%)	43
—	*s*-Butyl alcohol (—)	H_2SO_4 (—)	—	—	—	*p*- and *o*-*s*-Butylphenol	29
—	*s*-Butyl alcohol (—)	$AlCl_3$ (—)	—	120–140	6	*p*- and *o*-*s*-Butylphenol (52%), *s*-butylphenyl *s*-butyl ether (13%)	43
1.1	Isobutyl alcohol (1.1)	$ZnCl_2$ (1.6)	—	180	1	*p*-*t*-Butylphenol (70%)	179, 237, 238, 296

* References 93–350 appear on pp. 78–82.

TABLE IX—*Continued*

ALKYLATION OF PHENOL

Moles of Phenol	Alkylating Agent (moles)	Catalyst (moles)	Solvent	Temperature, ° C.	Time, hours	Products (% Yield)	Reference*
1.1	Isobutyl alcohol (—)	H_2SO_4 (70%) (—)	—	80	—	*p-t*-Butylphenol, (ca. 80%)	29
—	Isobutyl alcohol (—)	$AlCl_3$ (—)	—	—	—	*p-t*-Butylphenol (60–75%)	43, 208
—	*t*-Butyl chloride (—)	$AlCl_3$ (—)	—	—	—	*p-t*-Butylphenol (60–75%)	208
—	*t*-Butyl chloride (—)	HF (—)	—	—	—	*p-t*-Butylphenol (85%)	308
0.25	*t*-Butyl alcohol (0.25)	$AlCl_3$ (0.125)	Petroleum ether	25–30	3–4	*p-t*-Butylphenol (45–60%)	195, 208
—	Trimethylethylene (—)	H_2SO_4 (—)	—	—	—	*t*-Amylphenol	256
0.15	Amylene (0.15)	H_2SO_4 (0.12)	Acetic acid	—	96	*p-t*-Amylphenol (70%)	98, 223
0.1	Amylene (0.1)	*p*-Toluenesulfonic acid (0.005)		100	6	*p-t*-Amylphenol (65%)	342
—	2-Pentanol (—)	$AlCl_3$ (—)	—	100	2	2- and 3-(*p*-Hydroxyphenyl)pentane (58%)	43
0.2	Isoamyl chloride (0.2)	$AlCl_3$ (0.2)	—	90	5	*p*-Isoamylphenol (10%), *p*-isoamylphenyl isoamyl ether (15%)	321
0.2	Isoamyl chloride (0.2)	$AlCl_3$ (0.2)	—	Cold	—	*p-t*-Amylphenol (55%)	321
—	Isoamyl alcohol (—)	$ZnCl_2$ (—)	—	180	1	*p-t*-Amylphenol (40%)	179, 237, 238
0.2	Isoamyl chloroformate (0.2)	$FeCl_3$ (—)	—	25 → 80	—	*p-t*-Amylphenol	247
1	*t*-Amyl alcohol (1)	$ZnCl_2$ (2)	—	180	—	*p-t*-Amylphenol (65%)	157

0.25	*t*-Amyl alcohol (0.25)	$AlCl_3$ (0.125)	Petroleum ether	25–30	3–4	*p-t*-Amylphenol (45–60%)	195
—	3-Hexene (—)	? (—)	—	—	—	*s*-Hexylphenol, di-*s*-hexylphenol, tri-*s*-hexylphenol	315
0.25	2-Methyl-2-pentanol (0.25)	$AlCl_3$ (0.125)	Petroleum ether	25–30	3–4	2-(*p*-Hydroxyphenyl)-2-methylpentane (45–60%)	195
0.25	3-Methyl-3-pentanol (0.25)	$AlCl_3$ (0.125)	Petroleum ether	25–30	3–4	3-(*p*-Hydroxyphenyl)-2-methylpentane (45–60%)	195
0.25	2,3-Dimethyl-2-butanol (0.25)	$AlCl_3$ (0.125)	Petroleum ether	25–30	3–4	2-(*p*-Hydroxyphenyl)-2,3-dimethylbutane (45–60%)	195
0.25	Cyclohexene (0.25)	H_2SO_4 (0.1)	Acetic acid	80	1	*p*-Cyclohexylphenol (17%)	289
2	Cyclohexene (1.5)	$AlCl_3$ (0.45)	CS_2	25	3	*o*-Cyclohexylphenol (15%), *p*-cyclohexylphenol (4%), cyclohexylphenyl ether (12%)	58
5	Cyclohexene (1.5)	$AlCl_3$ (0.45)	—	25	3	*o*-Cyclohexylphenol (56%), *p*-cyclohexylphenol (20%)	58
1.0	Cyclohexyl chloride (1.0)	$ZnCl_2$ (1.0)	—	80	—	*p*-Cyclohexylphenol (20%)	112
0.1	Cyclohexanol (0.15)	*p*-Toluenesulfonic acid (0.002)	—	155	0.5	Cyclohexene (73%), *p*-cyclohexylphenol	342
0.1	Cyclohexanol (—)	H_2SO_4 (70%) (—)	—	80	—	*p*-Cyclohexylphenol (50%)	29
0.15	1-Methylcyclohexene (0.15)	H_2SO_4 (0.1)	Acetic acid	80	1	*p*-(Methylcyclohexyl)phenol † (55%)	289
0.15	3-Methylcyclohexene (0.15)	H_2SO_4 (0.1)	Acetic acid	80	1	*p*-(Methylcyclohexyl)phenol † (55%)	289
0.15	4-Methylcyclohexene (0.15)	H_2SO_4 (0.1)	Acetic acid	80	1	*p*-(Methylcyclohexyl)phenol † (55%)	289

* References 93–350 appear on pp. 78–82.

† The products obtained by Schrauth and Quasebarth (289) by condensation of the three isomeric methylcyclohexenes with phenol are identical and have the same melting point as the product prepared by Meyer and Bernhauer (29) from 4-methylcyclohexanol. The most probable structure would appear to be 1-methyl-1-(*p*-hydroxyphenyl)-cyclohexane.

TABLE IX—*Continued*

ALKYLATION OF PHENOL

Moles of Phenol	Alkylating Agent (moles)	Catalyst (moles)	Solvent	Temperature, ° C.	Time, hours	Products (% Yield)	Reference*
0.2	4-Methylcyclohexanol (0.2)	H_2SO_4 (80%) (6)	—	70	5	*p*-(Methylcyclohexyl)phenol † (55%)	29
0.5	Benzyl alcohol (0.5)	$AlCl_3$ (0.25)	Petroleum ether (CS_2)	20–30	18	*p*-Benzylphenol (43–45%)	191
3	Benzyl alcohol (—)	H_2SO_4 (70%) (—)	—	40	—	*p*- and *o*-Benzylphenols (40%)	29
—	Benzyl alcohol (—)	$ZnCl_2$ (—)	—	—	—	*p*-Benzylphenol	237, 238
—	Benzyl alcohol (—)	H_2SO_4 (—)	Acetic acid	—	—	*p*-Benzylphenol	267
2.7	Benzyl *n*-propyl ether (1)	BF_3 (0.5)	—	—	—	*p*-Benzylphenol (48%)	255
—	Benzyl chloride (—)	Zn (—)	—	—	—	*p*-Benzylphenol	266
0.5	Benzyl chloride (0.4)	$AlCl_3$ (0.25)	Petroleum ether	30	24	*p*-Benzylphenol (36%)	191
—	Benzyl chloride (—)	Ti (—)	—	—	—	*p*-Benzylphenol	297
—	Δ^5-1,3-Dimethylcyclohexene (—)	H_2SO_4 (—)	Acetic acid	80	—	1,3-Dimethyl-*x*-(*p*-hydroxyphenyl)-cyclohexane (62%)	289
1	Styrene (1)	H_2SO_4 (1)	Acetic acid	25	24–48	*p*-Hydroxy-1,1-diphenylethane (40%)	223
0.5	2-Phenyl-2-propanol (0.16)	$AlCl_3$ (0.08)	—	90	1	*p*-Hydroxy-2,2-diphenylpropane (68–72%)	332
0.4	$\Delta^{1\ (\text{or}\ 2)}$-Octalin (0.08)	HCl (—)	—	80	5	*p*-(1- (or 2-)-Decahydronaphthyl)-phenol (70%)	289

0.3	Dihydronaphthalene (0.3)	H_2SO_4 (0.6)	Acetic acid	25	24	Tetrahydronaphthylphenol (70%)	224
0.75	Pinene (0.15)	HCl (—)	—	80	5	Addition product (86%)	289
0.75	Limonene (0.15)	HCl (—)	—	80	5	Addition product (86%)	289
—	Benzhydrol (—)	$SnCl_4$ (—)	—	—	—	*p*-Hydroxytriphenylmethane	123
0.04	Benzhydrol (0.08)	H_2SO_4 (0.3)	Acetic acid	90	4	2,4,6-Tribenzhydrylphenol (ca. 100%)	299
0.5	1,1-Diphenyl-1-ethanol (0.16)	$AlCl_3$ (0.08)	—	90	1	*p*-Hydroxy-1,1,1-triphenylethane (80%)	332
0.75	1,1-Diphenyl-1-propanol (0.5)	$AlCl_3$ (0.25)	Ligroin	25	80–90	*p*-Hydroxy-1,1,1-triphenylpropane (87%)	196
0.75	1,1-Diphenyl-1-butanol (0.5)	$AlCl_3$ (0.25)	Ligroin	25	80–90	*p*-Hydroxy-1,1,1-triphenylbutane (46%)	196
0.75	1,1-Diphenyl-2-methyl-1-propanol (0.5)	$AlCl_3$ (0.25)	Ligroin	25	80–90	*p*-Hydroxy-1,1,1-triphenyl-2-methylpropane (73%)	196
0.75	1,1-Diphenyl-1-pentanol (0.5)	$AlCl_3$ (0.25)	Ligroin	25	80–90	*p*-Hydroxy-1,1,1-triphenylpentane (30%)	196
0.75	1,1-Diphenyl-2-methyl-1-butanol (0.5)	$AlCl_3$ (0.25)	Ligroin	25	80–90	*p*-Hydroxy-1,1,1-triphenyl-2-methylbutane (13%)	196
0.75	1,1-Diphenyl-3-methyl-1-butanol (0.5)	$AlCl_3$ (0.25)	Ligroin	25	80–90	*p*-Hydroxy-1,1,1-triphenyl-3-methylbutane (40%)	196
0.75	1,1-Diphenyl-2-2-dimethyl-1-propanol (0.5)	$AlCl_3$ (0.25)	Ligroin	25	80–90	3-(*p*-Hydroxyphenyl)-2,2-diphenyl-3-methylbutane ‡ (6%)	196
0.75	1,1-Diphenyl-1-hexanol (0.5)	$AlCl_3$ (0.25)	Ligroin	25	80–90	*p*-Hydroxy-1,1,1-triphenylhexane (30%)	196

* References 93–350 appear on pp. 78–82.

† The products obtained by Schrauth and Quasebarth (289) by condensation of the three isomeric methylcyclohexenes with phenol were identical and had the same melting point as the product prepared by Meyer and Bernhauer (29) from 4-methylcyclohexanol. The most probable structure would appear to be 1-methyl-1-(*p*-hydroxyphenyl)-cyclohexane.

‡ The formation of this product involved a rearrangement of the carbon skeleton of the substituting group.

TABLE IX—*Continued*

ALKYLATION OF PHENOL

Moles of Phenol	Alkylating Agent (moles)	Catalyst (moles)	Solvent	Temperature, °C.	Time, hours	Products (% Yield)	Reference*
—	Triphenylmethyl chloride (—)	Cu (—)	—	80	—	*p*-Hydroxytetraphenylmethane (80%)	103, 174
0.1	Triphenylcarbinol (0.01)	H_2SO_4 (0.2)	Acetic acid	25	24–48	*p*-Hydroxytetraphenylmethane	102
—	Triphenylcarbinol (—)	H_2SO_4 (trace)	—	80	0.8	*p*-Hydroxytetraphenylmethane (80–90%)	174
0.05	Triphenylcarbinol (0.02)	— (—)	—	Boiling	1	*p*-Hydroxytetraphenylmethane (97%)	131
0.1	*p*-Methyltriphenylcarbinol (0.01)	H_2SO_4 (0.2)	Acetic acid	25	24–48	*p*-Hydroxy-*p*′-methyltetraphenylmethane	122
0.1	9-Hydroxy-9-phenylfluorene (0.01)	H_2SO_4 (0.1)	Acetic acid	25	72	9-*p*-Hydroxyphenyl-9-phenylfluorene (95%)	221, 325
0.3	Di-α-naphthylmethyl bromide (0.03)	— (—)	—	Warm	—	*p*-Di-α-naphthylmethylphenol (75%)	243
0.1	Di-α-naphthylcarbinol (0.01)	— (—)	Acetic acid	115	6	*p*-Di-α-naphthylmethylphenol (75%)	243, 285

* References 93–350 appear on pp. 78–82.

TABLE X

Alkylation of Various Phenols and Phenolic Ethers

Aromatic Compound (moles)	Alkylating Agent (moles)	Catalyst (moles)	Solvent	Temperature, °C	Time, hours (unless otherwise noted)	Products (% Yield)	Reference
Anisole (—)	Isopropyl alcohol (—)	$AlCl_3$ (—)	—	120	4	*p*-Isopropylanisole (50%), *p*-isopropylphenol (38%)	43
Anisole (—)	Isopropyl alcohol (—)	$AlCl_3$ (—)	—	140	6	*p*-Isopropylanisole (30%), *p*-isopropylphenol (64%)	43
Anisole (0.2)	*n*-Butyl chloride (0.2)	$AlCl_3$ (0.2)	Ligroin	90	5	*n*-Butylanisole (65%)	321
Anisole (—)	*s*-Butyl alcohol (—)	$AlCl_3$ (—)	—	100	2	*s*-Butylanisole (55%), di-*s*-butylanisole (16%), *s*-butylphenol (13%)	43
Anisole (—)	Isobutyl chloride (—)	$AlCl_3$ (—)	—	—	—	*p*-*t*-Butylanisole	115
Anisole (0.5)	Isobutyl chloride (0.2)	$AlCl_3$ (0.2)	—	90	5	Isobutylanisole (40%)	321
Anisole (—)	*t*-Butyl chloride (—)	$AlCl_3$ (—)	—	Warm	—	*p*-*t*-Butylanisole	115
Anisole (0.1)	*t*-Butyl chloride (0.1)	ZnF_2 (—)	—	—	—	*p*-*t*-Butylanisole (30%)	18
Anisole (0.2)	Isoamyl chloride (0.2)	$AlCl_3$ (0.25)	Ligroin	90	5	Isoamylanisole (45%)	321
Anisole (1.5)	Cyclohexene (0.5)	$AlCl_3$ (0.25)	—	25	3	*o*- and *p*-Cyclohexylanisole (50%, 3 : 1)	58
Anisole (0.4)	Cyclohexyl chloride (0.25)	$AlCl_3$ (0.05)	—	70	4	Cyclohexylanisole (15–20%)	112
Anisole (—)	Benzyl chloride (—)	Zn (—)	—	—	—	*p*-Benzylanisole	266
Anisole (—)	Benzyl chloride (—)	$AlCl_3$ (1)	—	—	—	*p*-Benzylanisole	172
Anisole (—)	Benzyl chloride (—)	—	—	Boiling	3	*p*-Benzylanisole	259
Anisole (—)	Benzyl chloride (—)	Ti (—)	—	—	—	*p*-Benzylanisole (63%), 2,4-dibenzylanisole (12%)	297
Anisole (0.6)	Benzyl alcohol (0.5)	$AlCl_3$ (0.25)	Petroleum ether	20	48	*p*-Benzylanisole (46%)	191

* References 93–350 appear on pp. 78–82.

TABLE X—*Continued*

ALKYLATION OF VARIOUS PHENOLS AND PHENOLIC ETHERS

Aromatic Compound (moles)	Alkylating Agent (moles)	Catalyst (moles)	Solvent	Temperature, °C.	Time, hours (unless otherwise noted)	Products (% Yield)	Reference *
Anisole (0.1)	Triphenylcarbinol (0.01)	H_2SO_4 (0.2)	Acetic acid	25	120	*p*-Methoxytetraphenylmethane	102
o-Nitroanisole (1)	Isopropyl alcohol (1)	HF (12)	—	10–20	18	2-Nitro-4-isopropylanisole (84%)	71
o-Nitroanisole (2.45)	Cyclohexanol (2.25)	HF (18)	—	15–20	20	2-Nitro-4-cyclohexylanisole (55%)	71
Phenetole (1.5)	Propylene (1.5)	H_3PO_4 (0.6)	—	145	7	Isopropylphenetole (8%), diisopropylphenetole (15%)	207
Phenetole (—)	Cyclohexyl chloride (—)	$AlCl_3$ (—)	—	—	—	Cyclohexylphenetole (12%)	112
Phenetole (—)	Benzyl chloride (—)	Ti (—)	—	—	—	*p*-Benzylphenetole (76%)	297
Phenetole (0.6)	Benzyl alcohol (0.5)	$AlCl_3$ (0.25)	Petroleum ether	20	—	*p*-Benzylphenetole (57%)	191
Phenyl ether (0.6)	3-Hexene (1.8)	HF (6.5)	—	5 → 20	3 days	*s*-Hexylphenyl ether (61%)	71
Phenyl acetate (2)	Benzyl chloride (1)	$AlCl_3$ (—)	—	Warm	0.5	*p*-Acetoxydiphenylmethane (poor yield)	269
o-Cresol (—)	Isobutyl alcohol (—)	$ZnCl_2$ (—)	—	180	—	4-*t*-Butyl-2-methylphenol	115
o-Cresol (—)	Isobutyl chloride (—)	$ZnCl_2$ (—)	—	80	—	4-*t*-Butyl-2-methylphenol	115
o-Cresol (—)	Isobutyl alcohol (—)	H_2SO_4 (—)	—	—	—	4-*t*-Butyl-2-methylphenol	29
o-Cresol (—)	*t*-Butyl chloride (—)	$ZnCl_2$ (—)	—	80	—	4-*t*-Butyl-2-methylphenol	115
o-Cresol (—)	Benzyl alcohol (—)	H_2SO_4 (70%) (—)	—	—	—	4-Benzyl-2-methylphenol	29
o-Cresol (0.9)	Benzyl alcohol (0.9)	$AlCl_3$ (0.5)	Petroleum ether	30–35	18	4-Benzyl-2-methylphenol (30%), 6-benzyl-2-methylphenol (2%), 4,6-dibenzyl-2-methylphenol (20%)	77

Phenol	Alkylating agent	Catalyst	Solvent	Temp.	Time	Product	Ref.*
o-Cresol (1.5)	Benzyl ether (0.9)	HF (15)	—	5 → 25	20	Benzyl-o-cresol (54%), dibenzyl-o-cresol (10%)	71
o-Cresol (—)	Styrene (—)	H_2SO_4 (—)	Acetic acid	25	—	1-(4-Hydroxy-2-methylphenyl)-1-phenylethane	225
o-Cresol (0.04)	Benzhydrol (0.08)	H_2SO_4 (0.3)	Acetic acid	90	4	Benzhydryl-o-cresol (ca. 100%)	299
o-Cresol † (0.05)	Triphenylcarbinol (0.03)	H_2SO_4 (0.1)	Acetic acid	25	24	4-Hydroxy-3-methyltetraphenylmethane (ca. 100%)	131
o-Cresyl methyl ether (0.08)	Triphenylcarbinol (0.03)	H_2SO_4 (0.1)	Acetic acid	25	48	4-Methoxy-3-methyltetraphenylmethane (ca. 100%)	131
m-Cresol (3)	Propylene (3)	HF (27)	—	0–20	18	Isopropyl-m-cresols	71
m-Cresol ‡ (—)	Isopropyl alcohol (—)	H_2SO_4 (—)	—	—	—	3-Methyl-4-isopropylphenol	29
m-Cresol (—)	Isobutyl alcohol (—)	H_2SO_4 (—)	—	—	—	4-t-Butyl-3-methylphenol	29
m-Cresol (1.1)	Benzyl alcohol (0.9)	$AlCl_3$ (0.45)	Petroleum ether	35	24	4-Benzyl-3-methylphenol (19%), 6-benzyl-3-methylphenol (21%), 4,6-dibenzyl-3-methylphenol (35%)	75
m-Cresol (—)	Styrene (—)	H_2SO_4 (—)	Acetic acid	25	—	1-(4-Hydroxy-2-methylphenyl)-1-phenylethane	225
m-Cresol (0.05)	Triphenylcarbinol (0.03)	H_2SO_4 (0.1)	Acetic acid	48	25	4-Hydroxy-2-methyltetraphenylmethane (90%) §	131, 286
p-Cresol (1)	Benzyl alcohol (0.5)	$AlCl_3$ (0.25)	Petroleum ether	25–30	18	2-Benzyl-4-methylphenol (35%), 2,6-dibenzyl-4-methylphenol (36%)	76
p-Cresol (1.5)	Benzyl alcohol (0.5)	$AlCl_3$ (0.25)	Petroleum ether	25–30	18	2-Benzyl-4-methylphenol (35%), 2,6-dibenzyl-4-methylphenol (36%)	76
p-Cresol (0.05)	Benzhydrol (0.05)	H_2SO_4 (0.15)	Acetic acid	90	5	o,o′-Dibenzhydryl-p-cresol (70%)	299
m-n-Propylanisole (0.1)	t-Butyl chloride (0.1)	$AlCl_3$ (0.03)	—	0	2	2-t-Butyl-5-n-propylanisole (60%)	140

* References 93–350 appear on pp. 78–82.

† Similar treatment of p-cresol yields only triphenylmethane (90%) and polymerized quinomethane, $O{=}C_6H_4{=}CH_2$ (131, 286).

‡ p-Cresol is not alkylated by this procedure (29).

§ The structure of this condensation product has not been definitely established; it may be 2-hydroxy-4-methyltetraphenylmethane (286).

TABLE X—*Continued*

ALKYLATION OF VARIOUS PHENOLS AND PHENOLIC ETHERS

Aromatic Compound (moles)	Alkylating Agent (moles)	Catalyst (moles)	Solvent	Temperature, ° C.	Time, hours (unless otherwise noted)	Products (% Yield)	Reference *
Carvacrol (1)	Cyclohexene (0.5)	$AlCl_3$ (0.15)	—	25	3	Carvacryl cyclohexyl ether (15%), cyclohexylcarvacrol (20%)	58
Thymol (—)	Amylene (—)	H_2SO_4 (—)	Acetic acid	25	—	4-*t*-Amyl-2-isopropyl-5-methylphenol (50%)	225
α-Naphthol (—)	3-Hexene (—)	? (—)	—	—	—	*s*-Hexyl-α-naphthol	315
α-Naphthol (1)	Benzyl chloride (1)	Zn (—)	Benzene	—	5	Benzyl-α-naphthol (30%)	105
α-Naphthol (—)	Benzhydrol (—)	$SnCl_4$ or $ZnCl_2$ (—)	—	—	—	4-Benzhydryl-1-naphthol	328
β-Naphthol (1.11)	Isopropyl alcohol (4.44)	HF (25)	—	5	24	Diisopropyl-β-naphthol (94%)	71
β-Naphthol (—)	3-Hexene (—)	? (—)	—	—	—	*s*-Hexyl-β-naphthol	315
β-Naphthol (1)	Benzyl chloride (1)	Zn (—)	Benzene (alcohol)	—	6	Benzyl-β-naphthol (20%)	106
β-Naphthol (—)	Styrene (—)	H_2SO_4 (—)	Acetic acid	25	—	2-Hydroxy-1-(α-phenylethyl)-naphthalene	225
β-Naphthyl methyl ether (0.6)	Isobutyl bromide (0.7)	$AlCl_3$ (0.6)	CS_2	55–65	3	1-*t*-Butyl-2-methoxynaphthalene (70%)	137

* References 93–350 appear on pp. 78–82.

TABLE XI

Alkylation of Polyhydric Phenols

Aromatic Compound (moles)	Alkylating Agent (moles)	Catalyst (moles)	Solvent	Temperature, °C.	Time, hours	Products (% Yield)	Reference *
Catechol (0.1)	*t*-Butyl chloride (0.2)	$FeCl_3$ (0.02)	—	80	0.1	Di-*t*-butylcatechol	179
Catechol (0.03)	Amylene (0.08)	H_2SO_4 (—)	Acetic acid	25	120	Di-*t*-amylcatechol (15%)	226
Catechol (—)	3-Hexene (—)	? (—)	—	—	—	*s*-Hexylcatechol	315
Veratrol (1)	Allyl iodide (0.5)	Zn (0.015)	—	Warm	2.5	Methyl eugenyl ether	257
Resorcinol (0.5)	Acetylene (0.5)	$HgSO_4$ (—)	Methyl alcohol	25	—	Vinylresorcinol (83%)	159
Resorcinol (—)	Isopropyl alcohol (—)	H_2SO_4 (70%) (—)	—	80	—	4-Isopropylresorcinol, 4,6-diisopropylresorcinol	29
Resorcinol (0.1)	*t*-Butyl chloride (0.3)	$FeCl_3$ (0.02)	—	80	0.3–0.4	Di-*t*-butylresorcinol mono-*t*-butyl ether (40%)	179
Resorcinol (0.1)	*t*-Butyl chloride (0.3)	$AlCl_3$ (—)	—	—	—	Di-*t*-butylresorcinol	179
Resorcinol (0.1)	Amylene (0.25)	H_2SO_4 (—)	Acetic acid	25	120	Di-*t*-amylresorcinol	226
Resorcinol (0.1)	*t*-Amyl chloride (0.3)	$FeCl_3$ (0.02)	—	80	0.1	Di-*t*-amylresorcinol (5%)	179
Resorcinol (—)	3-Hexene (—)	$H_3BO_2F_2$ (—)	—	—	—	*s*-Hexylresorcinol (62%), di-*s*-hexylresorcinol (20%)	315
Resorcinol (0.8)	Cyclohexyl chloride (0.6)	$AlCl_3$ (0.15)	Nitrobenzene	70	4	Cyclohexylresorcinol (5%)	112

* References 93–350 appear on pp. 78–82.

TABLE XI—*Continued*

ALKYLATION OF POLYHYDRIC PHENOLS

Aromatic Compound (moles)	Alkylating Agent (moles)	Catalyst (moles)	Solvent	Temperature, °C.	Time, hours	Products (% Yield)	Reference*
Resorcinol (—)	Benzyl chloride (—)	Zn (—)	—	—	—	Benzylresorcinol, dibenzylresorcinol	104
Resorcinol (0.2)	Benzyl chloride (0.1)	$AlCl_3$ (0.1)	Nitrobenzene	50–70	2	4-Benzylresorcinol (50%)	220
Resorcinol monomethyl ether (—)	Isopropyl alcohol (—)	H_2SO_4 (—)	—	—	—	Monomethyl ether of diisopropylresorcinol	29
Resorcinol dimethyl ether (—)	Isopropyl alcohol (—)	H_2SO_4 (—)	—	—	—	Dimethyl ethers of isopropyl- and diisopropylresorcinol	29
Hydroquinone (5)	Isopropyl alcohol (6)	HF (42)	—	$5 \rightarrow 20$	24	Isopropylhydroquinone (39%)	71
Hydroquinone (1.65)	Isopropyl alcohol (7.6)	HF (—)	—	—	—	2,4,6-Triisopropylphenol (83%)	71

Hydroquinone (0.1)	*t*-Butyl chloride (0.2)	$FeCl_3$ (0.02)	—	25	0.2	2,5-Di-*t*-butylbenzoquinone	179
Hydroquinone (0.25)	Amylene (0.65)	H_2SO_4 (—)	Acetic acid	25	24	2,5-Di-*t*-amylhydroquinone (50%)	226
Hydroquinone (—)	3-Hexene (—)	? (—)	—	—	—	*s*-Hexylhydroquinone, di-*s*-hexylhydroquinone	315
Hydroquinone dimethyl ether (0.2)	Benzyl chloride (0.15)	Ti (0.1)	—	130–140	8	Benzylhydroquinone dimethyl ether (70%)	297
2-Methyl-1,4-naphthohydroquinone (—)	Cinnamyl alcohol (—)	Oxalic acid (—)	Dioxane	100	24	3-Cinnamyl-2-methyl-1,4-naphthohydroquinone (30%)	153
2-Methyl-1,4-naphthohydroquinone (—)	Phytol (—)	Oxalic acid (—)	Dioxane	75	36	2-Methyl-3-phytyl-1,4-naphthohydroquinone (30%)	152
Pyrogallol (0.1)	*t*-Butyl chloride (0.4)	$FeCl_3$ (0.02)	—	80	0.5	Di-*t*-butylpyrogallol	282
Pyrogallol (—)	Amylene (—)	H_2SO_4 (—)	Acetic acid	25	120	Di-*t*-amylpyrogallol	226

* References 93–350 appear on pp. 78–82.

TABLE XII

Alkylation of Miscellaneous Aldehydes, Acids, and Quinones

Aromatic Compound (moles)	Alkylating Agent (moles)	Catalyst (moles)	Solvent	Temperature, °C.	Time, hours	Products (% Yield)	Reference*
Benzaldehyde (0.2)	Isopropyl chloride (0.2)	$AlCl_3$ (0.4)	CS_2	25	12	*m*-Isopropylbenzaldehyde (8% conversion, 30% yield)	32
Benzaldehyde (—)	*t*-Butyl chloride (—)	$AlCl_3$ (—)	CS_2	25	12	*m*-*t*-Butylbenzaldehyde	32
Benzoquinone (0.1)	Benzhydrol (0.1)	H_2SO_4 (0.01)	Acetic acid	80	12	2,5-Dibenzhydrylbenzoquinone	254
α-Naphthoquinone (0.1)	Benzhydrol (0.1)	H_2SO_4 (0.01)	Acetic acid	80	3	2-Benzhydryl-α-naphthoquinone (ca. 100%)	254
Benzoic acid (1.5)	Isopropyl ether (3)	HF (45)	—	10 → 75	8	*m*-Isopropylbenzoic acid	71
Anisaldehyde (0.1)	Isopropyl chloride (0.1)	$AlCl_3$ (0.2)	CS_2	—	—	3-Isopropyl-4-methoxybenzaldehyde (22%)	32
Methyl anisate (0.08)	Isopropyl chloride (0.08)	$AlCl_3$ (0.16)	CS_2	—	—	Methyl 3-isopropyl-4-methoxybenzoate (33%)	168
Ethyl α-naphthoate (0.05)	Isopropyl chloride (0.05)	$AlCl_3$ (0.1)	CS_2	—	—	Ethyl isopropyl-α-naphthoate (33%)	168
Ethyl α-naphthoate (0.05)	*n*-Butyl chloride (0.05)	$AlCl_3$ (0.1)	CS_2	—	—	Ethyl butyl-α-naphthoate	168
Salicylic acid (1)	Isopropyl alcohol (2.5)	H_2SO_4 (80%) (60)	—	75	5	2-Hydroxy-5-isopropylbenzoic acid (50%)	29
Salicylic acid (1)	Isobutyl alcohol (2)	$ZnCl_2$ (—)	—	180	1	*p*-*t*-Butylphenol + CO_2 †	238
Salicylic acid (—)	Isobutyl alcohol (—)	H_2SO_4 (80%) (—)	—	70	—	2-Hydroxy-5-*t*-butylbenzoic acid (80%)	29
Salicylic acid (—)	*t*-Butyl alcohol (—)	H_2SO_4 (80%) (—)	—	70	—	2-Hydroxy-5-*t*-butylbenzoic acid (80%)	29
3-Hydroxy-2-naphthoic acid (1)	Isopropyl alcohol (1.2)	HF (33)	—	15–20	20	Isopropyl-3-hydroxy-2-naphthoic acid	71
Methyl salicylate (0.04)	Triphenylcarbinol (0.02)	— (—)	—	Boiling	1	3-Carboxy-4-hydroxytetraphenylmethane ‡ (40%)	131

* References 93–350 appear on pp. 78–82.

† On distillation of the crude product.

‡ After hydrolysis.

TABLE XIII

Alkylation of Aniline

Moles of Aniline	Alkylating Agent (moles)	Catalyst (moles)	Solvent	Temperature, ° C.	Time, hours	Products (% Yield)	Reference*
1	Methyl chloride (—)	$AlCl_3$ (1)	—	—	—	Dimethyltoluidine	164
1	*n*-Propyl alcohol (1)	$ZnCl_2$ (1)	—	260	8	*p*-*n*-Propylaniline	240
1	Isopropyl alcohol (1)	$ZnCl_2$ (1)	—	260	—	*p*-Isopropylaniline	240, 283
1	Isobutyl alcohol (1)	P_2O_5 (1)	—	260	8	*p*-*t*-Butylaniline	240, 296
1	Isobutyl alcohol (1)	$ZnCl_2$ (1)	—	260	8	*p*-*t*-Butylaniline (40–50%)	240, 338
—	Isoamyl alcohol (—)	$ZnCl_2$ (—)	—	280	—	*p*-Isoamylaniline (40%)	249, 296, 337
—	Isoamyl alcohol (—)	P_2O_5 (—)	—	250	—	*p*-Isoamylaniline (40%)	249, 296
0.2	*t*-Amyl alcohol (0.1)	$ZnCl_2$ (—)	—	270	9	*p*-*t*-Amylaniline	98
—	Benzyl chloride (—)	$ZnCl_2$ (—)	—	120	—	*p*-Benzyl-N,N-dibenzylaniline	248
0.1	*n*-Octyl alcohol (0.1)	$ZnCl_2$ (0.05)	—	270–280	8	*p*-*n*-Octylaniline	120
0.1	*s*-Octyl alcohol (0.1)	$ZnCl_2$ (0.05)	—	280	8	*p*-*s*-Octylaniline (15%)	120
—	Benzhydrol (—)	$ZnCl_2$ (—)	—	150	—	*p*-Aminotriphenylmethane	155
0.6	9-Hydroxy-9-phenylfluorene (0.02)	HCl (0.6)	Acetic acid	115	1	9-*p*-Aminophenyl-9-phenylfluorene (80%)	325
—	Di-α-naphthylmethyl bromide (—)	HCl (—)	—	Warm	—	*p*-Di-α-naphthylmethylaniline	243
—	Di-α-naphthylcarbinol (—)	HCl (—)	—	Warm	—	*p*-Di-α-naphthylmethylaniline	243, 285
0.1	Triphenylcarbinol (0.02)	HCl (0.1)	Acetic acid	115	5	*p*-Aminotetraphenylmethane	320

* References 93–350 appear on pp. 78–82.

TABLE XIV

Alkylation of Miscellaneous Aromatic Amines

Aromatic Compound (moles)	Alkylating Agent (moles)	Catalyst (moles)	Solvent	Temperature, ° C.	Time, hours	Products (% Yield)	Reference *
Dimethylaniline (—)	Methyl chloride (—)	$AlCl_3$ (—)	—	—	—	Dimethyltoluidine	164
Dimethylaniline (—)	Benzyl alcohol (—)	$ZnCl_2$ (—)	—	150	—	*p*-Dimethylaminodiphenylmethane	155
Dimethylaniline (—)	Benzhydrol (—)	$ZnCl_2$ (—)	—	150	—	*p*-Dimethylaminotriphenylmethane	155
Dimethylaniline 0.012	9-Hydroxy-9-phenylfluorene (0.004)	HCl (—)	Acetic acid	115	4	9-*p*-Dimethylaminophenyl-9-phenylfluorene (90%)	325
Diphenylamine (1)	Benzyl chloride (1)	$ZnCl_2$ (1)	—	80	1	*p*-Benzyldiphenylamine	248
Diphenylamine (1)	Benzyl chloride (2)	$ZnCl_2$ (1)	—	80	—	Dibenzyldiphenylamine	248
Acetanilide (—)	Benzyl chloride (—)	$ZnCl_2$ (—)	—	120	—	*p*-Benzyl-N,N-dibenzylaniline	248
o-Toluidine (—)	Isobutyl alcohol (—)	$ZnCl_2$ (—)	—	280	—	2-Amino-3-*t*-butyltoluene	145
o-Toluidine (—)	Isobutyl alcohol (—)	HCl (—)	—	280–300	—	2-Amino-5-*t*-butyltoluene	145
o-Toluidine (—)	*n*-Octyl alcohol (—)	$ZnCl_2$ (—)	—	280	—	*n*-Octyl-*o*-toluidine (40–50%)	120
o-Toluidine (0.15)	Triphenylcarbinol (0.1)	HCl (0.15)	Acetic acid	115	5	4-Amino-3-methyltetraphenylmethane	97, 131
N-Methyl-*o*-toluidine (0.012)	9-Hydroxy-9-phenylfluorene (0.004)	HCl (—)	Acetic acid	115	2	9-(3-Methyl-4-methylaminophenyl)-9-phenylfluorene (90%)	325

2,6-Dimethyl-aniline (0.15)	Triphenylcarbinol (0.08)	HCl (0.15)	Acetic acid	115	0.3	4-Amino-3,5-dimethyltetra-phenylmethane (ca. 100%)	113
β-Naphthylamine (0.3)	Methanol (1.0)	HCl (0.3)	—	240–250	12	1-Methyl-2-naphthol (15%), β-dimethylaminonaphtha-lene, etc.	189
p-Aminophenol (3)	Isopropyl ether (5)	HF (100)	—	10 → 75	5	Diisopropyl-*p*-aminophenol (12%), 4,4′-dihydroxytetra-isopropyldiphenylamine (62%)	71
p-Anisidine (2)	Isopropyl ether (3)	HF (60)	—	10 → 25	20	Diisopropyl-*p*-anisidine (38%), 4,4′-dimethoxytetraisopro-pyldiphenylamine (50%)	71
p-Anisidine (0.77)	Cyclohexanol (2)	HF (19)	—	10–20	18	Cyclohexyl-*p*-anisidine (23%)	71
N-Dimethyl-*p*-aminophenol (2)	Isopropyl ether (2.1)	HF (60)	—	10 → 25	20	Isopropyl-N-dimethyl-*p*-aminophenol (42%), diiso-propyl-N-dimethyl-*p*-amino-phenol (9%)	71
N-Diethyl-*m*-phe-netidine (0.45)	Isopropyl ether (0.5)	HF (15)	—	10–20	20	Isopropyl-N-diethyl-*m*-phe-netidine (80%)	71
2-Methoxy-1-naph-thylamine (0.6)	Isopropyl ether (1)	HF (22)	—	5 → 20	20	Triisopropyl-2-methoxy-1-naphthylamine (46%)	71

* References 93–350 appear on pp. 78–82.

TABLE XV

Alkylation of Heterocyclic Aromatic Compounds

Aromatic Compound (moles)	Alkylating Agent (moles)	Catalyst (moles)	Solvent	Temperature, °C.	Time, hours	Products (% Yield)	Reference *
2-Furfural (0.5)	Isopropyl chloride (0.5)	$AlCl_3$ (0.6)	CS_2	25	—	4-Isopropyl-2-furfural (11%)	169
2-Furfural (0.5)	*t*-Butyl chloride (0.5)	$AlCl_3$ (0.6)	CS_2	25	2	5-*t*-Butyl-2-furfural (12%)	32
2-Furfural (0.5)	*n*-Butyl chloride (0.5)	$AlCl_3$ (0.6)	CS_2	25	2	5-*t*-Butyl-2-furfural (12%)	32
2-Furfural (0.5)	Isobutyl chloride (0.5)	$AlCl_3$ (0.6)	CS_2	25	2	5-*t*-Butyl-2-furfural (12%)	32
2-Furfural (0.5)	*n*-Amyl chloride (0.5)	$AlCl_3$ (0.6)	CS_2	25	2	5-Amyl-2-furfural (10%)	32
5-Bromo-2-furfural (—)	Isopropyl chloride (—)	$AlCl_3$ (—)	—	—	—	5-Bromo-4-isopropyl-2-furfural	169
2-Furyl phenyl ketone (0.05)	*t*-Butyl chloride (0.05)	$AlCl_3$ (0.1)	CS_2	25	24	5-*t*-Butyl-2-furyl phenyl ketone (30%)	168
2-Furoic acid (0.5)	*t*-Butyl chloride (0.5)	$AlCl_3$ (1.0)	CS_2	—	—	5-*t*-Butyl-2-furoic acid (6%)	168
Methyl 2-furoate (0.1)	*n*-Propyl chloride (0.1)	$AlCl_3$ (0.1–0.2)	CS_2	0	24	Methyl 5-isopropyl-2-furoate (48%)	168
Methyl 2-furoate (0.1)	Isopropyl chloride (0.1)	$AlCl_3$ (0.1–0.2)	CS_2	0	24	Methyl 5-isopropyl-2-furoate (45%)	168
Methyl 2-furoate (0.1)	*n*-Butyl chloride (0.1)	$AlCl_3$ (0.1–0.2)	CS_2	0	24	Methyl 5-*t*-butyl-2-furoate (45%)	168
Methyl 2-furoate (0.1)	*s*-Butyl chloride (0.1)	$AlCl_3$ (0.1–0.2)	CS_2	0	24	Methyl 5-*t*-butyl-2-furoate (2%)	168
Methyl 2-furoate (0.1)	*t*-Butyl chloride (0.1)	$AlCl_3$ (0.1–0.2)	CS_2	0	24	Methyl 5-*t*-butyl-2-furoate (46%)	168
Methyl 2-furoate (0.1)	Isobutyl chloride (0.1)	$AlCl_3$ (0.1–0.2)	CS_2	0	24	Methyl 5-*t*-butyl-2-furoate (66%)	168
Methyl 2-furoate (0.1)	*n*-Amyl chloride (0.1)	$AlCl_3$ (0.1–0.2)	CS_2	0	24	Methyl 5-*t*-amyl-2-furoate (31%)	168

Methyl 2-furoate (0.1)	*t*-Amyl chloride (0.1)	$AlCl_3$ (0.1–0.2)	CS_2	0 → 25	24	Methyl 5-*t*-amyl-2-furoate (82%)	278
Methyl 2-furoate (0.1)	*n*-Hexyl chloride (0.1)	$AlCl_3$ (0.1–0.2)	CS_2	25	24	Methyl 5-hexyl-2-furoate (57%)	168
Methyl 2-furoate (0.1)	1-Methylcyclohexyl chloride (0.1)	$AlCl_3$ (0.1–0.2)	CS_2	0 → 25	24	Methyl 5-(1-methylcyclohexyl)-2-furoate (55%)	278
Ethyl 2-furoate (—)	*t*-Butyl chloride (—)	HF (—)	CCl_4	—	150	Ethyl 5-*t*-butyl-2-furoate (54%)	308
Ethyl 5-bromo-2-furoate (0.1)	Isopropyl chloride (0.1)	$AlCl_3$ (0.1–0.2)	CS_2	0	24	Ethyl 5-bromo-4-isopropyl-2-furoate (35%)	169
Ethyl 5-bromo-2-furoate (0.74)	*t*-Butyl chloride (0.74)	$AlCl_3$ (1.68)	CS_2	25	24	Ethyl 5-bromo-4-*t*-butyl-2-furoate (3%)	32
Ethyl 5-bromo-2-furoate (0.12)	*n*-Amyl chloride (0.12)	$AlCl_3$ (0.25)	CS_2	25	24	Ethyl 5-bromo-4-*t*-butyl-2-furoate (10% conversion, 30% yield)	32
Ethyl 5-bromo-2-furoate (—)	*n*-Amyl bromide (—)	$AlCl_3$ (—)	—	—	—	5-*t*-Butyl-2-furoic acid † (31–40%)	33
Ethyl 5-bromo-2-furoate (—)	*t*-Amyl alcohol (—)	$AlCl_3$ (—)	CS_2	—	—	4-*t*-Butyl-5-bromo-2-furoic acid † (10%)	33
Ethyl 5-bromo-2-furoate (0.12)	*n*-Hexyl chloride (0.12)	$AlCl_3$ (0.25)	CS_2	25	24	Ethyl 5-bromo-4-*t*-butyl-2-furoate (5% conversion, 15% yield)	32
Ethyl 5-bromo-2-furoate (—)	*n*-Octodecyl bromide (—)	$AlCl_3$ (—)	—	—	—	Ethyl 5-bromo-4-*t*-butyl-2-furoate (46%)	32
Thiophene (0.1)	Benzhydryl ethyl ether (0.1)	$SnCl_4$ (0.1)	CS_2	Cold	—	Dibenzhydrylthiophene (50%), benzhydrylthiophene (5%)	317
Thiophene (0.7)	Benzhydrol (0.6)	P_2O_5 (—)	—	—	24	Benzhydrylthiophene	236

* References 93–350 appear on pp. 78–82.
† After hydrolysis.

REFERENCES TO TABLES

[93] Adam, *Ann. chim.*, [6] **15,** 224 (1888); *Bull. soc. chim.*, [2] **49,** 98 (1888).
[94] Ador and Rilliet, *Bull. soc. chim.*, [2] **31,** 244 (1879); *Ber.*, **12,** 331 (1879).
[95] Albright, Morgan, and Woodworth, *Compt. rend.*, **86,** 887 (1878).
[96] Allen and Underwood, *Bull. soc. chim.*, [2] **40,** 100 (1883).
[97] van Alphen, *Rec. trav. chim.*, **46,** 501 (1927).
[98] Anschütz and Beckerhoff, *Ann.*, **327,** 218 (1903).
[99] Auer, *Ber.*, **17,** 670 (1884).
[100] Auger, *Bull. soc. chim.*, [2] **47,** 48 (1887).
[101] Austin, *Bull. soc. chim.*, [2] **32,** 12 (1879).
[102] Baeyer and Villiger, *Ber.*, **35,** 3018 (1902).
[103] Baeyer, *Ber.*, **42,** 2625 (1909).
[104] Bakunin and Alfano, *Gazz. chim. ital.*, **37,** II, 250 (1907).
[105] Bakunin and Barberio, *Gazz. chim. ital.*, **33,** II, 470 (1903).
[106] Bakunin and Altieri, *Gazz. chim. ital.*, **33,** II, 488 (1903).
[107] Balsohn, *Bull. soc. chim.*, [2] **31,** 539 (1879).
[108] Balsohn, *Bull. soc. chim.*, [2], **32,** 618 (1879).
[109] Bandrowski, *Ber.*, **7,** 1016 (1874).
[110] Barbier, *Compt. rend.*, **79,** 660 (1874).
[111] Barkenbus, Hopkins, and Allen, *J. Am. Chem. Soc.*, **61,** 2452 (1939).
[112] Bartlett and Garland, *J. Am. Chem. Soc.*, **49,** 2098 (1927).
[113] Battegay and Kappeler, *Bull. soc. chim.*, [4] **35,** 992 (1924).
[114] Baur, *Ber.*, **24,** 2832 (1891); **27,** 1606 (1894).
[115] Baur, *Ber.*, **27,** 1614 (1894).
[116] Baur, *Ber.*, **27,** 1623 (1894).
[117] Beaurepaire, *Bull. soc. chim.*, [2] **50,** 677 (1888).
[118] von der Becke, *Ber.*, **23,** 3191 (1890).
[119] Behal and Choay, *Bull. soc. chim.*, [3] **11,** 207 (1894).
[120] Beran, *Ber.*, **18,** 132 (1885).
[121] Bialobrzeski, *Ber.*, **30,** 1773 (1897).
[122] Bistrzycki and Gyr, *Ber.*, **37,** 659 (1904).
[123] Bistrzycki and Herbst, *Ber.*, **35,** 3137 (1902).
[124] Bodroux, *Bull. soc. chim.*, [3] **19,** 888 (1898).
[125] Bodroux, *Compt. rend.*, **132,** 155 (1901).
[126] Bodroux, *Compt. rend.*, **132,** 1334 (1901).
[127] Bodroux, *Bull. soc. chim.*, [3] **25,** 496 (1901).
[128] Boedtker, *Bull. soc. chim.*, [3] **31,** 965 (1904).
[129] Boedtker and Rambech, *Bull. soc. chim.*, [4] **35,** 631 (1924).
[130] Boeseken, *Rec. trav. chim.*, **22,** 311 (1903).
[131] Boyd and Hardy, *J. Chem. Soc.*, **1928,** 630.
[132] von Braun and Deutsch, *Ber.*, **45,** 1273 (1912).
[133] von Braun and Deutsch, *Ber.*, **45,** 2182 (1912).
[134] Brochet, *Compt. rend.*, **117,** 115 (1894).
[135] Brown and Marvel, *J. Am. Chem. Soc.*, **59,** 1248 (1937).
[136] Brunel, *Ber.*, **17,** 1180 (1884).
[137] Cahen, *Bull. soc. chim.*, [3] **19,** 1007 (1898).
[138] Claus and Foecking, *Ber.*, **20,** 3097 (1887).
[139] Clemo and Walton, *J. Chem. Soc.*, **1928,** 728.
[140] Cousin and Lions, *J. Proc. Roy. Soc. N.S. Wales*, **70,** 413 (1937).
[141] Dillingham and Reid, *J. Am. Chem. Soc.*, **60,** 2606 (1938).
[142] Dilthey, Henkels, and Leonhard, *J. prakt. Chem.*, **151,** 114 (1938).
[143] Dziewonski and Dotta, *Bull. soc. chim.*, [3] **31,** 377 (1904).
[144] Dziewonski and Rychlik, *Ber.*, **58,** 2239 (1925).
[145] Effront, *Ber.*, **17,** 419, 2320 (1884).

[146] Elbs, *J. prakt. Chem.*, [2] **35**, 476 (1886).
[147] Epelberg and Lowy, *J. Am. Chem. Soc.*, **63**, 101 (1941).
[148] Errera, *Gazz. chim. ital.*, **14**, 484 (1884).
[149] Essner, *Bull. soc. chim.*, [2] **36**, 212 (1881).
[150] Essner and Gossin, *Bull. soc. chim.*, [2] **42**, 213 (1884).
[151] Estreicher, *Ber.*, **33**, 436 (1900).
[152] Fieser, *J. Am. Chem. Soc.*, **61**, 3467 (1939).
[153] Fieser, Campbell, Fry, and Gates, *J. Am. Chem. Soc.*, **61**, 3222 (1939).
[154] Fieser and Price, *J. Am. Chem. Soc.*, **58**, 1838 (1936).
[155] Fischer, *Ann.*, **206**, 113, 155 (1881).
[156] Fischer and Fischer, *Ann.*, **194**, 263 (1878).
[157] Fischer and Grützner, *Ber.*, **26**, 1646 (1893).
[158] Fisher and Eisner, *J. Org. Chem.*, **6**, 171 (1941).
[159] Flood and Nieuwland, *J. Am. Chem. Soc.*, **50**, 2566 (1928).
[160] Fortner, *Monatsh.*, **25**, 450 (1904).
[161] Fournier, *Bull. soc. chim.*, [3] **7**, 651 (1892).
[162] Frankland and Turner, *J. Chem. Soc.*, **43**, 357 (1883).
[163] Friedel and Crafts, *Bull. soc. chim.*, [2] **39**, 195, 306 (1883).
[164] Friedel and Crafts, *Ann. chim.*, [6] **1**, 449 (1884).
[165] Friedel and Crafts, *Ann., chim.*, [6] **10**, 417 (1887).
[166] Galle, *Ber.*, **16**, 1744 (1883).
[167] Gattermann, Fritz, and Beck, *Ber.*, **32**, 1122 (1899).
[168] Gilman and Calloway, *J. Am. Chem. Soc.*, **55**, 4197 (1933).
[169] Gilman, Calloway, and Burtner, *J. Am. Chem. Soc.*, **57**, 906 (1935).
[170] Gleditsch, *Bull. soc. chim.*, [3] **35**, 1095 (1906).
[171] Goldschmidt, *Ber.*, **15**, 1067 (1886).
[172] Goldschmidt and Larsen, *Z. physik. Chem.*, [A] **48**, 429 (1904).
[173] Goldschmiedt, *Monatsh.*, **2**, 433 (1881).
[174] Gomberg and Kamm., *J. Am. Chem. Soc.*, **39**, 2013 (1917).
[175] Gossin, *Bull. soc. chim.*, [2] **38**, 99 (1882).
[176] Grosse and Ipatieff, *J. Am. Chem. Soc.*, **57**, 2415 (1935).
[177] Grosse, Mavity, and Ipatieff, *J. Org. Chem.*, **3**, 448 (1938).
[178] Gump, *J. Am. Chem. Soc.*, **53**, 380 (1931).
[179] Gurewitsch, *Ber.*, **32**, 2424 (1899).
[180] Gustavson, *Compt. rend.*, **140**, 940 (1905).
[181] Gustavson, *Compt. rend.*, **146**, 640 (1908).
[182] Halse, *J. prakt. Chem.*, [2] **89**, 451 (1914).
[183] Hartmann and Gattermann, *Ber.*, **25**, 3532 (1892).
[184] Haworth, Letsky, and Mavin, *J. Chem. Soc.*, **1932**, 1784.
[185] Hemilian, *Ber.*, **11**, 202 (1878).
[186] Hemilian, *Ber.*, **13**, 678 (1880).
[187] Hemilian, *Ber.*, **16**, 2360 (1883).
[188] Hemilian, *Ber.*, **19**, 3061 (1886).
[189] Hey and Jackson, *J. Chem. Soc.*, **1936**, 1783.
[190] Hirst and Cohen, *J. Chem. Soc.*, **67**, 827 (1895).
[191] Huston, *J. Am. Chem. Soc.*, **46**, 2775 (1924).
[192] Huston and Friedemann, *J. Am. Chem. Soc.*, **38**, 2527 (1916).
[193] Huston and Friedemann, *J. Am. Chem. Soc.*, **40**, 785 (1918).
[194] Huston and Goodemoot, *J. Am. Chem. Soc.*, **56**, 2432 (1934).
[195] Huston and Hsieh, *J. Am. Chem. Soc.*, **58**, 439 (1936).
[196] Huston and Jackson, *J. Am. Chem. Soc.*, **63**, 541 (1941).
[197] Ipatieff and Corson, *J. Am. Chem. Soc.*, **59**, 1417 (1937).
[198] Ipatieff, Corson, and Pines, *J. Am. Chem. Soc.*, **58**, 919 (1936).
[199] Ipatieff and Grosse, *J. Am. Chem. Soc.*, **58**, 2339 (1936).
[200] Ipatieff and Komarewsky, *J. Am. Chem. Soc.*, **56**, 1926 (1934).
[201] Ipatieff, Komarewsky, and Pines, *J. Am. Chem. Soc.*, **58**, 918 (1936).

[202] Ipatieff, Orlov, and Petrov, *Ber.*, **60,** 1006 (1927).
[203] Ipatieff, Orlov, and Razoubaiev, *Bull. soc. chim.*, [4] **37,** 1576 (1925).
[204] Ipatieff, Pines, and Komarewsky, *Ind. Eng. Chem.*, **28,** 222 (1936).
[205] Ipatieff, Pines, and Schmerling, *J. Am. Chem. Soc.*, **60,** 353 (1938).
[206] Ipatieff, Pines, and Schmerling, *J. Am. Chem. Soc.*, **60,** 577 (1938).
[207] Ipatieff, Pines, and Schmerling, *J. Am. Chem. Soc.*, **60,** 1161 (1938).
[208] Isagulyants and Bagryantseva, *Neftyanoe Khoz.*, **1938,** No. 2, 36 [*C. A.*, **33,** 8183 (1939)].
[209] Jacobsen, *Ber.*, **14,** 2624 (1881).
[210] Jacobsen, *Ber.*, **20,** 896 (1887).
[211] Jacobsen, *Ber.*, **21,** 2819 (1888).
[212] Jannasch and Bartels, *Ber.*, **31,** 1716 (1898).
[213] Kamienski and Lewiowna, *Roczniki Chem.*, **14,** 1348 (1934).
[214] Kane and Lowy, *J. Am. Chem. Soc.*, **58,** 2605 (1936).
[215] Kelbe, *Ann.*, **210,** 25 (1881).
[216] Kekulé and Schrötter, *Ber.*, **12,** 2279 (1879).
[217] Khashtanov, *J. Gen. Chem. U.S.S.R.*, **2,** 515 (1932) [*C.A.*, **27,** 975 (1933)].
[218] Kirrmann and Graves, *Bull. soc. chim.*, [5] **1,** 1494 (1934).
[219] Klages, *J. prakt. Chem.*, [2] **65,** 394 (1902).
[220] Klarmann, *J. Am. Chem. Soc.*, **48,** 791 (1926).
[221] Kliegl, *Ber.*, **38,** 290 (1905).
[222] Koch and Steinbrink, *Brennstoff Chem.*, **19,** 277 (1938).
[223] Koenigs, *Ber.*, **23,** 3145 (1890).
[224] Koenigs, *Ber.*, **24,** 179 (1891).
[225] Koenigs and Carl, *Ber.*, **24,** 3889 (1891).
[226] Koenigs and Mai, *Ber.*, **25,** 2654 (1892).
[227] Konowalow, *J. Russ. Phys. Chem. Soc.*, **30,** 1036 (1898) [*Chem. Zentr.*, **I,** 777 (1899)].
[228] Konowalow and Jegerow, *J. Russ. Phys. Chem. Soc.*, **30,** 1031 (1898) [*Chem. Zentr.*, **I,** 776 (1899)].
[229] Kraemer, Spilker, and Eberhardt, *Ber.*, **23,** 3269 (1890); **24,** 2788 (1891).
[230] Krafft, *Ber.*, **19,** 2986 (1886).
[231] Kunckell and Ulex, *J. prakt. Chem.*, [2] **87,** 228 (1913).
[232] Kursanow, *Ann.*, **318,** 311 (1901).
[233] Kursanow, *J. Russ. Phys. Chem. Soc.*, **38,** 1304 (1907).
[234] Kursanow and Zel'vin, *J. Gen. Chem. U.S.S.R.*, **9,** 2173 (1939) [*C. A.*, **34,** 4062 (1940)].
[235] Lehne, *Ber.*, **13,** 358 (1880).
[236] Levi, *Ber.*, **19,** 1624 (1886).
[237] Liebmann, *Ber.*, **14,** 1842 (1881).
[238] Liebmann, *Ber.*, **15,** 150 (1882).
[239] Lippmann and Fritsch, *Monatsh.*, **25,** 793 (1904).
[240] Louis, *Ber.*, **16,** 105 (1883).
[241] Louis, *Compt. rend.*, **95,** 1163 (1882).
[242] Louis, *Ann. chim.*, [6] **6,** 177 (1885).
[243] Magidsohn, *J. Russ. Phys. Chem. Soc.*, **47,** 1304 (1915) [*Chem. Zentr.*, **II,** 129 (1916)]
[244] Malishev, *J. Am. Chem. Soc.*, **57,** 883 (1935).
[245] Marchetti, *Gazz. chim. ital.*, **11,** 439 (1881).
[246] Mayes and Turner, *J. Chem. Soc.*, **1929,** 500.
[247] Meissel, *Ber.*, **32,** 2423 (1899).
[248] Meldola, *J. Chem. Soc.*, **41,** 200 (1882).
[249] Merz and Weith, *Ber.*, **14,** 2343 (1881).
[250] Meyer and Wurster, *Ber.*, **6,** 963 (1873).
[251] Meyer, *J. prakt. Chem.*, [2] **82,** 539 (1910).
[252] Milligan and Reid, *J. Am. Chem. Soc.*, **44,** 206 (1922).
[253] Miquel, *Bull. soc. chim.*, [2] **26,** 2 (1876).
[254] Möhlau, *Ber.*, **31,** 2351 (1898); Möhlau and Klopfer, *Ber.*, **32,** 2149 (1899).

[255] Monacelli and Hennion, *J. Am. Chem. Soc.*, **63,** 1722 (1941).
[256] Monsanto Chemical Company, Brit. pat., 452,335 [*C. A.*, **31,** 485 (1937)].
[257] Moureu, *Bull. soc. chim.*, [3] **15,** 652 (1896).
[258] Nef, *Ann.*, **298,** 254 (1897).
[259] Ninetzescu, Isacescu, and Ionescu, *Ann.*, **491,** 210 (1931).
[260] Noelting, *Ber.*, **25,** 791 (1892).
[261] Norris and Arthur, *J. Am. Chem. Soc.*, **62,** 874 (1940).
[262] Norris and Ingraham, *J. Am. Chem. Soc.*, **62,** 1298 (1940).
[263] Norris and Klemka, *J. Am. Chem. Soc.*, **62,** 1432 (1940).
[264] O'Connor and Sowa, *J. Am. Chem. Soc.*, **60,** 125 (1938).
[265] *Org. Syntheses, Coll. Vol.* **2,** 248, John Wiley & Sons, New York, New York, 1943.
[266] Paterno, *Ber.*, **5,** 288 (1872); **5,** 435 (1872).
[267] Paterno and Fileti, *Gazz. chim. ital.*, **5,** 382 (1875).
[268] Pavelkina, *J. Applied Chem. U.S.S.R.*, **12,** 1422 (1939) [*C.A.*, **34,** 3485 (1940)].
[269] Perkin and Hodgkinson, *J. Chem. Soc.*, **37,** 725 (1880).
[270] Pines, Schmerling, and Ipatieff, *J. Am. Chem. Soc.*, **62,** 2901 (1940).
[271] Pokrovskaya and Sushchik, *J. Gen. Chem. U.S.S.R.*, **9,** 2291 (1939) [*C. A.*, **34,** 5433 (1940)].
[272] Potts and Carpenter, *J. Am. Chem. Soc.*, **61,** 663 (1939).
[273] Price and Lund, *J. Am. Chem. Soc.*, **62,** 3105 (1940).
[274] Radziewanowski, *Ber.*, **27,** 3235 (1894).
[275] Radziewanowski, *Ber.*, **28,** 1137, 1139 (1895).
[276] Radziszewski, *Ber.*, **7,** 141 (1874).
[277] Rayman and Preis, *Ann.*, **223,** 315 (1884).
[278] Reichstein, Rosenberg, and Eberhardt, *Helv. Chim. Acta*, **18,** 721 (1935).
[279] Rennie, *J. Chem. Soc.*, **41,** 33 (1882).
[280] Roux, *Bull. soc. chim.*, [2] **41,** 379 (1884).
[281] Roux, *Ann. chim.*, [6] **12,** 289 (1887).
[282] Rozycki, *Ber.*, **32,** 2428 (1899).
[283] Sachs and Weigert, *Ber.*, **40,** 4360 (1907); Constam and Goldschmidt, *Ber.*, **21,** 1157 (1888).
[284] Savard and Hösögüt, *Rev. faculté sci. univ. Istanbul*, [N.S.] **3,** 27 (1937) [*C.A.*, **32,** 3348 (1938)].
[285] Schmidlin and Massini, *Ber.*, **42,** 2390 (1909).
[286] Schorigin, *Ber.*, **60,** 2373 (1927).
[287] Schramm, *Monatsh.*, **9,** 613 (1888).
[288] Schramm, *Ber.*, **26,** 1706 (1893).
[289] Schrauth and Quasebarth, *Ber.*, **57,** 854 (1924).
[290] Schreiner, *J. prakt. Chem.*, [2] **81,** 557 (1910).
[291] Schreiner, *J. prakt. Chem.*, [2] **82,** 294 (1910).
[292] Schroeter, *Ann.*, **48,** 199 (1919).
[293] Semptowski, *Ber.*, **22,** 2662 (1889).
[294] Senff, *Ann.*, **220,** 225 (1883).
[295] Senkowski, *Ber.*, **23,** 2413 (1890).
[296] Senkowski, *Ber.*, **24,** 2974 (1891).
[297] Sharma and Dutt, *J. Indian Chem. Soc.*, **12,** 774 (1935).
[298] Shoesmith and McGechen, *J. Chem. Soc.*, **1930,** 2231.
[299] Shorigin, *Ber.*, **61,** 2516 (1928).
[300] Silva, *Bull. soc. chim.*, [2] **38,** 529 (1877).
[301] Silva, *Bull. soc. chim.*, [2] **29,** 193 (1878).
[302] Silva, *Bull. soc. chim.*, [2] **43,** 317 (1885).
[303] Simons and Archer, *J. Am. Chem. Soc.*, **60,** 2952 (1938).
[304] Simons and Archer, *J. Am. Chem. Soc.*, **60,** 2953 (1938).
[305] Simons and Archer, *J. Am. Chem. Soc.*, **61,** 1521 (1939).
[306] Simons and Archer, *J. Am. Chem. Soc.*, **62,** 1623 (1940).
[307] Simons, Archer, and Adams, *J. Am. Chem. Soc.*, **60,** 2955 (1938).

[308] Simons, Archer, and Passino, *J. Am. Chem. Soc.*, **60,** 2956 (1938).
[309] Simons, Archer, and Randall, *J. Am. Chem. Soc.*, **61,** 1821 (1939).
[310] Slanina, Sowa, and Nieuwland, *J. Am. Chem. Soc.*, **57,** 1547 (1935).
[311] Smith, *J. Am. Chem. Soc.*, **59,** 899 (1937).
[312] Smith and Guss, *J. Am. Chem. Soc.*, **62,** 2625 (1940).
[313] Smith and Rodden, *J. Am. Chem. Soc.*, **59,** 2353 (1937).
[314] Sowa, Hennion, and Nieuwland, *J. Am. Chem. Soc.*, **57,** 709 (1935).
[315] Spiegler and Tinker, *J. Am. Chem. Soc.*, **61,** 1002 (1939).
[316] Stadnikov and Kashtanov, *J. Russ. Phys. Chem. Soc.*, **60,** 1117 (1928) [*C. A.*, **23,** 2170 (1929)].
[317] Stadnikov and Goldfarb, *Ber.*, **61,** 2341 (1928).
[318] Stahl, *Ber.*, **23,** 992 (1890).
[319] Tcheou and Yung, *Contrib. Inst. Chem., Nat. Acad. Peiping,* **2,** No. 8, No. 9, 127, 149 (1936) [*C. A.*, **31,** 6646 (1937)].
[320] Tsukervanik and Sidorova, *J. Gen. Chem. U.S.S.R.*, **7,** 641 (1937) [*C. A.*, **31,** 5780 (1937)].
[321] Tsukervanik and Tambovtseva, *Bull. univ. Asie centrale,* **22,** 221 (1938) [*C. A.*, **34,** 4729 (1940)].
[322] Tsukervanik and Terent'eva, *J. Gen. Chem. U.S.S.R.*, **7,** 637 (1937) [*C. A.*, **31,** 5780 (1937)].
[323] Uhlhorn, *Ber.*, **23,** 3142 (1890).
[324] Ullmann and Münzhuber, *Ber.*, **36,** 407 (1903).
[325] Ullmann and von Wurstemberger, *Ber.*, **37,** 77 (1904).
[326] Verley, *Bull. soc. chim.*, [3] **19,** 67 (1898).
[327] Vincent and Roux, *Bull. soc. chim.*, [2] **40,** 163 (1883).
[328] Vlekke, dissertation, Freiburg, p. 46, 1905.
[329] Voswinkel, *Ber.*, **21,** 2829 (1888); **22,** 315 (1889).
[330] Walker, *Ber.*, **5,** 686 (1872).
[331] Wegscheider, *Monatsh.*, **5,** 236 (1884).
[332] Welsh and Drake, *J. Am. Chem. Soc.*, **60,** 58 (1938).
[333] Werner and Grob, *Ber.*, **37,** 2897 (1904).
[334] Wertyporoch and Firla, *Ann.*, **500,** 287 (1933).
[335] Wertyporoch and Sagel, *Ber.*, **66,** 1306 (1933).
[336] Willgerodt and Albert, *J. prakt. chem.*, [2] **84,** 393 (1911).
[337] Willgerodt and Damann, *Ber.*, **34,** 3678 (1901).
[338] Willgerodt and Rampacher, *Ber.*, **34,** 3667 (1901).
[339] Wispek and Zuber, *Ann.*, **218,** 379 (1883).
[340] Wispek and Zuber, *Bull. soc. chim.*, [2] **43,** 588 (1885).
[341] Wunderly, Sowa, and Nieuwland, *J. Am. Chem. Soc.*, **58,** 1007 (1936).
[342] Wuyts, *Bull. soc. chim. Belg.*, **26,** 308 (1912).
[343] Zincke, *Ann.*, **159,** 374 (1871); *Ber.*, **6,** 119 (1873).
[344] Zincke, *Ann.*, **161,** 93 (1872); *Ber.*, **6,** 906 (1873).
[345] Zincke, *Ber.*, **5,** 799 (1872).
[346] Zonew, *J. Russ. Phys. Chem. Soc.*, **48,** 550 (1916) [*Chem. Zentr.*, **I,** 1497 (1923)].
[347] Diuguid, *J. Am. Chem. Soc.*, **63,** 3527 (1941).
[348] Snyder, Adams, and McIntosh, *J. Am. Chem. Soc.*, **63,** 3280 (1941).
[349] Kleene and Wheland, *J. Am. Chem. Soc.*, **63,** 3321 (1941).
[350] Corson and Ipatieff, *J. Am. Chem. Soc.*, **59,** 645 (1937).
[351] Burwell and Archer, *J. Am. Chem. Soc.*, **64,** 1032 (1942).

CHAPTER 2

THE WILLGERODT REACTION

MARVIN CARMACK

University of Pennsylvania

AND

M. A. SPIELMAN

Abbott Laboratories

CONTENTS

* Numbering of nuclei follows current practice of Chemical Abstracts. In this example, as well as in several others, the numbering differs from common usage.

INTRODUCTION

The name of Conrad Willgerodt is associated with a group of closely related reactions which have as a common feature the conversion of a carbonyl compound into an amide with the same number of carbon atoms. The original process involved the reaction of an appropriately substituted alkyl aryl ketone with an aqueous solution of yellow ammonium polysulfide at an elevated temperature to form an aryl-substituted aliphatic acid amide, together with a smaller amount of the corresponding ammonium salt of the carboxylic acid. An example is the conversion of acetophenone into phenylacetamide and ammonium phenylacetate.[1]

$$C_6H_5COCH_3 \xrightarrow[H_2O]{(NH_4)_2SS_x} C_6H_5CH_2CONH_2 + (C_6H_5CH_2COONH_4)$$

The net result of the reaction is the reduction of the carbonyl group and the oxidation of the terminal methyl group.

In the first work [2] on the reaction 1-acetylnaphthalene was heated with ammonium polysulfide solution in a sealed tube at 210–230° for three or four days to form a substance later characterized [3] as 1-naphthylacetamide. Other methyl ketones such as acetophenone [1] and 2,4-dimethylacetophenone [2] were found to behave in a similar manner. In each case a mixture of amide and acid salt was obtained. Extension of the reaction to ethyl, *n*-propyl, and *n*-butyl aryl ketones led to the remarkable finding that the terminal methyl is always converted into a carbonamide group, even though it may be several carbon atoms removed from the original carbonyl group. Thus propiophenone gives β-phenylpropionamide,[1] butyrophenone yields γ-phenylbutyramide,[1] and *n*-butyl *p*-tolyl ketone yields δ-*p*-tolylvaleramide.[4] The publications of

$$C_6H_5C(=O)—CH_2CH_3 \rightarrow C_6H_5CH_2CH_2C(=O)—NH_2$$

$$C_6H_5C(=O)—CH_2CH_2CH_3 \rightarrow C_6H_5CH_2CH_2CH_2C(=O)—NH_2$$

$$(p\text{-})CH_3C_6H_4C(=O)—CH_2CH_2CH_2CH_3 \rightarrow (p\text{-})CH_3C_6H_4CH_2CH_2CH_2CH_2C(=O)—NH_2$$

Willgerodt and collaborators extending over a period of nearly twenty-five years [1–7] described efforts to develop the procedure into a useful syn-

[1] Willgerodt and Merk, *J. prakt. Chem.*, [2] **80,** 192 (1909).
[2] Willgerodt, *Ber.*, **20,** 2467 (1887).
[3] Willgerodt, *Ber.*, **21,** 534 (1888).
[4] Willgerodt and Hambrecht, *J. prakt. Chem.*, [2] **81,** 74 (1910).
[5] Willgerodt, *J. prakt. Chem.*, [2] **80,** 183 (1909).
[6] Willgerodt and Scholtz, *J. prakt. Chem.*, [2] **81,** 382 (1910).
[7] Willgerodt and Albert, *J. prakt. Chem.*, [2] **84,** 387 (1911).

thetic tool. Approximately forty ketones were investigated, but the final procedures did not differ greatly from those originally described, and the fundamental chemistry of the process was not elucidated.

Although the Willgerodt reaction was known through standard references,[8] it was used by only a few workers [9, 10, 11, 12] and remained a chemical curiosity until increasing interest in complex polynuclear systems led to a search for additional methods of synthesizing aryl-substituted aliphatic acids of unequivocal structure. Interest in the reaction revived after its application to the preparation of 3-acenaphthylacetic acid from 3-acetylacenaphthene.[11] The requisite temperature was lowered to 160° by the use of purified dioxane to increase the mutual solubility of the ketone and aqueous ammonium polysulfide, and the yield of acid compared favorably with that realized by an alternative synthesis involving the Arndt-Eistert reaction. The Willgerodt reaction in the presence of dioxane has been used by several investigators [13–21] in the synthesis of a variety of aryl-substituted aliphatic acids and amides.

The Kindler variation,[22, 23] which promises to be more useful than the original Willgerodt procedure, consists in heating the ketone with approximately equimolecular amounts of sulfur and a dry amine instead of aqueous ammonium polysulfide. A thioamide is formed as the principal product and on hydrolysis with acid or alkali affords the carboxylic acid, usually in good yield. Generally a secondary aliphatic amine but sometimes a primary amine or even anhydrous ammonia [24] is used; the development of a method for the electrolytic reduction of the thioamides to amines [25] extended the usefulness of the reaction as a new route to the synthesis of many important nitrogen bases. Early descriptions of this

[8] Houben, *Die Methoden der organischen Chemie*, 3d ed., Vol. III, pp. 867, 872, Georg Thieme, Leipzig, 1930.

[9] Weitzenböck and Lieb, *Monatsh.*, **33**, 556, 563 (1912).

[10] Mosettig and van de Kamp, *J. Am. Chem. Soc.*, **55**, 3444 (1933).

[11] Fieser and Kilmer, *J. Am. Chem. Soc.*, **62**, 1354 (1940).

[12] Smith and MacMullen, *J. Am. Chem. Soc.*, **58**, 633 (1936).

[13] Bachmann and Sheehan, *J. Am. Chem. Soc.*, **62**, 2688 (1940).

[14] Bachmann and Carmack, *J. Am. Chem. Soc.*, **63**, 2494 (1941).

[15] Hartmann and Bosshard, *Helv. Chim. Acta*, **24**, 28E (1941).

[16] Bachmann and Cortes, *J. Am. Chem. Soc.*, **65**, 1329 (1943).

[17] Bachmann and Cronyn, *J. Org. Chem.*, **8**, 461 (1943).

[18] (*a*) Arnold and Barnes, *J. Am. Chem. Soc.*, **65**, 2395 (1943); (*b*) R. T. Arnold, private communication.

[19] Riegel, Gold, and Kubico, *J. Am. Chem. Soc.*, **65**, 1775 (1943).

[20] (*a*) DeTar and Carmack, *J. Am. Chem. Soc.*, **68**, 2025 (1946); (*b*) Carmack and DeTar, *J. Am. Chem. Soc.*, **68**, 2029 (1946).

[21] Cavalieri, Pattison and Carmack, *J. Am. Chem. Soc.*, **67**, 1783 (1945)

[22] Kindler, *Ann.*, **431**, 193, 222 (1923).

[23] Kindler, *Arch. Pharm.*, **265**, 389 (1927).

[24] Kindler, Ger. pat., 405,675; *Chem. Zentr.*, **96**, I, 1529 (1925).

[25] Kindler and Peschke, *Arch. Pharm.*, **270**, 340 (1932).

procedure were placed inconspicuously in communications dealing with other subjects,[22–26] and the possibilities of the process have been appreciated only recently.[27]

$$ArCOCH_3 \xrightarrow[S]{(CH_3)_2NH} ArCH_2C(=S)N(CH_3)_2 \xrightarrow{H_2O} ArCH_2COOH$$

$$ArCH_2C(=S)N(CH_3)_2 \xrightarrow{4[H]} ArCH_2CH_2N(CH_3)_2$$

Morpholine is well suited to the Kindler version of the Willgerodt reaction;[28] it is cheap, and its boiling point (128°) makes possible the use of open apparatus in place of an autoclave or bomb tube.

The Willgerodt reaction has been applied to a number of completely aliphatic ketones.[21] For example, pinacolone is converted into *t*-butylacetamide and 2-heptanone into heptanamide.

$$(CH_3)_3CCOCH_3 \rightarrow (CH_3)_3CCH_2CONH_2$$

$$CH_3(CH_2)_4COCH_3 \rightarrow CH_3(CH_2)_5CONH_2$$

Aryl-substituted olefins and acetylenes are transformed into amides under the conditions of both the Willgerodt and Kindler procedures.[20]

$$C_6H_5C{\equiv}CH \searrow C_6H_5CH_2CONH_2 \nearrow C_6H_5CH{=}CH_2$$

$$C_6H_5C{\equiv}CCH_3 \searrow C_6H_5CH_2CH_2CONH_2 \nearrow C_6H_5CH{=}CHCH_3$$

MECHANISM

The mechanism of the Willgerodt reaction is not clear. The possibility that the ketone first undergoes reduction at the carbonyl group to form a hydrocarbon which is subsequently oxidized at the terminal methyl group was rejected when it was found that an alkyl substituent such as the ethyl group is unaffected under the conditions that bring about the reaction with ketones.[1, 3] Willgerodt considered it unlikely that the oxidation of the terminal methyl group of the ketone could precede the final

[26] Kindler and Peschke, *Arch. Pharm.*, **272**, 236 (1934).

[27] Kindler and Li, *Ber.*, **74**, 321 (1941).

[28] Schwenk and Bloch, *J. Am. Chem. Soc.*, **64**, 3051 (1942).

reductive step in which the carbonyl group would be converted to a methylene unit, since there is no evidence for intermediate keto acids and since the latter cannot be converted into amides by the ammonium polysulfide reagent.[3] He concluded that the oxygen atom of the alkyl aryl ketone can, in some unknown way, wander to the end of the chain, or, in effect, exchange place with two hydrogen atoms of the methyl group to form an aldehyde isomeric with the ketone. The aldehyde could then react with sulfur and ammonia to produce the amide and hydrogen sulfide; indeed, aldehydes are known to yield amides under these conditions.

Kindler [22] suggested that the reaction may proceed by a migration of the aryl group to the carbon atom alpha to the carbonyl group; the original carbonyl group would thus become the thioamide function of the final product. To accommodate ketones higher than acetophenone, e.g., propiophenone, he postulated [27] migration of the phenyl group to the end of the chain, *two* or more atoms removed from the original carbonyl group. First, he stated, there is the preliminary formation of the hydramine (I), which adds sulfur to give an amine sulfide (II). This is dehydrated to III,

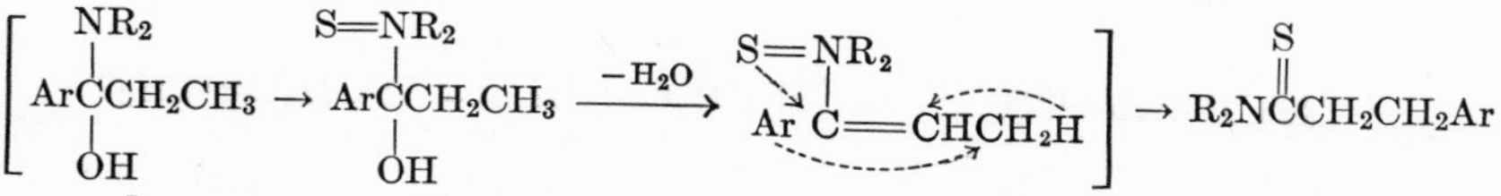

$$\left[\underset{\text{I}}{ArC(NR_2)(OH)CH_2CH_3} \rightarrow \underset{\text{II}}{ArC(S{=}NR_2)(OH)CH_2CH_3} \xrightarrow{-H_2O} \underset{\text{III}}{Ar\,C(S{=}NR_2){=}CHCH_2H}\right] \rightarrow \underset{\text{IV}}{R_2NC({=}S)CH_2CH_2Ar}$$

and then the final thioamide is formed in a rearrangement which results in the simultaneous migration of the sulfur atom, the aryl radical, and a terminal hydrogen atom. However, evidence against this mechanism is recorded in Willgerodt's observation that isovalerophenone gives (after hydrolysis) α-methyl-γ-phenylbutyric acid, VI. According to Kindler's hypothesis the β-methyl isomer VII should result. That VI is the product seems highly probable.[11]

$$\underset{\text{V}}{C_6H_5COCH_2CH(CH_3)_2} \rightarrow \underset{\text{VI}}{C_6H_5CH_2CH_2CH(CH_3)COOH}$$

$$\underset{\text{VII}}{HOOCCH_2CH(CH_3)CH_2C_6H_5}$$

On the basis of three facts—that no change in the carbon skeleton occurs during the reaction; that all members of a family of isomeric aliphatic carbonyl compounds, differing from one another only in the position of the oxygen atom, form the same final product; and that unsaturated hydrocarbons can undergo reactions very similar to the

Willgerodt and Kindler reactions of ketones—Carmack and DeTar [20] have argued that there must be one fundamental mechanism involving the preliminary formation of a labile intermediate which has an unsaturated carbon-carbon bond in the side chain. They have postulated a series of steps involving the stepwise addition, elimination, and readdition of the elements of simple molecules such as ammonia, amines, sulfur, water, or hydrogen sulfide, the net result being the migration of the functional group along the chain. Irreversible oxidation by the action of sulfur when the function reaches the terminal position produces a thioamide. The type of process is illustrated schematically as follows:

$$\mathrm{R'COCH_2CH_3 + R_2NH \rightleftharpoons R'C(OH)(NR_2)CH_2CH_3 \rightleftharpoons}$$

$$\mathrm{R'C(NR_2){=}CHCH_3 \rightleftharpoons R'C{\equiv}CCH_3 \rightleftharpoons R'CH{=}C(NR_2)CH_3}$$

$$\mathrm{R'CH_2CH{=}CHNR_2 \rightleftharpoons R'CH_2C{\equiv}CH \rightleftharpoons R'CH_2C(NR_2){=}CH_2}$$

$$\mathrm{R'CH_2CH{=}CHNR_2 \xrightarrow{S} R'CH_2CH_2C({=}S)NR_2}$$

R = alkyl or H.

That a carbonamide rather than a thioamide is isolated in the Willgerodt reaction with aqueous ammonia does not constitute an argument against the above scheme, for hot aqueous ammonia [29] is known to convert thioamides to carbonamides. The isomerization of straight-chain acetylenic compounds (with and without aromatic substituents) to products having the acetylene function in the terminal position is known to take place in the presence of sodium amide.[30, 31] The assumption that such unsaturated substances are intermediates in the Willgerodt reaction offers an explanation of the appearance of certain by-products. Tetrahydronaphthoic acid, isolated in small amounts from the reaction of ethyl 6-tetralyl ketone with morpholine and sulfur,[32] may arise from an oxidative attack by sulfur on an unsaturated intermediate. The presence of traces of thiophenes in the reaction mixtures is explicable when it

[29] Bernthsen, *Ann.*, **184**, 297 (1877).
[30] Bourguel, *Compt. rend.*, **179**, 686 (1925), **192**, 686 (1931); *Ann. chim.*, (10) **3**, 207 (1925).
[31] Vaughn, *J. Am. Chem. Soc.*, **55**, 3455 (1933).
[32] Arnold, Schultz, and Klug, *J. Am. Chem. Soc.*, **66**, 1606 (1944).

is considered that olefins and sulfur react at elevated temperatures to give hydrogen sulfide and thiophenes [33] and that acetylenes also give thiophenes but with little evolution of hydrogen sulfide. Styrene and phenylacetylene both undergo transformation to substituted thiophenes.[20]

SCOPE, LIMITATIONS, AND SIDE REACTIONS

Application of the reaction under the conditions originally specified by Willgerodt usually results in yields of 20–50% of arylacetic acids or amides from acetophenone and substituted acetophenones. The modified procedure in which a solvent is used gives somewhat higher yields, and when applied to the aceto derivatives of naphthalene and especially of phenanthrene, acenaphthene, and pyrene affords yields of 57–92%. When the earlier reaction conditions were applied to the higher homologs of acetophenone, such as propiophenone or butyrophenone, more by-products resulted and the yields of acids dropped to 7–40%. The three isomers, propiophenone, phenylacetone, and hydrocinnamaldehyde, all react to form β-phenylpropionamide.[20] The reaction appears to be unsuccessful for homologs higher than amyl, although the earlier experimentation was very limited and the improved procedures have not been investigated.

It should be kept in mind that reactive functions such as amino, nitro, and formyl groups may undergo oxidation, reduction, or condensation under conditions of the Willgerodt reaction, hence their presence as substituents on the starting compounds may lead to various side reactions. Alkyl groups, alkoxyls, halogens (if inert) and similar unreactive groups appear to have no effect on the course of the reaction.

Ketones with branched chains have been reported to undergo reaction in low yields (0.5–20%) [1] in a manner analogous to the straight-chain ketones without rearrangement of the carbon skeleton. Isopropyl phenyl ketone and isobutyl phenyl ketone may be cited as examples.

$$C_6H_5COCH(CH_3)_2 \rightarrow C_6H_5CH_2\underset{\displaystyle CH_3}{\underset{|}{C}}HCONH_2$$

$$C_6H_5COCH_2CH(CH_3)_2 \rightarrow C_6H_5CH_2CH_2\underset{\displaystyle CH_3}{\underset{|}{C}}HCONH_2$$

However, subsequent investigators [11, 14, 34] have reported experiments with branched-chain ketones in which little or no amide was obtained.

[33] Baumann and Fromm, *Ber.*, **28**, 891 (1895).

[34] Carmack, doctoral dissertation, University of Michigan, 1940.

Derivatives of pyridine have been studied, particularly 3-acetylpyridine [15, 35] and other heterocyclic compounds such as 5-acetyl-1-phenyl-4-methylpyrazole and 8-acetylquinoline.[35] The yield of methyl 3-pyridylacetate from 3-acetylpyridine was about 70%.

The Willgerodt reaction is apparently not limited to aromatic aliphatic ketones. A few completely aliphatic ketones have been found to undergo the reaction, though in general the yields are lower. Pinacolone reacts with ammonium polysulfide solution containing dioxane and a large excess of sulfur to form *t*-butylacetamide in 58% yield. Methyl cyclohexyl ketone yields 40% of cyclohexylacetamide, and ethyl cyclohexyl ketone 27% of β-cyclohexylpropionamide. The four isomeric carbonyl compounds, heptanal, 2-heptanone, 3-heptanone, and 4-heptanone, all give heptanamide in varying yields, the highest yields being obtained from the aldehyde (50%) and the methyl ketone (38%).

$$\left.\begin{array}{l} CH_3(CH_2)_5CHO \\ CH_3(CH_2)_4COCH_3 \\ CH_3(CH_2)_3COCH_2CH_3 \\ CH_3(CH_2)_2COCH_2CH_2CH_3 \end{array}\right\} \rightarrow CH_3(CH_2)_5CONH_2$$

The conversion of unsaturated compounds into acids has been studied in a very limited way. The transformation of phenylacetylene into phenylacetamide proceeds under comparable conditions and in about the same yield as the conversion of acetophenone into phenylacetamide. From styrene the yield is somewhat less. 1-Phenylpropyne and 1-phenylpropene give β-phenylpropionamide in good yields. Phenylacetylene and styrene both produce phenylacetothiomorpholide when treated with morpholine and sulfur.

$$\left.\begin{array}{l} C_6H_5C{\equiv}CH \\ C_6H_5CH{=}CH_2 \end{array}\right\} \xrightarrow{HN(CH_2CH_2)_2O\ +\ S} C_6H_5CH_2\overset{\overset{S}{\|}}{C}N(CH_2CH_2)_2O$$

The Kindler procedure has not been applied extensively. It reportedly gives somewhat higher yields with certain compounds than the Willgerodt procedure. However, compounds containing active methylene groups, such as 3-acetylacenaphthene or 2-acetylfluorene, do not react satisfactorily,[36] though good yields of amides result from the same ketones by reaction with ammonium polysulfide in dioxane-water solution.[11, 13] Only one example of an ethyl aryl ketone in the morpholine-sulfur procedure is reported;[32] yields of 30–58% have been obtained with ethyl aryl ketones, dimethylamine, and sulfur.[23, 25, 27]

[35] Brit. pat., 558,774; *Brit. C. A.*, **BII,** 102 (1944).

[36] Zaugg and Rapala, private communication.

It is of interest to note the behavior of molecules containing other functional groups. Carbinols form amides at somewhat higher temperatures than the corresponding ketones, probably by way of unsaturated intermediates. Aldehydes are converted into the corresponding carboxylic acid amides when heated with aqueous ammonium polysulfide,[3, 20] and they form substituted thioamides under conditions of the Kindler procedure. Aldimines [22, 23] likewise are converted to acid derivatives. Two imines derived from methyl ketones and methylamine are reported to react with sulfur to form N-methylarylthioacetamides in a manner analogous to the reaction of methyl ketones in the presence of the amine.

By-Products. The commonest by-products accompanying the amides prepared from ketones are the corresponding hydrocarbons.[3, 11]

$$RCOCH_3 \rightarrow RCH_2CH_3$$

A high concentration of hydrogen sulfide probably favors this side reaction.

Methyl aryl ketones in the Willgerodt reaction produce minor amounts of thiophenes, probably mixtures of 2,4- and 2,5-diarylthiophenes.[20]

Ar Ar S   Ar Ar S

Substituted thiophenes of this type constitute the principal products isolated when colorless ammonium sulfide is used in place of ammonium polysulfide.[1, 33]

Side chains may be degraded, as in the example already cited in which 5,6,7,8-tetrahydro-2-naphthoic acid appears as a by-product in the reaction of ethyl 6-tetralyl ketone with morpholine and sulfur.[32] Ammonium polysulfide and long-chain alkyl phenyl ketones give some benzoic acid.[1] Ethyl 9-anthryl ketone,[20] on the other hand, produces anthracene in 85% yield, possibly owing to the great lability of a substituent in the 9-position of anthracene.

EXPERIMENTAL CONDITIONS AND REAGENTS

Ammonium Polysulfide. Most of the published procedures for the Willgerodt reaction specify the use of aqueous ammonium polysulfide reagent prepared by "saturating" concentrated aqueous ammonia with hydrogen sulfide and dissolving in the solution 10% by weight of sulfur to form a clear, deep red reagent containing the complex polysulfide. In nearly all experiments 5 cc. of such a solution has been used for each gram of ketone. With aliphatic ketones [20, 21] higher yields are obtained when the proportion of sulfur is increased to as much as 10 to 20 gram atoms for each mole of ketone.

It has been demonstrated [20] that "saturation" of aqueous ammonia by bubbling gaseous hydrogen sulfide through the liquid is a slow process and may produce almost any concentration of hydrogen sulfide up to 7 moles per liter; the concentration of ammonia also changes during the process, so that the composition of the reagent may vary widely, depending upon the conditions. To ensure reproducibility of results the actual composition of the reagent should be determined by analysis. Ammonia can be titrated directly with acid; hydrogen sulfide (or its equivalent) can be determined iodometrically; and the sulfur present in free elementary state or combined as polysulfide is known from the weight of sulfur used in the preparation of the reagent.

In spite of the implications of most published procedures, high concentrations of hydrogen sulfide are not desirable, except perhaps with completely aliphatic compounds. It is known that ammonium sulfide can cause reduction of carbonyl compounds.[37]

A convenient and reproducible method of preparing a satisfactory polysulfide reagent consists in suspending finely powdered sulfur in about ten times its weight of concentrated aqueous ammonia (15 *M*) and passing a stream of hydrogen sulfide through the agitated suspension until all the sulfur dissolves. This process requires only a short time and produces a reagent containing approximately 0.7 mole of hydrogen sulfide (or the equivalent) per liter.

Highest yields are obtained from some ketones, e.g., acetophenone,[20] with a reagent to which no hydrogen sulfide is added; the reagent consists of a solution or suspension of flowers of sulfur in a mixture of concentrated aqueous ammonia and a solvent such as pyridine or dioxane. Better results are obtained with aliphatic ketones and some ketones derived from complex polycyclic hydrocarbons when a moderate concentration of hydrogen sulfide is present initially in the reagent. When hydrogen sulfide is not added it probably is formed as a reaction product and is present during most of the reaction period.

Attempts to use colorless ammonium sulfide (no added free sulfur) have been unsuccessful,[6] as the yields of amide are always lower than with the polysulfide reagent, and mixtures of by-products such as diarylthiophenes and hydrocarbons predominate among the products isolated.

The use of sodium polysulfide in place of ammonium polysulfide [1] in the reaction of acetophenone at 220° results in the formation of only a very small amount of sodium phenylacetate contaminated with sodium benzoate.

[37] Baumann and Fromm, *Ber.*, **28**, 907 (1895).

Added Organic Solvents. The addition of 4 volumes of dioxane to every 5 volumes of ammonium polysulfide reagent [11] has the advantage of allowing the reaction to proceed at a much lower temperature than would be possible without the organic solvent. Side reactions, in particular the formation of tarry material, are minimized, so that higher yields of amide are obtained; the amide is purer, and less hydrolysis of the amide to ammonium salt takes place.

Pyridine has been found [20] to be similarly effective in making possible a lower temperature of reaction. Since neither dioxane nor pyridine has been shown to take part in the Willgerodt reaction, it is presumed that their beneficial influence is due to their solvent properties, which increase the mutual solubility of the immiscible ketones and the polysulfide reagent.

The choice of dioxane or pyridine in a given case is governed to some extent by the type of procedure to be followed in isolating the product. The amides often precipitate directly from dioxane-water solutions upon cooling, and can be isolated by direct filtration in a state of fair purity, but many amides are soluble in pyridine-water mixtures.

The Kindler Modification with Amines and Sulfur. The theoretical molecular proportions of reactants in Kindler's procedure are 1 mole of amine and 1 gram atom of sulfur for each mole of ketone. The proportions which have been used vary from almost the theoretical to ratios of 1.5/1.5/1 for amine, sulfur, and ketone.[23, 25, 26, 27, 28, 38]

The amines which have been used most frequently are dimethylamine and morpholine, although methylamine,[24] piperidine,[23, 28] and anhydrous ammonia [24] have been mentioned.

Apparatus. All reactions with aqueous reagents must be carried out in closed systems capable of withstanding pressure. For this reason most reported experiments have been limited to runs with small amounts, usually 1 to 4 g. of ketone, in sealed glass tubes. Most procedures at present call for temperatures below 180°; at temperatures of 160–180° the pressures developed in sealed tubes seldom appear to be dangerously high; it has been estimated [6] that at 230° the pressure may reach as high a value as 41 atmospheres. When the tubes are opened there is little residual pressure, and sometimes air is drawn into the tube. However, it is advisable to observe the precautions usual in such work.

The limitations placed upon the scale of preparative reactions in sealed glass tubes have led to attempts to carry out the Willgerodt reaction in a lead-lined autoclave,[6] with disappointing results. Unfortunately, in these experiments a reagent containing only colorless ammonium sulfide instead of ammonium polysulfide was used. The colorless reagent is known

[38] M. S. Newman, private communication; Newman, *J. Org. Chem.*, **9**, 521 (1944).

to give poor results even in small-scale runs. Less satisfactory results have been reported for a reaction carried out in an autoclave than for the same reaction carried out on a smaller scale in a sealed glass tube.[11]

Excellent results have been obtained when the Willgerodt reaction (dioxane present) was carried out in a simple autoclave consisting of a short length of 2-in. iron pipe threaded on both ends and fitted with iron screw caps.[18] The caps are sealed on the tube with pipe cement, and the tube with its contents is heated in a liquid metal bath. There is no reason to believe that the Willgerodt reaction could not be carried out on a still larger scale in suitable equipment.

Kindler [23, 26] has described a special apparatus for carrying out the reaction of ketones, sulfur, and volatile aliphatic amines. When an amine is used which boils at approximately the desired temperature of reaction, no special closed apparatus is required, the reaction mixture being heated in conventional glass equipment under reflux condenser. A large-scale preparation starting with 373 g. of 2-acetylnaphthalene in a single run has been carried out (for experimental procedure see p. 97).[38]

Time and Temperature. Earlier experiments were usually carried out at temperatures above 200°. More recently, in runs with added dioxane, temperatures in the range 150–160° have been generally employed. The time required for complete reaction is dependent upon the temperature. It appears likely, however, that the reaction periods of twelve to twenty-four hours which frequently have been used are longer than necessary, and that most reactions are complete in three to four hours at 160°. For a relatively unreactive ketone like pinacolone,[21] a temperature above 200° may be required to obtain a satisfactory yield in a convenient time. The conditions in the Kindler modification with amines have been approximately the same as those in the Willgerodt reaction in aqueous solution, usually four to six hours of heating at 140–160°; occasionally reaction times have been longer—up to fifteen hours. When morpholine is employed the reaction mixture is simply heated to boiling under reflux.

Information in the literature does not indicate how closely the experimental times and temperatures have approached the minimal values. There is reason to believe that, once the reaction to form the amide is complete, continued heating of the mixture produces little further change except for the slow hydrolysis of the amide to ammonium carboxylate salt. In the absence of specific information about optimum conditions with individual compounds, it is probably safest to err on the side of an overly long reaction period.

Isolation of Product. The methods of isolating and purifying the products of the Willgerodt reaction depend upon the solubility behavior of the products, the presence of added organic solvents, the extent of side reactions, and upon whether the amide or the free carboxylic acid is the desired final product. In general the procedures fall into two main categories: (1) the amide or thioamide is isolated and purified as such; (2) the amide is hydrolyzed to the acid, which either is isolated as such or is converted into an ester that can be further purified by distillation.

When the amide is insoluble in the cooled reaction mixture, as amides of high molecular weight are likely to be, it can be isolated by direct filtration from the reaction mixture. Often the yield can be improved by working up the filtrates for dissolved amide or for the ammonium salt resulting from hydrolysis of a portion of the amide.

In working up a complete reaction mixture, or filtrates from the amide, it is advantageous to remove water, organic solvent, and as much of the volatile ammonium sulfide as possible by evaporation to dryness on a water bath or by distillation under reduced pressure; the residue contains the amide mixed with excess sulfur, small amounts of the ammonium salt of the acid, and other by-products. Separation of the amide from the sulfur is accomplished usually by extraction with a solvent such as hot water, ethanol, or carbon tetrachloride which will dissolve the amide but not the sulfur. When such a separation is not feasible, it may be necessary to hydrolyze the amide to the acid by heating with aqueous or ethanolic alkali or with a mineral acid. A mixture of acetic acid and concentrated hydrochloric acid is particularly effective [14] for the hydrolysis of insoluble amides.

The reaction mixture from the Kindler modification is usually taken up in ether and washed with dilute alkali, acid, and water, after which the ether solution is dried. The residual thioamide often can be crystallized from ethanol or benzene-petroleum ether. When the thioamide does not crystallize, it is purified by distillation at low pressure or is hydrolyzed to a carboxylic acid with either mineral acid or alkali. The carboxylic acid can then be separated from neutral by-products and purified by standard methods.

EXPERIMENTAL PROCEDURES

Phenylacetamide from Acetophenone (Use of Ammonium Polysulfide).[1] An ammonium sulfide solution is prepared by passing hydrogen sulfide into concentrated aqueous ammonia until the solution is saturated. A mixture of 2 g. of acetophenone with 10 g. of the colorless ammonium sulfide solution and 1 g. of sulfur is heated in a closed tube for four hours at 200–220°. After the reaction mixture has cooled, it is treated with sufficient hydrochloric acid to decompose the ammonium polysulfide completely, refluxed with carbon black in a large volume of water to decolorize the solution and coagulate the sulfur, and then filtered. The clear, hot filtrate is made alkaline with sodium carbonate and when cool is repeatedly extracted with ether to remove phenylacetamide. When the amide has been thoroughly extracted, the solution is made strongly acid with hydrochloric acid and is again thoroughly extracted with ether to remove phenylacetic acid. On distillation of the ether the two groups of combined extracts give, respectively, 50% of phenylacetamide, m.p. 155°, and 13.5% of phenylacetic acid, m.p. 76°.

1-Pyrenylacetamide and 1-Pyrenylacetic Acid from 1-Acetylpyrene (Use of Ammonium Polysulfide in Dioxane-Water).[14, 34] The reagent is prepared by suspending 1 g. of sulfur in 10 cc. of concentrated aqueous ammonia and passing hydrogen sulfide gas through the mixture until the sulfur has dissolved to form a clear, deep red solution. To this solution are added 8 cc. of dioxane and 2 g. of 1-acetylpyrene. The mixture is sealed in a glass bomb tube and heated at 160–165° for twelve hours. When the tube has cooled to room temperature, a process which requires eight hours in the heavy furnace, it is found to be filled with large, golden-brown prisms, which are filtered and washed with a solution of colorless ammonium sulfide in dioxane-water. The product is practically pure 1-pyrenylacetamide; yield 1.95 g. (92%); m.p. 250–252° (cor.). The material purified by sublimation at low pressure and by several recrystallizations from acetic acid-chlorobenzene forms colorless needles melting at 252–253° (cor.) in an evacuated capillary tube.

A total of 13.7 g. of crude amide obtained directly from several runs as described above can be hydrolyzed to the free acid by the following procedure: The solid amide is dissolved in 200 cc. of glacial acetic acid in a 1-l. round-bottomed flask. Concentrated hydrochloric acid (100 cc.) is cautiously added to the boiling solution through the reflux condenser. The solution, containing a little suspended material, is refluxed for seventy-five minutes, after which the addition (through the condenser) of 100 cc. of concentrated hydrochloric acid causes the precipitation of crystals of the acid. After the mixture has been chilled for several hours, 13.4 g. of crude acid (98%) is obtained by filtration; m.p. 223.5–225° (cor.). The acid is purified by treatment of the aqueous solution in dilute potassium hydroxide with Norit and Filter-Cel, followed by precipitation of the free acid and recrystallization from chlorobenzene. The first crop of crystalline acid amounts to 12.3 g. (90%); m.p. 227.5–228° (cor.) in an evacuated tube.

Methyl β-(6-Tetralyl)propionate from 6-Propionyltetralin[18] **(Use of Ammonium Polysulfide in Dioxane-Water).** A mixture of 20 g. of 6-propionyltetralin, 80 cc. of dioxane, and 100 cc. of concentrated aqueous ammonia saturated with hydrogen sulfide and containing 10 g. of sulfur is heated in an iron tube 2 in. in diameter fitted with an iron screw cap and having a capacity of 350 cc. The screw cap is sealed with pipe cement, and the tube is heated at 165° for twenty-four hours in a Wood's metal bath. When the tube has cooled it is opened, and the product is washed out with methanol. The solvents are removed by evaporation on the steam bath, and the residue is hydrolyzed by heating with 150 cc. of 25% aqueous potassium hydroxide until the odor of ammonia is no longer evident. The alkaline solution is treated with Norit, filtered, and acidified. The crude solid acid is esterified by refluxing for four hours with 200 cc. of methanol and 3 cc. of concentrated sulfuric acid. The reaction mixture is poured into 800 cc. of water and extracted with ether. The ether extract is washed with sodium bicarbonate solution and water, and the ether is removed by distillation. Distillation of the residue gives 15.5 g. (67%) of the methyl ester of β-(6-tetralyl)propionic acid, boiling at 165–168°/12 mm. A portion of the above-mentioned crude acid after recrystallization melts at 81.5–82.5°.

Phenylacetamide from Acetophenone (Use of Sulfur, Aqueous Ammonia, and Pyridine).[20] A mixture of 25 g. of acetophenone, 50 cc. of concentrated (15 *M*) aqueous ammonia, 37.5 g. of sulfur, and 30 cc. of pyridine is heated in a sealed glass tube at 150° for one hour and at 163° for three and one-half hours (heating at 165° for four hours is equally effective). The tube is cooled and opened, the contents removed, and the mixture evaporated to dryness on a water bath. The residue is extracted with approximately 500 cc. of boiling water in several portions. From the filtrate, upon cooling, 20.0 g. of phenylacetamide, m.p. 156–158° (cor.), separates. Concentration of the filtrate affords 2.7 g. of additional amide. The oily residue from evaporation of the filtrate is washed with ether, whereupon 0.32 g. of amide separates, and from the ether layer 1.2 g. of phenylacetic acid is isolated. The acid melts at 76.3–77.3° (cor.) after recrystallization. The total yield of amide is 23.0 g. (82%), and the combined yield of amide and acid is 86%.

Phenylacetamide from Styrene (Use of Sulfur, Aqueous Ammonia, and Pyridine).[20] In a sealed glass tube 21.7 g. of styrene (99.5% material) is heated for four hours at 165° with the same amounts of reagents as described in the previous experiment for acetophenone; two crops of phenylacetamide are obtained, amounting to 16.1 g. (57%) of colorless plates; m.p. 158.6–160.1° (cor.). From the filtrate a second crop of 2.0 g. of crystalline phenylacetamide is obtained. This fraction contains some phenylacetic acid. The total yield of acid and amide is 64%.

2-Naphthylacetothiomorpholide and 2-Naphthylacetic Acid from 2-Acetylnaphthalene (Use of Morpholine and Sulfur; Kindler Procedure).[38] A mixture of 373 g. (2.2 moles) of 2-acetylnaphthalene, 105 g. (3.3 moles) of sulfur, and 290 g. (3.3 moles) of morpholine is cautiously heated (in the hood) in an Erlenmeyer flask fitted with a ground-in reflux condenser. The first heating has to be moderated to prevent frothing due to evolution of hydrogen sulfide. After one hour the mixture is heated to vigorous refluxing, which is continued for ten to fifteen hours. The hot reaction mixture, which has separated into two layers, is poured into 1200 cc. of warm ethanol and left to crystallize. The crystals are collected and liberally washed with cold ethanol. The 2-naphthylacetothiomorpholide at this stage is pure enough for hydrolysis; yield 534 g. (90%); m.p. 102–108°. When only theoretical amounts of sulfur and morpholine are used the yield varies from 53% to 65%.

A mixture of 388 g. (1.43 moles) of the thiomorpholide, 800 cc. of acetic acid, 120 cc. of concentrated sulfuric acid, and 180 cc. of water is brought carefully to the boiling point, then refluxed for five hours. The solution is decanted from a little tarry material into 6 l. of water and left overnight. The solid acid is removed by filtration and washed well with water. It is dissolved in aqueous alkali, filtered, and reprecipitated with hydrochloric acid. The yield at this step is 225 g. (85% based on the crude amide). The product has a slight purple cast but has a satisfactory melting point, 137–140°. Recrystallization from benzene raises the melting point to 142–143°. The overall yield of pure acid from the ketone is 76%.

Note added in proof. After this chapter had gone to press two papers by King and McMillan relating to the Willgerodt reaction, *J. Am. Chem. Soc.*, **68**, 525, 632 (1946), described their independent observation that olefins are converted into carbonamides under the conditions of the Willgerodt reaction and postulated the following sequence of steps to account for the reaction of ketones: ketone → thioketone → mercaptan → olefin → isomercaptan → thioaldehyde → dithioacid → carboxylic acid → carbonamide. According to this picture the reagent functions first as a reducing agent, then subsequently as an oxidizing agent. The labile functional units are assumed to be thiol groups.

EXAMPLES OF THE WILLGERODT AND KINDLER REACTIONS

TABLE I

Examples of the Willgerodt Reaction

(Aqueous Ammonia)

Types of procedure are abbreviated as follows:

A. Ammonium polysulfide in water (original Willgerodt).
B. Colorless ammonium sulfide in water.
C. Ammonium polysulfide in dioxane-water.
D. Ammonium hydroxide, sulfur, and pyridine-water.

Methyl Aryl Ketones

Ketone Formula	Aryl Group	Procedure	Total Yield *	References
C_7H_7NO	3-Pyridyl	C	70%	15, 35
C_8H_8O	Phenyl	A	63%	1, 2, 3
		B	31%	1, 6
		D	86%	20
C_9H_9BrO	2-Bromo-5-methylphenyl	A	—	5
	4-Bromo-5-methylphenyl	A	—	5
C_9H_9ClO	2-Chloro-5-methylphenyl	A	—	5
	4-Chloro-5-methylphenyl	A	—	5
$C_9H_{10}O$	4-Methylphenyl	A	53–55%	3, 4, 5, 39
		B	31%	4, 6
$C_{10}H_{12}O$	2,4-Dimethylphenyl	A	—	2, 3, 5
	2,5-Dimethylphenyl	B	—	6
$C_{11}H_{14}O$	2,4,5-Trimethylphenyl	A	—	5, 12
		B	22%	6
	2,4,6-Trimethylphenyl	A	—	5
		B	—	6
$C_{12}H_{10}O$	1-Naphthyl	A	34%	2, 3, 5, 9
		B	—	6
	2-Naphthyl	A	23–25%	5, 9
$C_{12}H_{12}N_2O$	5-(1-Phenyl-4-methylpyrazolyl)	C	—	35
$C_{12}H_{16}O$	5-Isopropyl-2-methylphenyl	A	—	5
	3-Isopropyl-4-methylphenyl	A	—	5
$C_{14}H_{12}O$	3-Acenaphthyl	C	57%	11
	4-Biphenyl [40]	B	20%	6
		C	66%	20

* The total yield refers to the sum of the yields of amide and of free acid.

[39] Claus and Wehr, *J. prakt. Chem.*, [2] **44**, 85 (1891).

[40] The 4-biphenyl ketone series was incorrectly referred to as "3-biphenyl" by Willgerodt cf. Vorländer, *Ber.*, **40**, 4535 (1907).

TABLE I—*Continued*

EXAMPLES OF THE WILLGERODT REACTION

Methyl Aryl Ketones—Continued

Ketone Formula	Aryl Group	Procedure	Total Yield *	References
$C_{15}H_{12}O$	2-Fluorenyl	C	70%	13
$C_{16}H_{12}O$	2-Phenanthryl	A	—	10
		C	82%	20
	3-Phenanthryl	A	—	10
		C	40–82%	16
		C	76%	20
	9-Phenanthryl †	A	—	10
$C_{16}H_{16}O$	7-(1,2,3,4-Tetrahydro)phenanthryl	C	66%	17
	9-(1,2,3,4-Tetrahydro) phenanthryl	C	56%	17
$C_{18}H_{12}O$	1-Pyrenyl	C	92%	14
$C_{18}H_{16}O$	3-(6-Ethyl)phenanthryl	C	82%	16

Methyl Alkyl Ketones

Ketone Formula	Aryl Group	Procedure	Total Yield *	References
$C_5H_{10}O$	*n*-Propyl	C	31%	21
$C_6H_{12}O$	*t*-Butyl	C	58%	21
$C_7H_{14}O$	*n*-Amyl	C	38%	21
$C_8H_{14}O$	Cyclohexyl	C	40%	21
$C_9H_{10}O$	Benzyl	D	72%	20

Ethyl Aryl Ketones

Ketone Formula	Aryl Group	Procedure	Total Yield *	References
$C_9H_{10}O$	Phenyl	A	50%	1
		B	—	6
		D	82%	20
$C_{10}H_{12}O$	4-Methylphenyl	A	36–38%	3, 4
$C_{11}H_{14}O$	2,4-Dimethylphenyl	A	—	5, 41, 42
$C_{12}H_{14}O$	5-Indanyl	C	68%	18*b*
$C_{12}H_{16}O$	2,4,5-Trimethylphenyl	B	6%	6
$C_{13}H_{12}O$	1-Naphthyl	A	—	3, 5
	2-Naphthyl	A	—	5
$C_{13}H_{16}O$	6-Tetralyl	C	67%	18

* The total yield refers to the sum of the yields of amide and of free acid.

† Willgerodt and Albert (Ref. 7) reported a reaction with a ketone to which they assigned the structure of 9-acetylphenanthrene. The correctness of the structure has been questioned by Mosettig and van de Kamp (Ref. 10)

[41] Bornhäuser, dissertation, Freiburg, 1891.

[42] Claus, *J. prakt. Chem.*, [2] **46,** 475 (1892).

TABLE I—*Continued*

EXAMPLES OF THE WILLGERODT REACTION

Ethyl Aryl Ketones—Continued

Ketone Formula	Aryl Group	Procedure	Total Yield *	References
$C_{15}H_{14}O$	4-Biphenyl [40]	B	6%	6
$C_{17}H_{14}O$	2-Phenanthryl	C	57%	19
		C	66%	20
	9-Anthryl †	C	0	20
$C_{19}H_{14}O$	1-Pyrenyl	C	67%	14

Ethyl Alkyl Ketones

Ketone Formula	Aryl Group	Procedure	Total Yield *	References
$C_7H_{14}O$	*n*-Butyl	C	23%	21
$C_7H_{14}O$	*t*-Butyl	C	30%	21
$C_9H_{16}O$	Cyclohexyl	C	27%	21

n-Propyl Aryl Ketones

Ketone Formula	Aryl Group	Procedure	Total Yield *	References
$C_{10}H_{12}O$	Phenyl	A	37%	1
		D	42%	20
$C_{11}H_{14}O$	4-Methylphenyl	A	23–25%	4
$C_{12}H_{16}O$	2,4-Dimethylphenyl	A	7%	5, 41, 42
	2,5-Dimethylphenyl	A	7%	5, 41, 42
$C_{13}H_{18}O$	2,4,5-Trimethylphenyl	B	6%	6
$C_{14}H_{14}O$	1-Naphthyl	A	—	3, 5
$C_{16}H_{16}O$	4-Biphenyl [40]	B	—	6
$C_{20}H_{16}O$	1-Pyrenyl	C	46%	14

n-Propyl Alkyl Ketones

Ketone Formula	Aryl Group	Procedure	Total Yield *	References
$C_7H_{14}O$	*n*-Propyl	C	21%	21

n-Butyl Aryl Ketones

Ketone Formula	Aryl Group	Procedure	Total Yield *	References
$C_{11}H_{14}O$	Phenyl	D	29%	20
$C_{12}H_{16}O$	4-Methylphenyl	A	2%	4

* The total yield refers to the sum of the yields of amide and of free acid.

† Ethyl 9-anthryl ketone was cleaved in a unique manner, yielding 85% of anthracene.

TABLE I—*Continued*

EXAMPLES OF THE WILLGERODT REACTION

Other n-Alkyl Aryl Ketones

Formula	Ketone	Procedure	Products	References
$C_{13}H_{18}O$	*n*-Hexyl phenyl ketone	A	Heptanamide	1
$C_{22}H_{36}O$	*n*-Pentadecyl phenyl ketone	A	$C_6H_5CONH_2$; C_6H_5-COOH; impure $C_{15}H_{31}COOH$	1
$C_{23}H_{38}O$	*n*-Pentadecyl 4-methylphenyl ketone	A	S-containing oils or decomposition products	5
$C_{26}H_{44}O$	*n*-Heptadecyl 2,4-dimethylphenyl ketone	A	S-containing oils or decomposition products	5

Isopropyl Aryl Ketones

Ketone Formula	Aryl Group	Procedure	Products	Yield	References
$C_{10}H_{12}O$	Phenyl	A	Amide, m.p. 108°	19%	1
$C_{11}H_{14}O$	4-Methylphenyl	A	Amide, m.p. 130°	—	4
$C_{12}H_{16}O$	2,4-Dimethylphenyl	A	Amide, m.p. 120°	2%	5, 41, 42
$C_{13}H_{18}O$	2,4,5-Trimethylphenyl	B	Amide, m.p. 158°	0.5%	6
$C_{16}H_{16}O$	4-Biphenyl [40]	B	No identified product	—	6
$C_{20}H_{16}O$	1-Pyrenyl	C	Trace of high-melting S-containing solid	0 amide	14, 34

Isobutyl Aryl Ketones

Ketone Formula	Aryl Group	Procedure	Products	Yield	References
$C_{11}H_{14}O$	Phenyl	A	Amide, m.p. 118°, and benzoic acid	16–17%	1
		A	Amide, m.p. 121°	1.8%	11
$C_{12}H_{16}O$	4-Methylphenyl	A	Amide, m.p. 150°	3–4%	4
$C_{14}H_{20}O$	2,4,5-Trimethylphenyl	B	Solid, m.p. 158°	0.1%	6
$C_{17}H_{18}O$	4-Biphenyl [40]	B	None isolated	0	6
$C_{21}H_{18}O$	1-Pyrenyl	C	No amide	0	34

TABLE I—*Continued*

REACTIONS RELATED TO THE WILLGERODT REACTION

Unsaturated Hydrocarbons

Formula	Hydrocarbon	Procedure	Products	Yield	References
C_8H_6	Phenylacetylene	D	Phenylacetamide	80%	20
C_8H_8	Styrene	D	Phenylacetamide	64%	20
C_9H_8	1-Phenylpropyne	D	β-Phenylpropionamide	—	20
C_9H_{10}	1-Phenylpropene	D	β-Phenylpropionamide	—	20

Aldehydes

Formula	Aldehyde	Procedure	Products	Yield	References
C_7H_6O	Benzaldehyde	A	Benzamide	—	3
$C_7H_{14}O$	Heptaldehyde	A	Heptanamide	—	3, 21
C_8H_8O	Phenylacetaldehyde	D	Phenylacetamide	48%	20
$C_9H_{10}O$	β-Phenylpropionaldehyde	D	β-Phenylpropionamide	48%	20

TABLE II

EXAMPLES OF THE KINDLER MODIFICATION

(Sulfur and Amine)

Methyl Aryl Ketones

Ketone Formula	Aryl Group	Amine	Thioamide Formed	Yield	References
C_7H_7NO	3-Pyridyl	—	N-Alkyl-3-pyridylacetothioamide	—	23
		Diethyl	N,N-Diethyl-3-pyridylacetothioamide	—	35
C_8H_7BrO	4-Bromophenyl	Morpholine	4-Bromophenylacetothiomorpholide	(10%) *	28
C_8H_7ClO	4-Chlorophenyl	Morpholine	4-Chlorophenylacetothiomorpholide	31%	36, 43
C_8H_8O	Phenyl	Methyl	N-Methylphenylacetothioamide	—	24
		Dimethyl	N,N-Dimethylphenylacetothioamide	70%	22, 23
		Diethyl	N,N-Diethylphenylacetothioamide	—	22
		Morpholine	Phenylacetothiomorpholide	92%	28
$C_9H_{10}O$	4-Methylphenyl	Dimethyl	N,N-Dimethyl-4-methylphenylacetothioamide	80%	23
		Morpholine	4-Methylphenylacetothiomorpholide	57%	36, 43
$C_9H_{10}O_2$	2-Methoxyphenyl	Morpholine	2-Methoxyphenylacetothiomorpholide	(55%) *	28
	3-Methoxyphenyl	Morpholine	3-Methoxyphenylacetothiomorpholide	85%	28
	4-Methoxyphenyl	Dimethyl	N,N-Dimethyl-4-methoxyphenylacetothioamide	75%	22, 23, 24
		Diethyl	N,N-Diethyl-4-methoxyphenylacetothioamide	—	22
		Piperidine	4-Methoxyphenylacetothiopiperidide	48%	23
		Morpholine	4-Methoxyphenylacetothiomorpholide	—	43
$C_{10}H_{12}O$	4-Ethylphenyl	Dimethyl	N,N-Dimethyl-4-ethylphenylacetothioamide	40%	23

* Yields given in parentheses are for the free acids isolated after hydrolysis of the crude thioamide

[43] Haller and Barthel, U. S. pat., 2,358,925; *C. A.*, **39**, 1948 (1945).

TABLE II—*Continued*

EXAMPLES OF THE KINDLER MODIFICATION

Methyl Aryl Ketones—Continued

Ketone Formula	Aryl Group	Amine	Thioamide Formed	Yield	References
$C_{10}H_{12}O_3$	3,4-Dimethoxyphenyl	Methyl	N-Methyl-3,4-dimethoxyphenylacetothioamide	—	25
		Dimethyl	N,N-Dimethyl-3,4-dimethoxyphenylacetothioamide	68%	23, 26
	2,5-Dimethoxyphenyl	Morpholine	2,5-Dimethoxyphenylacetothiomorpholide	(28%) *	28
$C_{11}H_9NO$	4-Quinolyl	—	N-Alkylquinolylacetothioamide	—	23
	8-Quinolyl	Diethyl	N,N-Diethylquinolylacetothioamide	—	35
$C_{12}H_{10}O$	1-Naphthyl	—	N-Alkyl-1-naphthylacetothioamide	—	23
	2-Naphthyl	Morpholine	2-Naphthylacetothiomorpholide	85%	28
				90%	33
		—	N-Alkylnaphthylacetothiomorpholide	—	23
$C_{12}H_{11}NO_2$	6-Methoxy-4-quinolyl	—	N-Alkyl-6-methoxy-4-quinolylacetothioamide	—	23
$C_{14}H_{12}O$	3-Acenaphthyl	Morpholine	No amide isolated	0	36
	4-Biphenyl	Morpholine	4-Biphenylacetothiomorpholide	82%	36
$C_{15}H_{12}O$	2-Fluorenyl	Morpholine	Much tar formation	0	36
$C_{15}H_{14}O_2$	2-Benzyloxyphenyl	Morpholine	2-Benzyloxyphenylacetothiomorpholide	72%	28
$C_{16}H_{12}O$	2-Phenanthryl	Morpholine	2-Phenanthrylacetothiomorpholide	(41%) *	28
	9-Phenanthryl	—	N-Alkyl-9-phenanthrylacetothioamide	—	23

Ethyl Aryl Ketones

Ketone Formula	Aryl Group	Amine	Thioamide Formed	Yield	References
C_9H_9BrO	4-Bromophenyl	Dimethyl	N,N-Dimethyl-4-bromophenylpropiothioamide	—	27
C_9H_9ClO	4-Chlorophenyl	Dimethyl	N,N-Dimethyl-4-chlorophenylpropiothioamide	—	27
C_9H_9FO	4-Fluorophenyl	Dimethyl	N,N-Dimethyl-4-fluorophenylpropiothioamide	40%	27

* Yields given in parentheses are for the free acids isolated after hydrolysis of the crude thioamide

TABLE II—*Continued*

EXAMPLES OF THE KINDLER MODIFICATION

Ethyl Aryl Ketones—Continued

Ketone Formula	Aryl Group	Amine	Thioamide Formed	Yield	References
C_9H_9IO	4-Iodophenyl	Dimethyl	N,N-Dimethyl-4-iodophenylpropiothioamide	—	27
$C_9H_{10}O$	Phenyl	Dimethyl	N,N-Dimethylphenylpropiothioamide	58%	23
$C_{10}H_{12}O$	4-Methylphenyl	Dimethyl	N,N-Dimethyl-4-methylphenylpropiothioamide	58%	27
$C_{10}H_{12}OS$	4-Methylthiophenyl	Dimethyl	N,N-Dimethyl-4-methylthiophenylpropiothioamide	—	27
$C_{10}H_{12}O_2$	4-Methoxyphenyl	Dimethyl	N,N-Dimethyl-4-methoxyphenylpropiothioamide	—	25, 27
$C_{11}H_{14}O$	4-Ethylphenyl	Dimethyl	N,N-Dimethyl-4-ethylphenylpropiothioamide	—	27
$C_{11}H_{14}O_2$	3-Methyl-4-methoxyphenyl	Dimethyl	N,N-Dimethyl-3-methyl-4-methoxyphenylpropiothioamide	—	27
$C_{11}H_{14}O_3$	3,4-Dimethoxyphenyl	Dimethyl	N,N-Dimethyl-3,4-dimethoxyphenylpropiothioamide	42%	25, 27
$C_{13}H_{16}O$	6-Tetralyl	Morpholine	β-(6-Tetralyl)propiothiomorpholide	35%	32
$C_{14}H_{14}O_2$	4-Methoxy-1-naphthyl	Dimethyl	N,N-Dimethyl-4-methoxy-1-naphthylpropiothioamide	—	27

EXAMPLES OF THE KINDLER MODIFICATION AND RELATED REACTIONS

Aldehydes

Formula	Compound	Amine	Product Formed	Yield	References
C_7H_6O	Benzaldehyde	Ammonia	Thiobenzamide	—	22, 24
		Dimethyl	N,N-Dimethylthiobenzamide	80%	22, 23
		Diethyl	N,N-Diethylthiobenzamide	—	22
		2-Naphthyl	N-(2-Naphthyl)thiobenzamide	—	22

TABLE II—*Continued*

EXAMPLES OF THE KINDLER MODIFICATION AND RELATED REACTIONS

Aldehydes—Continued

Formula	Compound	Amine	Product Formed	Yield	References
C_8H_8O	4-Methylbenzaldehyde	Methyl	N-Methyl-4-methylthiobenzamide	—	22
	Phenylacetaldehyde	Dimethyl	N,N-Dimethylphenylacetothioamide	—	22, 24
$C_8H_8O_2$	4-Methoxybenzaldehyde	Methyl	N-Methyl-4-methoxythiobenzamide	—	24
		Dimethyl	N,N-Dimethyl-4-methoxythiobenzamide	—	22

Hydrocarbons, Imines, and Other Compounds

Formula	Compound	Amine	Product Formed	Yield	References
C_8H_6	Phenylacetylene	Morpholine	Phenylacetothiomorpholide	60%	20
C_8H_8	Styrene	Morpholine	Phenylacetothiomorpholide	52%	20
C_8H_9N	N-Methylbenzaldimine	None	N-Methylthiobenzamide	80%	22, 23
$C_9H_{11}N$	N-Methylacetophenonimine	None	N-Methylphenylacetothioamide	30%	22, 23
$C_9H_{11}NO$	N-Methyl-4-methoxybenzaldimine	None	N-Methyl-4-methoxythiobenzamide	40%	22, 23
$C_{10}H_{11}NO_2$	N-Methyl-3,4-methylenedioxyacetophenonimine	None	N-Methyl-3,4-methylenedioxyphenylacetothioamide	45%	23
$C_{10}H_{12}O$	*n*-Propyl phenyl ketone	—	N-Alkyl-γ-phenylbutyrothioamide	—	23
$C_{11}H_{14}O$	*n*-Butyl phenyl ketone	Dimethyl	N,N-Dimethyl-δ-phenylvalerothioamide	—	24
$C_{13}H_{11}N$	Benzalaniline	None	Thiobenzanilide	—	22

CHAPTER 3

PREPARATION OF KETENES AND KETENE DIMERS

W. E. Hanford * and John C. Sauer

E. I. du Pont de Nemours and Company

CONTENTS

* Present address, M. W. Kellogg Co., 225 Broadway, New York, N. Y.

INTRODUCTION

Ketenes are substances containing the functional group $\overset{|}{—C}=C=O$ (with a single bond drawn down from the first C). They have been classified as aldoketenes (RCH=C=O) and ketoketenes ($R_2C=C=O$). Although these terms carry the implication of a nonexistent similarity to aldehydes and ketones, respectively, they have become generally accepted. Carbon suboxide, O=C=C=C=O, probably is best considered in a class of its own.

The ketenes are prepared by modifications of the general methods for the synthesis of olefins. The ketenes are much more reactive than simple olefins, however, and are more likely to enter into combination with the reagents from which they are prepared or with the solvents used or into self-condensation to yield dimers or polymers. Many of the aldoketenes, which generally are more reactive than ketoketenes, have not been isolated as the pure monomers. The dimers of aldoketenes (p. 127) have some of the properties of ketenes, and certain of them are useful reagents.

PREPARATION OF KETENES

Pyrolysis of Acids, Anhydrides, Ketones, Esters, etc.

Ketene, $CH_2=C=O$, the first member of this class, apparently can be obtained by the pyrolysis of any compound which contains the group $CH_3CO—$. The method is of no value for the synthesis of higher homologs, although some have been obtained by pyrolysis, but it is the basis of the best preparations, both laboratory and commercial, of the first member. Ketene was first prepared by the decomposition of acetone, ethyl acetate, or acetic anhydride by means of a hot platinum wire immersed in the liquid.[1] In the pyrolysis of acetone better results are obtained by passing the vapor over a heated surface.[2] The commercial preparation of ketene consists in the pyrolysis of acetone or acetic acid at temperatures of 550° or higher. The most useful laboratory method [3] consists in passing acetone over Chromel A wire heated at 700–750°, the

[1] Wilsmore, *J. Chem. Soc.*, **91**, 1938 (1907); Wilsmore and Stewart, *Proc. Chem. Soc.*, **23**, 229 (1907); *Nature*, **75**, 510 (1907).

[2] Schmidlin and Bergman, *Ber.*, **43**, 2821 (1910).

[3] Williams and Hurd, *J. Org. Chem.*, **5**, 122 (1940).

yield of ketene being 90–95% (see p. 132). The other product of the reaction is methane.

$$CH_3COCH_3 \xrightarrow{>550^\circ} CH_2{=}C{=}O + CH_4$$

The thermal decomposition of acetone is a free-radical chain reaction. The initiating process may consist in the generation of carbon monoxide and methyl radicals.

$$CH_3COCH_3 \rightarrow 2CH_3\cdot + CO$$

The chain process then can be represented as follows.[4]

$$CH_3COCH_3 + CH_3\cdot \rightarrow CH_3COCH_2\cdot + CH_4$$
$$CH_3COCH_2\cdot \rightarrow CH_3\cdot + CH_2{=}C{=}O$$

As ordinarily prepared, ketene contains 5–10% of ethylene along with carbon monoxide and methane, all of which can be removed by careful fractionation. Only partial purification can be effected by freezing the ketene (m.p. −134°) and holding the solid under diminished pressure; the ketene purified in this way contains about 5% of an unsaturated hydrocarbon, which can be separated by fractionation.

Principally because of the ease with which it dimerizes, ketene (b.p.* −41°) is seldom isolated. The mixture of gases from the generator is passed into a reaction vessel in which the ketene is converted to the desired derivative. The most important industrial uses are in the manufacture of acetic anhydride and of the dimer, known as diketene.

$$CH_2{=}C{=}O + CH_3CO_2H \rightarrow (CH_3CO)_2O$$
$$2CH_2{=}C{=}O \rightarrow (CH_2{=}C{=}O)_2$$

The preparation of acetic anhydride from acetic acid at a high temperature [5, 6] probably depends upon the primary formation of ketene and its reaction with acetic acid.

The use of ketene as an acetylating agent is restricted by the tendency of the compound to dimerize (p. 127). Diketene is an important industrial intermediate in the manufacture of derivatives of acetoacetic acid (see p. 127).

There have been extensive investigations of the preparation of ketene by the pyrolysis of acetone, acetic acid, acetic anhydride, and other substances. The various compounds which have been subjected to pyrolysis in studies of the production of ketene and its homologs are listed in Table I. A list of the various substances whose pyrolysis to ketene and higher ketenes is described in the patent literature is given separately in Table II.

* The boiling point of ketene has been recorded as −56° also, but this figure apparently is incorrect (see ref. 17).

[4] Rice and Walters, *J. Am. Chem. Soc.*, **63**, 1701 (1941).

[5] For an example see U. S. pat., 2,278,537 [*C. A.*, **36**, 4831 (1942)].

[6] Hurd and Martin, *J. Am. Chem. Soc.*, **51**, 3614 (1929).

TABLE I

FORMATION OF KETENES BY THE PYROLYSIS OF KETONES, ACIDS, ACID ANHYDRIDES, ESTERS, AND OTHER SUBSTANCES

A. *Ketene* ($CH_2{=}C{=}O$)

Raw Material	Conditions					Yield	Reference
	Phase	Filament or Hot Wire	Tube	Packing	Temp.		
Acetone	Liq.	Pt	Glass	None	—	10%	1, 2
	Vap.	None	Glass	Pumice	500–600	10%	2
	Vap.	Chromel A	Glass	None	750	90%	3
	Vap.	None	Glass	Porcelain	600	17.5%	7
	Vap.	Pt	Glass	None	—	9.8%	8
	Vap.	None	Glass	Porcelain	700	35–45%	9
	Vap.	None	Glass	Porcelain	ca. 650	25–30%	10
	Vap.	None	Glass	Silica gel	650	—	11
	Vap.	Pt	Glass	None	—	—	12
	Vap.	Fe	Glass	None	—	5–7%	13
	Vap.	Ni	Glass	None	—	12%	13
	Vap.	W	Glass	None	—	50%	13
		(Brush discharge)			—	11%	14
	Vap.	—	Glass	Various catalysts	600–700	*	15
	Vap.	—	Quartz	Various catalysts	675–690	†	16
	Vap.	None	Quartz or Pyrex	Quartz or Pyrex	650–750	70%	17
	Vap.	Pt or Ni	Glass	None	—	—	17*a*
	Vap.	—	SiO_2	Cu	—	—	18
	Vap.	None	Glass	V_2O_5 on pumice	700	3%	19
	Vap.	W	Glass	None	—	—	20
	Vap.	None	Cu	None	520–670	High ‡	21
	Vap. §	None	Glass	Glass	506–540	—	4
	Vap.	—	—	CeO_2	—	85%	22
	Vap.	None	Pt	None	1150	—	23
	Vap. ‖	None	Quartz	None	588, 635	25–60%	24
	Vap.	Chromel A	Glass	None	—	—	25, 26
	Vap.	None	Glass	Porcelain	—	—	27
Acetic acid	Vap.	None	Quartz	Porcelain	800	"Low"	6
Acetic anhydride	Liq.	Pt	Glass	None	—	—	1

* The best catalyst (77% yield) was pumice containing V_2O_5.

† The best catalyst (96.5% yield) was pumice containing V_2O_5.

‡ The yield approaches 100%.

§ In the presence of biacetyl.

‖ Nitrogen saturated with acetone.

TABLE I—*Continued*

Formation of Ketenes by the Pyrolysis of Ketones, Acids, Acid Anhydrides, Esters, and Other Substances

A. *Ketene* ($CH_2{=}C{=}O$)—*Continued*

Raw Material	Conditions					Yield	Reference
	Phase	Filament or Hot Wire	Tube	Packing	Temp.		
Ethyl acetate	Liq.	Pt	Glass	None	—	—	1
Phenyl acetate	Vap.	None	Glass	None	625–645	84§ ;63§	28*a*
Methyl ethyl ketone	Vap.	None	Glass	Porcelain	600	1–3.5%	28
	Vap.	Pt	Glass	None	—	3.4–3.7% *	8
Diethyl ketone	Vap.	Pt	Glass	None	—	7% *	8
Acetylacetone	Vap.	None	Glass	Porcelain	635	16%	29
Biacetyl	Vap.	None	Glass	Porcelain	605–625	10–14%	29, 30
Pinacolone	Vap.	None	Glass	Porcelain	705	"Small"	29
Diglycolic anhydride	Vap.	None	Glass	None	450–500	4%	31
Acetylphthalimide †		(Heated under reflux)			—	Low	32, 33
Acetylcarbazole		(Heated under reflux)			—	0% ‡	32

B. *Higher Ketenes*

Ketene	Raw Material	Conditions	Yield	Reference
$(CH_3)_2C{=}C{=}O$	Isobutyrylphthalimide	Reflux, 225°	30%	32, 33
$(C_6H_5)_2C{=}C{=}O$	Diphenylacetylphthalimide	Reflux, 300°	Low	32, 33
	Benzilic acid	Reflux, ca. 250°	Low	34
	Diphenylacetyl chloride	Distil	Low	35
$(C_2H_5)(C_2H_5O_2C)C{=}C{=}O$	$C_2H_5CH(CO_2H)CO_2C_2H_5$	Heat, 180–200°, P_2O_5	23%	36
$O{=}C{=}C{=}C{=}O$	$CH_2(CO_2C_2H_5)_2$	Heat, P_2O_5	—	37
	$CH_2(CO_2H)_2$	Heat, P_2O_5	12%	38
	Diacetyltartaric anhydride	200°	41%	39
	Diacetoxymaleic anhydride	Heat	2%	39*a*
$(CH_3)(CH_2{=}CH)C{=}C{=}O$	Carvone	Heat	—	40

* Product contained methylketene.

† Aldoketenes were not obtained from the propionyl, butyryl or caproyl derivatives.

‡ The principal product was ketene dimer.

§ Based on ester decomposed.

REFERENCES FOR TABLE I

[7] Hurd and Cochran, *J. Am. Chem. Soc.*, **45**, 515 (1923).
[8] Hurd, *J. Am. Chem. Soc.*, **45**, 3095 (1923).
[9] Hurd and Tallyn, *J. Am. Chem. Soc.*, **47**, 1427 (1925).
[10] Hurd, *Org. Syntheses*, *Coll. Vol.* **I**, 330, 2nd ed. (1941).
[11] Goldschmidt and Orthner, *Z. angew. Chem.*, **42**, 40 (1929).
[12] Herriot, *J. Gen. Physiol.*, **18**, 69 (1934).
[13] Ott, Schröter, and Packendorff, *J. prakt. Chem.*, **130**, 177 (1931).
[14] Davis, *J. Phys. Chem.*, **35**, 3330 (1931).
[15] Berl and Kullman, *Ber.*, **65**, 1114 (1932).
[16] Al, *Angew. Chem.*, **45**, 545 (1932).
[17] Rice, Greenberg, Waters, and Vollrath, *J. Am. Chem. Soc.*, **56**, 1760 (1934).
[17a] Rosenblum, *J. Am. Chem. Soc.*, **63**, 3323 (1941).
[18] Hale, *Nature*, **140**, 1017 (1937).
[19] Pearson, Purcell, and Saigh, *J. Chem. Soc.*, **1938**, 409.
[20] Li, *Science*, **90**, 143 (1939).
[21] Morey, *Ind. Eng. Chem.*, **31**, 1129 (1939).
[22] Nametkin and Fedoseeva, *Khim. Referat. Zhur.*, **1940**, No. 4, 116 [*C. A.*, **36**, 3783 (1942)].
[23] Peytral, *Bull. soc. chim.*, **31**, 122 (1922).
[24] Rice and Vollrath, *Proc. Natl. Acad. Sci.*, **15**, 702 (1929).
[25] Dunbar and Bolstad, *J. Org. Chem.*, **9**, 219 (1944).
[26] Bolstad and Dunbar, *Ind. Eng. Chem.*, *Anal. Ed.*, **15**, 498 (1943).
[27] Freri and Maximoff, *Gazz. chim. ital.*, **70**, 836 (1940) [*C. A.*, **36**, 1024 (1942)].
[28] Hurd and Kocour, *J. Am. Chem. Soc.*, **45**, 2167 (1923).
[28a] Hurd and Blunck, *J. Am. Chem. Soc.*, **60**, 2423 (1938).
[29] Hurd and Tallyn, *J. Am. Chem. Soc.*, **47**, 1779 (1925).
[30] Rice and Walters, *J. Chem. Phys.*, **7**, 1015 (1939).
[31] Hurd and Glass, *J. Am. Chem. Soc.*, **61**, 3490 (1939).
[32] Hurd and Dull, *J. Am. Chem. Soc.*, **54**, 2432 (1932).
[33] Hurd, Dull, and Williams, *J. Am. Chem. Soc.*, **57**, 774 (1935).
[34] Staudinger, *Ber.*, **44**, 543 (1911).
[35] Staudinger, *Ber.*, **44**, 1619 (1911).
[36] Hurd, Jones, and Blunck, *J. Am. Chem. Soc.*, **57**, 2033 (1935).
[37] Diels and Wolf, *Ber.*, **39**, 689 (1906).
[38] Diels and Meyerheim, *Ber.*, **40**, 355 (1907).
[39] Ott and Schmidt, *Ber.*, **55**, 2126 (1922).
[39a] Ott, *Ber.*, **47**, 2388 (1914).
[40] Staudinger, "Die Ketene," p. 29, Ferdinand Enke, Stuttgart, 1912.

TABLE II

Substances Whose Conversion to Ketenes is Described in the Patent Literature

Ketene	Raw Material	References
$CH_2{=}C{=}O$	Acetone and/or similar compounds	41–73*a*
	Isopropyl alcohol	70, 71, 74
	Acetic acid and/or similar compounds	75–91
	Acetic anhydride	67, 72, 92
	Acetaldehyde	93, 94
	Mesityl oxide	95, 96
	Vinyl esters	97
	Carbon monoxide and hydrogen	98–101
	Alcohols and carbon monoxide	102
	Diketene	103
	Methyl acetate	104, 105
$CH_3CH{=}C{=}O$	Methyl propionate	104, 105
	Methyl ethyl ketone	106
$RRC{=}C{=}O$	Diazoketones	107

[41] U. S. pat., 1,723,724 [*C. A.*, **23,** 4485 (1929)].
[42] Brit. pat., 309,577 [*C. A.*, **24,** 630 (1930)].
[43] Ger. pat., 556,367 [*C. A.*, **26,** 5579 (1932)].
[44] Fr. pat., 673,051 [*C. A.*, **24,** 2474 (1930)].
[45] Ger. pat., 536,423 [*C. A.*, **26,** 999 (1932)].
[46] Fr. pat., 730,724 [*C. A.*, **27,** 306 (1933)].
[47] Brit. pat., 377,574 [*C. A.*, **27,** 3946 (1933)].
[48] U. S. pat., 1,926,642 [*C. A.*, **27,** 5753 (1933)].
[49] U. S. pat., 1,879,497 [*C. A.*, **27,** 313 (1933)].
[50] Fr. pat., 749,245 [*C. A.*, **27,** 5757 (1933)].
[51] Brit. pat., 413,709 [*C. A.*, **29,** 482 (1935)].
[52] Brit. pat., 397,025 [*C. A.*, **28,** 780 (1934)].
[53] Fr. pat., 750,804 [*C. A.*, **28,** 1052 (1934)].
[54] Ger. pat., 646,408 [*C. A.*, **31,** 6260 (1937)].
[55] Can. pat., 338,162 [*C. A.*, **28,** 1718 (1934)].
[56] U. S. pat., 1,975,663 [*C. A.*, **28,** 7268 (1934)].
[57] Ger. pat., 598,953 [*C. A.*, **28,** 7268 (1934)].
[58] Ger. pat., 604,910 [*C. A.*, **29,** 813 (1935)].
[59] Can. pat., 355,618 [*C. A.*, **30,** 2578 (1936)].
[60] U. S. pat., 2,053,286 [*C. A.*, **30,** 7127 (1936)].
[61] Brit. pat., 472,988 [*C. A.*, **32,** 1278 (1938)].
[62] U. S. pat., 2,069,243 [*C. A.*, **31,** 1826 (1937)].
[63] U. S. pat., 2,080,562 [*C. A.*, **31,** 4994 (1937)].
[64] U. S. pat., 2,184,963 [*C. A.*, **34,** 2866 (1940)].
[65] U. S. pat., 2,232,705 [*C. A.*, **35,** 3651 (1941)].
[66] U. S. pat., 2,258,985 [*C. A.*, **36,** 497 (1942)].
[67] Brit. pat., 237,573 [*C. A.*, **20,** 1415 (1926)].
[68] Ger. pat., 468,402 [*C. A.*, **23,** 1142 (1929)]

[69] U. S. pat., 1,602,699 [*C. A.*, **20**, 3697 (1926)]
[70] Brit. pat., 396,568 [*C. A.*, **28**, 483 (1934)].
[71] Fr. pat., 742,985 [*C. A.*, **27**, 3722 (1933)].
[72] Fr. pat., 722,477 [*C. A.*, **26**, 4063 (1932)].
[73] U. S. pat., 2,305,652 [*C. A.*, **37**, 3108 (1943)].
[73a] U. S. pat., 2,376,748 [*C. A.*, **39**, 4621 (1945)].
[74] U. S. pat., 2,086,582 [*C. A.*, **31**, 6260 (1937)].
[75] Fr. pat., 777,483 [*C. A.*, **29**, 4029 (1935)].
[76] Ger. pat., 687,065 [*C. A.*, **37**, 5988 (1943)].
[77] Ger. pat., 734,349 [*C. A.*, **38**, 1250 (1944)].
[78] Brit. pat., 435,219 [*C. A.*, **30**, 1072 (1936)].
[79] Fr. pat., 46,965 [*C. A.*, **31**, 7893 (1937)].
[80] Brit. pat., 478,213 [*C. A.*, **32**, 4610 (1938)].
[81] Brit. pat., 478,303 [*C. A.*, **32**, 4610 (1938)].
[82] U. S. pat., 2,108,829 [*C. A.*, **32**, 2961 (1938)].
[83] U. S. pat., 2,176,419 [*C. A.*, **34**, 1037 (1940)].
[84] U. S. pat., 2,249,543 [*C. A.*, **35**, 6604 (1941)].
[85] Brit. pat., 478,325 [*C. A.*, **32**, 4610 (1938)].
[86] Brit. pat., 509,778 [*C. A.*, **34**, 4080 (1940)].
[87] Brit. pat., 509,777 [*C. A.*, **34**, 4080 (1940)].
[88] U. S. pat., 2,202,046 [*C. A.*, **34**, 6656 (1940)].
[89] Brit. pat., 478,326 [*C. A.*, **32**, 4610 (1938)].
[90] U. S. pat., 2,295,644 [*C. A.*, **37**, 1133 (1943)].
[91] Fr. pat., 878,651.
[92] U. S. pat., 2,045,739 [*C. A.*, **30**, 5597 (1936)].
[93] Brit. pat., 273,622 [*C. A.*, **22**, 1981 (1928)].
[94] U. S. pat., 1,870,104 [*C. A.*, **26**, 5315 (1932)].
[95] U. S. pat., 2,143,489 [*C. A.*, **33**, 2914 (1939)].
[96] Fr. pat., 851,816 [*C. A.*, **36**, 1944 (1942)].
[97] Ger. pat., 515,307 [*C. A.*, **25**, 1537 (1931)].
[98] Brit. pat., 262,364 [*C. A.*, **21**, 3626 (1927)].
[99] U. S. pat., 1,773,970 [*C. A.*, **24**, 5046 (1930)].
[100] Fr. pat., 617,428 [*Chem. Zentr.*, **I**, 2686 (1927)].
[101] Fr. pat., 617,433 [*Chem. Zentr.*, **I**, 2686 (1927)].
[102] Brit. pat., 537,480 [*C. A.*, **36**, 1336 (1942)].
[103] U. S. pat., 2,218,066 [*C. A.*, **35**, 1072 (1941)].
[104] Brit. pat., 504,626 [*C. A.*, **33**, 7818 (1939)].
[105] U. S. pat., 2,175,811 [*C. A.*, **34**, 776 (1940)].
[106] U. S. pat., 2,235,561 [*C. A.*, **35**, 4042 (1941)].
[107] Ger. pat., 220,852 [*C. A.*, **4**, 2188 (1910)].

Decomposition of Malonic Acid Derivatives

A method of synthesis of ketoketenes which is closely related to the pyrolysis described in the preceding section consists in the thermal decomposition of disubstituted malonic anhydrides, of either the simple or mixed types.

$$\left.\begin{array}{c}\left(-\mathrm{O}\overset{\mathrm{O}}{\overset{\|}{\mathrm{C}}}-\overset{\mathrm{R}}{\overset{|}{\underset{\underset{\mathrm{R}}{|}}{\mathrm{C}}}}-\overset{\mathrm{O}}{\overset{\|}{\mathrm{C}}}-\right)_x \\ \text{or} \\ \mathrm{R_2C}\langle\begin{array}{c}\mathrm{CO}\\ \mathrm{CO}\end{array}\rangle\mathrm{O}\end{array}\right\} \rightarrow \mathrm{R_2C{=}C{=}O} + \mathrm{CO_2}$$

$$\mathrm{R_2C(COOCOR')_2} \rightarrow \mathrm{R_2C{=}C{=}O} + \mathrm{R'COOCOR'} + \mathrm{CO_2}$$

Monosubstituted malonic anhydrides have not yielded aldoketenes,[108] but malonic acid itself yields carbon suboxide when heated with phosphorus pentoxide.[38]

The disubstituted malonic anhydrides can be prepared from the corresponding malonic acids and acetic anhydride in the presence of a little sulfuric acid, with neutralization of the mineral acid by treatment with barium carbonate and removal of acetic acid and acetic anhydride by distillation.[109] The residual malonic anhydride is decomposed by heating under low pressure. This method appears to have been used only for dimethylketene (80% yield), diethylketene (55% yield), methylethylketene (65% yield), and dipropyl- and diisopropyl-ketenes (50% yields).

A more common method involves the decomposition of mixed anhydrides, nearly all of which have been obtained by treating the dialkylmalonic acid, dissolved in dry ether, with diphenylketene. The resulting mixed anhydrides, derived from the malonic acids and diphenylacetic acid, are nearly insoluble in ether and separate in almost quantitative yields. They are decomposed by heating under diminished pressure until

[108] Staudinger, Anthes, and Schneider, *Ber.*, **46,** 3539 (1913).
[109] Staudinger, *Helv. Chim. Acta*, **8,** 306 (1925).

the evolution of carbon dioxide is complete. If the ketene being prepared is easily volatile it may distil with the carbon dioxide. If a ketene of low volatility is prepared in this way it is separated from the diphenylacetic anhydride by extraction rather than by distillation, in order to prevent the occurrence of ketene interchange. For example, distillation (under diminished pressure) of a mixture of dibenzylketene and diphenylacetic anhydride results in the formation of diphenylketene and dibenzylacetic anhydride.

$$2(C_6H_5CH_2)_2C{=}C{=}O + [(C_6H_5)_2CHCO]_2O \rightleftharpoons 2(C_6H_5)_2C{=}C{=}O + [(C_6H_5CH_2)_2CHCO]_2O$$

Decomposition of the mixed anhydrides prepared by means of diphenylketene has been used for the production of simple dialkylketenes [108, 110] (30–60% yields), diallylketene [110] (80% yield), dibenzylketene [110] (73.5% yield), and ethylchloroketene [108] [$C_2H_5C(Cl){=}C{=}O$] (50% yield). Methylphenyl ketene has been made in 75% yield, and other unsymmetrical ketoketenes [110] (RR′C=C=O) have been prepared in unspecified yields. Attempts to prepare ketenes containing additional cumulative double bonds [e.g., isopropylideneketene,[108, 111] $(CH_3)_2C{=}C{=}C{=}O$] from alkylidenemalonic acids have failed. Methylethoxymalonic and diethoxymalonic acids have yielded none of the ketenes, but ethylphenoxymalonic and diphenoxymalonic acids appeared to give some of the corresponding ketenes.[112] Cyclopropane-1,1-dicarboxylic acid gave none of the ketene.[110]

Dimethylketene has been obtained in unspecified yield by heating the monochloride of dimethylmalonic acid; [113] it is probable that the malonic anhydride was formed as an intermediate. This method failed in attempted applications to diethylketene and carbon suboxide. Low yields of carbon suboxide have been obtained by treating malonyl chloride with lead, silver, or zinc oxide or with silver oxalate or malonate, and by treating silver malonate with cinnamoyl chloride; [114] malonic anhydrides or mixed anhydrides may be intermediates.

The ketenes which have been prepared by these methods are listed in Table III; unsuccessful attempts mentioned above are not repeated in the table.

[110] Staudinger, Schneider, Schotz, and Strong, *Helv. Chim. Acta*, **6**, 291 (1923).

[111] Staudinger and Schneider, *Helv. Chim. Acta*, **6**, 316 (1923).

[112] Staudinger and Schneider, *Helv. Chim. Acta*, **6**, 304 (1923).

[113] Staudinger and Ott, *Ber.*, **41**, 2208 (1908).

[114] Staudinger and St. Bereza, *Ber.*, **41**, 4461 (1908).

TABLE III

Ketoketenes Prepared from Malonic Acid Derivatives

A. *From Simple Malonic Anhydrides*

$$[\text{—OCOCR(R')CO—}]_x \xrightarrow{\text{Heat}} \text{R(R')C=C=O} + CO_2$$

Ketene	Yield	Reference
$(CH_3)_2C{=}C{=}O$	80%	109
$CH_3CH_2C(CH_3){=}C{=}O$	65%	109
$(CH_3CH_2)_2C{=}C{=}O$	55%	109
$(n\text{-}C_3H_7)_2C{=}C{=}O$	50%	109
$(iso\text{-}C_3H_7)_2C{=}C{=}O$	50%	109

B. *From Mixed Anhydrides Prepared from Malonic Acids and Diphenylketene*

$$\text{R(R')C}(CO_2H)_2 + 2(C_6H_5)_2C{=}C{=}O \rightarrow \text{R(R')C}[COOCOCH(C_6H_5)_2]_2 \xrightarrow{\text{Heat}} \text{R(R')C=C=O} + [(C_6H_5)_2CHCO]_2O$$

Ketene	Yield	Reference
$(CH_3)_2C{=}C{=}O$	49%	108
$CH_3CH_2C(CH_3){=}C{=}O$	(?)	110
$(CH_3CH_2)_2C{=}C{=}O$	64%	108
$CH_2{=}CHCH_2C(CH_3){=}C{=}O$	(?)	110
$(n\text{-}C_3H_7)_2C{=}C{=}O$	32%	110
$(CH_2{=}CHCH_2)_2C{=}C{=}O$	80%	110
$C_6H_5CH_2C(CH_3){=}C{=}O$	(?)	110
$(C_6H_5CH_2)_2C{=}C{=}O$	73.5%	110
$C_6H_5C(CH_3){=}C{=}O$	75%	110
$C_2H_5C(Br){=}C{=}O$	9%	112
$C_2H_5C(Cl){=}C{=}O$	50%	108
$Cl_2C{=}C{=}O$	0	108

TABLE III—*Continued*

KETOKETENES PREPARED FROM MALONIC ACID DERIVATIVES

C. *Related Preparations*

Ketene	Prepared from	Reagent	Yield	Reference
$(CH_3)_2C{=}C{=}O$	$(CH_3)_2C(CO_2H)COCl$	Heat	(?)	113
$O{=}C{=}C{=}C{=}O$	$CH_2(COCl)_2$	Ag_2O	63%	114
		PbO	"Low"	114
		ZnO	5.5%	114
		$(CO_2Ag)_2$	10.5%	114
		$CH_2(CO_2Ag)_2$	5.7%	114
	$CH_2(CO_2Ag)_2$	$C_6H_5CH{=}CHCOCl$	1–2%	114
	$CH_2(CO_2H)_2$	P_2O_5	(?)	2, 37

Regeneration of Ketenes from the Dimers

Because of the ease with which many ketenes dimerize, the reconversion of the dimers to the monomers is an important adjunct to the methods of synthesis of ketenes. In general, the regeneration of the monomers is effected by pyrolysis, but the process is smoother than the thermal decomposition of ketones, acids, etc. The dilution of the dimer with an inert gas has proved advantageous in some preparations.[115, 116]

The pyrolysis of diketene produces ketene in quantitative yield,[117] and the product is not contaminated with hydrocarbons, carbon monoxide, etc., which are present in ketene produced by the cracking of acetone. In other instances also it may be possible to prepare ketenes in the state of highest purity by utilization of the dimers (for the preparation of the dimers, see p. 127).

Relatively few such preparations have been reported. The dimers of ketene, methylketene, and dimethylketene have been converted to the monomers in yields of 86–100% by decomposition over hot filaments or in hot (550–600°) tubes. Ethylcarbethoxyketene has been prepared in 80–90% yield by heating the dimer under a pressure of 15 mm. in an oil

[115] Private communication from Professor J. R. Johnson, Cornell University, and taken from the doctoral thesis of C. M. Hill, entitled "Studies of Ketenes and Their Derivatives," 1941.

[116] Private communication from Professor J. R. Johnson, Cornell University, and taken from the doctoral thesis of J. M. Witzel, entitled "Dimethyl Ketene and Its Reaction with Cyclopentadiene," 1941.

[117] Boese, *Ind. Eng. Chem.*, **32**, 16 (1940).

bath at 180–200°. A complete list of the ketenes prepared and the conditions employed (if reported) is given in Table IV.

TABLE IV

PREPARATION OF KETENES BY PYROLYSIS OF KETENE DIMERS

Ketene	Conditions of Depolymerization of the Dimer	Yield	Reference
$CH_2{=}C{=}O$	Hot platinum filament	Quant.	117
	Hot tube (550–600°)	Quant.	117
$CH_3CH{=}C{=}O$	Hot Nichrome wire	—	115
$(CH_3)_2C{=}C{=}O$	Hot Nichrome wire	86%	116
	Hot platinum spiral	—	118
$CH_3C(CO_2CH_3){=}C{=}O$	Treatment with $NaOCH_3$—CH_3OH	— *	119
$C_2H_5C(CO_2C_2H_5){=}C{=}O$	Heat at 200°/15 mm.	80–90%	120
	Distillation at 15 mm.	30%	36
	Treatment with C_6H_5MgBr	— †	36
$(C_2H_5O_2C)_2C{=}C{=}O$	Heat at 150°	—	121
$C_6H_5C(CO_2CH_3){=}C{=}O$	Distillation in "abs." vacuum	70%	122
	Heat at 150°	—	121
$C_6H_5C(CH_3){=}C{=}O$	Distillation	—	121, 123
$(C_6H_5)_2C{=}C{=}O$	Pyrolysis	—	121, 124

* The product isolated was $CH_3CH(CO_2CH_3)_2$, evidently formed from the ketene.
† The product isolated was ethyl α-benzoylbutyrate.

Dehalogenation of α-Haloacyl Halides

The oldest procedure for the synthesis of ketenes is the dehalogenation of α-haloacyl halides by treatment with zinc.[125] There have been no

$$RR'CX{-}C({=}O)X + Zn \rightarrow RR'C{=}C{=}O + ZnX_2$$

[118] Staudinger and Klever, *Ber.*, **44**, 2215 (1911).
[119] Schroeter, *Ber.*, **49**, 2697 (1916).
[120] Staudinger and St. Bereza, *Ber.*, **42**, 4908 (1909).
[121] Staudinger and Hirzel, *Ber.*, **50**, 1024 (1917).
[122] Staudinger and Hirzel, *Ber.*, **49**, 2522 (1916).
[123] Staudinger and Ruzicka, *Ann.*, **380**, 278 (1911).
[124] Staudinger, *Ber.*, **44**, 521 (1911).
[125] Staudinger, *Ber.*, **38**, 1735 (1905).

extensive studies of the relative yields from the various possible dihalo compounds such as bromoacid bromides, chloroacid chlorides, bromoacid chlorides, and chloroacid bromides. In the preparation of ketene the yields obtained from bromoacetyl bromide and bromoacetyl chloride were 12% and 3.7%, respectively, but none of the product was obtained from chloroacetyl bromide or chloroacetyl chloride.[126] However, a 13.5% yield of phenylketene was obtained from phenylchloroacetyl chloride.[127] Later attempts to prepare ketene by the dehalogenation of bromoacetyl bromide with zinc either in boiling ether solution or in the vapor phase at 200° were unsuccessful;[128] copper bronze, molten sodium, sodium iodide, or magnesium and magnesium iodide likewise failed to effect the dehalogenation.

Only carbon suboxide[114, 129] (yield up to 80%) and ketoketenes (yields up to 95%, see Table V) have been prepared in yields above 20%. Many of the aldoketenes have not been isolated from the reaction mixtures, their presence being demonstrated only by conversion to derivatives.[125, 127, 129, 129a] The method has given only negative results when applied to α,β-unsaturated α-haloacyl halides.[130]

The dehalogenation generally is carried out in pure ethyl ether or ethyl acetate at the reflux temperature. These solvents are especially useful because they dissolve the zinc halides and because their low boiling points facilitate control of the reaction temperature. The solvents used in this synthesis must, of course, be free from water and ethanol. Some ethyl ester may be formed through cleavage of ether (when it is used as the solvent) by the acyl halide in the presence of zinc halide. Mercury and silver have been used as dehalogenating agents instead of zinc, but they are less satisfactory.[131, *] Magnesium appears to have been used only with bromoacetyl bromide and α-bromoisobutyryl bromide; the yields were about the same as those obtained with zinc.

Various α-haloacyl halides which have been used in preparations or attempted preparations of ketenes are listed in Table V.

* See p. 7 of ref. 40.

[126] Staudinger and Kubinsky, *Ber.*, **42**, 4213 (1909).

[127] Staudinger, *Ber.*, **44**, 533 (1911).

[128] Hurd, Cashion, and Perletz, *J. Org. Chem.*, **8**, 367 (1943).

[129] Staudinger and Klever, *Ber.*, **41**, 906 (1908).

[129a] Fuson, Armstrong, and Shenk, *J. Am. Chem. Soc.*, **66**, 964 (1944).

[130] Staudinger and Ott, *Ber.*, **44**, 1633 (1911).

[131] Staudinger, *Ann.*, **356**, 51 (1908).

TABLE V

PREPARATION OF KETENES BY ZINC DEHALOGENATION OF α-HALOACYL HALIDES

$$R(R')CXCOX' + Zn \rightarrow R(R')C{=}C{=}O + ZnXX'$$

Ketene	α-Haloacyl Halide X	X′	Solvent	Yield	Reference
$CH_2{=}C{=}O$	Br	Br	$(C_2H_5)_2O$	7–13%	126, 132
	Br	Br	$CH_3CO_2C_2H_5$ *	12–14% *	126
	Br	Br	$(C_2H_5)_2O$ *	11–12% *	126
	Br	Br	$CH_3CO_2C_2H_5$	8–12%	126, 132
	Br	Cl	$(C_2H_5)_2O$	3.7%	126
	Br	Cl	$CH_3CO_2C_2H_5$	4.4%	126
	Cl	Cl	$(C_2H_5)_2O$	0	126
	Cl	Br	$(C_2H_5)_2O$	0	126
$CH_3CH{=}C{=}O$	Br	Br	$(C_2H_5)_2O$	6–8% †	127, 129
$C_2H_5CH{=}C{=}O$	Br	Br	$(C_2H_5)_2O$	4–6% †	129
$(CH_3)_2C{=}C{=}O$	Br	Br	$(C_2H_5)_2O$	38%	133
	Br	Br	$CH_3CO_2C_2H_5$	28%	133
$(C_2H_5)C(CH_3){=}C{=}O$	Br	Br	$(C_2H_5)_2O$	?	134
$HC(CO_2C_2H_5){=}C{=}O$	Br	Cl	—	0	135
$C_2H_5C(CO_2CH_3){=}C{=}O$	Br	Cl	$(C_2H_5)_2O$	34%	120
$C_6H_5CH{=}C{=}O$	Cl	Cl	$(C_2H_5)_2O$	13% †	125, 127
2,4,6-$(CH_3)_3C_6H_2CH{=}C{=}O$	Br	Br	$(C_2H_5)_2O$	— †	129*a*
2,4,6-$(C_2H_5)_3C_6H_2CH{=}C{=}O$	Br	Br	$(C_4H_9)_2O$	— †	129*a*
$C_6H_5C(CH_3){=}C{=}O$	Cl	Cl	$(C_2H_5)_2O$	80–90%	123
$(C_6H_5)_2C{=}C{=}O$	Cl	Cl	$(C_2H_5)_2O$	95%	125, 131
p-$CH_3C_6H_4C(C_6H_5){=}C{=}O$	Cl	Cl	$(C_2H_5)_2O$	?	134, 136
(*p*-$C_6H_5C_6H_4)_2C{=}C{=}O$	Cl	Cl	$(C_2H_5)_2O$	60%	137
C_6H_4—C_6H_4 (biphenylene) $>C{=}C{=}O$	Cl	Cl	$(C_2H_5)_2O$	90%	138
$(CH_3)_2C{=}C{=}C{=}O$	Br	Cl	$CH_3CO_2C_2H_5$	0	130
$C_6H_5CH{=}C{=}C{=}O$	Br	Cl	$CH_3CO_2C_2H_5$	0	130
	Br	Br	$CH_3CO_2C_2H_5$	0	130
$O{=}C{=}C{=}C{=}O$	$[Br_2C(COCl)_2]$		$(C_2H_5)_2O$	80% †	114
			$CH_3CO_2C_2H_5$	40–50%	114
	$[Br_2C(COBr)_2]$		$(C_2H_5)_2O$	?	129

* Magnesium was used instead of zinc.

† In solution—not isolated.

[132] Staudinger and Klever, *Ber.*, **41,** 594 (1908).

[133] Staudinger and Klever, *Ber.*, **39,** 968 (1906).

[134] McKenzie and Christie, *J. Chem. Soc.*, **1934,** 1070.

[135] Staudinger and Becker, *Ber.*, **50,** 1016 (1917).

[136] Weiss, *Monatsh.*, **40,** 391 (1920).

[137] Shilov and Burmistrov, *Ber.*, **68,** 582 (1935).

[138] Staudinger, *Ber.*, **39,** 3062 (1906).

Miscellaneous Methods

Decomposition of Diazo Ketones. Diphenylketene usually is prepared from benzil through the following series of reactions.[107, 139, 140]

$$C_6H_5COCOC_6H_5 + NH_2NH_2 \rightarrow C_6H_5COC(NNH_2)C_6H_5 \xrightarrow{HgO}$$

$$C_6H_5COC(N_2)C_6H_5 \rightarrow (C_6H_5)_2C{=}C{=}O + N_2$$

The last step is effected by slowly dropping a benzene solution of the diazo ketone into a distilling flask heated in a metal bath at 100–110°. The residual diphenylketene is then distilled (64% yield) and redistilled (58% yield). A somewhat lower yield (45%) results when the decomposition is effected in ligroin; *bis*-benzilketazine is a by-product of the decomposition.[141] Di-*p*-tolylketene has been prepared in unspecified yield by similar reactions.[142] Mesitylphenylketene has been prepared from the diazo compound in 35% yield, but dehydrohalogenation of mesitylphenylacetyl chloride is a much superior method (see p. 139).

This general method has been followed in the preparation of a few other ketoketenes from ethoxalylacetic ester and from acylacetic esters. The diazo ketones were prepared by nitrosation, reduction, and treatment with nitrous acid. The use of methyl acetoacetate is illustrative;[119] the ketene was isolated as the dimer.

$$CH_3COCH_2CO_2CH_3 \rightarrow \underset{\displaystyle NO}{CH_3CO\underset{|}{C}HCO_2CH_3} \rightarrow \underset{\displaystyle NH_2}{CH_3CO\underset{|}{C}HCO_2CH_3} \rightarrow$$

$$\underset{\displaystyle N_2}{CH_3CO\underset{\|}{C}CO_2CH_3} \xrightarrow[\text{xylene}]{\text{Heat in}} N_2 + \underset{\displaystyle CO_2CH_3}{CH_3\underset{|}{C}{=}C{=}O} \quad \text{(47\% yield of the dimer)}$$

The diazo compound from methyl benzoylacetate gives phenylcarbomethoxyketene in 70% yield when the final decomposition is carried out in refluxing xylene, but it is converted largely to the ester of phenylmalonic acid by heating in the absence of a solvent.[122] The ethyl ester of ethylmalonic acid is the principal product from the decomposition (in the absence of a solvent) of the diazo compound obtained from ethyl propionylacetate.[122] A small amount of the ketene evidently was formed also. The diazo compound obtained from ethyl ethoxalylacetate on decomposition in warm xylene gives 54% of dicarbethoxyketene.[122]

[139] Schroeter, *Ber.*, **42,** 2336, 3356 (1909).
[140] Smith and Hoehn, *Org. Syntheses*, **20,** 47 (1940).
[141] Ritter and Wiedeman, *J. Am. Chem. Soc.*, **51,** 3583 (1929).
[142] Gilman and Adams, *Rec. trav. chim.*, **48,** 464 (1929).

Small pieces of platinum have been used as catalyst for the decomposition of these diazo compounds.

Only the ketoketenes mentioned above have been obtained from the diazo ketones. Attempts to prepare the more highly unsaturated ketenes, $C_6H_5CH{=}CHC(CO_2R){=}C{=}O$ and $CH_3CH{=}CHC(CO_2R){=}C{=}O$ from cinnamoylacetic ester and crotonylacetic ester, respectively, were unsuccessful.[122] Aldoketenes could not be obtained from acetyldiazomethane (CH_3COCHN_2) and benzoyldiazomethane ($C_6H_5COCHN_2$),[119] nor could ketenes be obtained from diacetyldiazomethane, benzoylacetyldiazomethane,[119] mesitoyldiazomethane,[129a] and 2,4,6-triisopropylbenzoyldiazomethane. It is of interest that methyl 5-phenyl-1,2,3-thiodiazole-4-carboxylate and methyl 1,5-diphenyl-1,2,3-triazolecarboxylate do not yield ketene analogs on pyrolysis.[122]

The β-Lactone Method. Dimethylketene has been prepared in 50% yield by pyrolysis of α-carbomethoxy-α,β-dimethyl-β-butyrolactone.[143] The lactone was prepared from acetone and methylmalonic acid.[144] The

$$(CH_3)_2CO + CH_3CH(CO_2H)_2 \xrightarrow[H_2SO_4]{(CH_3CO)_2O} \underset{\displaystyle |\quad\ \ |\atop \displaystyle O\text{—}CO}{(CH_3)_2C\text{—}C(CH_3)CO_2H} \xrightarrow[CH_3I]{Ag_2O}$$

$$\underset{\displaystyle |\quad\ \ |\atop \displaystyle O\text{—}CO}{(CH_3)_2C\text{—}C(CH_3)CO_2CH_3} \xrightarrow{\text{Heat}} (CH_3)_2C{=}C{=}O + (CH_3)_2CO + CO_2$$

intermediate α-carboxy lactone did not give any methylketene upon pyrolysis. However, the lactone of α-carboxy-β-methyl-β-butyrolactone did give a little carbon suboxide (5.2% yield).[143] α-Carbomethoxy-α-

$$\underset{\displaystyle |\quad\ \ |\atop \displaystyle O\text{—}CO}{(CH_3)_2C\text{—}CHCO_2H} \rightarrow (CH_3)_2CO + O{=}C{=}C{=}C{=}O + H_2O$$

bromo-β-methyl-β-butyrolactone yielded an unspecified amount of a polymer of methylbromoketene.[143] The corresponding α-carboxy lactone gave none of the expected bromoketene.[143]

Dehydrohalogenation of Acyl Halides by Means of Tertiary Amines. One of the oldest methods of preparing diphenylketene consists in the dehydrohalogenation of diphenylacetyl chloride with tertiary amines.[145] The yield of the ketene was reported as quantitative when tripropylamine was the dehydrohalogenating agent, and considerably less with quinoline, whereas thermal dehydrohalogenation of the acid chloride

[143] Ott, *Ann.*, **401,** 159 (1913).
[144] The method is an adaptation of that of Meldrum, *J. Chem. Soc.*, **93,** 601 (1908).
[145] Staudinger, *Ber.*, **40,** 1148 (1907).

gave only a low yield.[35] However, certain unsymmetrical diarylketenes have been prepared by thermal dehydrohalogenation of the acid chlorides in the presence of not more than traces of pyridine hydrochloride.[146, 147] For example, mesitylphenylacetic acid, prepared from mesitylene and mandelic acid in the presence of stannic chloride, is converted into the ketene in excellent yield [146] by refluxing in benzene with thionyl chloride and a little pyridine, separation of the precipitated pyridine hydrochloride by filtration, and distillation of the acid chloride at reduced

$$2,4,6\text{-}(CH_3)_3C_6H_3 + HOCH(C_6H_5)CO_2H \xrightarrow{SnCl_4} 2,4,6\text{-}(CH_3)_3C_6H_2CH(C_6H_5)CO_2H \xrightarrow[(C_5H_5N)]{SOCl_2}$$

$$2,4,6\text{-}(CH_3)_3C_6H_2CH(C_6H_5)COCl \rightarrow 2,4,6\text{-}(CH_3)_3C_6H_2C(C_6H_5){=}C{=}O + HCl$$

pressure. It is of interest to note that this ketene was formed during an attempt to carry out a Rosenmund reduction of the acid chloride.[146]

In preparations of aliphatic ketoketenes [115, 148] the dehydrohalogenations have been accomplished by treatment with slightly more than equivalent amounts of tertiary aliphatic amines, the reactions being carried out by adding the amines to solutions of the acid chlorides in inert solvents like ether, benzene, toluene, ligroin, trichloroethylene, tetrachloroethylene, or carbon tetrachloride. Trimethylamine appears to be the most satisfactory base in the preparation of aliphatic ketoketenes, owing to the low solubility of the hydrochloride in organic solvents. The reaction is effected by allowing the mixture to stand at room temperature for several hours, after which time the amine salt is removed by filtration and the ketene is recovered by distillation at the lowest possible pressure. Dimethylaniline and pyridine are reported to be unsatisfactory for the preparation of dialkyl ketoketenes.[148]

The tertiary amines must be free of primary and secondary amines. The presence of small amounts of diethylamine in the triethylamine used in such preparations leads to formation of diethylamides. Such amides were originally mistaken for "ketenium" derivatives of tertiary amines.[149]

The applicability of this method is limited by the fact that the tertiary

[146] Fuson, Armstrong, Kneisley, and Shenk, *J. Am. Chem. Soc.*, **66**, 1464 (1944).
[147] Fuson, private communication.
[148] U. S. pat., 2,268,169 [*C. A.*, **36**, 2737 (1942)].
[149] For a discussion, see Miller and Johnson, *J. Org. Chem.*, **1**, 135 (1936).

amine salts catalyze the dimerization of ketenes.[132, 150] Consequently only those ketenes which have relatively low tendencies toward dimerization can be prepared in this way. Dialkylacetyl chlorides of low molecular weight, such as isobutyryl chloride,[149] and monoalkylacetyl chlorides give only dimers (see p. 129).[150] Evidently no aldoketene has been prepared by this method.

The ketenes which have been prepared by dehydrohalogenation of acyl halides are listed in Table VI.

TABLE VI

PREPARATION OF KETOKETENES BY DEHYDROHALOGENATION OF ACYL HALIDES

$$R(R')CHCOX + R_3''N \rightarrow R(R')C{=}C{=}O + R_3''N \cdot HX$$

Ketene	Dehydrohalogenating Agent	Yield	Reference
$(CH_3)_2C{=}C{=}O$	$(C_2H_5)_3N$	Dimer only (60%)	149
$(n\text{-}C_7H_{15})_2C{=}C{=}O$	$(CH_3)_3N$	58%	148
$n\text{-}C_{12}H_{25}C(C_2H_5){=}C{=}O$	$(CH_3)_3N$	29%	148
CH_2CH_2 CH_2 $C{=}C{=}O$ CH_2CH_2	$(C_2H_5)_3N$	32% *	115
CH CH_2 $=C{=}O$ $C(CH_3)_2$ CH_2 $=O$ C CH_3	C_9H_7N or $(C_2H_5)_3N$	56–58% †	151
$(C_6H_5)_2C{=}C{=}O$	$(C_3H_7)_3N$	Quant.	35
	C_9H_7N	—	35
	Heat	Low	35
$2,4,6\text{-}(CH_3)_3C_6H_2C(C_6H_5){=}C{=}O$	Distillation at reduced pressure	64–67%	146, 147

* The dimer was obtained in 66% yield.

† The yield is based on the formation of derivatives from the unisolated ketene.

[150] U. S. pat., 2,238,826 [*C. A.*, **35**, 4970 (1941)].

[151] Staudinger and Schotz, *Ber.*, **53**, 1105 (1920).

PREPARATION OF KETENE DIMERS

All known ketenes dimerize when heated or when allowed to stand at room temperature or below for a sufficient length of time. The dimers of ketoketenes undoubtedly are derivatives of cyclobutanedione. For example, the dimer of dimethylketene has a pleasant odor similar to that of ketones; it yields two isomeric (*cis* and *trans*) glycols upon reduction; and it yields mono- and di-oximes which give the expected products in the Beckmann transformation.[152]

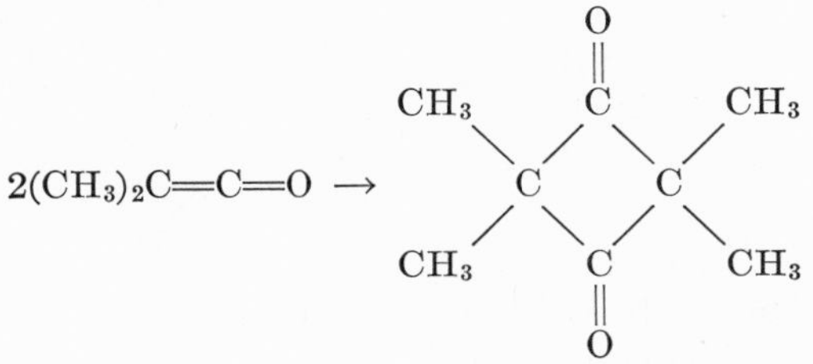

```
                            O
                            ‖
                     CH3    C     CH3
                        \  / \   /
2(CH3)2C=C=O  →          C     C
                        /  \ /   \
                     CH3    C     CH3
                            ‖
                            O
```

The dimers of aldoketenes are much more reactive. Diketene has a harsh, irritating odor entirely unlike that of dimethylketene dimer, and its characteristic reactions resemble those of ketenes or acid anhydrides rather than those of ketones. It reacts with water and alcohols (in the presence of catalytic amounts of strong acid) to give acetoacetic acid and its esters,[117] with ammonia and amines to give acetoacetamides,[117] and with ozone to give pyruvaldehyde,[153] reactions which are easily interpreted on the basis of formula I. Hydrogenation over Raney nickel catalyst converts it to β-butyrolactone,[154] a reaction most readily explicable on the basis of one of the lactone formulas (II and III). The addition of halogen leads to a γ-haloacetoacetyl halide,[155, 156] a result which might

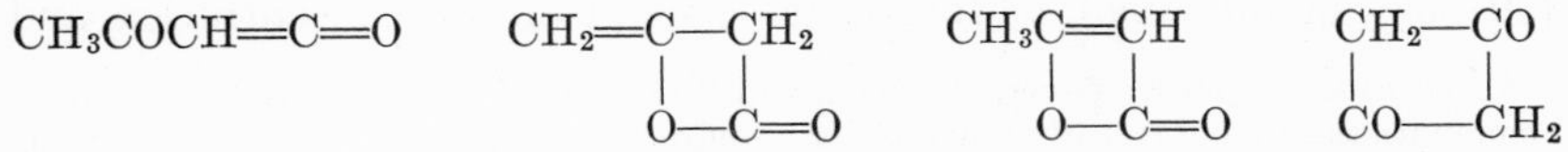

```
CH3COCH=C=O     CH2=C—CH2     CH3C=CH      CH2—CO
                    |  |          |  |       |   |
                    O—C=O         O—C=O      CO—CH2
     I              II            III          IV
```

be accounted for on the basis of formula II more easily than on the basis of formula III; however, the absorption spectrum appears to be in better

[152] Private communication from Professor J. R. Johnson, Cornell University, and taken from the doctoral thesis of L. L. Miller, entitled "The Structure of Some Derivatives of Dimethylketene," 1937.

[153] Hurd and Williams, *J. Am. Chem. Soc.*, **58**, 962 (1936).

[154] Johnson and Gross, paper presented at the American Chemical Society, Organic Division, in New York City on April 23, 1935.

[155] Chick and Wilsmore, *J. Chem. Soc.*, **97**, 1978 (1910).

[156] Hurd and Abernethy, *J. Am. Chem. Soc.*, **62**, 1147 (1940).

agreement with III.[157] The dipole moment of diketene agrees with values calculated for the most probable structures and does not serve to distinguish among them.[158] The behavior of diketene on pyrolysis is said to be compatible only with the cyclobutanedione formula, IV.[159, 160] The dimers of aldoketenes yield higher polymers on moderate heating. Dehydracetic acid is formed from diketene; if the acetylketene formula (I) is

```
          O                                        O
          ‖                                        ‖
          C                                        C
         //                                      /   \
       CH              CHCOCH3               CH      CHCOCH3
       |         +     ‖             →       ‖       |
     CH3C              C=O                 CH3C      C=O
         \\                                    \    /
          O                                      O
```

used the reaction can be written as a Diels-Alder condensation. Diketene can be stored indefinitely at temperatures of 0° or below.[117]

Apparently there is yet no agreement among students of the problem of the diketene structure,[117, 153–164] and it is possible that the substance actually is a mixture of readily interchangeable isomeric forms. The use of the acylketene formula I in the sequel is for convenience only. The dimers of aldoketenes undergo the same reactions as diketene and present the same problems of structure.[115, *]

In the laboratory preparation [165] of diketene the mixture of ketene, unchanged acetone, and methane from a ketene generator is passed into a condensing system which is cooled initially in Dry Ice, and the condensate is allowed to warm to room temperature over a period of about twenty-four hours. The resulting mixture of acetone, diketene, and dehydracetic acid is separated by distillation under reduced pressure (50–55% of diketene). More exact control of the concentration and

* *Note added in proof.* Bauer, Bregman, and Wrightson of Cornell University (private communication) have recently made electron diffraction studies of diketene vapor using the sector technique. They find that formulas II and III are compatible with the observed diffraction pattern and that formulas I and IV must be discarded. Since the evidence of Taufen and Murray from the Raman spectrum of liquid diketene eliminates formulas III and IV, only formula II satisfies both sets of experimental data, and it therefore appears to represent the most probable structure for the dimer.

[157] Calvin, Magel, and Hurd, *J. Am. Chem. Soc.*, **63,** 2174 (1941).

[158] Oesper and Smyth, *J. Am. Chem. Soc.*, **64,** 768 (1942).

[159] Rice and Roberts, abstract of paper presented at 104th meeting of the American Chemical Society, Organic Division, Buffalo, New York, p. 12M, September, 1942.

[160] Rice and Roberts, *J. Am. Chem. Soc.*, **65,** 1677 (1943).

[161] Hurd, Sweet, and Thomas, *J. Am. Chem. Soc.*, **55,** 337 (1933).

[162] Staudinger, *Ber.*, **53,** 1085 (1920).

[163] Angus, Leckie, LeFevre, LeFevre, and Wassermann, *J. Chem. Soc.*, **1935,** 1751.

[164] Taufen and Murray, *J. Am. Chem. Soc.*, **67,** 754 (1945).

[165] Williams and Krynitsky, *Org. Syntheses*, **21,** 64 (1941).

temperature in the commercial preparation probably permits a higher conversion to diketene. Several variations of the above procedure are disclosed in the patent literature.[166–176]

Dimers of other ketenes also can be prepared from the monomers, but frequently it is more convenient to prepare the dimers directly by extending the reaction time or increasing the reaction temperature. The most convenient preparation of higher aldoketene dimers is that of dehydrohalogenation of acyl halides with tertiary aliphatic amines.[115, 150, 177]

$$2RCH_2COCl + 2R'_3N \rightarrow \underset{\displaystyle R}{RCH_2CO\underset{|}{C}}{=}C{=}O + 2R'_3NH^+Cl^-$$

In many preparations nearly quantitative yields are obtained by allowing the reactions to run at room temperature for about twenty-four hours. This is one of the simplest methods of bringing about the formation of a new carbon-carbon bond, and it affords a very attractive route to derivatives of β-keto acids; for example, esters of the type $RCH_2COCHRCO_2C_2H_5$ are obtained from the acids (RCH_2CO_2H) by converting the acid chlorides to the ketene dimers and allowing these to react with ethanol.

$$\underset{\displaystyle R}{RCH_2CO\underset{|}{C}}{=}C{=}O + C_2H_5OH \xrightarrow{(H^+)} \underset{\displaystyle R}{RCH_2CO\underset{|}{C}H}CO_2C_2H_5$$

Mixed aldoketene dimers have been prepared by treating mixtures of two acid chlorides with tertiary aliphatic amines.[150] Presumably the two monomeric ketenes are formed and combine to give the simple and mixed dimers. Three of the four possible products have been isolated from the treatment of a mixture of acetyl and lauroyl chlorides with triethylamine.

$$\begin{array}{l} CH_3COCl \\ CH_3(CH_2)_{10}COCl \end{array} \xrightarrow{2(C_2H_5)_3N} \begin{array}{ll} CH_3COCH{=}C{=}O & (14\%) \\ CH_3(CH_2)_{10}COC(C_{10}H_{21}){=}C{=}O & (14\%) \\ CH_3(CH_2)_{10}COCH{=}C{=}O & (12\%) \\ [CH_3COC(C_{10}H_{21}){=}C{=}O, \text{ not identified}] & \end{array}$$

[166] U. S. pat., 2,019,983 [*C. A.*, **30**, 487 (1936)].
[167] Fr. pat., 761,731 [*C. A.*, **28**, 4072 (1934)].
[168] Can. pat., 352,920 [*C. A.*, **29**, 8008 (1935)].
[169] Brit. pat., 410,394 [*C. A.*, **28**, 6160 (1934)].
[170] U. S. pat., 1,998,404 [*C. A.*, **29**, 3689 (1935)].
[171] U. S. pat., 2,103,505 [*C. A.*, **32**, 1718 (1938)].
[172] Brit. pat., 498,280 [*C. A.*, **33**, 3820 (1939)].
[173] U. S. pat., 2,216,450 [*C. A.*, **35**, 757 (1941)].
[174] Ger. pat., 700,218 [*C. A.*, **35**, 6976 (1941)].
[175] Fr. pat., 835,162 [*C. A.*, **33**, 4274 (1939)].
[176] Brit. pat., 550,486 [*C. A.*, **38**, 1534 (1944)].
[177] U. S. pat., 2,369,919 [*C. A.*, **39**, 4086 (1945)].

The various ketene dimers which have been reported are listed in Table VII. No attempt has been made to give all the references to the preparation of a particular dimer; only those references which, in the authors' opinion, give the best preparative methods are listed. Experimental procedures for preparing ketene dimers are described on pages 137 and 140.

TABLE VII

KETENE DIMERS

A. *Aldoketene Dimers*

Dimer	Method of Preparation	Yield	Reference
$(CH_2{=}C{=}O)_2$	Monomer in acetone, low temperature	55%	165
	$CH_3COCl + (C_2H_5)_3N$ *	14% *	150
$(CH_3CH{=}C{=}O)_2$	$CH_3CH_2COCl + (C_2H_5)_3N$	60%, 74%	115, 177
		28%,†	150
		36% ‡	150
	$CH_3CHBrCOBr$ + Zn	?	127
$(iso\text{-}C_3H_7CH{=}C{=}O)_2$	$iso\text{-}C_3H_7CH_2COCl + (C_2H_5)_3N$	60%	177
$(n\text{-}C_4H_9CH{=}C{=}O)_2$	$n\text{-}C_4H_9CH_2COCl + (C_2H_5)_3N$	65%, 27% ‡	115, 150
$C_2H_5COC(n\text{-}C_4H_9){=}C{=}O$ and/or $n\text{-}C_5H_{11}COC(CH_3){=}C{=}O$	$CH_3CH_2COCl + CH_3(CH_2)_4COCl + (C_2H_5)_3N$	44% ‡	150
$C_2H_5COC(n\text{-}C_6H_{13}){=}C{=}O$ and/or $n\text{-}C_7H_{15}COC(CH_3){=}C{=}O$	$CH_3CH_2COCl + CH_3(CH_2)_6COCl + (C_2H_5)_3N$	26% †	150
$n\text{-}C_{11}H_{23}COCH{=}C{=}O$	$CH_3COCl + CH_3(CH_2)_{10}COCl + (C_2H_5)_3N$	12% *	150
$(n\text{-}C_6H_{13}CH{=}C{=}O)_2$	$CH_3(CH_2)_6COCl + (C_2H_5)_3N$	31% †	150
		75%	177
$(n\text{-}C_{10}H_{21}CH{=}C{=}O)_2$	$n\text{-}C_{10}H_{21}CH_2COCl + (C_2H_5)_3N$	90%	177
$(n\text{-}C_{16}H_{33}CH{=}C{=}O)_2$	$n\text{-}C_{16}H_{33}CH_2COCl + (C_2H_5)_3N$	97%	177
$(C_6H_5CH{=}C{=}O)_2$	$C_6H_5CHClCOCl$ + Zn	10%	127
$[2,4,6\text{-}(CH_3)_3C_6H_2CH{=}C{=}O]_2$	$2,4,6\text{-}(CH_3)_3C_6H_2CHBrCOBr$ + Zn	—	129*a*
$[(CO_2CH_3)CH{=}C{=}O]_2$	$H_2C(CO_2CH_3)(COCl)$ (heated)	Low	135

* From the preparation of simple and mixed dimers by the action of triethylamine on a mixture of acetyl and lauroyl chlorides.

† From the preparation of simple and mixed dimers by the action of triethylamine on a mixture of propionyl and capryloyl chlorides.

‡ From the preparation of simple and mixed dimers by the action of triethylamine on a mixture of propionyl and caproyl chlorides.

TABLE VII—*Continued*

KETENE DIMERS

B. *Ketoketene Dimers*

Dimer	Method of Preparation	Yield	Ref.
CO $(CH_3)_2C$ C$(CH_3)_2$ CO	$(CH_3)_2CHCOCl$ + $(C_2H_5)_3N$	57%	149
CH_3 CO CH_3 C C C_2H_5 CO C_2H_5	Heating of monomer	84%	110
CO $(C_2H_5)_2C$ C$(C_2H_5)_2$ CO	Heating of monomer	83%	110
CO $(CH_2)_5C$ C$(CH_2)_5$ CO	CH_2CH_2 CH_2 CHCOCl + CH_2CH_2 $(C_2H_5)_3N$	32–66%	115
CO $(n\text{-}C_3H_7)_2C$ C$(n\text{-}C_3H_7)_2$ CO	Heating of monomer	10%	110
CH_3 CO CH_3 C C $CH_2{=}CHCH_2$ CO $CH_2CH{=}CH_2$	Heating of monomer	78%	110
CO $(CH_2{=}CHCH_2)_2C$ C$(CH_2CH{=}CH_2)_2$ CO	Heating of monomer	96%	110
C_2H_5 CO C_2H_5 C C $C_2H_5O_2C$ CO $CO_2C_2H_5$	C_2H_5 Br C + Zn $C_2H_5O_2C$ COCl	80%	120, 121
	From the monomer	—	36

TABLE VII—*Continued*

KETENE DIMERS

B. *Ketoketene Dimers—Continued*

Dimer	Method of Preparation	Yield	Ref.
$(C_2H_5O_2C)_2C\langle(CO)_2\rangle C(CO_2C_2H_5)_2$	Heating of monomer	Low	121
$(C_6H_5)(C_2H_5O_2C)C\langle(CO)_2\rangle C(C_6H_5)(CO_2C_2H_5)$	Heating of monomer	"Nearly quantitative"	121
$(C_6H_5)_2C\langle(CO)_2\rangle C(C_6H_5)_2$	Heating of monomer	—	35, 124
$(CH_3)(C_6H_5)C\langle(CO)_2\rangle C(CH_3)(C_6H_5)$	Heating of monomer	"Quantitative"	123
$(C_6H_5CH_2)(CH_3)C\langle(CO)_2\rangle C(CH_2C_6H_5)(CH_3)$	Heating of monomer	"Quantitative"	110
$(C_6H_5CH_2)_2C\langle(CO)_2\rangle C(CH_2C_6H_5)_2$	Heating of monomer	"Nearly quantitative"	110

EXPERIMENTAL PROCEDURES

Pyrolysis

Ketene by Pyrolysis of Acetone.[3] *Description of Apparatus.* The apparatus consists essentially of a Chromel A filament (*O* in Fig. 1) suspended from the top portion of a ground-glass joint (*H*) so that it can be removed from the pyrolysis chamber (*E*) whenever desired. Filament *O* is prepared from 175 cm. of B. and S.* gauge 24 Chromel A wire (an

* B. and S. refers to Brown and Sharpe, Inc., 20 Vesey Street, New York, New York.

alloy of 80% nickel and 20% chromium) by wrapping the wire in a tight spiral around a rod 3 mm. in diameter and stretching the coil so formed to a length of 70 cm. The filament is held in position on 15-mm.-long platinum hooks (*N*) sealed into the Pyrex glass rod which supports

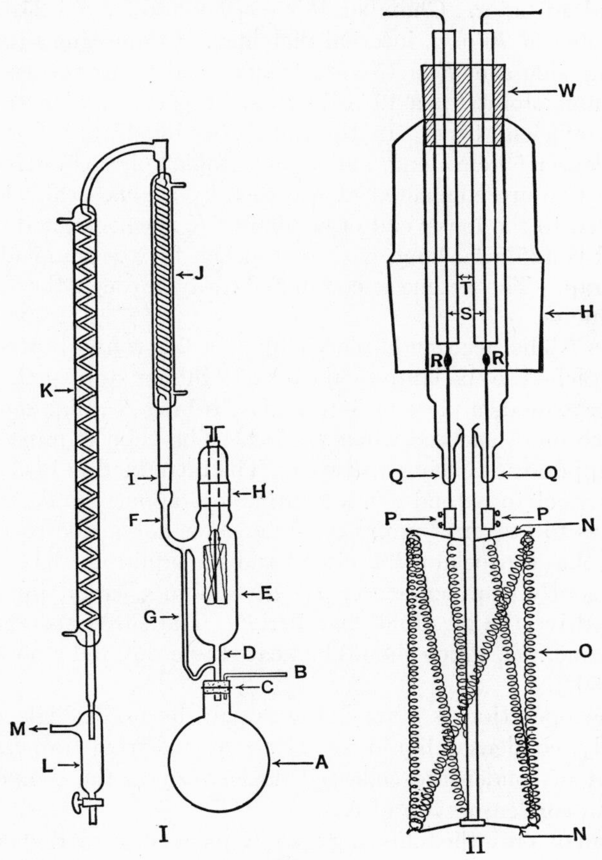

FIG. 1.

them. The three hooks at the bottom of the rod are spaced 120° apart. Two platinum hooks support the filament at a distance of 11 cm. above the end. The ends of the filament *O* are connected to tungsten leads by means of nickel sleeves *P*, 10 mm. in length and 3.5 mm. in internal diameter, equipped with two set screws. The tungsten leads are of B. and S. gauge 24 wire and are sealed into the glass at the points *Q*, and above these junctions are soldered to B. and S. gauge 24 copper wire (*S*) at the points *R*. The copper leads *S* are insulated by pieces of 6-mm.

glass tubing *T*, which are held by the cork stopper *W*. The copper wire leads are connected to a source of 110-volt alternating current, preferably through a variable resistance such as a Variac transformer.

All the glass in the apparatus is Pyrex. The ground-glass joint *H* is a 55/50 standard taper. Chamber *E* is constructed from a 25-cm. length of glass tubing of 70-mm. internal diameter. Connecting tube *D* is 12-mm. tubing, side arm *F* is 15-mm. tubing, and reflux return tube *G* is 6-mm. tubing. Joint *I* is a 19/38 standard taper. Condensers *J* and *K* are of any efficient type. In the apparatus illustrated *J* is a double spiral condenser 50 cm. long, and *K* is a single spiral condenser 90 cm. long. The two are connected at the tops by a glass seal. The liquid trap *L* sealed to the lower end of condenser *K* is constructed of 35-mm. tubing and is 125 mm. long, with a stopcock for the removal of liquid from the trap. The ketene is conducted away through the tube *M*, of 8-mm. diameter.

Operation. The acetone is placed in *A*, a 2-l. round-bottomed flask which is attached to the lamp by means of a rubber stopper *C*. Through this stopper extends a piece of 6-mm. glass tubing *B* which may be used to introduce more acetone when needed. The tube *B* must be closed when the apparatus is being operated. The introduction into *A* of sufficient glass wool to extend a few centimeters above the surface of the liquid serves to prevent bumping. After *M* is connected to the proper apparatus, the stopcock on *L* is closed and the liquid in *A* is heated until it refluxes gently from condenser *J*. Five minutes' refluxing should be allowed to drive the air from chamber *E*. The current is then passed through filament *O*, which should be heated to a dull red glow (temperature 700–750°).

After the operation is started the apparatus needs little attention. Occasionally, condensed liquid must be removed from trap *L*, in which the amount of condensate collected depends upon the temperature of the water in condensers *J* and *K*.

At the end of a run the following operations must be carried out rapidly in this order: (1) the source of heat is removed from flask *A*, (2) the filament current is turned off, and (3) the stopcock on *L* is opened.

Calibration. The amount of ketene produced per hour may be determined either by weighing the acetanilide produced by passing the effluent gas stream through excess aniline for a measured period of time or by passing the gas stream through standard alkali with subsequent titration of the unused alkali. By the second method the apparatus described was found to deliver 0.45 mole of ketene per hour. In a continuous run of ten hours 4.53 moles of ketene was produced with a net consumption of about 350 cc. of acetone from flask *A*. If the residual liquid and condensate were pure acetone, this would represent a 95% yield, but the figure is too high, for, although the liquid is chiefly acetone, it contains small amounts of acetic anhydride, acetic acid, and ketene dimer.

Malonic Anhydride Method

Dimethylketene.[109] To 25 g. of acetic anhydride containing a trace of concentrated sulfuric acid in a dry Claisen distilling flask protected from moisture is added 6.5 g. of dimethylmalonic acid. The solid dissolves when the mixture is shaken. The solution is allowed to stand at room temperature for two days. A small amount of powdered barium carbonate is added, and most of the acetic acid and acetic anhydride is removed by distillation at 1-mm. pressure while the flask is heated gently in an oil bath. The last traces of acetic acid and acetic anhydride are removed by heating at 60° under a pressure of 1 mm. or lower. The flask is then connected to a dry receiver cooled in a Dry Ice bath, and the residual, thoroughly dry dimethylmalonic anhydride is decomposed by slowly raising the temperature of the oil bath until vigorous evolution of carbon dioxide and dimethylketene occurs (about 100°). The pressure is maintained at the lowest possible point during the decomposition. The dimethylketene (b.p. 34° at atmospheric pressure) collected in the cold receiver weighs 2.3 g. (65%).

Dipropylketene.[110] To 5.6 g. of dipropylmalonic acid in 5 cc. of anhydrous ether is added 11.5 g. of diphenylketene (p. 123) with cooling in an ice bath. The clear solution begins to deposit crystals after one hour. Crystallization is completed by cooling in an ice bath, and a nearly quantitative yield of the mixed anhydride melting at 84° is obtained. The mixed anhydride can be recrystallized from a mixture of carbon disulfide and petroleum ether (b.p. 30–70°).

The mixed anhydride (10 g.) is placed in a small Claisen flask connected to a receiver cooled in Dry Ice and acetone and is heated under a pressure of about 11 mm. and at a bath temperature of 90–100°. Decarboxylation proceeds fairly rapidly, and dipropylketene (b.p. 30°/11 mm.) distils into the cooled receiver. Diphenylacetic anhydride remains in the distillation flask. On the basis of the amount of dipropylacetanilide formed when aniline is added to the distillate, the yield of dipropylketene is 32%.*

Dibenzylketene.[110] A solution of 8.5 g. of dibenzylmalonic acid in 8 cc. of anhydrous ether is mixed with 11.6 g. of diphenylketene (p. 123). The mixture is shaken mechanically for four hours, or until complete solution occurs. It is then transferred to an ice bath and cooled until

* This is the percentage yield cited by Staudinger (ref. 110); however, the weight of dipropylacetanilide reported by him corresponded to an 83% yield.

crystallization is complete. The yield of crude mixed anhydride is nearly quantitative. After recrystallization from a mixture of carbon disulfide and petroleum ether (b.p. 35–70°) it melts at 104°. The purified anhydride is placed in a Claisen flask and heated under reduced pressure at 110° until the evolution of carbon dioxide is complete. The dibenzylketene is extracted from the residue with petroleum ether (b.p. 35–70°). The yield of dibenzylketene in the filtered extract, calculated from the weight of dibenzylacetanilide obtained by treatment of an aliquot portion with excess aniline, is 73%; the yield of dibenzylketene (b.p. 121–122°/0.08 mm.) which can be isolated by distillation is 2.7 g. (40%).

Depolymerization

Dimethylketene.[116] A modification of the ordinary ketene lamp is necessary to permit the pyrolysis of the comparatively high-melting dimethylketene dimer (m.p. 115°), which tends to sublime out of the reaction zone. The apparatus illustrated in Fig. 2 has a triple filament made

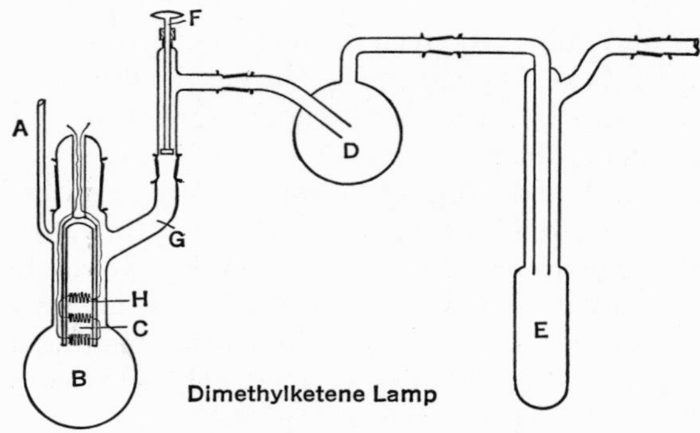

FIG. 2.

of No. 26 gauge Nichrome wire. For each filament (*C*), between 25 and 28 cm. of wire is wound around a microscope slide (2.5-cm. width) and then spot-welded to the tungsten supports (*H*). All joints are made of ground glass, and when the lamp is in operation they are held together by rubber bands. The circular bulb trap (*D*) is cooled by a stream of tap water. There are two traps (*E*) cooled in Dry Ice-acetone in the train (one shown in diagram); the final trap is connected to a calcium chloride tube. The filament is connected to a 110-volt a-c. source, with an ammeter and variable resistance in the circuit. The plunger (*F*) can be used if necessary to dislodge any sublimed dimethylketene dimer.

The nitrogen gas, employed to sweep the ketene and unchanged dimer and monomer away from the filament and into the traps, is passed through two gas wash bottles containing Fieser's solution,* two calcium chloride tubes, a third wash bottle containing concentrated sulfuric acid, finally a third calcium chloride tube, and then into the lamp at the nitrogen inlet (*A*). A weighed amount of the dimer is placed in the reaction flask (*B*), and the entire system is evacuated by a water pump. Nitrogen is then drawn through the system for approximately five minutes. The water pump is then disconnected, and the nitrogen is allowed to flow under the pressure of a few centimeters of mercury. Dry Ice and acetone are next placed in the Dewar flasks for cooling the traps (*E*). As soon as the temperature of these traps reaches $-70°$ the filament is heated, and an oil bath (90–100°) is placed around the reaction flask. The oil level reaches the outlet tube (*G*) of the reaction flask. The oil bath is heated to the desired temperature, usually 120°, for the duration of the run. Within a few minutes vapor is observed leaving the reaction flask, and the flow of nitrogen is regulated so that the vapor flows steadily and slowly into the circular bulb trap. The nitrogen current must not be strong enough to carry the vapor into the Dry Ice traps. At the end of the run the flow of nitrogen is stopped, the electric current is turned off, and a cork is placed in the calcium chloride tube at the end of the train. The monomeric dimethylketene, which collects for the most part in the first Dry Ice trap, may be stored in this condition until desired.

With the oil-bath temperature at 120° and the Nichrome filament at a dull red heat, there are collected 6 g. of dimethylketene in *E* and 3 g. of unchanged dimer in *D* from a charge of 10 g. of starting material (86% yield of dimethylketene based on dimer consumed). The recovered dimer is washed out of the apparatus with ether. The filament is cleaned with a camel's-hair brush after each run; less than 0.05 g. of carbon is deposited during a 10-g. run.

If the temperature of the oil bath is allowed to fall below 120° for an appreciable length of time or if the flow of nitrogen is slow, the yield is lower. Too strong heating of the filament also lowers the yield.

Ethylcarbethoxyketene.[120] To 32 g. (0.5 mole) of zinc shavings is added 104 g. (0.41 mole) of α-bromo-α-carbethoxybutyryl chloride (p. 138) in 600 cc. of absolute ether, and the mixture is refluxed for four hours. The ether solution is shaken with water, dilute hydrochloric acid, and dilute sodium hydroxide and is then dried over calcium chloride. The solvent is removed, and the residue is distilled in the highest vacuum. The yield of the dimer boiling at 113–116° ("absolute" vacuum) is 35 g. (61%). A 10-g. portion of the dimer is placed in a small distilling flask equipped with a short fractionating column connected to a receiver cooled

* For details of the preparation of the solution see Fieser, *J. Am. Chem. Soc.*, **46**, 2639 (1924).

in Dry Ice. Depolymerization is effected by heating in an oil bath at 180–200° under a pressure of 15 mm. for about five hours. The yield of ethylcarbethoxyketene (b.p. 48°/15 mm.) is nearly quantitative.

Dehalogenation of α-Haloacyl Halides

Ethylcarbethoxyketene.[120] *α-Carbethoxybutyryl Chloride.* To a solution of 300 g. (1.9 moles) of α-carbethoxybutyric acid in 500 cc. of absolute ether is added slowly with cooling 420 g. (2 moles) of phosphorus pentachloride. The mixture is refluxed two hours to complete the reaction. After removal of the ether and phosphorus oxychloride by distillation under reduced pressure, there is obtained 230 g. (69%) of the acid chloride boiling at 75–77°/13 mm.

α-Bromo-α-carbethoxybutyryl Chloride. Into a refluxing solution of 200 g. (1.13 moles) of the acid chloride in 200 cc. of carbon disulfide is slowly dropped 190 g. (1.18 moles) of bromine. Refluxing is continued for two hours after completion of the addition. After removal of the carbon disulfide by distillation under reduced pressure, there is obtained 250 g. (87%) of the bromo derivative boiling at 95–102°/14 mm.

Ethylcarbethoxyketene. A solution of 26 g. (0.1 mole) of the bromo acid chloride in 200 cc. of absolute ether is added to 15 g. (0.23 mole) of zinc shavings at such a rate that the ether refluxes gently. After the addition is complete the reaction mixture is refluxed briefly and 600 cc. of petroleum ether is added in order to precipitate the zinc chloride.

If the ketene is not isolated from the solvent but converted into the anilide by addition of aniline, an amount of anilide corresponding to a 34% yield of the ketene is isolated. However, if the ketene is isolated from the solvent by vacuum distillation, the yield of monomer is much lower (not given). If pure monomeric ethylcarbethoxyketene is desired, it is preferable to prepare the dimer and depolymerize it thermally (p. 137).

Dehydrohalogenation

Diheptylketene.[148] In a dry flask protected from the atmosphere 24 g. (0.09 mole) of diheptylacetyl chloride is added to a solution of 7.1 g. (0.12 mole) of trimethylamine in 150 g. (188 cc.) of anhydrous benzene. The mixture is allowed to stand at room temperature for twenty-nine hours, and the precipitated trimethylamine hydrochloride (6.8 g., 80%) is separated by rapid filtration.[178] The solvent is removed from the filtrate by distillation at room temperature under about 200 mm. pressure. Dis-

[178] For a simple technique of filtration with exclusion of moisture see Bost and Constable, *Org. Syntheses, Coll. Vol.* **2**, 610 (1943).

tillation of the residue yields 12.3 g. (60%) of diheptylketene boiling at 133–135°/5 mm. (n_D^{27} 1.4432).

Mesitylphenylketene.[146, 147] *Mesitylphenylacetic Acid.* A mixture of 152 g. (1 mole) of a good grade of dry mandelic acid and 353 g. (400 cc., 2.9 moles) of dry mesitylene is placed in a 1-l. round-bottomed three-necked flask fitted with a mechanical stirrer (grease seal), a 250-cc. separatory funnel, and a condenser protected from moisture by calcium chloride tubes. A thermometer is inserted in the reaction mixture by way of the condenser tube, the stirrer is started, and the temperature is raised to 70° by heating over an electric light. After this temperature has been maintained for one hour (to bring most of the mandelic acid into solution), 390 g. (175 cc., 1.5 mole) of anhydrous stannic chloride is added dropwise over a period of eighty minutes. Stirring and heating are continued for eight hours more. During this period large colorless stannic chloride hydrate crystals form on the upper parts of the flask.

After standing overnight at room temperature, the reaction mixture is treated with 500 cc. of water. The organic layer is separated, the aqueous portion is extracted with one 100-cc. portion of ether, and the combined organic layers are diluted with 1200 cc. of ether. The ethereal solution is washed twice with 100-cc. portions of water and is then shaken with 100-cc. portions of 7% aqueous sodium carbonate (about fourteen washings are required for complete separation). The first two or three portions of carbonate solution cause precipitation of stannic hydroxide, and they are collected separately and filtered. The filtrate is combined with the subsequent carbonate extracts. Acidification with concentrated hydrochloric acid precipitates the acid as a white solid. It is collected by filtration on a 15-cm. Büchner funnel, washed twice with 300-cc. portions of water, and dried in the air. It weighs about 190 g. and melts at 170–172°; it can be purified further by recrystallization from a mixture of 800 cc. of ethanol and 150 cc. of water. The yield of acid melting at 172–173° is 165 g. (65%).

Mesitylphenylketene. A mixture of 25 g. (0.1 mole) of dry mesitylphenylacetic acid, 200 cc. of dry benzene, 13 g. (0.11 mole) of thionyl chloride purified by distillation from cottonseed oil (2.5 l. of commercial thionyl chloride to 1 l. of Puritan oil), and 0.5 cc. of dry pyridine is placed in a 300-cc. flask fitted with a ground-glass joint. A condenser equipped with a drying tube is attached, and the solution is heated under reflux for five hours. Pyridine hydrochloride is precipitated on the sides of the flask. The mixture is filtered by suction, the filtrate is introduced into a 250-cc. Claisen flask, and the solvent is removed under the vacuum of a water pump. The residue is transferred to a 60-cc. Claisen flask and distilled at a good water pump (much hydrogen chloride is evolved). A golden yellow liquid boiling at 150–155°/13–14 mm. and weighing 18–19 g. (80%) is collected. Redistillation yields 15–16 g. of the ketene boiling at 125–126°/3 mm. The yellow liquid turns deep red upon storage but is regenerated upon distillation. It reacts rapidly with the moisture of the air to give mesitylphenylacetic acid.

***n*-Butylketene Dimer.**[115] Into a 2-l. three-necked round-bottomed flask equipped with a reflux condenser carrying a calcium chloride tube, a motor-driven stirrer with a mercury seal, and a 150-cc. graduated dropping funnel is poured 850 cc. of anhydrous ether. Stirring is commenced, and 134.5 g. (1.0 mole) of *n*-caproyl chloride, b.p. 45–45.5°/6 mm., is added rapidly through the condenser. To this well-agitated mixture is added dropwise from the funnel 99.9 g. (0.99 mole) of triethylamine, b.p. 88°, at a rate just sufficient to maintain gentle refluxing. During the addition of the first few cubic centimeters of the triethylamine, there is no noticeable evidence of reaction. However, as the proportion of triethylamine to *n*-caproyl chloride increases, the reaction proceeds with great vigor and triethylamine hydrochloride precipitates as a light orange-colored solid. The reaction mixture is stirred for one and one-half hours after the addition of the triethylamine and is then allowed to stand overnight at room temperature.

The solution of the ketene dimer is removed by the inverted filtration method.[178] The crude triethylamine hydrochloride can be purified by pressing firmly on a Büchner funnel and washing thoroughly with dry ether. The pure air-dried hydrochloride weighs 135 g. (98%). The ether is removed from the filtrate by fractionation through a helix-packed column (1.5 cm. by 60 cm.). About 75 cc. of a light yellow residue which remains is transferred to a modified Claisen flask. The *n*-butylketene dimer boiling at 115–116°/4 mm. weighs 64 g. (65%). The *n*-butylketene dimer is a colorless, oily liquid possessing no distinct odor. Its physical constants are as follows: D_4^{20} 0.91700; n_D^{20} 1.4513; MR_D calculated 57.19, observed 57.50; molecular weight calculated 196.2, found (cryoscopically in benzene) 191.4.

CHAPTER 4

DIRECT SULFONATION OF AROMATIC HYDROCARBONS AND THEIR HALOGEN DERIVATIVES

C. M. SUTER

Winthrop Chemical Company

AND

ARTHUR W. WESTON

Abbott Laboratories

CONTENTS

INTRODUCTION

This chapter deals with the direct replacement of the hydrogen atoms in aromatic hydrocarbons and their halogen derivatives by sulfonic acid, sulfonyl chloride, and sulfonyl fluoride groups. These sulfonations are more convenient and much more commonly used than indirect synthetic methods such as those which involve the reaction of an aryl halide with a sulfite, the oxidation of a disulfide, thiol, or sulfinic acid, or the conversion of a diazonium salt into a sulfonic acid. The reagents most often used for direct sulfonation are (1) sulfuric acid, (2) sulfur trioxide in an inert solvent, in sulfuric acid as oleum, or as an addition product with pyridine or dioxane, (3) chlorosulfonic acid, its salts, and its anhydride (pyrosulfuryl chloride), and (4) fluorosulfonic acid. Sulfamic acid, alkali bisulfates, and sodium trihydrogen sulfate, $NaH_3(SO_4)_2$, are employed less frequently. Combinations of reagents which have been used are sulfuric acid with phosphorus pentoxide, chlorosulfonic anhydride with aluminum chloride, sulfuryl chloride with aluminum chloride, and sulfuryl chloride with chlorosulfonic acid.

GENERAL ASPECTS OF THE REACTION

Sulfonation with Sulfuric Acid and Sulfur Trioxide. Various mechanisms for the reaction of aromatic hydrocarbons or aryl halides with sulfuric acid or with sulfur trioxide have been proposed.[1] Since the reaction is heterogeneous, it is not favorable for experimental study. Solvents that dissolve sulfuric acid or sulfur trioxide form addition compounds with the reagent; hence any conclusion drawn from a homogeneous sulfonation might not be applicable to the ordinary sulfonation. One possibility is that an electrophilic reagent such as sulfur trioxide with its relatively positive sulfur atom or an ion such as HO_3S^+ in the case of sulfuric acid [1g] attacks the negative center of the polarized form of the hydrocarbon, as illustrated for benzene.

$$C_6H_6 + O{\leftarrow}\overset{O}{\overset{\uparrow}{S}}{=}O \longrightarrow {}^{+}C_6H_6{-}\overset{O}{\overset{\uparrow}{S}}{-}O^- \xrightarrow{-H^+} C_6H_5{-}\overset{O}{\overset{\uparrow}{\underset{\downarrow}{S}}}{-}O^- \xrightarrow{H^+} C_6H_5{-}\overset{O}{\overset{\uparrow}{\underset{\downarrow}{S}}}{-}OH \qquad (1)$$

$$(HO)_2SO_2 \xrightarrow{H^+} \left[(HO)(H_2O^+)SO_2\right] \longrightarrow H_2O + {}^+SO_2OH \qquad (2)$$

$$C_6H_6 + {}^+SO_2OH \longrightarrow [C_6H_6SO_3H]^+ \xrightarrow{-H^+} C_6H_5SO_3H$$

The reaction with sulfuric acid is reversible; for example, the sulfonation of benzene at temperatures between 100° and 200° attains equilibrium when the concentration of sulfuric acid is 73–78%.[1c, 2] In order to obtain maximum yields it is necessary either to separate the sulfonic acid by continuous extraction or, more generally, to remove the water as the reaction proceeds. One industrial method of preparing benzenesulfonic acid is a modification of the Tyrer process,[3] which utilizes the latter principle. The reaction is carried out at temperatures of 170–180°; the water is removed by passing benzene vapor through the reactor at such a rate that unchanged benzene is present in the condensate. The reaction is carried to about 95% completion.[4] Two other expedients used in manufacturing processes consist in carrying out the reaction under such a vacuum as to remove the water as it is formed,[5] and in the intermittent addition of sulfur trioxide, which reacts with the water to form sulfuric acid.[6] The water can be removed also by entrainment with an inert gas that is passed through the reaction mixture.[7]

The aromatic sulfonic acids undergo hydrolysis (reversal of the sulfonation reaction) when they are heated with water or dilute acid. The sulfonic acids that are the most readily formed are the most readily hydrolyzed.[8] This accounts for the variation in the relative amounts of

[1] (*a*) Lantz, *Bull. soc. chim.*, [5] **6**, 302 (1939); (*b*) Spryskov, *J. Gen. Chem. U.S.S.R.*, **8**, 1857 (1938) [*C. A.*, **33**, 5820 (1939)]; (*c*) Guyot, *Chimie & industrie*, **2**, 879 (1919); (*d*) Courtot, *Rev. gén. mat. color.*, **33**, 177 (1929); (*e*) Courtot and Bonnet, *Compt. rend.*, **182**, 855 (1926); (*f*) Vorozhtzov, *Anilinokrasochnaya Prom.*, **4**, 84 (1934) [*C. A.*, **28**, 4652 (1934)]; (*g*) Price, *Chem. Revs.*, **29**, 37 (1941).

[2] Zakharov, *J. Chem. Ind. U.S.S.R.*, **6**, 1648 (1929) [*C. A.*, **25**, 5154 (1931)].

[3] Tyrer, U. S. pat. 1,210,725 [*C. A.*, **11**, 689 (1917)].

[4] Killeffer, *Ind. Eng. Chem.*, **16**, 1066 (1924).

[5] Downs, U. S. pats. 1,279,295 and 1,279,296 [*C. A.*, **12**, 2572 (1918)]; Bender, U. S. pat. 1,301,360 [*C. A.*, **13**, 1862 (1919)].

[6] Aylesworth, U. S. pat. 1,260,852 [*C. A.*, **12**, 1469 (1918)].

[7] Meyer, *Ann.*, **433**, 327 (1923); Gay, Aumeras, and Mion, *Chimie & industrie*, **19**, 387 (1928); Spruiskov, *J. Chem. Ind. U.S.S.R.*, **8**, 41 (1931) [*C. A.*, **26**, 2735 (1932)].

[8] (*a*) Ioffe, *Anilinokrasochnaya Prom.*, **3**, 296 (1933) [*C. A.*, **28**, 957 (1934)]; (*b*) *J. Gen. Chem. U.S.S.R.*, **3**, 437, 505 (1933) [*C. A.*, **28**, 1593 (1934)]; (*c*) Lantz, *Compt. rend.*, **201**, 149 (1935); (*d*) Fedorov and Spruiskov, *Org. Chem. Ind. U.S.S.R.*, **2**, 100 (1936) [*C. A.*, **31**, 678 (1937)].

isomeric sulfonic acids resulting from changes in the time allowed for reactions capable of producing isomers; an extended reaction time would be expected to favor the formation of the most stable isomer. The difference in the stability of α- and β-naphthalenesulfonic acid toward hydrolysis provides the basis for a convenient purification of the β-isomer.[9] When a mixture of the two substances is heated to 145–155° with water, the α-isomer is completely hydrolyzed and there is little loss of the more stable β-isomer. Since aromatic hydrocarbons or halogen derivatives are regenerated, usually in good yield, by hydrolysis of the sulfonates, sulfonation followed by hydrolysis is utilized in the separation of mixtures of aliphatic and aromatic compounds and in the separation of mixtures of aromatic compounds that differ in ease of sulfonation.[10]

The reaction of aromatic hydrocarbons with sulfur trioxide is practically instantaneous and occurs under much milder conditions than are needed for other sulfonating agents. For example, the reaction of benzene with sulfuric acid (equal volumes) at reflux temperature reaches equilibrium only after twenty to thirty hours when 80% of the benzene is sulfonated;[11] the reaction with sulfur trioxide (chloroform solution) is practically instantaneous even at 0–10°, and benzenesulfonic acid can be isolated in a yield of 90%.[1d, 1e, 1f] Sulfuric acid is the usual solvent for the trioxide (oleum), but certain chlorinated solvents, particularly ethylene chloride[12] and chloroform,[13] and liquid sulfur dioxide are used to advantage.

One interesting feature of the sulfonation reaction with sulfuric acid is that the temperature plays a striking role in the orientation. This effect has been examined most extensively in the sulfonation of toluene[14] and of naphthalene.[15] In the sulfonation of toluene at 0° three isomers are produced in the following proportions: *o*-toluenesulfonic acid, 43%; *m*-toluenesulfonic acid, 4%; *p*-toluenesulfonic acid, 53%. At this temperature there is only a slight preference for *para* substitution over *ortho* substitution. In the sulfonation at 100° the yields are 13% *o*-toluenesulfonic acid, 8% *m*-toluenesulfonic acid, and 79% *p*-toluenesulfonic

[9] Masters, U. S. pat. 1,922,813 [*C. A.*, **27**, 5085 (1933)]; Vorozhtzov and Krasova, *Anilinokrasochnaya Prom.*, **2**, 15 (1932) [*C. A.*, **27**, 5321 (1933)].

[10] Kruber, *Ber.*, **65**, 1382 (1932).

[11] Michael and Adair, *Ber.*, **10**, 585 (1877).

[12] I. G. Farbenind. A.-G., Ger. pat. 647,988 [*C. A.*, **31**, 8074 (1937)].

[13] Courtot and Lin, *Bull. soc. chim.*, [4] **49**, 1047 (1931); Kipping, *J. Chem. Soc.*, **91**, 209, 717 (1907); Luff and Kipping, *ibid.*, **93**, 2090 (1908); Kipping and Davies, *ibid.*, **95**, 69 (1909); Marsden and Kipping, *ibid.*, **93**, 198 (1908); Bygdén, *J. prakt. Chem.*, [2] **96**, 86 (1917); Wedekind and Schenk, *Ber.*, **44**, 198 (1911); Bad. Anilin- und Soda-Fabrik, Ger. pat. 260,562 [*Chem. Zentr.*, **84**, II, 104 (1913)]; Pschorr and Klein, *Ber.*, **34**, 4003 (1901); Hodgkinson and Matthews, *J. Chem. Soc.*, **43**, 163 (1883).

[14] Holleman and Caland, *Ber.*, **44**, 2504 (1911).

[15] Euwes, *Rec. trav. chim.*, **28**, 298 (1909).

acid. The extent of *meta* substitution is affected only slightly by the reaction temperature, but that of *para* substitution is increased markedly with increasing temperature, at the expense of *ortho* substitution. Both the *ortho* and the *para* isomers can be partially transformed into one another by heating at 100° with sulfuric acid containing a little water; the *meta* isomer is stable under similar conditions.[14, 16] The effect of temperature on the orientation undoubtedly is a result of the reversibility of the sulfonation reaction; the transformation of the isomers probably proceeds through hydrolysis followed by sulfonation. In the sulfonation of naphthalene, α-naphthalenesulfonic acid is the predominant product (96%) at temperatures below 80°, whereas β-naphthalenesulfonic acid is the main product (85%) at a temperature of 165°. Here again the α-isomer can be transformed into the more stable β-isomer by heating with sulfuric acid.

The discovery that the sulfonation of anthraquinone, which normally occurs in the β-position, is directed exclusively to the α-position by a small amount of mercury has prompted investigations of the effect of mercury on other sulfonations. No instances have been found in which the course of the reaction of hydrocarbons is altered drastically. The sulfonation of naphthalene [15] and of anthracene [17, 18] is unaffected. However, the course of the reaction of sulfur trioxide-sulfuric acid with *o*-xylene, *o*-dichlorobenzene, and *o*-dibromobenzene is affected to a certain extent.[19] The 4-sulfonic acid is the exclusive product of sulfonation in the absence of mercury; the 3-sulfonic acid is formed to the extent of 20–25% in the presence of 10% of mercury. The relative ineffectiveness of mercury in the sulfonation of hydrocarbons is understandable if it is true that the activity of mercury in the reactions of oxygen-containing compounds is due to mercuration followed by replacement with the sulfonic acid grouping. Phenols are known to be particularly susceptible to mercuration (in the *ortho* position), and mercury has been found to exert some effect in the sulfonation of phenols, such as α-naphthol.[20]

Many instances of the response of sulfonation to catalysts are known. The most active catalyst for the high-temperature sulfonation of benzene is a mixture of sodium sulfate and vanadium pentoxide.[21] The sulfates of mercury, cadmium, aluminum, lead, arsenic, bismuth, and iron increase the rate of sulfonation of benzenesulfonic acid, whereas manganous

16 Bradfield and Jones, *Trans. Faraday Soc.*, **37**, 731 (1941).

17 Battegay and Brandt, *Bull. soc. chim.*, [4] **31**, 910 (1922).

18 Battegay and Brandt, *Bull. soc. chim.*, [4] **33**, 1667 (1923).

19 Lauer, *J. prakt. Chem.*, [2] **138**, 81 (1933).

20 Holdermann, *Ber.*, **39**, 1250 (1906).

21 Ambler and Cotton, *Ind. Eng. Chem.*, **12**, 968 (1920); Häuser and Korovits'ka, *C. A.*, **33**, 159 (1939); Senseman, *Ind. Eng. Chem.*, **13**, 1124 (1921).

sulfate has little effect.[22, 23] Benzene and its homologs are said to be sulfonated quantitatively at room temperature in the presence of infusorial earth or animal charcoal.[24] The trisulfonation of benzene with sulfur trioxide-sulfuric acid is facilitated by the presence of mercury.[22, 25]

One notable feature of the sulfonation reaction is the tendency of the entering sulfonic acid group to avoid a position adjacent to certain substituents. *t*-Butylbenzene is substituted exclusively at the 4-position,[26] even under conditions where toluene is substituted to some extent at the 2-position. Under the most favorable conditions *p*-cymene is sulfonated to only a limited extent (15%) at the 3-position,[27] which is *ortho* to the more bulky alkyl substituent. In fact the first authentic sample of the 3-acid was prepared indirectly by sulfonating 2-bromocymene and subsequently removing the bromine from the product of sulfonation, 6-bromocymene-3-sulfonic acid.[28] Particular interest in the

CH_3, Br, $CH(CH_3)_2$ $\xrightarrow{H_2SO_4}$ CH_3, Br, SO_3H, $CH(CH_3)_2$ $\xrightarrow{Na—Hg}$ CH_3, SO_3H, $CH(CH_3)_2$

3-sulfonic acid stems from the fact that this substance, if it were readily available, would serve as a convenient starting material for the preparation of thymol.

Sulfonation with Addition Compounds of Sulfur Trioxide. In a broad sense all sulfonating agents are more or less stable addition products of sulfur trioxide. The more readily an atom donates an electron pair, or the more basic it is, the less active is the addition compound with sulfur trioxide as a sulfonating agent. The most active sulfonating agents are sulfur trioxide and its addition product with itself, the known sulfur β-trioxide, S_2O_6; the next most active are the addition compounds with the mineral acids, chloro- and fluoro-sulfonic acid, and with sulfuric acid, pyrosulfuric acid ($H_2S_2O_7$). Sulfuric acid is less active; this agent is not precisely a coordination compound of sulfur trioxide and water, but certain ethers such as di-(β-chloroethyl) ether and dioxane do form stable addition complexes with sulfur trioxide that are active sulfo-

[22] Behrend and Mertelsmann, *Ann.*, **378**, 352 (1911).

[23] Mohrmann, *Ann.*, **410**, 373 (1915).

[24] Wendt, Ger. pat. 71,556 [*Frdl.*, **3**, 19].

[25] Suter and Harrington, *J. Am. Chem. Soc.*, **59**, 2575 (1937).

[26] Senkowski, *Ber.*, **23**, 2412 (1890).

[27] (*a*) Schorger, *Ind. Eng. Chem.*, **10**, 259 (1918); (*b*) Phillips, *J. Am. Chem. Soc.*, **46**, 686 (1924); (*c*) Le Fèvre, *J. Chem. Soc.*, **1934**, 1501; (*d*) Kuan, *J. Chem. Soc. Japan*, **52**, 473 (1931).

[28] Remsen and Day, *Am. Chem. J.*, **5**, 154 (1883).

nating agents.[29] The addition compounds with bases, such as pyridine,[18, 30] are the least active. No data are available to distinguish between the behavior of the amine addition products, but the compound with trimethylamine would be expected to show little activity. A possible mechanism for the sulfonating action of these reagents that does not require preliminary dissociation into free sulfur trioxide involves the stereochemical inversion of the sulfur atom, the carbon atom attaching itself to the sulfur atom opposite the valence bond that is broken. This is analogous to the Walden inversion reactions by which

$$C_6H_6 + O_3SX \rightarrow C_6H_5SO_3H + X$$

replacement of a group attached to carbon frequently occurs.

Chlorosulfonic acid is not used widely for the preparation of sulfonic acids, partly because excess reagent reacts with the sulfonic acid to form the sulfonyl chloride; it is commonly employed for the preparation of sulfonyl chlorides.

$$C_6H_6 + ClSO_3H \rightarrow C_6H_5SO_3H + HCl$$

$$C_6H_5SO_3H + ClSO_3H \rightarrow C_6H_5SO_2Cl + H_2SO_4$$

The reaction of fluorosulfonic acid is probably similar [31, 32] but has not been investigated so extensively. The action of chlorosulfonic anhydride [33] leads to such a complex mixture of products that this reagent is of little value. Sulfonation with chlorosulfonic acid is often carried out in an inert solvent,[12, 13, 34] usually chloroform.

Sulfonation with Miscellaneous Reagents. Sodium hydrogen sulfate [35] and sodium trihydrogen disulfate [36] exert some sulfonating action, but their value is limited by the fact that they are solids at room temperature and insoluble in organic solvents. Sodium trihydrogen disulfate melts at approximately 100° and has been used in reactions carried out at higher temperatures. Sulfamic acid, which differs from sulfuric acid in that one hydroxyl group is replaced by an amino group, has only a slight sulfonating action; furthermore, sulfamic acid is a solid and is insoluble in anhydrous solvents.

[29] Suter, Evans, and Kiefer, *J. Am. Chem. Soc.*, **60,** 538 (1938).

[30] Baumgarten, *Ber.*, **59,** 1976 (1926); *Die Chemie*, **55,** 115 (1942); Ger. pat. 514,821 [*C. A.*, **25,** 2156 (1931)].

[31] Steinkopf *et al.*, *J. prakt. Chem.*, [2] **117,** 1 (1927).

[32] Meyer and Schramm, *Z. anorg. allgem. Chem.*, **206,** 24 (1932).

[33] Steinkopf and Buchheim, *Ber.*, **54,** 2963 (1921).

[34] Huntress and Autenrieth, *J. Am. Chem. Soc.*, **63,** 3446 (1941).

[35] Soc. St. Denis, Ger. pat. 72,226 [*Frdl.*, **3,** 195]; Ger. pat. 77,311 [*Frdl.*, **4,** 271].

[36] (*a*) Gebler, *J. Chem. Ind. U.S.S.R.*, **2,** 984 (1926) [*C. A.*, **21,** 1450 (1927)]; (*b*) Lamberts, Ger. pat. 113,784 [*Chem. Zentr.*, II, 883 (1900)].

Side Reactions. The most common side reaction is the formation of a sulfone, Ar_2SO_2. This reaction is favored by an excess of the hydrocarbon or aryl halide and by an active sulfonating agent, such as sulfur trioxide, oleum,[37] or chlorosulfonic acid.[38] The reaction between benzene and sulfur trioxide in the vapor phase has been patented as a method of preparing phenyl sulfone.[39] The formation of 2,2′-cyclic sulfones is characteristic of biphenyl and its derivatives,[40] where the structure is favorable for intramolecular sulfone formation. Sulfone formation,

$$C_6H_5-C_6H_5 + 6ClSO_3H \rightarrow$$

$$ClO_2S-C_6H_3(SO_2)C_6H_3-SO_2Cl + 3H_2SO_4 + 4HCl$$

like sulfonation, is a reversible process; phenyl sulfone, for example, is converted by sulfuric acid into benzenesulfonic acid.[41]

Compounds containing bromine,[42] iodine, [43, 44, 45] or an accumulation of alkyl groups [46, 47, 48] or of alkyl and halogen groups [49] attached to the aromatic nucleus frequently undergo rearrangement or disproportionation or both when treated with sulfuric acid. The redistribution of methyl and halo substituents in polysubstituted benzene derivatives under the influence of sulfuric acid is known as the Jacobsen reaction.[48] Bromobenzene on refluxing with sulfuric acid gives a complex mixture of products that includes 3,5-dibromobenzenesulfonic acid, two bromobenzenedisulfonic acids (structure not established), *p*-dibromobenzene, 1,2,4,5-tetrabromobenzene, and hexabromobenzene.[42]

[37] Spiegelberg, *Ann.*, **197**, 257 (1879); Koerner and Paternò, *Gazz. chim. ital.*, **2**, 448 (1872); Troeger and Hurdelbrink, *J. prakt. Chem.*, [2] **65**, 82 (1902).

[38] (*a*) Pollak, Heimberg-Krauss, Katscher, and Lustig, *Monatsh.*, **55**, 358 (1930); (*b*) Dziewonski, Grünberg, and Schoen, *Bull. intern. acad. polon. sci.*, **1930A**, 518 [*C. A.*, **25**, 5419 (1931)].

[39] Carr, U. S. pat. 2,000,061 [*C. A.*, **29**, 4027 (1935)]; Planovskiĭ and Kagan, *Org. Chem Ind. U.S.S.R.*, **7**, 296 (1940) [*C. A.*, **35**, 3985 (1941)].

[40] Courtot and Lin, *Bull. soc. chim.*, [4] **49**, 1047 (1931).

[41] Gericke, *Ann.*, **100**, 207 (1856); Kekulé, *Zeit. für Chem.*, **1867**, 195.

[42] Herzig, *Monatsh.*, **2**, 192 (1881).

[43] Huntress and Carten, *J. Am. Chem. Soc.*, **62**, 511 (1940).

[44] Neumann, *Ann.*, **241**, 33 (1887).

[45] Boyle, *J. Chem. Soc.*, **95**, 1683 (1909).

[46] Smith and Kiess, *J. Am. Chem. Soc.*, **61**, 989 (1939).

[47] Smith and Guss, *J. Am. Chem. Soc.*, **62**, 2631 (1940).

[48] Smith, *Org. Reactions*, **I**, 370 (1942).

[49] Jacobsen, *Ber.*, **22**, 1580 (1889).

The formation of by-products other than the sulfone usually can be decreased by the use of a more active sulfonating agent and of a lower reaction temperature. However, satisfactory yields of the sulfonic acid cannot be obtained under any conditions for certain reactions, among them the sulfonation of *p*-diiodobenzene;[43, 44, 45] iodine groups generally have been found to migrate more readily than bromine or methyl groups. The reaction of *p*-diiodobenzene with chlorosulfonic acid is abnormal in another respect, for the principal product is 2,3,5,6-tetrachloro-1,4-diiodobenzene.[43]

APPLICATION OF THE REACTION

Practically any aromatic hydrocarbon or aryl halide can be sulfonated if the proper conditions are chosen. As the compound becomes more complex, however, the tendency toward the production of by-products and mixtures of isomers is increased. It is usually difficult to prevent polysubstitution of a reactive hydrocarbon. For example, even when phenanthrene is sulfonated incompletely at room temperature, some disulfonic acids are formed.[50] The sulfonation of anthracene follows such a complex course that the 1- and 2-sulfonic acid derivatives are made from the readily available derivatives of anthraquinone. The following sections include comments on the accessibility of the reaction products of the commonly available hydrocarbons and aryl halides. The examples cited and still others are listed in Tables I–XIII.

Benzene (Table I, p. 165). Some of the factors involved in the industrial sulfonation of benzene have been discussed. In the small-scale, laboratory preparation, where the difference in cost between sulfuric acid and oleum is negligible, oleum is the preferred reagent. Benzene is added gradually to ice-cold sulfuric acid containing 5–8% of the anhydride; the reaction is complete after ten to fifteen minutes. Benzensulfonic acid is isolated readily as the sodium salt by the addition of the reaction mixture to a saturated sodium chloride solution.[51] The reaction of benzene with chlorosulfonic acid is not used for the preparation of benzenesulfonic acid because, under conditions that limit the formation of the sulfonyl chloride, the acid is always accompanied by phenyl sulfone.[52] Benzenesulfonyl chloride can be obtained in a yield of 75–77% by the addition of benzene to an excess of chlorosulfonic acid (room temperature).[53] Fluorosulfonic acid reacts less vigorously; the addi-

[50] Sandqvist, "Studien über die Phenanthrensulfosäuren," Dissertation, Upsala, 1912.

[51] Gattermann and Wieland, "Laboratory Methods of Organic Chemistry," translation by W. McCartney of the 22nd ed., p. 181, Macmillan, 1932.

[52] Knapp, *Zeit. für Chem.*, **1869**, 41.

[53] Ullmann, *Ber.*, **42**, 2057 (1909); Pummerer, *Ber.*, **42**, 1802, 2274 (1909); Clarke, Babcock, and Murray, *Org. Syntheses*, *Coll. Vol.* **1**, 85 (1941).

tion of 55 g. of benzene to 225 g. of fluorosulfonic acid at 16–20° affords benzenesulfonyl fluoride in 62% yield [31] (p. 164).

m-Benzenedisulfonic acid is readily prepared, either by treating benzene with 20–40% oleum at elevated temperatures (160–209°) [54, 55] or by treating a monosulfonate with 12–20% oleum at about 210°.[54] Less vigorous sulfonating agents that require a longer reaction time or a higher temperature lead to the formation of some of the *para* isomer; for example, barium benzenesulfonate when heated with 98% sulfuric acid for forty-eight hours at 209° is converted into the *m*- and *p*-disulfonic acids in the approximate ratio of 3 : 1.[54] The formation of the *para* isomer is favored also by the addition of mercury.[22] The *ortho* disulfonic acid cannot be prepared by sulfonation of benzene or benzenesulfonic acid under any conditions. Treatment of benzene with a large excess of chlorosulfonic acid at 150–160° for two hours affords benzene-*m*-disulfonyl chloride (28% yield) together with a small amount of the *para* isomer and some (phenyl sulfone)-disulfonyl chloride.[38a]

The introduction of a third sulfo group into benzene proceeds with difficulty, but benzene-1,3,5-trisulfonic acid can be prepared in 73% yield by heating sodium benzene-1,3-disulfonate with 15% oleum in the presence of mercury for twelve hours at 275° (p. 163).[22, 25]

Toluene (Table II, p. 168). Toluene is more readily sulfonated than benzene. The reaction mixture always contains the three possible monosulfonic acid derivatives; the *meta* isomer is present in such low amounts that its presence has been demonstrated only by indirect means.[14] The sulfonation reaction is employed for the production of both the *ortho* and *para* acids; as described earlier, by suitable control of the temperature it is possible to favor the production of one or of the other isomer. The preparation of the *para* sulfonic acid [56] is relatively simple since this isomer predominates in reactions carried out at temperatures above 75° with either sulfuric acid or oleum.[20] The *para* acid can be freed from the accompanying *ortho* isomer either by crystallization from cold concentrated hydrochloric acid, in which the *para* acid is practically insoluble, or by conversion into the sodium or calcium salt,[57] either of which crystallizes readily. The relative proportion of the *ortho* sulfonic acid in the reaction mixture is never higher than 35–45%, even under the optimum conditions for the formation of this isomer.[14, 58] The separation of the

[54] Holleman and Polak, *Rec. trav. chim.*, **29**, 416 (1910).

[55] Voluinkin, *J. Applied Chem. U.S.S.R.*, **9**, 885 (1936) [*C. A.*, **30**, 7555 (1936)].

[56] Gattermann and Wieland, *op. cit.*, p. 183; Fieser, "Experiments in Organic Chemistry," p. 136, Heath, Boston, 1941.

[57] Bourgeois, *Rec. trav. chim.*, **18**, 426 (1899).

[58] Fahlberg and List, Ger. pat. 35,211 [*Frdl.*, **1**, 509]; Lange, Ger. pat. 57,391 [*Frdl.*, **3**, 905].

two isomers, however, is relatively easy. On the addition of a little water the *para* isomer separates readily; when the mother liquor is cooled to $-5°$ the crude *ortho* acid is obtained and is then purified as the barium salt, which is practically insoluble in cold water, in contrast to that of the *para* acid, which is readily soluble.[14]

Toluene reacts with gaseous sulfur trioxide at 40–55° to yield a mixture containing 20–24% of *p*-tolyl sulfone, 8% of the *ortho*, 7% of the *meta*, and 55% of the *para* sulfonic acid.[59] The reaction of toluene with the calculated amount of chlorosulfonic acid at 35° results in the formation of the three isomeric acids in the following amounts: 59% of the *para* acid, 4% of the *meta* acid, and 37.5% of the *ortho* acid.[14] That is, the relative proportion of the three acids is roughly the same in the reaction at a given temperature with either sulfuric acid or chlorosulfonic acid. The reaction of toluene (60 g.) with excess chlorosulfonic acid (150 g.) at a low temperature leads to a mixture of monosulfonyl chlorides but gives mainly the 2,4-disulfonyl chloride at a high temperature.[38a] The reaction of toluene with chlorosulfonic anhydride leads to a complex mixture containing *p*-toluenesulfonic acid, *p*-toluenesulfonyl chloride, a chlorinated tolyl sulfone, and a mixture of isomeric dichlorotoluenes.[33] Toluene reacts with excess fluorosulfonic acid [31] at ordinary temperature to give a mixture of sulfonyl fluorides (89% yield), of which 40% is the *ortho* derivative; from the reaction at 130–140° the 2,4-disulfonyl fluoride can be isolated in 48% yield.

Only one of the six possible toluenedisulfonic acids is prepared by the sulfonation reaction, toluene-2,4-disulfonic acid. This acid is the predominant product of the sulfonation of toluene,[60] *o*- and *p*-toluenesulfonic acid,[61] and *o*- and *p*-toluenesulfonyl chloride.[62] Toluene-2,4,6-trisulfonic acid is obtained from the reaction of potassium toluene-2,4-disulfonate (1 mole) with chlorosulfonic acid (3 moles) at 240°.[63]

Xylenes (Table IV, p. 172). The 4-sulfonic acid is the exclusive product of the sulfonation of *o*-xylene [64] under ordinary conditions. In the presence of mercury some of the 3-isomer is also formed.[19] This isomer rearranges to the 4-isomer on heating either alone [65] or with sulfuric acid.[66] The sulfonation of *m*-xylene occurs more readily than

[59] Lauer and Oda, *J. prakt. Chem.*, [2] **143**, 139 (1935).

[60] Senhofer, *Ann.*, **164**, 126 (1872); Gnehm and Forrer, *Ber.*, **10**, 542 (1877).

[61] Claësson and Berg, *Ber.*, **13**, 1170 (1880).

[62] Fahlberg, *Am. Chem. J.*, **1**, 175 (1879); **2**, 182 (1880).

[63] Claësson, *Ber.*, **14**, 307 (1881).

[64] Jacobsen, *Ber.*, **11**, 17 (1878); **17**, 2374 (1884).

[65] Moody, *Chem. News*, **67**, 34 (1893).

[66] Kizhner, *J. Gen. Chem. U.S.S.R.*, **3**, 578 (1933) [*C. A.*, **28**, 2693 (1934)].

that of *o*- and *p*-xylene; the 4-sulfonic acid is the main product.[67] A small amount of the 2-sulfonic acid can be isolated from a reaction conducted at room temperature,[68] but this isomer rearranges rapidly to the 4-isomer when warmed with sulfuric acid,[69] and hence is not isolated in the usual preparation. The 4-position of *m*-xylene is also the point of attack in the reaction with fluorosulfonic acid.[31] The sulfonation of *p*-xylene proceeds less readily than that of either of the isomers; only one monosubstitution product, the 2-sulfonic acid,[70] is possible. The reaction with fluorosulfonic acid yields the 2-sulfonyl fluoride.[31] The difference in the ease of sulfonation and desulfonation of the xylenes is utilized for the separation of the pure hydrocarbons from the xylene fraction of coal tar.[71]

The structure of the only known disulfonate of *o*-xylene, obtained by heating barium *o*-xylene-4-sulfonate with chlorosulfonic acid,[72] is not established. The second sulfonic acid group would be expected to enter the position *meta* to the first to yield *o*-xylene-3,5-disulfonic acid. The dichloride of the same disulfonic acid is obtained from the reaction of *o*-xylene itself with excess chlorosulfonic acid.[38a] The disulfonic acid obtainable from *m*-xylene [73] or *m*-xylene-4-sulfonic acid [72] was originally considered to be the 2,4-disulfonic acid, partly because the same diacid was obtained by sulfonation of a sample of *m*-xylene-2-sulfonic acid [72] and also by the elimination of bromine from 6-bromo-*m*-xylene-2,4-disulfonic acid.[73] The former evidence, however, is not significant, for the 2-sulfonic acid has been shown to rearrange readily to the 4-sulfonic acid.[69] More recent work indicates that the sulfonic acid groups are in the 4- and 6-positions;[74] one piece of evidence is that the disulfonyl chloride can be converted into the known 4,6-dichloroisophthalic acid. Furthermore, a 2,4-structure would be very unlikely in view of the fact that the entering sulfo group is known to avoid a hindered position such as the 2-position in *m*-xylene. The second sulfonic acid group enters

[67] (*a*) Jacobsen, *Ber.*, **10,** 1009 (1877); *Ann.*, **184,** 179 (1877); (*b*) Crafts, *Ber.*, **34,** 1350 (1901).

[68] Pollak and Meissner, *Monatsh.*, **50,** 237 (1928).

[69] Moody, *Chem. News*, **58,** 21 (1888).

[70] Krafft and Wilke, *Ber.*, **33,** 3207 (1900); Karslake and Huston, *J. Am. Chem. Soc.*, **36,** 1245 (1914).

[71] Spielmann, "The Constituents of Coal Tar," pp. 56–60, Longmans, Green, London, 1924; Weissberger, "Chemische Technologie der Steinkohlenteers," pp. 57–58, Otto Spamer, Leipzig, 1923.

[72] Pfannenstill, *J. prakt. Chem.*, [2] **46,** 152 (1892).

[73] Wischin, *Ber.*, **23,** 3113 (1890).

[74] Pollak and Lustig, *Ann.*, **433,** 191 (1923); Holleman, *Anales soc. españ. fís. quím.*, **27,** 473 (1929) [*C. A.*, **24,** 85 (1930)]; Holleman and Choufoer, *Proc. Acad. Sci. Amsterdam*, **27,** 353 (1924) [*C. A.*, **18,** 3183 (1924)].

p-xylene in the 6-position to give *p*-xylene-2,6-disulfonic acid.[75, 76] The disubstitution of *p*-xylene by excess chlorosulfonic acid leads to the formation of both the 2,6- and the 2,5-disulfonyl chloride in the ratio of 10 : 1.[74]

Trimethylbenzenes (Table V, p. 175). Only one monosulfonic acid has been obtained from each of the trimethylbenzenes. 1,2,3-Trimethylbenzene (hemimellitene) is sulfonated in the 4-position,[77] 1,2,4-trimethylbenzene (pseudocumene) in the 5-position.[78, 79] Sulfonation of 1,3,5-trimethylbenzene (mesitylene) can lead to only one monosulfonic acid, obtainable in good yield by the reaction with either sulfuric acid (90% yield, preparation p. 162)[79] or oleum.[80] Mesitylenesulfonyl chloride has been made by the action of sulfuryl chloride and aluminum chloride (chloromesitylene is formed also); [81] the disulfonyl chloride is obtained from the reaction of mesitylene with chlorosulfonic acid [82] or with a mixture of chlorosulfonic acid and sulfuryl chloride.[76] Fluorosulfonic acid converts mesitylene into the sulfonyl fluoride,[31] which reacts with chlorosulfonic acid to form the disulfonyl chloride. Mesitylenedisulfonic acid has been made by treating mesitylene with oleum and phosphorus pentoxide; [83] the introduction of a third sulfonic acid group proceeds with difficulty but has been accomplished by the action of sulfur trioxide (low yield).[81]

Halobenzenes (Table I, p. 165). Halogen atoms attached to the benzene nucleus decrease the ease of sulfonation, and hence oleum is the preferred reagent for the sulfonation of halobenzenes, particularly since the use of the less potent sulfuric acid also favors the rearrangement of the halogen group (p. 148). Only one monosulfonic acid is obtained from any of the four monohalobenzenes, for the sulfonic acid group always enters the position *para* to the halogen group. *p*-Fluorobenzenesulfonic acid [84] and *p*-chlorobenzenesulfonic acid [85] are available from the sulfonation of the corresponding halobenzenes with 10% oleum at temperatures of 60–75°. *p*-Chlorobenzenesulfonic acid is obtained also

[75] Pollak and Schadler, *Monatsh.*, **39,** 129 (1918).

[76] Holleman, Choufoer, and Alozery, *Rec. trav. chim.*, **48,** 1075 (1929).

[77] (*a*) Jacobsen, *Ber.*, **15,** 1853 (1882); **19,** 2517 (1886); (*b*) v. Auwers and Wieners, *Ber.*, **58,** 2815 (1925).

[78] Jacobsen, *Ann.*, **184,** 179 (1877); Schultz, *Ber.*, **42,** 3602 (1909).

[79] (*a*) Smith and Cass, *J. Am. Chem. Soc.*, **54,** 1606, 1617 (1932); (*b*) Jacobsen, *Ann.*, **146,** 85 (1868).

[80] Moschner, *Ber.*, **34,** 1259 (1901).

[81] Töhl and Eberhard, *Ber.*, **26,** 2940 (1893).

[82] Backer, *Rec. trav. chim.*, **54,** 544 (1935).

[83] Barth and Herzig, *Monatsh.*, **1,** 807 (1880).

[84] Holleman, *Rec. trav. chim.*, **24,** 26 (1905).

[85] Baxter and Chattaway, *J. Chem. Soc.*, **107,** 1814 (1915).

from the reaction of chlorobenzene with one molecular equivalent of chlorosulfonic acid;[86] the sulfone and the sulfonyl chloride are formed in small amounts. *p*-Chlorobenzenesulfonyl chloride is obtainable in 84% yield by the reaction with excess chlorosulfonic acid at a temperature of 25°.[87] The sulfonyl chloride is converted by sulfuric acid at 160–180° into the 2,4-disulfonic acid[88] and by chlorosulfonic acid into the disulfonyl chloride.[38a] Disulfonation of chlorobenzene can be accomplished directly by the reaction of 20% oleum at 300°,[88, 89] but the reaction is abnormal, for these sulfonic acid groups are *meta* to the chlorine atom; the product is chlorobenzene-3,5-disulfonic acid. This same disulfonic acid is obtained under the same conditions from chlorobenzene-4-sulfonic acid[88] and from chlorobenzene-2,4-disulfonic acid.[89]

In contrast to the reaction of bromobenzene with sulfuric acid, which requires a high temperature and yields a mixture of products (p. 148), the reaction with oleum[85] or with chlorosulfonic acid in carbon disulfide solution[43] is normal and gives the 4-sulfonic acid and bis-(4-bromophenyl) sulfone. The 4-sulfonic acid is sulfonated in the 2-position by either pyrosulfuric acid[90] or sulfur trioxide; the reaction with oleum at high temperatures is abnormal, like that of chlorobenzene, and yields the 3,5-disulfonic acid.

p-Iodobenzenesulfonic acid is prepared by the action of sulfuric acid[44] or oleum[44, 85, 91] on iodobenzene at 100°; side reactions giving rise to *p*-diiodobenzene and benzenesulfonic acid[44] become appreciable above 100°.

Alkylhalobenzenes (Table II, p. 168; Table III, p. 171; Table IV, p. 172; Table V, p. 175). In the sulfonation of benzene derivatives containing alkyl and halogen groups, the sulfonic acid group appears in a position *para* to a halogen atom rather than *para* to an alkyl group; thus, 2-chlorotoluene yields the 5-sulfonic acid.[92, 93] However, if only *ortho* positions are available, the sulfonic acid produced in larger quantity is that in which substitution occurs *ortho* to the alkyl group; thus 4-chlorotoluene yields a mixture of the 2- and the 3-sulfonic acids in

[86] (*a*) Beckurts and Otto, *Ber.*, **11**, 2061 (1878); (*b*) Ullmann and Korselt, *Ber.*, **40**, 641 (1907).

[87] Pummerer, *Ber.*, **42**, 1802 (1909).

[88] Olivier, *Rec. trav. chim.*, **37**, 307 (1918).

[89] Olivier, *Rec. trav. chim.*, **38**, 351, 356 (1919).

[90] Fischer, *Ber.*, **24**, 3805 (1891).

[91] Langmuir, *Ber.*, **28**, 90 (1895); Troeger and Hurdelbrink, *J. prakt. Chem.*, [2] **65**, 82 (1902); Willgerodt and Waldeyer, *ibid.*, [2] **59**, 194 (1899)

[92] Hübner and Majert, *Ber.*, **6**, 790, 1672 (1873).

[93] Wynne, *J. Chem. Soc.*, **61**, 1073 (1892).

which the 2-sulfonic acid predominates.[94] Furthermore, 1,3-dimethyl-5-chlorobenzene [95] and 1,3-dimethyl-4,6-dichlorobenzene [96] are sulfonated exclusively in the 2-position.

As in the reaction with halobenzenes, sulfuric acid is likely to bring about rearrangement or elimination of bromine or iodine of alkylhalobenzenes. For example, 5-bromo-1,2,4-trimethylbenzene on long standing with sulfuric acid at room temperature is converted into the 3-bromo-5-sulfonic acid and trimethyltribromobenzene.[97] This reaction and similar rearrangements have been discussed in detail by Smith.[48]

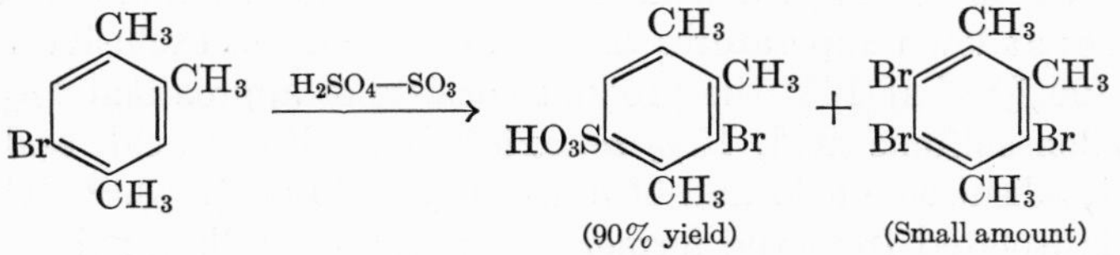

H_2SO_4—SO_3

(90% yield)

(Small amount)

The structures of many of the sulfonic acids obtained from dihalotoluenes (Table II) and also from other alkylhalobenzenes have not been established.

Biphenyl and Derivatives (Table VII). Biphenyl-4-sulfonic acid can be prepared very satisfactorily by sulfonation with sulfuric acid in nitrobenzene solution [98] (90% yield) or by the action of chlorosulfonic acid in tetrachloroethane at 50°.[38a] Sulfuric acid alone either gives a mixture of the 4-mono- and 4,4′-di-sulfonic acids with unchanged hydrocarbon or, with excess reagent, yields chiefly the di- derivative.[99] The monosulfonic acid is readily freed from the disulfonic acid through its sparingly soluble copper salt; the disulfonic acid remains in solution and can be crystallized

[94] Wynne and Bruce, *J. Chem. Soc.*, **73**, 731 (1898).

[95] Klages and Knoevenagel, *Ber.*, **27**, 3019 (1894); Klages, *Ber.*, **29**, 310 (1896).

[96] Koch, *Ber.*, **23**, 2319 (1890).

[97] Smith and Moyle, *J. Am. Chem. Soc.*, **58**, 1 (1936); Jacobsen, *Ber.*, **22**, 1580 (1889).

[98] Gebauer-Fülnegg, Riesz, and Ilse, *Monatsh.*, **49**, 41 (1928).

[99] McCullough, U. S. pat. 1,865,776 [*C. A.*, **26**, 4346 (1932); Stoesser and Marschner, U. S. pat. 1,981,337 [*C. A.*, **29**, 478 (1935)]; Fittig, *Ann.*, **132**, 209 (1864).

as the potassium salt. Potassium biphenyl-4-sulfonate is converted by heating into biphenyl and the 4,4′-disulfonate.[100] The reaction of biphenyl with excess chlorosulfonic acid at 0° gives the 4,4′-disulfonyl chloride (80% yield) and at 18° gives (dibenzothiophene dioxide)-2,7-disulfonyl chloride.[38a]

Arylalkanes and Arylalkenes (Table VIII, p. 181). Diphenylmethane is sulfonated exclusively in the *para* position rather than in the more hindered *ortho* position. The 4-sulfonic acid is prepared by treating diphenylmethane with chlorosulfonic acid in chloroform solution at 0°;[101] the 4,4′-disulfonic acid, by the action of oleum at 100°.[102] 1,2-Diphenylethane (bibenzyl) when heated with sulfuric acid[103] yields a mixture of a disulfonic acid (probably 4,4′) and a tetrasulfonic acid. Oleum reacts with stilbene without affecting the olefinic linkage to yield a disulfonic acid of unknown structure.[104] Triphenylmethane,[105] *sym*-tetraphenylethane,[106] and tetraphenylethylene[107] yield sulfonic acids containing one sulfo group for each benzene ring, probably in the *para* position.

Naphthalene (Table IX, p. 182). The course of the sulfonation of naphthalene is strikingly dependent upon both the reaction temperature and time; at low temperatures the product is almost exclusively the α-isomer (96%),[108] at 165° the product consists of approximately 85% β-naphthalenesulfonic acid, 15% α-naphthalenesulfonic acid, and traces of the 1,6-disulfonic acid and of β-naphthyl sulfone (1%).[109] The pure α-acid is isolated from the former sulfonation as follows: the reaction mixture is diluted with water, filtered from unchanged naphthalene, and evaporated somewhat under vacuum at a low temperature; the α-acid dihydrate separates slowly, and is recrystallized from dilute hydrochloric acid (m.p. 90°).[108] The pure β-acid is obtained from the high-temperature sulfonation as follows: the reaction mixture is diluted with water and filtered from the sulfone, then shaken with benzene to remove the last traces of the sulfone; the water layer is evaporated, and the β-acid separates as the trihydrate on cooling to 10°. The pure trihydrate (m.p. 83°) is obtained after several recrystallizations from 10% hydrochloric acid, in which it is practically insoluble at 10°. The trihydrate is converted into the monohydrate (m.p. 124°) on drying in a desiccator

[100] Engelhardt and Latschinow, *Zeit. für Chem.*, **1871**, 259.
[101] Wedekind and Schenk, *Ber.*, **44**, 198 (1911).
[102] Lapworth, *J. Chem. Soc.*, **73**, 402 (1898).
[103] Kade, *Ber.*, **6**, 953 (1873).
[104] Limpricht and Schwanert, *Ann.*, **145**, 330 (1868).
[105] Kekulé and Franchimont, *Ber.*, **5**, 908 (1872).
[106] Engler, *Ber.*, **11**, 926 (1878).
[107] Behr, *Ber.*, **5**, 277 (1872).
[108] Fierz and Weissenbach, *Helv. Chim. Acta*, **3**, 312 (1920).
[109] Witt, *Ber.*, **48**, 743 (1915).

over sulfuric acid or calcium chloride.[109] The α-isomer is transformed into the β-isomer by heating the reaction mixture obtained at a low temperature; at 129° equilibrium is established after forty-two hours when the ratio of the α-acid and β-acid is approximately 1 : 3.[15] It is noteworthy that the acid group of the more stable isomer is situated in the less hindered β-position.

In the polysubstitution of naphthalene the sulfo groups are never found *ortho, para,* or *peri* (1,8) to one another; even so, six disulfonic acids, three trisulfonic acids, and one tetrasulfonic acid are obtainable by sulfonation reactions.[110] Seventy-three polysulfonic acids are theoretically possible. The acids obtainable from naphthalene by sulfonation are indicated in the chart; the symbol S used in the formulas represents the sulfonic acid group.

CHART I

SULFONATION OF NAPHTHALENE

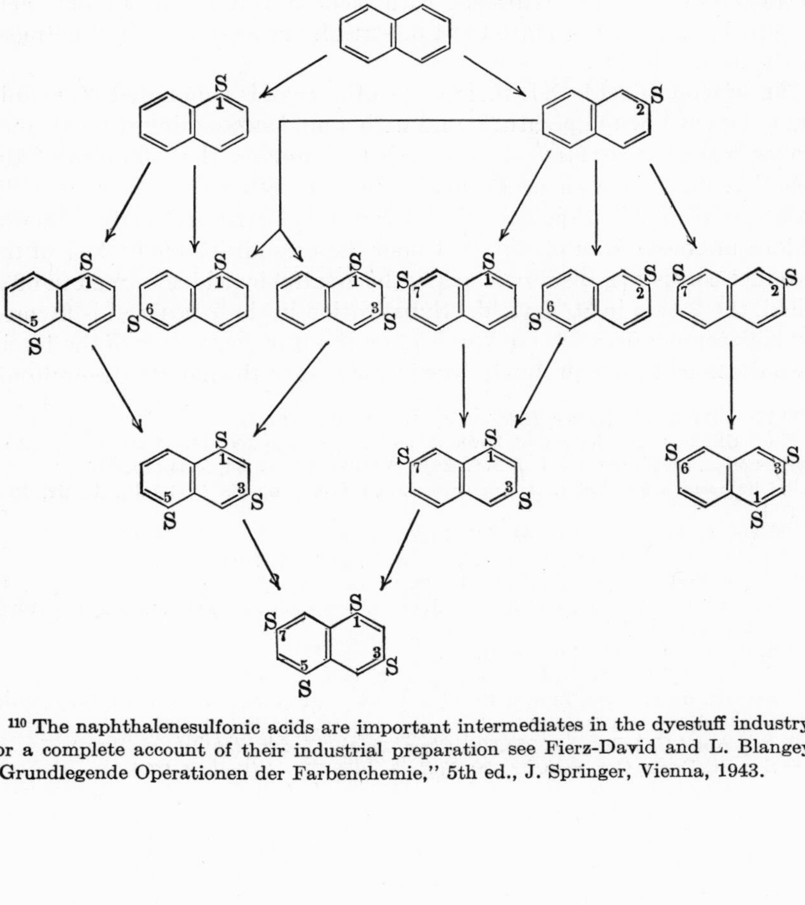

[110] The naphthalenesulfonic acids are important intermediates in the dyestuff industry, for a complete account of their industrial preparation see Fierz-David and L. Blangey "Grundlegende Operationen der Farbenchemie," 5th ed., J. Springer, Vienna, 1943.

The disulfonation of naphthalene below 40° with oleum yields 70% of the 1,5- and 25% of the 1,6-disulfonic acid.[111] In the reaction at 130°, the 1,6- and 2,7-acids predominate;[111] minor amounts of the 1,3-, the 1,5-, and 1,7-acids are present.[112] On sulfonation with 98% sulfuric acid at 60°, the 2-sulfonic acid is converted into the 1,6-disulfonic acid (80%) and into the 1,7-isomer (20%).[113] The 2,6-disulfonic acid is formed in sulfonations carried out above 140°,[111] but in a yield that never exceeds 42%;[114] the main product is the 2,7-acid, which has been shown to rearrange at the reaction temperature into the 2,6-acid.[114] The 2,7-acid can be obtained in high yield (78–85%) by sulfonation at 220–245° with 80–95% sulfuric acid.[115]

Direct high-temperature (180°) sulfonation of naphthalene with 24% oleum gives the 1,3,6-trisulfonic acid;[116] the 1,3,5-trisulfonic acid[116] is made by treating the 1,5-diacid with 67% oleum at 90°;[117] the 1,3,7-triacid is obtained by further sulfonation of the 2,6-diacid by oleum at 100°.[118] Both the 1,3,5- and 1,3,7-trisulfonic acids yield the 1,3,5,7-tetrasulfonic acid on treatment with oleum.[119] A fourth sulfonic acid group is not introduced into the 1,3,6-trisulfonic acid, even by treatment with sulfur trioxide.

Anthracene (Table XI, p. 188). Anthracene is sulfonated so readily that even at low temperatures and with a mild sulfonating reagent some polysubstitution occurs. It is striking, therefore, that dilution of the reaction mixture with acetic acid (but not with water) decreases the extent of disubstitution, even with the more reactive sulfonating agents, chlorosulfonic acid or oleum.[120] Under these conditions only 20% of the product consists of disulfonic acids; the 1-sulfonic acid is formed in 50% yield, the 2-acid in 30% yield. Substitution in the 2-position is favored by high temperatures,[121] but this is not a result of conversion of the 1-acid into the 2-acid (as is probably true in the case of the naphthalenesulfonic

[111] Fierz-David and Hasler, *Helv. Chim. Acta*, **6**, 1133 (1923).

[112] (*a*) Ufimtzew and Krivoschlykowa, *J. prakt. Chem.*, [2] **140**, 172 (1934); (*b*) Chuksanova, *Compt. rend. acad. sci. U.R.S.S.*, **26**, 445 (1940) [*C. A.*, **34**, 5834 (1940)].

[113] Chuksanova and Bilik, *Anilinokrasochnaya Prom.*, **4**, 488 (1934) [*C. A.*, **29**, 1085 (1935)].

[114] Heid, *J. Am. Chem. Soc.*, **49**, 844 (1927).

[115] Ambler, Lynch, and Haller, *Ind. Eng. Chem.*, **16**, 1264 (1924).

[116] Busse, Bregman, and Trokhimovskaya, *Khim. Farm. Prom.*, No. 1, 31 (1934) [*C. A.*, **28**, 5432 (1934)]; Ufimtzew and Krivoschlykowa, *Org. Chem. Ind. U.S.S.R.*, **2**, 144 (1936) [*C. A.*, **31**, 1021 (1937)].

[117] Erdmann, *Ber.*, **32**, 3186 (1899).

[118] Cassella and Co., Ger. pat. 75,432 [*Frdl.*, **3**, 484].

[119] Schmid, dissertation, Zurich, 1920 [*C. A.*, **16**, 2141 (1922)]; Fierz and Schmid, *Helv. Chim. Acta*, **4**, 381 (1921); Bayer and Co., Ger. pat. 80,464 [*Frdl.*, **4**, 605].

[120] Bayer and Co., Ger. pat. 251,695 [*Chem. Zentr.*, II, 1413 (1912)].

[121] Soc. St. Denis, Ger. pats. 72,226 [*Frdl.*, **3**, 195]; 77,311 [*Frdl.*, **4**, 271].

acids), for the 1-acid on heating with sulfuric acid at 150–180° is not converted into the 2-acid, but into the 1,5- and 1,8-disulfonic acids.[18]

SO_3H $\xrightarrow[150\text{-}180°]{H_2SO_4}$ SO_3H, SO_3H + SO_3H, SO_3H

(9 parts) (1 part)

Another striking observation is that the formation of the 2-acid can be depressed to as little as 1% by the use of pyridine-sulfur trioxide as the sulfonating agent, even when the reaction is carried out at temperatures (150–175°) that, with oleum, favor substitution in the 2-position.[17, 18] Although the two sulfonic acids can be separated from each other and from polysulfonic acids fairly readily by fractional crystallization of the sodium or barium salts, the sulfonation reaction of anthracene is not employed commonly, since the monosulfonic acids are prepared more conveniently from the corresponding derivatives of anthraquinone.

Phenanthrene (Table XII, p. 189). Phenanthrene is as readily sulfonated as anthracene; when the reaction is carried out for three hours at 120–125° with concentrated sulfuric acid, more than 40% of the phenanthrene is converted into disulfonic acids.[122] Two monosulfonic acids are isolated under these experimental conditions: phenanthrene-2-sulfonic acid (25% yield) and phenanthrene-3-sulfonic acid (27% yield).[122, 123] The same acids are obtained by sulfonating at 100° for eight hours (2-acid, 7% yield; 3-acid, 9% yield), and in addition a third acid, phenanthrene-9-sulfonic acid (6% yield) [124] is formed. The 9-acid is formed in larger amounts at lower temperatures (14.5% at 20°, twenty days).[125] A fourth monosulfonic acid, the 1-acid, is isolated from the sulfonation reaction conducted at 60° for several days.[122] The yields of the four monosulfonic acids isolated under these conditions are 4% of the 1-acid, 18% of the 2-acid, 19% of the 3-acid, and 13% of the 9-acid. There is no indication that the only other possible monosulfonic acid, the 4-isomer, is ever formed, probably because the 4-position of phenanthrene is particularly hindered.

The extent of disulfonation can be decreased by decreasing the time interval and, within certain limits, the quantity and strength of the sulfuric acid.[126] Thus far no pure phenanthrenedisulfonic acids have been

[122] Fieser, *J. Am. Chem. Soc.*, **51,** 2460 (1929).

[123] Fieser, *Org. Syntheses, Coll. Vol.* **2,** 482 (1943).

[124] Werner *et al.*, *Ann.*, **321,** 248 (1902).

[125] Sandqvist, *Ann.*, **392,** 76 (1912).

[126] Ioffe, *J. Gen. Chem. U.S.S.R.*, **3,** 448 (1933) [*C. A.*, **28,** 1694 (1934)].

prepared, by the sulfonation either of phenanthrene or of a phenanthrenesulfonic acid, but the formation of the 2,6-, 2,7-, 2,8-, 3,6-, and 3,8-disulfonic acids is inferred by the isolation of the corresponding dihydroxy compounds from mixtures resulting from alkali fusion.[127]

SELECTION OF EXPERIMENTAL CONDITIONS

In the sulfonation of the less reactive aromatic hydrocarbons or aryl halides, it is desirable to use 5–20% oleum, which brings about reaction at a convenient rate at moderate temperatures (0–50°); furthermore, if oleum is used, less sulfuric acid remains at the completion of the reaction to interfere with the isolation of the product. In the preparation of salts, however, this factor is of less significance. Although sulfur trioxide is even more active than oleum, it can be used to advantage only occasionally because it favors the formation of a sulfone. The formation of by-products is decreased by use of a solvent; a suitable solution can be prepared by passing the gaseous material, obtained by warming 60% oleum, into cold ethylene dichloride.

Sulfuric acid is a satisfactory reagent for the sulfonation of the more reactive aromatic hydrocarbons; the reaction, however, is reversible, and, as ordinarily carried out, a large amount of reagent must be employed to obtain a fairly complete reaction. The excess is undesirable since it promotes polysubstitution. The use of excess reagent can be avoided by carrying out the reaction in an ingenious apparatus that permits removal of the water as it is formed.[128] The use of a solvent in sulfonation with sulfuric acid is sometimes desirable. For example, in the sulfonation of biphenyl [38a, 98] the presence of a sulfonic acid group in one ring does not greatly reduce the rate of sulfonation in the other ring but does increase the solubility in sulfuric acid and therefore the chance of further sulfonation. This and similar compounds containing two or more substantially independent aromatic nuclei are preferably monosulfonated by using a solution of chlorosulfonic acid in chloroform, ethylene dichloride, or tetrachloroethane. The presence of one sulfo group in naphthalene decreases the rate of sulfonation in the other ring to such an extent that a solvent is not essential;[108, 109] but in the monosulfonation of anthracene a solvent is desirable.[120] When chlorosulfonic acid is used to prepare the sulfonic acid of polynuclear hydrocarbons a solvent such as chloroform seems to minimize the formation of the sulfonyl chloride.[38a, 129, 130]

[127] Fieser, *J. Am. Chem. Soc.*, **51**, 2471 (1929).

[128] Meyer, *Ann.*, **433**, 327 (1923); see also p. 183 of ref. 51.

[129] Armstrong, *J. Chem. Soc.*, **24**, 176 (1871).

[130] Pschorr, *Ber.*, **34**, 3998 (1901).

The progress of a sulfonation reaction can be followed by determining the acidic titer of a given weight of reaction mixture at suitable intervals,[131] since for every mole of sulfonic acid produced the acidity is decreased by one equivalent. If a sulfonation yields a mixture of mono- and di-sulfonic acids, neutralization of the diluted reaction mixture with barium hydroxide, filtration of the insoluble barium sulfate, and analysis for barium of a sample of the dried barium sulfonates obtained by evaporation of the filtrate will indicate the composition of the mixture.

ISOLATION AND IDENTIFICATION OF SULFONIC ACIDS

In a few instances it is possible to isolate the free sulfonic acid directly from the reaction mixture. The solubility of the acid is usually decreased by the addition of an inorganic acid. Several sulfonic acids have been isolated from the reaction mixture by the addition of hydrochloric acid: for example, *p*-toluenesulfonic acid,[56] β-naphthalenesulfonic acid,[109] and *m*-xylene-4-sulfonic acid.[67b] Sometimes the acid can be isolated by treating an aqueous solution of the lead salt with hydrogen sulfide, removing the insoluble lead sulfide, and evaporating the filtrate, preferably under reduced pressure. The free acids are comparable in acidic strength to sulfuric acid; they are hygroscopic liquids or solids that are difficult to purify, and some are not even isolable. They usually form hydrates when crystallized from solvents containing water. For most purposes the alkali or ammonium salts serve equally well, and these are readily obtainable by adding a concentrated solution of the chlorides to the reaction mixture after partial neutralization with the carbonate.[132] The remaining acid is converted into the salt by displacement of the equilibrium

$$ArSO_3H + NaCl \rightleftarrows ArSO_3Na + HCl$$

An excess of the inorganic salt has a strong salting-out effect. An isolation procedure that is suitable for di- and tri-sulfonic acids as well as monosulfonic acids consists in neutralizing the diluted reaction mixture with a base that forms an insoluble sulfate (e.g., barium carbonate) and in treating the filtrate with an exact equivalent of dilute sulfuric acid; the insoluble sulfate is again precipitated, and the filtered solution containing the free sulfonic acid is then treated with the desired carbonate or sulfate and evaporated. The separation of isomers is often possible by fractional crystallization of various salts. The sulfonates prepared by either procedure are usually contaminated by the inorganic salt; salt-free

[131] Simpson and Olsen, *Ind. Eng. Chem.*, **29**, 1350 (1937).

[132] Gattermann, *Ber.*, **24**, 2121 (1891).

material can often be obtained by crystallization from anhydrous ethanol. Another procedure applicable to polysulfonates, particularly azo dyes, consists in resalting the sodium sulfonate several times with sodium acetate (or ammonium bromide) and then removing the salting agent from the dried, ground sulfonate by repeated extraction with ethanol.[133]

The identification and purity of a sulfonate are difficult to establish since the salts do not melt without decomposition; the melting points of the free acids or hydrates are often not sharp. In the precise work of Holleman and Caland [14] on the quantitative determination of the course of the sulfonation of toluene where the pure sulfonic acids were required as standards, the purity was established by conversion into the sulfochloride or into the sulfonamide, both of which derivatives in general exhibit satisfactory melting characteristics. The sulfonic acid is readily regenerated by hydrolysis of the sulfonyl chloride; in fact, if the sulfonyl chloride is readily available, it may serve as a convenient source of the free sulfonic acid.[14, 134] Identification through conversion into the sulfonyl chloride or into the ester has the disadvantage that an anhydrous sample of the sulfonate is required. A solid derivative that can be made from an aqueous solution of the free acid or from the sodium, potassium, or ferrous salt is the *p*-toluidine salt, prepared by adding *p*-toluidine and hydrochloric acid and allowing crystallization to occur.[125, 126, 135] The amine salts are sparingly soluble in water and can be recrystallized from ethanol or ethanol-water mixtures. The amine salt of an impure acid remains as an oil almost indefinitely, and this property is very characteristic of a mixture of isomers.

EXPERIMENTAL PROCEDURES

2,4,6-Trimethylbenzenesulfonic Acid (Mesitylenesulfonic Acid).[78a] A mixture of 100 cc. (87.6 g.) of mesitylene and 200 cc. of concentrated sulfuric acid, contained in a 500-cc. flask fitted with a short air-cooled condenser, is shaken vigorously. The temperature rises rapidly to 60°, and solution of the hydrocarbon is complete in five to ten minutes. The clear yellowish liquid that results is poured, while still warm, into 400 cc. of concentrated hydrochloric acid, kept at 10° or lower, or onto 300 g. of ice, and stirred vigorously. The sulfonic acid that precipitates is filtered with suction through a cloth filter and pressed as dry as possible. The yield of air-dried crude acid, which usually has a slight color, is 150 g. (90%); m.p. 76–78°. It may be purified by crystallization from chloro-

[133] Hartwell and Fieser, *Org. Syntheses, Coll. Vol.* **2,** 145 (1943).

[134] Sandqvist, *Ann.*, **379,** 79 (1911).

[135] Dermer and Dermer, *J. Org. Chem.*, **7,** 581 (1942).

form (50 g. acid, 200 g. chloroform); the acid (46 g.) then melts sharply at 78° and is snow white.

Sodium 1,3,5-Benzenetrisulfonate.[25] A mixture of 50 g. of crude sodium *m*-benzenedisulfonate, 50 cc. of 15% oleum, and 2 g. of mercury is placed in a 300-cc. Kjeldahl flask and is heated in a salt bath at 275° for twelve hours with occasional shaking. The cooled mixture is poured into 1 l. of water. The resulting solution is heated and treated with solid calcium carbonate until neutral to litmus. The calcium sulfate is filtered and washed with three 200-cc. portions of boiling water. The combined filtrates and washings are treated with a saturated solution of sodium carbonate until they are just alkaline to phenolphthalein. The mixture is digested on a steam bath and filtered through a Norit pad, and the filtrate is evaporated to dryness. The residue, which is practically pure sodium *sym*-benzenetrisulfonate, is dried in an oven at 140° for four hours. The yield is 50 g. (73%).

4,4′-Dibromobiphenyl-3-sulfonic Acid.[40] To a mechanically stirred solution of 20 g. of 4,4′-dibromobiphenyl in 50 cc. of anhydrous chloroform, 20 g. of chlorosulfonic acid is added slowly so that the temperature is maintained at 40°. The solution becomes dark green, and hydrogen chloride gas is steadily evolved. At the end of three hours the reaction product is hydrolyzed, and the insoluble material is removed by centrifugation. Crystallization of this solid from acetic acid gives 6 g. (25% yield) of 4,4′-dibromobiphenylene-2,2′-sulfone. The solution is neutralized with sodium carbonate. From the chloroform layer there is obtained by evaporation 5 g. (25% yield) of the unchanged dibromobiphenyl. The addition of acid precipitates the 4,4′-dibromobiphenyl-3-sulfonic acid in small orange crystals. The yield is 8 g. (32%). The acid can be crystallized from boiling water.

Doubling the quantity of chlorosulfonic acid increases the yield of acid to 11 g. There is obtained also 8 g. of sulfone together with 2.5 g. of unchanged starting material. When 20 g. of the dibromide and 40 g. of chlorosulfonic acid are heated at 60° for fifteen minutes in the absence of a solvent, the reaction product consists of 13 g. (41.5% yield) of the 3,3′-disulfonic acid, 4 g. (12.5% yield) of the corresponding disulfonyl chloride, and 10 g. (42% yield) of the sulfone mentioned above.

Sodium Pyrene-3-sulfonate.[136, 137] To a cooled solution of 1 equivalent of pyrene in 6 volumes of *s*-tetrachloroethane there is added dropwise with stirring the calculated amount of chlorosulfonic acid (2 equivalents) dissolved in an equal volume of *s*-tetrachloroethane. The temperature is maintained at 0–5° during the addition. The mixture is stirred for fifteen

[136] Volmann, Becker, Corell, and Streeck, *Ann.*, **531**, 1 (1937).

[137] Tietze and Bayer, *Ann.*, **540**, 189 (1939).

to twenty hours at 10–20°, and the gray-green mass is poured on ice. The original solvent is removed under reduced pressure, and the aqueous solution is heated and then filtered to remove a small amount of unchanged pyrene. Finally the hot filtrate is mixed with a boiling solution of the calculated amount of sodium sulfate in water, which precipitates the almost insoluble sodium sulfonate. This is filtered and dried. The yield is 90–92%.

2,5-Dichlorobenzenesulfonyl Chloride.[138] A mixture of 1 mole of *p*-dichlorobenzene and 5 moles of chlorosulfonic acid is heated at 150° for one hour in a flask equipped with an air-cooled condenser. The flask is then cooled and the contents are poured on crushed ice; the chlorosulfonyl derivative separates as a solid. This is filtered and dried. The yield of crude material is 85%. After crystallization from ethanol the substance is obtained as colorless needles that melt at 39°.

Benzenesulfonyl Fluoride.[31] For experiments with fluorosulfonic acid, Steinkopf recommends the use of an iron vessel with a screw top fitted with a mercury-seal stirrer, dropping funnel, thermometer well, and gas-exit tube. A small open-top iron or platinum container without a stirrer can be used only in very small-scale fluorosulfonations.

To 225 g. (2.25 moles) of fluorosulfonic acid in an iron container is added 55 g. (0.7 mole) of benzene with stirring during six hours at 16–20°. After an additional nine hours at the same temperature, with continued stirring, the reaction mixture is poured on ice and extracted with ether; the ether layer is washed with water to which sufficient calcium carbonate is added to neutralize the acid, the ether solution is separated and concentrated, and the residue is distilled with steam. There is obtained 77.5 g. (62% yield) of an oil that distils at 90–91°/14 mm. and 203–204°/760 mm.; $d_4^{20°}$ 1.3286 and n_D^{18} 1.4932. The residue from the steam distillation contains 9.5 g. of phenyl sulfone. Benzenesulfonyl fluoride may be obtained also by allowing benzenesulfonyl chloride to stand with four times its weight of fluorosulfonic acid at room temperature for twenty-four hours.

[138] Stewart, *J. Chem. Soc.*, **121**, 2555 (1922).

TABLE I

Benzene and Its Halogen Derivatives

Compound Sulfonated	Reagent * and Reference †	Experimental Conditions	Position of Sulfo Group(s)	Remarks
Benzene	A (1*c*, 1*d*, 1*e*, 2, 4, 11, 51, 139, 140)	Various conditions	—	Mono-SO_3H
	B, 5–9.5% (132, 141, 142)	3.7 parts B, warm	—	Mono-SO_3H, mainly
	SO_3 (1*d*, 1*e*, 1*f*)	$CHCl_3$ solution, 0–10°	—	Mono-SO_3H, 90%
	SO_3 dioxane (29)	CCl_4 solution, room temperature; 1 day	—	Mono-SO_3H, high yield
	C (53)	3 moles C, 20–25°, 1 hr.	—	Mono-SO_2Cl, 76%; some sulfone
	C (52)	Excess benzene	—	Mono-SO_3H and sulfone
	D (31)	4 parts of D, 9 hr. at 16–20°	—	Mono-SO_2F, 62%; also sulfone
	$NaH_3(SO_4)_2$ (36)	2.5 parts reagent, reflux, various times	—	Mono-SO_3H, 33–40%
	Nitryl sulfate $(O_2NOSO_2\text{-}OSO_2)_2$ (143)	—	—	Mono-SO_3H
	A, then SO_3 (144)	Excess A	1,3-	Di-SO_3H
	$NaH_3(SO_4)_2$ (36)	Excess reagent, heat	1,3-	Di-SO_3H
	B, 20% (54, 55)	2 vol. B, 200–220°, 3 hr.	1,3-	Di-SO_3H
	B, 66% (110)	75°, 2 hr.; 90°, 1 hr.	1,3-	Di-SO_3H, 90%
	C (38*a*)	10 parts C, 150–160°, 2 hr.	1,3-	Di-SO_2Cl
	A, 97 or 100% (19, 22)	2–4 parts A, 235–250°, Hg catalyst	1,3- and 1,4-	1,3-Di-SO_3H, 67–69% 1,4-Di-SO_3H, 31–33%
	A (145)	7 parts A, 4 parts P_2O_5, 280–290°, 5–6 hr.	1,3,5-	Tri-SO_3H
Benzenesulfonic acid	A (146)	210–275°, 60 mm., 3 hr.	1,3- and 1,4-	82.5% of di-SO_3H mixture
	$NaH_3(SO_4)_2$ (36*b*)	1.5 parts A, 240°, 2–3 hr.	1,3-	Di-SO_3H, 100%
Benzenesulfonyl chloride	D (31)	4 parts D, 20°, 24 hr.	—	$C_6H_5SO_2F$
Sodium benzene-1,3-disulfonate	B, 15% (25)	1 part B, 2% Hg, 275°, 12 hr.	1,3,5-	Tri-SO_3H, 73%
Potassium benzene-1,3-disulfonate	A (147)	High temperature	1,3,5-	Tri-SO_3H, 44%
Benzene-1,3-disulfonic acid	$NaH_3(SO_4)_2$ (36*b*)	280–30C°	1,3,5-	Tri-SO_3H
Benzene-1,3-disulfonyl chloride	D (31)	5 parts D; 95°, 19 hr.	1,3-	Di-SO_2F
Bromobenzene	A (42)	10 parts A, reflux	—	Complex mixture
	B, 10% (27*d*, 85)	1 mole SO_3, 60°, 1 hr.	4-	Trace of 4,4′-sulfone
	C (86)	1 mole C	4-	-SO_3H, smaller amounts of the 4-SO_2Cl and sulfone
	C (43, 148, 149)	5 parts C, $CHCl_3$ solution, 25°, 20 min.	4-	-SO_2Cl

* A refers to concentrated sulfuric acid; B, to oleum; C, to chlorosulfonic acid; and D, to fluorosulfonic acid.

† References 139–406 appear on pp. 192–197.

TABLE I—*Continued*

BENZENE AND ITS HALOGEN DERIVATIVES

Compound Sulfonated	Reagent * and Reference †	Experimental Conditions	Position of Sulfo Group(s)	Remarks
Bromobenzene-4-sulfonic acid	SO_3(150)	200–220°, 10 hr.	2,4-	Di-SO_3H, 73%
	$H_2S_2O_7$ (90)	8–10 parts reagent, 220–240°, 6 hr.	2,4-	Di-SO_3H
	A (151)	10 parts A, reflux 10 hr.	3,5-	Di-SO_3H, 40% (crude)
Chlorobenzene	A (152)	Excess A, 100°, 3–4 hr.	4-	-SO_3H
	B, 10% (85)	1 mole SO_3, $< 60°$, 1 hr.	4-	-SO_3H
	C (86*a*)	1 mole C	4-	-SO_3H, small amounts of the 4-SO_2Cl and sulfone
	C (43, 86*b*, 87)	4 vol. C, 25°, 1–3 hr.	4-	-SO_2Cl, 84%; sulfone, 6.2%
	B, 20% (88, 89)	5 vol. B, 300°, 6 hr.	3,5-	Di-SO_3H, 30%
Chlorobenzene-4-sulfonyl chloride	A, 100% (89, 153)	160–180°	2,4-	Di-SO_3H
	C (38)	150–180°	2,4-	Di-SO_2Cl
Chlorobenzene-4-sulfonic acid	B, 20% (88, 89)	Excess B, 300°	3,5-	Di-SO_3H, mainly
Chlorobenzene-2,-4-disulfonic acid	B, 20% (88, 89)	Excess B, 300°	3,5-	Di-SO_3H, mainly
Fluorobenzene	B, 10% (84)	70°	4-	—
	C (43)	5 parts C, $CHCl_3$ solution, 25°, 20 min.	4-	-SO_2Cl
		5 parts C, 40°, 1 hr.	—	100% of 4,4′-sulfone
Iodobenzene	A (44)	10 parts A, 25°, several days	4-	Mixture
	A (44)	1 part A, 170–180°, 2 hr.	—	50% $C_6H_4I_2$, some 4-SO_3H and $C_6H_5SO_3H$
	B (85)	1 mole SO_3, $< 60°$, 1 hr.	4-	-SO_3H and some 4,4′-sulfone
	C (43)	5 parts C, $CHCl_3$ solution, 25°, 20 min.	—	4,4′-Sulfone
1,2-Dibromobenzene	B (19)	—	4-	-SO_3H
	B (19)	10% Hg	3- and 4-	3-SO_3H, 24%
	C (43)	5 parts C, 50°	—	3,4,3′,4′-Sulfone
		5 parts C, $CHCl_3$ solution, 25°, 20 min.	4-	-SO_2Cl, also 3% of sulfone
1,3-Dibromobenzene	C (43)	5 parts C, $CHCl_3$ solution, 25°, 20 min.	4-	-SO_2Cl
1,4-Dibromobenzene	B (154)	Various conditions	2-	-SO_3H
	C (43)	5 parts C, reflux, 1 hr.	2-	-SO_2Cl, 80%
1,2-Dichlorobenzene	B (155, 156, 157)	25°, 100°, or 210°	4-	-SO_3H
	B (19)	2% or 10% Hg	3- and 4-	3-SO_3H, 16%; 4-SO_3H, 26%

* A refers to concentrated sulfuric acid; B, to oleum; C, to chlorosulfonic acid; and D, to fluorosulfonic acid.

† References 139–406 appear on pp. 192–197.

TABLE I—*Continued*

Benzene and Its Halogen Derivatives

Compound Sulfonated	Reagent * and Reference †	Experimental Conditions	Position of Sulfo Group(s)	Remarks
1,2-Dichlorobenzene	C (43)	5 parts C, 50°	—	3,4,3′,4′-Sulfone
	C (43)	5 parts C, $CHCl_3$ solution, 25°, 20 min.	4-	$-SO_2Cl$, also 8% of sulfone
1,3-Dichlorobenzene	B, 7% (156, 157)	230° or 100°	4-	$-SO_3H$
	B, 45% (158)	2.3 vol. B, 145°, 5 hr.	4,6-	Di-SO_3H
	C (43)	5 parts C, $CHCl_3$ solution, 25°, 20 min.	4-	$-SO_2Cl$
1,4-Dichlorobenzene	B, 10% (157, 159, 160)	25°, shake 24 hr.	2-	$-SO_3H$; almost quantitative
	SO_3 (161)	—	2-	$-SO_3H$
	C (138, 162)	5 parts C, reflux, 1 hr.	2-	$-SO_2Cl$, 80%
	C (162)	140°, 48 hr.	2,5- and 2,6-	Di-SO_2Cl, mainly 2,6-
1,4-Diiodobenzene	SO_3 (45)	Warm	2-	$-SO_3H$, <10%, mainly polyiodo compounds
	C (43)	5 parts C, 50°, 5 min.	—	2,3,5,6-Tetrachloro-1,4-diiodobenzene
1,4-Bromochlorobenzene	B (163)	—	2- and 3-	Equal amounts of two $-SO_3H$
	C (43)	5 parts C, reflux, 1 hr.	2- and 3-	$-SO_2Cl$, 86%, mainly the 2-
1,2,4-Tribromobenzene	$H_2S_2O_7$ (164)	6.6 parts reagent	5-(?)	Anhydride of a mono-SO_3H
1,3,5-Tribromobenzene	B (165, 166, 167)	3 or 4 parts B, 100°, 3–4 hr.	2-	$-SO_3H$, good yield
	C (43)	5 parts C, $CHCl_3$ solution, 25°, 20 min.	2-	$-SO_2Cl$
1,2,3-Trichlorobenzene	C (43)	5 parts C, $CHCl_3$ solution, 25°, 20 min., then 80°, 1 hr.	4-	$-SO_2Cl$
1,2,4-Trichlorobenzene	C (43)	5 parts C, $CHCl_3$ solution, 25°, 20 min., then 150°, 1 hr.	5-	$-SO_2Cl$
1,3,5-Trichlorobenzene	C (43)	5 parts C, $CHCl_3$ solution, 25°, 20 min., then 150°, 30 min.	2-	$-SO_2Cl$
	B (158)	3 vol. B, 100°, 15 hr.	2, 4-	Di-SO_3H
1,2,3,5-Tetrabromobenzene	B (166)	3-4 vol. B, 100°, 14 days	—	Mono-SO_3H
1,2,4,5-Tetrachlorobenzene	C (43)	4 parts C, reflux, 1 hr.	—	Hexachlorobenzene, 78%

* A refers to concentrated sulfuric acid; B, to oleum; C, to chlorosulfonic acid; and D, to fluorosulfonic acid.

† References 139–406 appear on pp. 192–197.

TABLE II

Toluene and Its Halogen Derivatives

Compound Sulfonated	Reagent * and Reference †	Experimental Conditions	Position of Sulfo Group(s)	Remarks
Toluene	A, 84–100% (14, 16, 62, 168)	Various conditions	2-, 3-, 4-	Yield of each isomer determined for each condition
	B, 8% (20, 169)	2.3 parts B with or without 3% $HgSO_4$	2- and 4-	82% yield (69% 4- and 31% 2-)
	C (86*a*)	1 mole of C	2- and 4-	Two $-SO_3H$, some 4,4′-sulfone
	C (14, 16, 34, 170, 171)	Various conditions	2-, 3-, and 4-	$-SO_2Cl$
	D (31)	4 parts D; 10 hr. at 25°	2- and 4-	89% of $-SO_2F$ (40% of 2-isomer)
	SO_3 (59)	40–55°	2-, 3-, and 4-	$-SO_3H$; 8%, 7%, and 55% respectively, also 22% of 4,4′-sulfone
	$NaH_3(SO_4)_2$ (36*a*)	2.5 parts reagent, reflux, 15–16 hr.	4-	$-SO_3H$, 87%
	$S_2O_5Cl_2$ (33)	1 mole reagent, 60°, 1 hr.	4-	$-SO_3H$ and $-SO_2Cl$, also sulfone and dichlorotoluenes
	B, 66% (110)	125°, 4 hr.	2,4-	Di-SO_3H
	B (60, 62, 63, 172)	3-4 parts B, 150–180°, 2 hr., then 200°	2,4- and 2,5-	Di-SO_3H, mostly 2,4-
	C (38*a*)	8 parts C, 140–150°, 5 hr.	2,4-	Di-SO_2Cl, 60%
	C (38*a*)	1 mole C, heat, then 10 moles, 150–160°, 5–6 hr.	—	4,4′-sulfone-3,3′-di-SO_2Cl, 42%
Toluene-2-sulfonyl chloride	B, 40–50% (173)	4 parts B, heat slowly to 200°	2,4-(?)	$-SO_3H$ derivatives of $-SO_2Cl$
Toluene-4-sulfonyl chloride	B (62)	140–150°	2,4-	Di-SO_3H
	D (31)	4 parts D	4-	$-SO_2F$
Toluene-4-sulfonyl fluoride	D (31)	4 parts D, 130–140°, 3 hr.	2,4-	Di-SO_2F, 48%
Toluene-3-sulfonic acid	B (94, 172)	2.5 parts B, 180°, 3–4 hr.	2,5- and 3,5-	Di-SO_3H
Toluene-2,4-disulfonyl fluoride	C (31)	4 parts C, 100°, 10 hr.	2,4-	Di-SO_2Cl
Potassium toluene-2,4-disulfonate	C (63)	3 moles C, 240°	2,4,6-	Tri-SO_3H
2-Bromotoluene	B (174)	Warm, shake	5- and 6-	5-SO_3H, mainly
	C (43)	5 parts C, $CHCl_3$ solution, 25°, 20 min.	5-	$-SO_2Cl$
3-Bromotoluene	B (175)	100°	6-	$-SO_3H$
	C (43)	5 parts C, $CHCl_3$ solution, 25°, 20 min., then 50°, 10 min.	6-	$-SO_2Cl$
4-Bromotoluene	B (176)	1–4 vol. B, 60°, 4 days	2- and 3-	2-SO_3H, mainly

* A refers to concentrated sulfuric acid; B, to oleum; C, to chlorosulfonic acid; and D, to fluorosulfonic acid.

† References 139–406 appear on pp. 192–197.

TABLE II—*Continued*

TOLUENE AND ITS HALOGEN DERIVATIVES

Compound Sulfonated	Reagent * and Reference †	Experimental Conditions	Position of Sulfo Group(s)	Remarks
4-Bromotoluene	C (43)	5 parts C, $CHCl_3$ solution, 25°, 20 min., then 50°, 10 min.	2-	$-SO_2Cl$
	B (177)	Heat, 24 hr.	2,6-(?)	Di-SO_3H, 37%
2-Chlorotoluene	A, 100% (93)	3 parts A, 60°, 10 min.	5-	$-SO_3H$
	B (92)	Dissolve in B	5-	$-SO_3H$
	C (43)	5 parts C, $CHCl_3$ solution, 25°, 20 min.	5-	$-SO_2Cl$
Potassium 2-chlorotoluene-4-sulfonate	B, 35% (94)	1.4 parts B, 150°, 2 hr.	5- and 6-	6-SO_3H, mainly
Potassium 2-chlorotoluene-5-sulfonate	B, 20% (94)	1.7 parts B, 150°, 2 hr.	3-	$-SO_3H$
3-Chlorotoluene	A, 100% (93)	3 parts A, 70°, 10 min.	6-(?)	$-SO_3H$
	C (43)	5 parts C, $CHCl_3$ solution, 25°, 20 min., then 50°, 10 min.	6-	$-SO_2Cl$
4-Chlorotoluene	A, 100% (92, 93, 94, 178)	3 parts A, 100°, 40 min.	2- and 3-	2-SO_3H, 86%
	C (43)	5 parts C, $CHCl_3$ solution, 25°, 20 min., then 50°, 10 min.	2-	$-SO_2Cl$
Potassium 4-chlorotoluene-2-sulfonate	B, 20% (94)	1.7 parts B, 150°, 2 hr.	2,5- and 2,6-	Di-SO_3H
Potassium 4-chlorotoluene-3-sulfonate	B, 20% (94)	1.7 parts B, 150°, 2 hr.	3,5- and 3,6-	Di-SO_3H
2-Fluorotoluene	C (43)	5 parts C, $CHCl_3$ solution, 25°, 20 min.	5-	$-SO_2Cl$
2-Iodotoluene	A (44)	1 part A, 100°, 4 hr.	5-(?)	$-SO_3H$
	SO_3 (179)	Cold, then heat	5-(?)	Also diiodo compounds
4-Iodotoluene	SO_3 (180)	1 mole SO_3, $CHCl_3$ solution	2- and 3-	$-SO_3H$
2,3-Dibromotoluene	B (181)	2 parts B, 100°	5-(?)	$-SO_3H$
2,4-Dibromotoluene	B (181)	2 parts B, 100°	5-(?)	$-SO_3H$
2,5-Dibromotoluene	B (181)	2 parts B, 100°	4-(?)	$-SO_3H$
2,6-Dibromotoluene	B (181)	2 parts B, 100°	3-(?)	$-SO_3H$
3,4-Dibromotoluene	B (181)	2 parts B, 100°	6-(?)	$-SO_3H$
3,5-Dibromotoluene	B (181)	2 parts B, 100°	2-(?)	$-SO_3H$
2,3-Dichlorotoluene	B (182)	3 parts B, heat	5- and 4- or 6-	$-SO_3H$

* A refers to concentrated sulfuric acid; B, to oleum; C, to chlorosulfonic acid; and D, to fluorosulfonic acid.

† References 139–406 appear on pp. 192–197.

TABLE II—*Continued*

Toluene and Its Halogen Derivatives

Compound Sulfonated	Reagent * and Reference †	Experimental Conditions	Position of Sulfo Group(s)	Remarks
2,4-Dichloro-toluene	B (182, 183)	2 parts B, heat	5-	$-SO_3H$
	C (43)	5 parts C, $CHCl_3$ solution, 25°, 20 min., then 50°, 10 min.	5-	$-SO_2Cl$
2,5-Dichloro-toluene	B, 10% (93)	2 parts B, 60–70°, then 2 parts more, 100°	4-	$-SO_3H$
2,6-Dichloro-toluene	B (182)	2 parts B, heat	3-(?)	$-SO_3H$
	C (43)	5 parts C, $CHCl_3$ solution, 25°, 20 min., then 50°, 10 min.	3-	$-SO_2Cl$
3,4-Dichloro-toluene	B, 5% (93)	3 parts B, dissolve	6-	$-SO_3H$
3,5-Dichloro-toluene	B (182)	2 parts B, heat	2-(?)	$-SO_3H$
2-Bromo-3-chlorotoluene	B (184)		6-(?)	$-SO_3H$
2-Bromo-4-chlorotoluene	B (184)		5-(?)	$-SO_3H$
2-Bromo-5-chlorotoluene	B (184)		4-(?)	$-SO_3H$
2-Bromo-6-chlorotoluene	B (184)		3-(?) or 5-(?)	$-SO_3H$
3-Bromo-2-chlorotoluene	B (184)	3 parts B, 100°	6-(?)	$-SO_3H$
3-Bromo-4-chlorotoluene	B (184)		6-(?)	$-SO_3H$
3-Bromo-5-chlorotoluene	B (184)		6-(?)	$-SO_3H$
3-Bromo-6-chlorotoluene	B (184)		4-(?)	$-SO_3H$
4-Bromo-2-chlorotoluene	B (184)		5-(?)	$-SO_3H$
4-Bromo-3-chlorotoluene	B (184)		6-(?)	$-SO_3H$
2,3,4-Trichloro-toluene	B (183)	80–100°	5- and 6-	Structures undetermined
3,4,5-Trichloro-toluene ‡	B, 10% (93)	3 parts B, 70–80°	2-	$-SO_3H$

* A refers to concentrated sulfuric acid; B, to oleum; C, to chlorosulfonic acid; and D, to fluorosulfonic acid.

† References 139–406 appear on pp. 192–197.

‡ The sulfonic acid was isolated from the sulfonation of a chlorinated toluene fraction boiling above 165°.

TABLE III

Higher Alkylbenzenes ‡ and Their Halogen Derivatives

Compound Sulfonated	Reagent * and Reference †	Experimental Conditions	Position of Sulfo Group(s)	Remarks
Ethylbenzene	A (185)	Equal volume A added slowly to boiling compound	4-	$-SO_3H$
	B (186, 187)	By dissolving in B	4-	$-SO_3H$
	C (186, 187)	1 mole C	4-	—
	D (188)	4 parts D, standing	4-	$-SO_2F$, 86%; trace of sulfone
	B, 50% (189)	—	2,4-	Di-SO_3H
Ethylbenzene-2-sulfonic acid	Heat (187)	100°	—	Rearranges to the 4-SO_3H
2- and 4-Bromo-ethylbenzene	B (185, 187)	1.5 vol. B added slowly to boiling mixture	(2) 5- and (4) 2-	2-SO_3H, mainly
n-Propylbenzene	A (190)	—	4- and 2-	$-SO_3H$
	B (191, 192)	Dissolve in B	4- and 2-	$-SO_3H$
Isopropylbenzene	A (193)	100°	4-	$-SO_3H$; trace of 2-SO_3H
	B (79*b*, 191, 194)	1–2 parts B, stir	4-	$-SO_3H$
n-Butylbenzene	B (195)	Warming	4- and 2-	$-SO_3H$
sec-Butylbenzene	B, "very strong" (196*a*)	24 hr.	4-	$-SO_3H$
	B, 6% (196*b*)	5 parts B, 50°	Unknown	$-SO_3H$
t-Butylbenzene	A (197)	Warm	4-(?)	$-SO_3H$
	B (26)	Dissolve, cooling	4-	—
	C (34)	Excess C, $CHCl_3$ solution	4-	$-SO_2Cl$, 100%
Isoamylbenzene	B (199)	Warm slightly	4-(?)	Cryst. acid
2-Phenylpentane	B, 6% (200)	Warm slightly	4-(?)	$-SO_3H$
3-Phenylpentane	B, 6% (200, 201)	Warm	4-(?)	$-SO_3H$
2-Phenyl-3-methylbutane	B, 6% (200)	Warm	4-(?)	Rapid reaction
Neopentyl-benzene	B, 6% (202)	2 parts B, room temperature	4-	Ba salt, 95%
2-Phenylhexane	B (203)	—	?	$-SO_3H$
1-Phenyl-3-methylpentane	B, 6% (204)	40° approximately	4-(?)	Oily product
2-Phenyl-4-methylpentane	B, "weak" (205)	Warm	4-(?)	$-SO_3H$
n-Octylbenzene	B (206)	Room temperature	4-(?)	$-SO_3H$
n-Dodecylbenzene	C or SO_3 (207)	$C_2H_4Cl_2$ solution	4-(?)	Washing agent
n-Hexadecylbenzene	B (208)	35–40°	4-	$-SO_3H$
n-Octadecylbenzene	B (208)	Approximately 40°; excess B	4-	$-SO_3H$

* A refers to concentrated sulfuric acid; B, to oleum; C, to chlorosulfonic acid; and D, to fluorosulfonic acid.

† References 139–406 appear on pp. 192–197.

‡ Mixtures of alkylbenzenesulfonic acids, obtained by the sulfonation of mixed *sec*-alkylbenzenes which in turn have been prepared by the condensation of a mixture of olefins or alkyl chlorides with benzene, have been patented as washing or emulsifying agents.[12,209] The condensation of acid chlorides with benzene, followed by reduction and sulfonation, has also been employed for this purpose.[207]

In a number of instances, alkylbenzenesulfonic acids have been obtained by the alkylation of benzene-, toluene-, or xylene-sulfonic acids.[210]

TABLE IV

Dialkylbenzenes and Their Halogen Derivatives

Compound Sulfonated	Reagent * and Reference †	Experimental Conditions	Position of Sulfo Group(s)	Remarks
1,2-Dimethylbenzene	A (64)	1 vol. A, warm	4-	$-SO_3H$
	A (19)	2% and 10% $HgSO_4$ as catalyst	4- and 3-	$3-SO_3H$, 8 and 22%
	A (66)	1.2 vol. A, room temperature	4-	82% dissolves in 2 hr.
	C (34)	$CHCl_3$ solution	4-	$-SO_2Cl$, 74–86%
	C (38*a*)	Excess C	3,5-	Di-SO_2Cl
Barium 1,2-dimethylbenzene-4-sulfonate	C (72)	2 parts C, 150°	3,5-(?)	Di-SO_3H
1,2-Dimethyl-3-chlorobenzene	B (211, 212)	By shaking	6-	Mixed chloroxylenes used
1,2-Dimethyl-4-chlorobenzene	B (211, 212)	By shaking	5-	Mixed chloroxylenes used
1,2-Dimethyl-3-bromobenzene	B (213)	Dissolve in B	6- and 4-	$6-SO_3H$, mostly
1,2-Dimethyl-4-bromobenzene	B (64)	By warming	5-	A reacts very slowly
1,2-Dimethyl-4,5-dibromobenzene	B, 15% (65)	10 parts B; 75°, shaking	3-	$-SO_3H$
1,3-Dimethylbenzene	A (67*b*, 68, 69, 214)	2 parts A; 100° or less; 2 hr.	4-	$2-SO_3H$, trace
	D (31)	4 parts D; 5 hr. 5°; 15 hr. 20–30°	4-	$-SO_2F$, 86%
	$H_2S_2O_7$ (73)	4 parts reagent; 150°	4,6-	Di-SO_3H
1,3-Dimethylbenzene-4-sulfonyl fluoride	D (31)	4 parts D; 100°	4,6-	Di-SO_2F, 70%
1,3-Dimethylbenzene-2-sulfonic acid	C (68, 74)	10 parts C; 80–90°; 4 hr.	4,6- and 2,4-	Di-SO_2Cl; mostly 4,6-
	C (68)	10 parts C; 150–160°; 5 hr.	4,6-	Di-SO_2Cl
1,3-Dimethylbenzene-4-sulfonic acid	C (68)	7 parts C; 150–160°; 5 hr.	4,6-	Di-SO_2Cl
1,3-Dimethyl-4-chlorobenzene	B (215)	Dissolve in B	6-	$-SO_3H$
	$H_2S_2O_7$ (73)	Heat	2,6-	Di-SO_3H
1,3-Dimethyl-5-chlorobenzene	B, 15% (95*b*)	30–40°, shaking	2-	$-SO_3H$; anhydride is by-product
1,3-Dimethyl-4-bromobenzene	B (216)	Cold	6-	$-SO_3H$
1,3-Dimethyl-4-iodobenzene	A (217)	4–6 weeks; room temperature	6-	Diiodoxylene also
1,3-Dimethyl-2,4-dichlorobenzene	C (96)	—	6-	$-SO_3H$
1,3-Dimethyl-2,4-dibromobenzene	C (218)	Excess C	6-	$-SO_2Cl$

* A refers to concentrated sulfuric acid; B, to oleum; C, to chlorosulfonic acid; and D, to fluorosulfonic acid.

† References 139–406 appear on pp. 192–197.

TABLE IV—*Continued*

DIALKYLBENZENES AND THEIR HALOGEN DERIVATIVES

Compound Sulfonated	Reagent * and Reference †	Experimental Conditions	Position of Sulfo Group(s)	Remarks
1,3-Dimethyl-4,6-dichlorobenzene	C (96)	—	2-	A causes rearrangement
1,3-Dimethyl-4,6-dibromobenzene	B (219)	70–80°	2-	$-SO_3H$
1,3-Dimethyl-4,6-diiodobenzene	B (220)	25°, 6 days	6-	Iodine to 2,4-
1,4-Dimethylbenzene	A (66)	Room temperature	2-	$-SO_3H$, 68%
	B (70, 221)	2 vol. B	2-	$-SO_3H$
	D (31)	4 parts D, 16 hr., 25°	2-	$-SO_2F$, 85%
	B, 50% (75, 76)	140–150°	2,6-	Di-SO_3H
	C (74)	Excess C	2,6- and 2,5-	Di-SO_2Cl; ratio 10 : 1; also sulfone (38),
1,4-Dimethylbenzene-2-sulfonyl chloride	B (221)	Warm	2,6-(?)	Di-SO_3H
1,4-Dimethylbenzene-2-sulfonyl fluoride	C (31)	4 parts C, 36 hr., 25°	2- and 2,6-di-	SO_2Cl compounds
1,4-Dimethyl-2-chlorobenzene	B (222)	By shaking	5-	$-SO_3H$
1,4-Dimethyl-2,3-dichlorobenzene	A (223)	Reacts readily	5-	$-SO_3H$
1,4-Dimethyl-2,6-dichlorobenzene	A (223)	Reacts readily	3-	$-SO_3H$
1,4-Dimethyl-2,5-dichlorobenzene	B (223)	100°	3-	$-SO_3H$
1,4-Dimethyl-2,5-dibromobenzene	B, 20% (224)	80–85°	3-	$-SO_3H$
1,2-Diethylbenzene	B (225)	50–60°	4-(?)	$-SO_3H$
1,3-Diethylbenzene	B (226)	Dissolve in B	4-	Mixture of isomers sulfonated
1,4-Diethylbenzene	B (226, 227)	Dissolve in B	2-	(Mixture of isomers sulfonated)
1,4-Di-*n*-propylbenzene	B (228)	Dissolve in B	2-	$-SO_3H$
1,2-Diisopropylbenzene	A (229)	Long shaking	4-(?)	$-SO_3H$
1,3-Diisopropylbenzene	A (229)	Long shaking	4-	$-SO_3H$
	C (230)	CCl_4 solution	4-	$-SO_2Cl$
1,4-Diisopropylbenzene	C (230)	CCl_4 solution	2-	$-SO_2Cl$
1,4-Di-*t*-butylbenzene	A (231)	By warming	2-	$-SO_3H$

* A refers to concentrated sulfuric acid; B, to oleum; C, to chlorosulfonic acid; and D, to fluorosulfonic acid.

† References 139–406 appear on pp. 192–197.

TABLE IV—*Continued*

DIALKYLBENZENES AND THEIR HALOGEN DERIVATIVES

Compound Sulfonated	Reagent * and Reference †	Experimental Conditions	Position of Sulfo Group(s)	Remarks
2-Ethyltoluene	B (232)	Cold or at 100°	—	Mixture, two $-SO_3H$
3-Ethyltoluene	A (233)	Dissolve in A	—	Mixture, two $-SO_3H$
4-Ethyltoluene	A (234)	2.5 parts A at 100°	2- and 3-	$2-SO_3H$, mostly
	B (235)	130°	—	$-SO_3H$
4-Ethyl-2(?)-chlorotoluene	B (235)	130°	5-(?)	$-SO_3H$
4-Ethyl-2-bromotoluene	B (235)	130°	5-(?)	$-SO_3H$
3-*n*-Propyltoluene	A (236)	By warming	4- and 6-(?)	$-SO_3H$
4-*n*-Propyltoluene	A (237)	100°	2- and 3-	$2-SO_3H$, mostly
2-Isopropyltoluene	B (238)	50°	4- and 5-(?)	$-SO_3H$
3-Isopropyltoluene	A (239, 240)	By warming	4- and 6-	$6-SO_3H$, mostly
3-Isopropyl-6-bromotoluene	B (240)	By warming	4-	$-SO_3H$
4-Isopropyltoluene	A (27*a*, 241, 242)	100°	2- and 3-	$2-SO_3H$, mostly
	A (27*b*, 27*c*)	3 parts A, 100°	2- and 3-	$3-SO_3H$, 15.6%
	B, 15% (27*b*, 27*c*)	0°	2- and 3-	$2-SO_3H$, 90%; $3-SO_3H$, 2.5%
	A (27*d*)	2.8 equivalents of A	2- and 3-	$3-SO_3H$, 20%
	C (27*c*)	—	2-	—
4-Isopropyl-2-chlorotoluene	B, 20% (243)	10 parts B, shaking	5-(?)	$-SO_3H$
4-Isopropyl-3-chlorotoluene	C (243*a*, 244)	Add C	6-	$-SO_2Cl$
4-Isopropyl-2-bromotoluene	B (28, 242*a*, 245)	—	5-	Trace of a second compound
	C (246)	1 part C	5-	$-SO_3H$ and $-SO_2Cl$
3-*t*-Butyltoluene	A (247)	50°	6-(?)	$-SO_3H$
	B, 15% (248)	Dissolve in B	6-(?)	$-SO_3H$
"*p*-Butyltoluene"	A (247*a*, 249)	50°	—	$-SO_3H$
4-Isoamyltoluene	A (250)	—	2-(?)	$-SO_3H$
4-*n*-Octyltoluene	B (251)	By dissolving	2-(?)	$-SO_3H$
4-*n*-Hexadecyltoluene	B (252)	By dissolving	2-(?)	$-SO_3H$
1-Ethyl-4-*n*-propylbenzene	A (253)	100°	2- and 3-	$-SO_3H$
1-Ethyl-3-isopropylbenzene	B (254)	By dissolving	6-(?)	$-SO_3H$
1-Ethyl-4-isopropylbenzene	B, 6% (255)	By warming	2-(?)	$-SO_3H$
1-Ethyl-(?)-*t*-butylbenzene	B (231, 256)	By dissolving	—	$-SO_3H$
1-*n*-Propyl-4-isopropylbenzene	B (256, 257)	By warming	2- and 3-	$-SO_3H$

* A refers to concentrated sulfuric acid; B, to oleum; C, to chlorosulfonic acid; and D, to fluorosulfonic acid.

† References 139–406 appear on pp. 192–197.

TABLE V

TRIALKYLBENZENES AND HALOGEN DERIVATIVES

Compound Sulfonated	Reagent * and Reference †	Experimental Conditions	Position of Sulfo Group(s)	Remarks
1,2,3-Trimethylbenzene (hemimellitene)	A (77)	2.5 parts A, 100°	4-	High yield
4-Chloro-1,2,3-trimethylbenzene	B, 20% (97)	5 parts B, 15 hr., 75°	5-	$-SO_3Na$, 46%
1,2,4-Trimethylbenzene (pseudocumene)	A (79*a*)	2 vol. A, 60°, 5 to 10 min.	5-	$-SO_3H$, 85%
	$SO_2Cl_2 + AlCl_3$ (81)	36 hr., cold	5-	$-SO_2Cl$, etc.
	D (31)	5 parts D, 25°, 3 hr.	5-	$-SO_2F$, 37%
3-Bromo-1,2,4-trimethylbenzene	A or B (218, 258)	100°	5-	Anomalous substitution
	C (218, 258)	—	5-	$-SO_2Cl$
5-Bromo-1,2,4-trimethylbenzene	B (49, 258, 259)	Warm	6-	Rearranges on standing
	B, 20% (97*a*)	6 parts B, 6 weeks; 70°, then 25°	5-	$-SO_3H$, 90%; Br to 3-position
6-Bromo-1,2,4-trimethylbenzene	B (49, 259)	Heat	3-	From dibromo compound
3-Chloro-1,2,4-trimethylbenzene	B (97)	3 parts B, shaking	5-	$-SO_3Na$, 80%
5-Chloro-1,2,4-trimethylbenzene	B (260)	Long standing	?	—
	B, 20% (97*a*)	6 parts B, 4 hr., 65–70°	5-	$-SO_3H$, 71%; Cl to 3-position
6-Chloro-1,2,4-trimethylbenzene	B (97*a*)	16 parts B, 3 days, 25°	5-	$-SO_3H$, 44%; Cl to 3-position
5-Fluoro-1,2,4-trimethylbenzene	A (261)	Warm	6-(?)	No rearrangement in 3 months
	B (261)	Warm	6-(?)	—
5-Iodo-1,2,4-trimethylbenzene	A (262)	Long standing	6-(?)	Also rearranges
	B (262)	Long standing	—	—
6-Bromo-5-fluoro-1,2,4-trimethylbenzene	A (261)	Room temperature, long standing	—	Rearrangement
	C (261)	—	3-	—
6-Chloro-5-fluoro-1,2,4-trimethylbenzene	A (261)	Long standing	—	Chlorine slowly rearranges
	B (261)	Long standing	3-	—
	C (261)	—	3-	—
5,6-Dibromo-1,2,4-trimethylbenzene	B (49, 259)	Heat at high temperature	—	Decomposition and formation of SO_2
	C (49, 259)	Stand 1 to 2 hr.	3-	Also other products

* A refers to concentrated sulfuric acid; B, to oleum; C, to chlorosulfonic acid; and D, to fluorosulfonic acid.

† References 139–406 appear on pp. 192–197.

TABLE V—*Continued*

TRIALKYLBENZENES AND HALOGEN DERIVATIVES

Compound Sulfonated	Reagent * and Reference †	Experimental Conditions	Position of Sulfo Group(s)	Remarks
1,3,5-Trimethylbenzene (mesitylene)	A (79*a*, 263, 264)	2 vol. A, < 60°, 5 to 10 min.	2-	$-SO_3H$, 90%
	B (79*b*, 80)	20–30°	2-	—
	$SO_2Cl_2 + AlCl_3$ (81)	—	2-	$-SO_2Cl$
	B—P_2O_5 (83)	30–40°, 2–3 days	2,4-	Di-SO_3H
	C (82)	−5°	2,4-	Di-SO_3H
	C + SO_2Cl_2 (76)	100°, 10 hr.	2,4-	Di-SO_3H
	C (34)	$CHCl_3$ solution	2-	$-SO_2Cl$, 65–72%
	D (31)	5.5 parts D, 25°, 3 hr.	2-	$-SO_2F$
1,3,5-Trimethylbenzene-2-sulfonyl fluoride	C (31)	4 parts C, 20°	2,4-	Di-SO_2Cl
1,3,5-Trimethylbenzene-2,4-disulfonic acid	SO_3 (82)	120°	2,4,6-	Tri-SO_3H, low yield
2-Bromo-1,3,5-trimethylbenzene	A (264, 265)	20°, 1 week	—	$C_9H_{10}Br_2$ and $C_9H_{11}SO_3H$
	B (264, 265)	20°	4-	Also $C_9H_{10}Br_2$
2-Chloro-1,3,5-trimethylbenzene	B, 20% (97*a*)	9 parts B, 70°, 6 hr.	4-	—
	B, 20% (97*a*)	8 parts B, 60°, then 25°, 6 weeks	4-	—
2-Iodo-1,3,5-trimethylbenzene	A (265)	5 parts A, 20°, 12 hr.	—	$C_9H_{10}I_2$ and $C_9H_{11}SO_3H$
	B (265)	5 parts B, 20°, 48 hr.	—	$C_9H_9I_3$
	SO_3 (265)	Cold	4-	Also other products
	C (265)	Excess C, many days	—	$C_9H_9Cl_3$
1,2,4-Triethylbenzene	A (47)	3 parts A, 100°, 3 hr.	—	No rearrangement
	B, 8% (266)	1.6 parts B, 50°	5-	—
1,3,5-Triethylbenzene	A (47, 266)	2 vol. A, warm	2-	$-SO_3H$ as an oil
1,2,4-Triisopropylbenzene	C (230)	CCl_4 solution, 30–50°	5-	$-SO_2Cl$, 99%
1,3,5-Triisopropylbenzene	B (267)	2 vol. B, shaking	2-	Free acid isolated
	C (230)	CCl_4 solution, 30–50°	2-	—
1,2-Dimethyl-4-ethylbenzene	A (77*a*, 268, 269)	Dissolve	3- and 5- (?)	Cryst. acid
1,3-Dimethyl-4-ethylbenzene	A (77*a*, 270)	Warm, dissolve	6-(?)	—
1,3-Dimethyl-5-ethylbenzene	A (271, 272)	Dissolve	2-	—
2-Bromo-1,3-dimethyl-5-ethylbenzene	C (272)	1 mole of C	4-	$-SO_3H$ and $-SO_2Cl$

* A refers to concentrated sulfuric acid; B, to oleum; C, to chlorosulfonic acid; and D, to fluorosulfonic acid.

† References 139–406 appear on pp. 192–197.

TABLE V—*Continued*

TRIALKYLBENZENES AND HALOGEN DERIVATIVES

Compound Sulfonated	Reagent * and Reference †	Experimental Conditions	Position of Sulfo Group(s)	Remarks
1,4-Dimethyl-2-ethylbenzene	A (77*a*, 268)	Dissolve	3-	—
1,2-Dimethyl-4-*n*-propylbenzene	— (273)	—	5-(?)	—
1,4-Dimethyl-2-*n*-propylbenzene	— (273)	—	5-(?)	—
1,3-Dimethyl-4-*n*-propylbenzene	— (273)	—	6-(?)	—
1,2-Dimethyl-4-isopropylbenzene	B, 6% (198)	—	3- and 5-(?)	2 isomers
1,3-Dimethyl-4-isopropylbenzene	— (273)	—	6-(?)	—
1,3-Dimethyl-5-*tert*-butylbenzene	B (31, 231, 248, 274)	1 part B, 24 hr., 20–25°	2-(?)	Also other conditions
	C (34)	$CHCl_3$	6-(?)	$-SO_2Cl$, 97%
	D (31)	2.5 parts D; 18–22°, 16 hr.	2-(?)	$-SO_2F$
1-Methyl-2-*n*-propyl-4-isopropylbenzene	B, 6% (275)	Warm	5-(?)	$-SO_3H$
1-Methyl-3,5-diisopropylbenzene	C (276)	—	2-(?)	$-SO_2Cl$

* A refers to concentrated sulfuric acid; B, to oleum; C, to chlorosulfonic acid; and D, to fluorosulfonic acid.

† References 139–406 appear on pp. 192–197.

TABLE VI

Polyalkylbenzenes and Halogen Derivatives

Compound Sulfonated	Reagent * and Reference †	Experimental Conditions	Position of Sulfo Group	Remarks
1,2,3,4-Tetramethylbenzene (prehnitine)	A (258, 277)	2 vol. A, 10 min., shake	5-	5-SO_3H, 91%; no rearrangement
	C (34)	$CHCl_3$ solution	5-	-SO_2Cl, 95%
5-Chloro-1,2,3,4-tetramethylbenzene	B (97*a*, 278)	5 hr., 25–30°	—	$C_6H(CH_3)_3ClSO_3H$ and $C_6(CH_3)_5Cl$
1,2,3,5-Tetramethylbenzene (isodurene)	A (277*a*)	4 parts A, 10 min., 25°	4-	4-SO_3H, 60–70%; slowly rearranges
	B (279)	2 vol. B, warm	4-	—
4-Chloro-1,2,3,5-tetramethylbenzene	A (97, 278)	6 parts A, 65°, 4 hr.	—	$C_6H(CH_3)_3ClSO_3H$ and $C_6(CH_3)_5Cl$
1,2,4,5-Tetramethylbenzene (durene)	B (277*a*, 280)	40°, 5 min.	3-	3-SO_3H, 94%; slowly rearranges
	C (281)	2.5 parts C, cold	3-	Some -SO_2Cl and sulfone
	C (34)	$CHCl_3$ solution	3-	-SO_2Cl, 100%
3-Bromo-1,2,4,5-tetramethylbenzene	A (282, 283)	—	—	Rearrangement
3-Chloro-1,2,4,5-tetramethylbenzene	A (97*a*, 278)	6 parts A, 65°, 4 hr.	—	$C_6HCl(CH_3)_3SO_3H$ and $C_6(CH_3)_5Cl$
1-Ethyl-2,4,6-trimethylbenzene	A (46)	6 hr., 60–70°	—	Rearrangement
	B (284, 285, 286)	—	3-	—
1-Ethyl-2,4,5-trimethylbenzene	A (46, 287)	—	3-(?)	Rearranges slowly
	B, 10% (46, 284)	1 vol. B, to 45°	3-(?)	-SO_3H, 95%
	C (46)	—	3-(?)	—
3-Ethyl-1,2,4-trimethylbenzene	A (46)	2 vol. A, 2 min., 55°	6-(?)	-SO_3H, high yield
	A (46)	6 hr., 70°	6-(?)	No rearrangement
1-*n*-Propyl-2,4,6-trimethylbenzene	— (286)	—	—	—
1-Isobutyl-2,4,6-trimethylbenzene	— (286)	—	—	—
1-Isopentyl-2,4,6-trimethylbenzene	— (286)	—	—	—

* A refers to concentrated sulfuric acid; B, to oleum; C, to chlorosulfonic acid; and D, to fluorosulfonic acid.

† References 139–406 appear on pp. 192–197.

TABLE VI—*Continued*

POLYALKYLBENZENES AND HALOGEN DERIVATIVES

Compound Sulfonated	Reagent * and Reference †	Experimental Conditions	Position of Sulfo Group	Remarks
1-*n*-Heptyl-2,4,6-trimethylbenzene	B (286)	Dissolves	4-	—
1,2,3,5-Tetraethylbenzene	C (47)	1.4 parts C, 20–30°	4-	Rearranges with A
1,2,4,5-Tetraethylbenzene	A (47, 288*a*)	Cold or warm	3-	Rearranges
	C (47)	1.4 parts C, 20–30°	3-	$-SO_3H$, 90%
1,2,4,5-Tetraisopropylbenzene	C (34, 230)	Excess C, in $CHCl_3$ or alone	5-	Loss of 5-C_3H_7; $-SO_2Cl$, 97%
Pentamethylbenzene	A (282, 288*b*)	—	6-	Rearranges on standing
	C (34)	$CHCl_3$ solution	6-	$-SO_2Cl$, 98%
Pentaethylbenzene	C (47)	5 parts C, or 1 part C in $CHCl_3$	6-	$-SO_3H$, 89%

* A refers to concentrated sulfuric acid; B, to oleum; C, to chlorosulfonic acid; and D, to fluorosulfonic acid.

† References 139–406 appear on pp. 192–197.

TABLE VII

Biphenyl and Its Derivatives

Compound Sulfonated	Reagent * and Reference †	Experimental Conditions	Position of Sulfo Group(s)	Remarks
Biphenyl	A (98, 99)	$C_6H_5NO_2$ solution, heat	4-	4-SO_3H, 90%
	C (38*a*)	1 mole of C in $Cl_2CHCHCl_2$, 50°	4-	Good yield
	A (289)	Excess A, heat	4,4′-	Nearly quantitative
	C (38*a*)	Excess C, 0°	4,4′-	Di-SO_2Cl, 80%
	C (38*a*)	5 parts C, 24 hr., 18°	—	Dibenzothiophene dioxide 2,7-di-SO_2Cl
Potassium biphenyl-4-sulfonate	(100)	Heat, no reagent	4,4′-	Also biphenyl
Biphenyl-4-sulfonyl chloride	B, 4% (173)	15–20°	4′-	No loss of halogen
3-Methylbiphenyl ‡	A, 98% (10)	0.1 part A, 40–45°, 2 hr.	4-	—
4-Methylbiphenyl ‡	A, 98% (10)	0.1 part A, 40–45°, 2 hr.	2′-(?)	—
3,4′-Dimethylbiphenyl ‡	A, 98% (10)	0.1 part A, 40–45°	2′-(?)	—
4,4′-Dimethylbiphenyl ‡	A, 98% (10)	0.1 part A, 40–45°	2′-(?)	—
2-Methyl-5-isopropylbiphenyl	B, 6% (275)	5 parts B, cold	?	Mono-SO_3H
2,2′3,3′4,4′6,6′-Octamethylbiphenyl	C (290)	5 parts C, 0°, 1 hr.	5,5′-	Di-SO_2Cl, 77%
4,4′-Dibromobiphenyl	C (40)	1 part C, $CHCl_3$ solution, 40°	3-	-SO_3H, 32%; 2,2′-sulfone, 25%
	A (40)	Excess A, 80°, 4 hr.	3,3′-	Only product isolated
	B, 30% (40)	6.6 parts B, 80°, 4 hr.	3,3′-	Di-SO_3H, 73%; sulfone-di-SO_3H, 13.5%
	C (40)	5.3 moles C, 60° 15 min.	3,3′-	3,3′-Di-SO_3H, 41.5%; 3,3′-di-SO_2Cl, 12.5%; 2,2′-sulfone, 42%

* A refers to concentrated sulfuric acid; B, to oleum; C, to chlorosulfonic acid; and D, to fluorosulfonic acid.

† References 139–406 appear on pp. 192–197.

‡ The sulfonic acids of these hydrocarbons were obtained from the sulfonation of high-boiling fractions of coal tar. The pure hydrocarbons were regenerated from these acids by high-temperature hydrolysis.

TABLE VIII

Arylalkanes, Arylalkenes, and Derivatives

Compound Sulfonated	Reagent * and Reference †	Experimental Conditions	Position of Sulfo Group(s)	Remarks
Diphenylmethane	C (101)	1.3 moles C, $CHCl_3$ solution, 0°, several hours	4-	-SO_3H, 82% and some sulfone
	B (102)	Excess B, 90°, 2 days	4,4′-	—
4-Methyldiphenylmethane	B (291)	Warm	?	Mixture; a di-SO_3H isolated
2-Methyl-5-isopropyldiphenylmethane	B (292)	5 vol. B	—	Mono-SO_3H
	B (293)	100°, several hours	—	Di-SO_3H
Bibenzyl	A (103)	2 vol. A, warm	4,4′-(?)	Trace of a tetra-SO_3H
Stilbene	B (104)	Warm, 12 hr.	4,4′-(?)	—
1,1-Diphenyl-1-propene	A (294)	—	—	4-Phenyl-5,6-benzothio-α-pyran-1-dioxide
α,α-*bis*-(2,4,5-Trimethylphenyl)-β,β-dichloroethylene	B, 20% (295)	Room temperature, many hours	3,3′- or 6,6′-(?)	Good yield
1,1-Diphenyl-2,2,3-trichlorobutane	B (296)	Warm	*p,p*′-(?)	Di-SO_3H
Triphenylmethane	B (105)	Hot or cold	4,4′,4″-(?)	Tri-SO_3H
1,1,2,2-Tetraphenylethane	A (106)	8 parts A, warm	—	Tetra-SO_3H
Tetraphenylethylene	A (107)	Heat	—	Tetra-SO_3H

* A refers to concentrated sulfuric acid; B, to oleum; C, to chlorosulfonic acid; and D, to fluorosulfonic acid.

† References 139–406 appear on pp. 192–197.

TABLE IX

Naphthalene and Naphthalenesulfonic Acids

Compound Sulfonated	Reagent * and Reference †	Experimental Conditions	Position of Sulfo Group(s)	Remarks
Naphthalene	A (15, 297)	1 mole A, various conditions	1- and 2-	By-products and % yield determined for each condition
	A, 90%, 96%, 100% (15)	129°, 2 or 7–8 hr.	1- and 2-	% determined for each reagent and time
	A, 100% (108, 298, 299)	2 parts A, 0°, 1 hr.	1- and 2-	1-SO_3H, mainly
	A, 94% (8*a*, 8*d*, 109, 300, 301)	1.6 parts A, 160°, 5 min.	1- and 2-	2-SO_3H, 80%; 1-SO_3H, 15%; 2,2′-sulfone, trace
	B, 15% (299)	Below 70°	1- and 2-	1-SO_3H, chiefly
	B, 12% (15)	129°, 2 or 7–8 hr.	1- and 2-	1-SO_3H, respectively, 70% and 62%
	$NaH_3(SO_4)_2$ (36)	1.5 parts reagent, various conditions	1- and 2-	1-SO_3H, mainly, all temperatures
	C (148)	<1 part C, 10% CS_2 solution	1- and 2-	-SO_3H, a little 1,5-di-SO_3H
	$SO_3 \cdot C_5H_5N$ (30)	0.86 mole, SO_3, 170°, 11 hr.	1- and 2-	1-SO_3H, 38%; 2-SO_3H, 10%
	D (31)	1.6 parts D, 2.4 parts of CS_2, 14 hr., 20°	1-	1-SO_2F, 16%
	A, 100% or 86% (111, 302)	40°, 70°, 100°, 8 hr.	1,5-	99%, 97%, 85% respectively
	B, 30% (303)	4 parts B, short time	1,5-	Almost quantitative
	C (148, 304, 305)	2 moles C, 15–45°	1,5-	Di-SO_3H; some di-SO_2Cl
	C (38*a*)	10 parts C, 0°, short time	1,5-	Di-SO_2Cl, 59%
	D (31)	4 parts D, 75°, 6 hr.	?	Di-SO_2F, not the 1,5-; also other products
	A (111)	165°	1,6-	1,6-Di-SO_3H, 40–45%
	A, 100%, then B, 64% (111, 306)	2.3 parts A, then 2.3 parts of B, <40°	1,5- and 1,6-	1,5-Di-SO_3H, 70%; 1,6-Di-SO_3H, 25%
	A, 80–95% (115)	Vapor phase, 220–245°	2,7- and 2,6-	2,7-Di-SO_3H, 78–85%; a mono-SO_3H, traces
	A, 100% (111, 305, 307)	4.7 parts A, 180°, 8 hr.	1,6-, 2,6-, and 2,7-	1,6-Di-SO_3H, 10%; 2,6-Di-SO_3H, 27%; 2,7-Di-SO_3H, 65%
	A (112*b*)	4 parts A, 130°, 4 hr.	1,3-, 1,5-, 1,6-, 1,7-, 2,6-, and 2,7-	—

* A refers to concentrated sulfuric acid; B, to oleum; C, to chlorosulfonic acid; and D, to fluorosulfonic acid.

† References 139–406 appear on pp. 192–197.

TABLE IX—*Continued*

NAPHTHALENE AND NAPHTHALENESULFONIC ACIDS

Compound Sulfonated	Reagent * and Reference †	Experimental Conditions	Position of Sulfo Group(s)	Remarks
Naphthalene	B, 24% or 40% (116)	8 parts B, 180°, 1 hr. or 6 parts, 100° respectively	1,3,6-	No further reaction
Naphthalene-1-sulfonic acid	A (15)	1 mole A, 129°, 7 hr.	1- and 2-	47% of 1-isomer converted to 2-isomer
Sodium naphthalene-1-sulfonate	D (31)	4 parts D, 1 hr., 50–60°	1-	—
Naphthalene-1-sulfonyl fluoride	C (31)	4 parts C, 1 day	1,5-	1-SO_2F-5-SO_2Cl
Naphthalene-1-sulfonyl chloride	D (31)	4 parts D, 24 hr., 100°	1,5-	1,5-Di-SO_2F
Naphthalene-2-sulfonic acid	C (305)	3 moles C, 100°	1,6-	1,6-Di-SO_3H
	A, 98% (111, 113, 308)	55–60°, 2 and 10 hr.	1,6- and 1,7-	1,6-Di-SO_3H, 80%; 1,7-Di-SO_3H, 20%
	A, 100% and $K_2S_2O_7$ (309)	10 moles A and 1 mole $K_2S_2O_7$, 160–170°	2,6- and 2,7-	2,6-Di-SO_3H, 12%; 2,7-Di-SO_3H, 87%
	D (31)	4 parts D, 1 hr., 50°	2-	-SO_2F, 33%
Naphthalene-2-sulfonyl chloride	B, 4% (173)	8 parts B, 15–20°	—	-SO_3H derivatives of -SO_2Cl
Naphthalene-2-sulfonyl fluoride	C (31)	2.4 parts C, 2 days	2,6-	2-SO_2F-6-SO_2Cl
Naphthalene-1,5-disulfonic acid	A, 100%, then B, 67% (117)	1.5 parts A, 56°, then 1.4 parts B, 90°, 3.5 hr.	1,3,5-	—
Naphthalene-1,5-disulfonyl fluoride	C (31)	4 parts C, 24 hr., 100°	1,3,5-	Tri-SO_2Cl
Naphthalene-1,6-disulfonic acid	A (111)	160°, 8 hr.	—	2,6-Di-SO_3H, 20%
Naphthalene-2,6-disulfonic acid	B (118)	120°	1,3,7-	—
Naphthalene-2,7-disulfonic acid	A, 95% (114)	1 mole A, 160°, 1–24 hr.	2,6- and 2,7-	Conversion to 2,6-isomer determined for various times
	B, 25% (119)	3 parts B, 90°, 4 hr., then 250°, 6 hr.	1,3,5,7-	End product of sulfonation
Naphthalene-1,3,5-trisulfonic acid	B (119)	High temperature	1,3,5,7-	—
Naphthalene-1,3,7-trisulfonic acid	B (119)	High temperature	1,3,5,7-	—

* A refers to concentrated sulfuric acid; B, to oleum; C, to chlorosulfonic acid; and D, to fluorosulfonic acid.

† References 139–406 appear on pp. 192–197.

TABLE X

Alkyl and Halonaphthalenes ‡

Compound Sulfonated	Reagent * and Reference †	Experimental Conditions	Position of Sulfo Group(s)	Remarks
1-Methylnaphthalene	A (316)	0.75 part A, warm, 5–6 hr.	3-	3-SO_3H, 32%
	A (317)	1.8 parts A, room temperature, 5–6 hr.	4-	Good yield
	A (316)	110°	3- and 7-	Former predominates
	A (318, 319)	165–170°, 5–6 hr.	6-	—
	B (320)	1 vol. B, room temperature	—	Mono-SO_3H
	C (316, 321, 322)	CCl_4 solution, cold	4- and 5-	73% of mixture, mainly 4-; some sulfone
2-Methylnaphthalene	A (323)	0.75 part A, 95°, 6 hr.	6-	6-SO_3H, 80%, no other isomers isolated
	A (324*a*)	1 mole A, shake, room temperature	—	Mixture of two mono-SO_3H
	B, 21% (324*b*)	3 parts B, shake	?	Mono-SO_3H
	C (325)	1 mole C, $C_6H_5NO_2$ solution, 35°	8-	-SO_3H
1-Ethylnaphthalene	B (320)	1 vol. B, room temperature	—	Mono-SO_3H
2-Ethylnaphthalene	A (326)	2 moles A, 70–80°	—	Mono-SO_3H
	A, 66% (327)	1.3 moles A, heat	6-	6-SO_3H, 86%
1-Isopropylnaphthalene	A, 96% (312)	40–45°	4-	—
2-Isopropylnaphthalene	A (312)	—	1-	—
1-Benzylnaphthalene	A (328)	2.5 moles A, 66°	4-	SO_3H, sole product
	C (328)	$C_6H_5NO_2$ solution, room temperature	4-	Sole product
	A (329)	140°	—	Not 4-SO_3H
Coal-tar fraction (b.p. 260–365°)	A (330)	0.6 part A, 40–45°, 10 hr.	—	Some 1,6-dimethylnaphthalene-4-SO_3H
	A, 98% (330)	1 part A, 135–140°, 3 hr.	—	Some 2,6-dimethylnaphthalene-7-SO_3H and 2,3-dimethyl-?-SO_3H
2,6-Dimethylnaphthalene	A, 98% (330)	1 part A, 35–40°, long stirring	8-	8-SO_3H, 60%, perhaps some 1-SO_3H
2,7-Dimethylnaphthalene	A (330)	1 part A, 100°, 1 hr.	—	Mixture of 3-SO_3H and other -SO_3H

* A refers to concentrated sulfuric acid; B, to oleum; C, to chlorosulfonic acid; and D, to fluorosulfonic acid.

† References 139–406 appear on pp. 192–197.

‡ A number of nuclear alkylated naphthalenesulfonic acids has been prepared by treating the hydrocarbon with alcohols in the presence of chlorosulfonic acid[310, 311] or oleum.[311, 312] Successive alkylation and sulfonation[313] or the reverse[314] has also been employed. Other procedures involve the chloromethylation of naphthalene before, during, or after the sulfonation, and the condensation of an unsaturated alcohol or hydrocarbon with the sulfonated naphthalene.[315]

TABLE X—*Continued*

ALKYL AND HALONAPHTHALENES ‡

Compound Sulfonated	Reagent * and Reference †	Experimental Conditions	Position of Sulfo Group(s)	Remarks
1,4-Dimethyl-naphthalene	A (331)	2 parts A, 120°	—	Unknown structure
2,6-Dimethyl-naphthalene-8-sulfonic acid	A, 78% (330)	135°, short time	—	Rearranges to 7-isomer
1,8-Dibenzyl-naphthalene	C (332)	100–110°	4-(?)	$-SO_3H$
Diisopropylnaphthalene	— (312)	—	—	Mono-SO_3H
1-Chloronaphthalene	C (333, 334)	CS_2 solution	4-	4-SO_3H, mainly
	A, 100% (335)	2.5 moles A, 10°	4-	4-SO_3H, 84%, some of 5-isomer
	A (336)	56°, 78°, 98°	4-	4-SO_3H, 70%, 57%, 31% respectively
	C (336)	Excess C, 30°	—	Mixture of $-SO_2Cl$; 4-SO_2Cl is present
	C (43)	$CHCl_3$ solution, 5 parts, 25°, 20 min.	4-	$-SO_2Cl$
	A, 66° Bé. (336, 337)	1-1.5 parts A, 160–170°, several hours	6- and 7-	—
	B (333, 335*a*)	160°	4- and 5-	Equal amounts
	B, 45% (338)	5 parts B, 80°, 8 hr.	2,4,7-	Some di-SO_3H, probably 4,7-
1-Chloronaphthalene-3-sulfonic acid	B, 20% (339)	100°	3,5-	—
1-Chloronaphthalene-4-sulfonic acid	A (333)	150°	—	Rearranges to 5-SO_3H
	B, 20% (340)	100°	4,7-	Di-SO_3H
	B, 20% (338)	5 parts B, 170°, 8 hr.	2,4,7-	Tri-SO_3H
1-Chloronaphthalene-6-sulfonic acid	B, 10% (341)	3–4 parts B, 110°, 6 hr.	4,6-	Di-SO_3H
2-Chloronaphthalene	A and B (342)	130–140°, long heating	6- and 8-	8-SO_3H predominates
	B (335*a*)	Excess B, 160–180°	6,8-	Di-SO_3H
	C (343)	CS_2 solution, cold	6- and 8-	8-SO_3H, mainly; 6-isomer, 4%
	C (43)	$CHCl_3$ solution, 5 parts C, 25°, 20 min.	8-	$-SO_2Cl$

* A refers to concentrated sulfuric acid; B, to oleum; C, to chlorosulfonic acid; and D, to fluoro sulfonic acid.

† References 139–406 appear on pp. 192–197.

‡ A number of nuclear alkylated naphthalenesulfonic acids has been prepared by treating the hydrocarbon with alcohols in the presence of chlorosulfonic acid[310, 311] or oleum.[311, 312] Successive alkylation and sulfonation[313] or the reverse[314] has also been employed. Other procedures involve the chloromethylation of naphthalene before, during, or after the sulfonation, and the condensation of an unsaturated alcohol or hydrocarbon with the sulfonated naphthalene.[315]

TABLE X—*Continued*

ALKYL AND HALONAPHTHALENES ‡

Compound Sulfonated	Reagent * and Reference †	Experimental Conditions	Position of Sulfo Group(s)	Remarks
2-Chloronaphthalene-6-sulfonic acid	$H_2S_2O_7$ (344)	—	6,8-	Di-SO_3H
	B, 20% (344)	—	—	4,6-Di-SO_3H as by-product
2-Chloronaphthalene-7-sulfonic acid	$H_2S_2O_7$ (344)	100°	4,7-	Di-SO_3H
2-Chloronaphthalene-8-sulfonic acid	A (345, 346)	150°, 5 hr.	—	53% of 6-isomer by rearrangement
	$H_2S_2O_7$ (344)	—	6,8-	Di-SO_3H
1-Bromonaphthalene	B (347, 348, 349)	2 parts B, warm, few minutes	4- and 5-(?)	-SO_3H
	C (350)	CS_2 solution	4- and 5-(?)	-SO_3H (and SO_2Cl?)
	C (43)	$CHCl_3$ solution, 5 parts C, 25°, 20 min.	4-	-SO_2Cl
2-Bromonaphthalene	C (343, 346, 351)	CS_2 solution	6- and 8-(?)	-SO_3H (and -SO_2Cl?)
	C (43)	$CHCl_3$ solution, 5 parts C, 25°, 20 min.	8-	-SO_2Cl
2-Bromonaphthalene-8-sulfonic acid	(346)	Heat	—	Rearranges to 6-isomer
1-Iodonaphthalene	C (352)	CS_2 solution	4-(?)	-SO_3H (and -SO_2Cl?)
2-Iodonaphthalene	C (343, 346, 353)	CS_2 solution	8- and 5-	-SO_3H
	C (343, 346)	Cold, then heat to 150°	6-	-SO_3H
2-Iodonaphthalene-5- and 8-sulfonic acids	A (346)	150°	—	Rearranges to 6-isomer
1,2-Dichloronaphthalene	C (346, 354)	10% CS_2 solution	5- and 6-	-SO_3H
1,3-Dichloronaphthalene	C (354)	In CS_2	5- and 7-	-SO_3H
1,4-Dichloronaphthalene	C (354)	In CS_2	6- and (?)	-SO_3H
	C (355)	In CS_2	—	Sulfone, mainly
	A, 100% (356)	12 parts A, room temperature	6-(?)	-SO_3H
	B (357)	160°	6-	-SO_3H

* A refers to concentrated sulfuric acid; B, to oleum; C, to chlorosulfonic acid; and D, to fluorosulfonic acid.

† References 139–406 appear on pp. 192–197.

‡ A number of nuclear alkylated naphthalenesulfonic acids has been prepared by treating the hydrocarbon with alcohols in the presence of chlorosulfonic acid[310, 311] or oleum.[311, 312] Successive alkylation and sulfonation[313] or the reverse[314] has also been employed. Other procedures involve the chloromethylation of naphthalene before, during, or after the sulfonation, and the condensation of an unsaturated alcohol or hydrocarbon with the sulfonated naphthalene.[315]

TABLE X—*Continued*

ALKYL AND HALONAPHTHALENES ‡

Compound Sulfonated	Reagent * and Reference †	Experimental Conditions	Position of Sulfo Group(s)	Remarks
1,5-Dichloro-naphthalene	C (354)	CS_2 solution	3- and (?)	$-SO_3H$
	A, 100% (356)	12 parts A, room temperature	3-	$-SO_3H$
1,6-Dichloro-naphthalene	C (354)	CS_2 solution	4-	$-SO_3H$
	A and B (358)	Equal volumes of A and B, warm	4-	$-SO_3H$
1,7-Dichloro-naphthalene	C (354, 359)	CS_2 solution, low temperature	4-	$-SO_3H$
1,8-Dichloro-naphthalene	C (354)	CS_2 solution, low temperature	4-	$-SO_3H$
2,3-Dichloro-naphthalene	C (354)	CS_2 solution, low temperature	5- and 6-	$-SO_3H$
2,6-Dichloro-naphthalene	C (354)	CS_2 solution, low temperature	4-	$-SO_3H$
2,7-Dichloro-naphthalene	C (354)	CS_2 solution, low temperature	3- and (?)	$-SO_3H$
1,3-Dibromo-naphthalene	A (360)	2 parts A, 100°	5- and 7-	$-SO_3H$
1,4-Dibromo-naphthalene	A, 100% (360, 367*a*)	100°	6-	$-SO_3H$
	B, 2% (361)	2 parts B, 60°, 8 hr.	6-	$6-SO_3H$, 46%
1,5-Dibromo-naphthalene	A (360)	2 parts, 100°	7-(?)	$-SO_3H$
1,6-Dibromo-naphthalene	A (360)	100°	4-(?)	$-SO_3H$
1,7-Dibromo-naphthalene	A (360)	100°	4-(?)	$-SO_3H$
1-Chloro-4-bromo-naphthalene	C (355)	CS_2 solution	—	Sulfone (?), chiefly
1,2,3-Trichloro-naphthalene	B, 10% (354)	100°	—	$-SO_3H$
1,2,4-Trichloro-naphthalene	A or C (354)	100°	—	$-SO_3H$
1,2,7-Trichloro-naphthalene	? (362)	—	?	No details given
1,3,6-Trichloro-naphthalene	? (362)	—	—	No details given
?-Tetrachloro-naphthalene	B (348)	—	—	$-SO_3H$

* A refers to concentrated sulfuric acid; B, to oleum; C, to chlorosulfonic acid; and D, to fluorosulfonic acid.

† References 139–406 appear on pp. 192–197.

‡ A number of nuclear alkylated naphthalenesulfonic acids has been prepared by treating the hydrocarbon with alcohols in the presence of chlorosulfonic acid [310, 311] or oleum.[311, 312] Successive alkylation and sulfonation [313] or the reverse [314] has also been employed. Other procedures involve the chloromethylation of naphthalene before, during, or after the sulfonation, and the condensation of an unsaturated alcohol or hydrocarbon with the sulfonated naphthalene.[315]

TABLE XI

ANTHRACENE AND DERIVATIVES

Compound Sulfonated	Reagent * and Reference †	Experimental Conditions	Position of Sulfo Group(s)	Remarks
Anthracene	B, 20% (18, 120)	1.3 parts B, AcOH solution, 95°, 3 hr.	1- and 2-	1-SO_3H, 50%; 2-SO_3H, 30%
	C (18, 120)	0.7 part C, $(CH_3CO)_2O$ solution, 95°, 5 hr.	1- and 2-	Equal amounts
	$SO_3 \cdot C_5H_5N$ (17, 18)	Various solvents and conditions	1-	1-SO_3H; 2-SO_3H, traces (1%)
	A (363)	3 parts A, 100°	1- and 2-	-SO_3H
	A, 53° Bé. (121)	2 parts A, 120–135°	2-	-SO_3H
	$MHSO_4$ (121)	1.4 parts reagent, 140°, 5.5 hr.	2-	Some di-SO_3H
	A (18, 363)	3 parts A, 100°, 1 hr.	1,5- and 1,8-	Di-SO_3H
	A, 53–58° (364)	4.5 parts A, 140°	2-, 2,6-, and 2,7-	Mainly the 2,7-di-SO_3H
Anthracene-2-sulfonyl chloride	B, 4% (365)	—	—	Mixture
Anthracene-1-sulfonic acid	A, 96% (18)	150–180°, 1 hr.	1,5- and 1,8-	Mixture: 1,5-di-SO_3H, 90%; 1,8-di-SO_3H, 10%
9-Benzylanthracene	A (366)	100°	—	Mono-SO_3H
9,10-Dichloroanthracene	A, 100%, and C (367)	3 parts A, 0.5 part C, 30°, 3 hr.	2-	-SO_3H
	B, 20% (368, 369, 370)	2 parts B, $C_6H_5NO_2$, 10–15°	2-	-SO_3H
	C (367)	0.5 part C, $CHCl_3$ solution, 40°, 4 hr.	2-	-SO_3H
	B (370)	5 parts B, 100°	2,6- and 2,7-(?)	Di-SO_3H
9,10-Dibromoanthracene	C (367)	0.6 part C, $CHCl_3$ solution	2-	-SO_3H
	B (369, 370)	2 parts B, $C_6H_5NO_2$ solution, 10–15°	2-	-SO_3H
	B (370)	6–7 parts B, 100°, 1.5 hr.	2,6- and 2,7-(?)	Di-SO_3H

* A refers to concentrated sulfuric acid; B, to oleum; C, to chlorosulfonic acid; and D, to fluorosulfonic acid.

† References 139–406 appear on pp. 192–197.

TABLE XII

Phenanthrene and Derivatives

Compound Sulfonated	Reagent * and Reference †	Experimental Conditions	Position of Sulfo Group(s)	Remarks
Phenanthrene	A (122, 123, 126)	2 moles A, 120–125°, 3.5 hr.	2- and 3-	2-SO_3H, 20%; 3-SO_3H, 25%; di-SO_3H, >40%
	A (124, 126)	100°, 8 hr.	2-, 3-, and 9-	2-SO_3H, 7%; 3-SO_3H, 9%; 9-SO_3H, 6%
	A (122, 371)	0.6 cc. A per g., 60°, 3 days	1-, 2-, 3-, and 9-	1-SO_3H, 4%; 2-SO_3H, 18%; 3-SO_3H, 19%; 9-SO_3H, 13%
	C (130)	1 mole C in boiling $CHCl_3$	2- and 3-	-SO_3H, 85% of mixture
Phenanthrene-2-sulfonic acid	A (127)	1 cc. A per g., 130°, 30 min.	2,6-, 2,7-, and 2,8-	2,6-Di-SO_3H, 54%; 2,7-, 2.1%; 2,8-, 1%. Isolated as diacetates
Phenanthrene-3-sulfonic acid	A (127)	1 cc. A per g., 130°, 1.5 hr.	2,6-, 3,6-, and 3,8-	2,6-Di-SO_3H, 10%; 3,6-, 59%; 3,8-, 0.9%. Isolated as diacetates
Ammonium phenanthrene-9-sulfonate	(125)	250–260°	—	2-SO_3H, phenanthrene, and a di-SO_3H
1-Methyl-7-isopropylphenanthrene	A (373*a*, 373*b*)	1 part A, 100°, 5 min.	2- and 6-	-SO_3H
	A (373*b*, 374)	1 part A, 190°, 2 min.	6-	6-SO_3H, 69%
	A and B (375)	Room temperature, 2–3 weeks	—	Di-SO_3H
	B (375)	100°, 24 hr.	—	Tri-SO_3H
9-Bromo- and 9-chloro-phenanthrene	A, 96% (372, 376)	0.9 part A, 100°, 2.5 hr. then 0.6 part, 150°, 0.5 hr.	3- or 6-	-SO_3H, 65–75%

* A refers to concentrated sulfuric acid; B, to oleum; C, to chlorosulfonic acid; and D, to fluorosulfonic acid.

† References 139–406 appear on pp. 192–197.

TABLE XIII

Miscellaneous Compounds

Compound Sulfonated	Reagent * and Reference †	Experimental Conditions	Position of Sulfo Group(s)	Remarks
Benzal chloride	A (377)	—	2-, 3-, and 4-	2-SO_3H, 10%; 3-, 30%; 4-, 60%
Benzotrichloride	SO_3 (377)	—	3-	-SO_3H
Benzotrifluoride	SO_3 (378)	—	3-(?)	-SO_3H
4-Chlorobenzotrifluoride	SO_3 (378)	—	?	-SO_3H
Phenylcyclohexane	B (379)	7 vol. B, cool, shake	4-	Substitution in benzene ring
3-Phenylmethylcyclopentane	B (380)	—	—	Mono-SO_3H
Bornylbenzene	A (379)	Room temperature	4-(?)	Quantitative, substitution probably in benzene ring
m-Tolylcyclohexane	A (381)	—	6-(?)	Substitution in tolyl ring
Hydrindene	A (382)	2 parts A, shake	4- and 5-	-SO_3H
	C (383)	4.3 moles C, −10°, 15 min.	4- and 5-	76% yield of mixed -SO_3H
4,7-Dimethylhydrindene	A (384)	11.5 parts A, 100°, 15 min.	5-	1,5-Di-SO_3H, 79%
Tetralin	A (385, 386)	1.2 parts A, 100°	5- and 6-	6-SO_3H, mainly
	C (386)	4.3 moles C, −5–10°	5- and 6-	80% of mixed -SO_2Cl
	D (31)	4 parts D, 15–20°, 12 hr.	5- and 6-	-SO_2F, 13% of 5-
6-Methyltetralin	A (387)	1.25 parts A, 100°	7-	-SO_3H
1,1-Dimethyltetralin	A (388)	1 vol. A, 90°, 2 hr.	—	Two mono-SO_3H
1,1,6-Trimethyltetralin (ionene)	A (389)	1 vol. A, 90°, 2 hr., then stand at room temperature	7-(?)	-SO_3H, 50%
Fluorene	A (390)	—	2-	-SO_3H; mostly 2,7-di-SO_3H
	C (391, 392)	1 mole C with or without $CHCl_3$	2-	-SO_3H
	C (391)	$CHCl_3$ solution	2,7-	Di-SO_3H
	A (390, 393)	4 parts A, 100°	2,7-	Also two other di-SO_3H, probably 2,6- and 3,6-
	SO_3 (1*d*, 390)	$CHCl_3$ solution	2-	-SO_3H
2,7-Dibromofluorene	C (392)	1 mole C in $CHCl_3$	3-(?)	-SO_3H
Acenaphthene	A (394)	0.8 part A, 100°, 2 hr.	3-	-SO_3H
	C (38*b*)	0.5 part C, 125–130°, 10 hr.	3,3′-	Sulfone
	C (394, 395)	1 mole C, inert solvent, near 0°	5-	-SO_3H, ca. 40%
	A (394*c*)	2 parts A, 100°, 8 hr.	—	Di-SO_3H
	A (394*c*)	5 parts A, 20°, 20 hr.	—	Di-SO_3H, different from above acid

* A refers to concentrated sulfuric acid; B, to oleum; C, to chlorosulfonic acid; and D, to fluorosulfonic acid.

† References 139–406 appear on pp. 192–197.

TABLE XIII—*Continued*

MISCELLANEOUS COMPOUNDS

Compound Sulfonated	Reagent * and Reference †	Experimental Conditions	Position of Sulfo Group(s)	Remarks
5-Chloroace-naphthene	A (396)	0.5 part A, 70°, 2 hr.	8-(?)	$-SO_3H$
5-Bromoace-naphthene	C (38*b*, 397)	Room temperature	3- and 8-	$-SO_3H$
	A (38*b*, 397)	80–90°	—	Di-SO_3H
Octahydro-anthracene	A (398)	1.07 moles A, 75°, 50 min.	—	Rearranges to oct-anthrene-9-SO_3H, 66%
	C (398*b*)	2.5 parts C, cool	9-	$-SO_2Cl$, 98%
9-Bromooöctahy-droanthracene	C (398*b*)	3 parts C, cool and stir	10-	$-SO_2Cl$, 82%
9,10-Dihydro-phenanthrene	A (399)	80°, 50 min.	—	Mixture of two di-SO_3H
Octahydro-phenanthrene (octanthrene)	A (399)	1.8 parts A, 70°, 15 min.	9-	$-SO_3H$, 76%
Fluoranthene (idryl)	A (400)	2 parts A, 100°	—	Di-SO_3H
1,3,5-Triphenyl-benzene	B (401)	100°	—	Di-SO_3H
Pyrene	C (136, 137)	1 mole C, CCl_4, or Cl_2CH-$CHCl_2$ solution, 15 hr.	3-	$-SO_3H$, 90–92%
	$H_2S_2O_7$ (402)	—	—	Di-SO_3H
	A, 66% Bé. (137)	4.8 moles A, 15°, 2 days	3,8-	$-SO_3H$, 32%
	A, 100%, then B, 65% (137)	13 moles A with 2.1 moles Na_2SO_4, then 4 parts B, 63°, stir 5 hr.	3,5,8,10-	Tetra-SO_3H, 70%
Sodium pyrene-3-sulfonate	A, 66° Bé. (137)	19 moles A, 5–10°, 1 hr.	3,8-	3,8-Di-SO_3H, 42%; 3,5-isomer, 5.7%
	A, 100% (137)	22.4 moles A, 15°, 1 day	3,5,8-	Tri-SO_3H, 10%
	A, 100%, then B, 65% (137)	8.8 moles A, then 2.6 parts B, 20°, 15 hr.	3,5,8,10-	Tetra-SO_3H, 80%
3-Chloropyrene	A, 100%, then B, 65% (137)	13 moles A with 2.1 moles Na_2SO_4, then 3.3 parts B at 50°, 3 hr.	5,8,10-	Tri-SO_3H, 76%
2,2′-Binaphthyl	A (403*b*)	0.2 part A, 200°, 5–6 hr.	—	Two mono-SO_3H
	A (403)	0.7 part A, 200°, 5–6 hr.	—	Two di-SO_3H
	B (403*b*)	Excess B, 200°, 5–6 hr.	—	Tetra-SO_3H
Decacyclene	A (404)	—	—	Tri-SO_3H
"Abietene"	A (405)	2 parts A, 0–15°, 20 hr.	—	Mono-SO_3H
"Abietanes"	A (406)	—	—	—

* A refers to concentrated sulfuric acid; B, to oleum; C, to chlorosulfonic acid; and D, to fluorosulfonic acid.

† References 139–406 appear on pp. 192–197.

REFERENCES TO TABLES

[139] Mohrmann, *Ann.*, **410,** 373 (1915).
[140] Martinsen, *Z. physik. Chem.*, **59,** 619 (1907).
[141] Hochstetter, *J. Am. Chem. Soc.*, **20,** 549 (1898).
[142] Dennis, Can. pat. 177,138 [*C. A.*, **11,** 3278 (1917)].
[143] Pictet and Karl, *Compt. rend.*, **145,** 239 (1907); *Bull. soc. chim.*, [4] **3,** 1114 (1908).
[144] Grillet, U. S. pat. 1,956,571 [*C. A.*, **28,** 4071 (1934)].
[145] Senhofer, *Ann.*, **174,** 243 (1874).
[146] Kamens'kiĭ-Shmidt, *Mem. Inst. Chem. Ukrain. Acad. Sci.*, **3,** 21 (1937) [*C. A.*, **31,** 5777 (1937)].
[147] Jackson and Wing, *Am. Chem. J.*, **9,** 325 (1887).
[148] Armstrong, *J. Chem. Soc.*, **24,** 173 (1871).
[149] Armstrong, *Chem. News*, **23,** 188 (1871).
[150] Meyer and Noelting, *Ber.*, **7,** 1308 (1874).
[151] Olivier and Kleermaeker, *Rec. trav. chim.*, **39,** 640 (1920).
[152] Glutz, *Ann.*, **143,** 181 (1867).
[153] Farbw. v. Meister, Lucius, and Brünning, Ger. pat. 260,563 [*C. A.*, **7,** 3198 (1913)].
[154] Hübner and Williams, *Ann.*, **167,** 118 (1873); Woelz, *Ann.*, **168,** 81 (1873); Borns, *Ann.*, **187,** 350 (1877).
[155] Friedel and Crafts, *Ann. chim.*, [6] **10,** 413 (1887).
[156] Beilstein and Kurbatow, *Ann.*, **176,** 27 (1875); **182,** 94 (1876).
[157] Holleman and van der Linden, *Rec. trav. chim.*, **30,** 334 (1911).
[158] Davies and Poole, *J. Chem. Soc.*, **1927,** 1122.
[159] Crauw, *Rec. trav. chim.*, **50,** 753 (1931).
[160] Seel, U. S. pat. 2,171,166 [*C. A.*, **34,** 272 (1940)].
[161] Lesimple, *Zeit. für Chemie*, **1868,** 226.
[162] Gebauer-Fülnegg and Figdor, *Monatsh.*, **48,** 627 (1927).
[163] Armstrong, *J. Chem. Soc.*, **97,** 1578 (1910).
[164] Rosenberg, *Ber.*, **19,** 652 (1886).
[165] Reinke, *Ann.*, **186,** 271 (1877).
[166] Bässeman, *Ann.*, **191,** 206 (1878).
[167] Kohlhase, *J. Am. Chem. Soc.*, **54,** 2441 (1932).
[168] Engelhardt and Latschinoff, *Zeit. für Chemie*, **1869,** 617; Wolkow, *ibid.*, **1870,** 321; Vallin, *Ber.*, **19,** 2952 (1886).
[169] Remsen and Fahlberg, *Am. Chem. J.*, **1,** 426 (1879).
[170] Klaesson and Vallin, *Ber.*, **12,** 1848 (1879); Heumann and Köchlin, *Ber.*, **15,** 1114 (1882).
[171] (*a*) Noyes, *Am. Chem. J.*, **8,** 176 (1886); (*b*) Harding, *J. Chem. Soc.*, **119,** 1261 (1921).
[172] Klason, *Ber.*, **19,** 2887 (1886).
[173] I. G. Farbenind. A.-G., Fr. pat. 837,855 [*C. A.*, **33,** 6349 (1939)].
[174] Hübner, Retschy, Müller, and Post, *Ann.*, **169,** 31 (1873); Miller, *J. Chem. Soc.*, **61,** 1029 (1892).
[175] Hübner and Grete, *Ber.*, **6,** 801 (1873); **7,** 795 (1874); Grete, *Ann.*, **177,** 231 (1875); Wroblevski, *Ber.*, **7,** 1063 (1874).
[176] Hübner and Post, *Ann.*, **169,** 1 (1873); Jenssen, *Ann.*, **172,** 230 (1874); v. Pechmann, *Ann.*, **173,** 195 (1874); Schäfer, *Ann.*, **174,** 357 (1874).
[177] Kornatzki, *Ann.*, **221,** 191 (1883).
[178] Vogt and Henninger, *Ann.*, **165,** 362 (1873).
[179] Mabery and Palmer, *Am. Chem. J.*, **6,** 170 (1884).
[180] Hübner and Glassner, *Ber.*, **8,** 560 (1875).
[181] Cohen and Dutt, *J. Chem. Soc.*, **105,** 501 (1914).
[182] Cohen and Dakin, *J. Chem. Soc.*, **79,** 1129 (1901); Wynne and Greeves, *Chem. News*, **72,** 58 (1895).
[183] Seelig, *Ann.*, **237,** 129 (1887).
[184] Cohen and Smithells, *J. Chem. Soc.*, **105,** 1907 (1914).

[185] Sempotowski, *Ber.*, **22**, 2663 (1889).
[186] Chrustschoff, *Ber.*, **7**, 1166 (1874).
[187] Moody, *Chem. News*, **71**, 197 (1895).
[188] Steinkopf and Hübner, *J. prakt. Chem.*, [2] **141**, 193 (1934).
[189] Pollak, Fiedler, and Roth, *Monatsh.*, **39**, 182 (1918).
[190] Moody, *Chem. News*, **79**, 81 (1899).
[191] Fittig, Schaeffer, and König, *Ann.*, **149**, 324 (1869).
[192] Spica, *Gazz. chim. ital.*, **8**, 406 (1878).
[193] Meyer and Baur, *Ann.*, **219**, 299 (1883).
[194] Spica, *Ber.*, **12**, 2367 (1879).
[195] Balbiano, *Gazz. chim. ital.*, **7**, 343 (1877).
[196] (*a*) Estreichner, *Ber.*, **33**, 436 (1900); (*b*) Klages, *Ber.*, **39**, 2131 (1906).
[197] Kelbe and Pfeiffer, *Ber.*, **19**, 1723 (1886); Baur, *Ber.*, **24**, 2832 (1891).
[198] Klages and Sommer, *Ber.*, **39**, 2306 (1906).
[199] Tollens and Fittig, *Ann.*, **131**, 315 (1884).
[200] Klages, *Ber.*, **36**, 3688 (1903).
[201] Dafert, *Monatsh.*, **4**, 616 (1883).
[202] Bygdén, *J. prakt. Chem.*, [2] **100**, 1 (1919).
[203] Brochet, *Compt. rend.*, **117**, 117 (1893); *Bull. soc. chim.*, [3] **9**, 687 (1893).
[204] Klages and Sautter, *Ber.*, **37**, 654 (1904).
[205] Klages, *Ber.*, **37**, 2308 (1904).
[206] Schweinitz, *Ber.*, **19**, 642 (1886).
[207] I. G. Farbenind. A.-G., Brit. pat. 453,778 [*C. A.*, **31**, 1122 (1937)].
[208] Krafft, *Ber.*, **19**, 2982 (1886).
[209] Kyrides, U. S. pat. 2,161,173 [*C. A.*, **33**, 7438 (1939)]; Stirton and Peterson, *Ind. Eng. Chem.*, **31**, 856 (1939).
[210] Günther and Hetzer, U. S. pat. 1,737,792 [*C. A.*, **24**, 864 (1930)].
[211] Krüger, *Ber.*, **18**, 1755 (1885).
[212] Claus and Bayer, *Ann.*, **274**, 304 (1893).
[213] Stallard, *J. Chem. Soc.*, **89**, 808 (1906).
[214] Kizhner and Vendelshtein, *J. Russ. Phys.-Chem. Soc., Chem. Part*, **57**, 1 (1926) [*C. A.*, **20**, 2316 (1926)].
[215] Jacobsen, *Ber.*, **18**, 1760 (1885).
[216] Weinburg, *Ber.*, **11**, 1062 (1878).
[217] Bauch, *Ber.*, **23**, 3117 (1890).
[218] Jacobsen, *Ber.*, **21**, 2821 (1888).
[219] Jacobsen and Weinberg, *Ber.*, **11**, 1534 (1878).
[220] Töhl and Bauch, *Ber.*, **26**, 1105 (1893).
[221] Holmes, *Am. Chem. J.*, **13**, 371 (1891).
[222] Kluge, *Ber.*, **18**, 2098 (1885).
[223] Wahl, *Compt. rend.*, **200**, 936 (1936).
[224] Moody and Nicholson, *J. Chem. Soc.*, **57**, 974 (1890).
[225] Voswinkel, *Ber.*, **21**, 3499 (1878).
[226] Voswinkel, *Ber.*, **21**, 2829 (1878); Fournier, *Bull. soc. chim.*, [3] **7**, 651 (1892); Allen and Underwood, *ibid.*, [2] **40**, 100 (1883).
[227] Fittig and König, *Ann.*, **144**, 286 (1867); Aschenbrandt, *Ann.*, **216**, 214 (1883): Remsen and Noyes, *Am. Chem. J.*, **4**, 197 (1883).
[228] Körner, *Ann.*, **216**, 224 (1883); Remsen and Keiser, *Am. Chem. J.*, **5**, 161 (1883); *see also* Heise, *Ber.*, **24**, 768 (1891).
[229] Uhlhorn, *Ber.*, **23**, 3142 (1890).
[230] Newton, *J. Am. Chem. Soc.*, **65**, 2439 (1943).
[231] Baur, *Ber.*, **27**, 1606 (1894).
[232] Claus and Pieszcek, *Ber.*, **19**, 3090 (1886).
[233] Wroblewski, *Ann.*, **192**, 199 (1878).
[234] Bayrac, *Bull. soc. chim.*, [3] **13**, 890 (1895); *Ann. chim.*, [7] **10**, 28 (1897).
[235] Defren, *Ber.*, **28**, 2648 (1895).

[236] Claus and Stüsser, *Ber.*, **13,** 899 (1880).
[237] Widman, *Ber.*, **24,** 444 (1891); Claus, *Ber.*, **14,** 2139 (1881).
[238] Sprinkmeyer, *Ber.*, **34,** 1950 (1901).
[239] Kelbe, *Ann.*, **210,** 30 (1881); Kelbe and Czarnomski, *Ber.*, **17,** 1747 (1884); *Ann.*, **235,** 285 (1896).
[240] Spica, *Ber.*, **14,** 652 (1881); *Gazz. chim. ital.*, **12,** 487, 546 (1882); Armstrong and Miller, *Ber.*, **16,** 2748 (1883).
[241] Claus and Cratz, *Ber.*, **13,** 901 (1880); Claus, *Ber.*, **14,** 2139 (1881).
[242] (*a*) Kelbe and Koschnitsky, *Ber.*, **19,** 1730 (1886); (*b*) Dinesmann, Ger. pat. 125,097 [*Chem. Zentr.*, **72,** II, 1030 (1901)].
[243] (*a*) Jünger and Klages, *Ber.*, **29,** 314 (1896); (*b*) Klages and Kraith, *Ber.*, **32,** 2555 (1899).
[244] Carrara, *Gazz. chim. ital.*, **19,** 173, 502 (1889).
[245] Claus and Christ, *Ber.*, **19,** 2162 (1886).
[246] Paternò and Canzoneri, *Gazz. chim. ital.*, **11,** 124 (1881).
[247] (*a*) Kelbe and Baur, *Ber.*, **16,** 2559 (1883); (*b*) Baur, *Ber.*, **24,** 2832 (1891); **27,** 1614 (1894).
[248] Noelting, *Ber.*, **25,** 785 (1892).
[249] Noelting, *Chimie & industrie*, **6,** 722 (1921).
[250] Bigot and Fittig, *Ann.*, **141,** 166 (1867).
[251] Lipinski, *Ber.*, **31,** 938 (1898).
[252] Krafft and Göttig, *Ber.*, **21,** 3183 (1888).
[253] Widman, *Ber.*, **23,** 3080 (1890); **24,** 456 (1891).
[254] von der Becke, *Ber.*, **23,** 3191 (1890).
[255] Klages and Keil, *Ber.*, **36,** 1641 (1903).
[256] Heise, *Ber.*, **24,** 768 (1891).
[257] Fileti, *Gazz. chim. ital.*, **21,** I, 4 (1891).
[258] Kelbe and Pathe, *Ber.*, **19,** 1546 (1886).
[259] Jacobsen, *Ber.*, **19,** 1218 (1886).
[260] Franke, dissertation, Rostock; *see* Töhl and Müller, ref. 261.
[261] Töhl and Müller, *Ber.*, **26,** 1108 (1893).
[262] Kürzel, *Ber.*, **22,** 1586 (1889).
[263] Ravikovich, *J. Russ. Phys.-Chem. Soc.*, **62,** 177 (1930) [*C. A.*, **24,** 5588 (1930)].
[264] Rose, *Ann.*, **164,** 53 (1872).
[265] Töhl and Eckel, *Ber.*, **26,** 1099 (1893).
[266] Klages, *J. prakt. Chem.*, [2] **65,** 394 (1902).
[267] Gustavsen, *J. prakt. Chem.*, [2] **72,** 57 (1905).
[268] Stahl, *Ber.*, **23,** 988 (1890).
[269] Armstrong and Miller, *Ber.*, **16,** 2259 (1883).
[270] Ernst and Fittig, *Ann.*, **139,** 184 (1866).
[271] Jacobsen, *Ber.*, **7,** 1433 (1874); *Ann.*, **195,** 284 (1879).
[272] Töhl and Geyger, *Ber.*, **25,** 1533 (1892).
[273] Uhlhorn, *Ber.*, **23,** 2349 (1890).
[274] Darzens and Rost, *Compt. rend.*, **152,** 607 (1911); Valentiner, Ger. pat. 69,072 [*Frdl.*, **3,** 881].
[275] Klages, *Ber.*, **40,** 2370 (1907).
[276] Schorger, *J. Am. Chem. Soc.*, **39,** 2678 (1917).
[277] (*a*) Smith and Cass, *J. Am. Chem. Soc.*, **54,** 1603, 1609, 1614 (1932); (*b*) Jacobsen, *Ber.*, **19,** 1209 (1886).
[278] Töhl, *Ber.*, **25,** 1527, 2759 (1892).
[279] Bielefeldt, *Ann.*, **198,** 381 (1879); Jacobsen, *Ber.*, **15,** 1853 (1882).
[280] Markownikoff, *Ann.*, **234,** 101 (1886).
[281] Jacobsen and Schnapauff, *Ber.*, **18,** 2841 (1885).
[282] Smith and Lux, *J. Am. Chem. Soc.*, **51,** 2994 (1929).
[283] Jacobsen, *Ber.*, **20,** 2837 (1887); Smith and Moyle, *J. Am. Chem. Soc.*, **55,** 1676 (1933)
[284] Klages and Keil, *Ber.*, **36,** 1632 (1903).

[285] Töhl, *Ber.*, **28,** 2459 (1895).

[286] Klages and Stamm, *Ber.*, **37,** 1715 (1904).

[287] Töhl and Karchowski, *Ber.*, **25,** 1530 (1892).

[288] Jacobsen, *Ber.*, (*a*) **21,** 2821 (1888); (*b*) **20,** 896 (1887).

[289] Feldmann, *Helv. Chim. Acta*, **14,** 751 (1931); Latschinow, *J. Russ. Phys.-Chem. Soc.*, **5,** 50 (1873); *Ber.*, **6,** 193 (1873); Fittig, *Ann.*, **132,** 209 (1864).

[290] Knauf and Adams, *J. Am. Chem. Soc.*, **55,** 4704 (1933).

[291] Zincke, *Ber.*, **5,** 683 (1872).

[292] Klages, *Ber.*, **40,** 2371 (1907).

[293] Mazzara, *Gazz. chim. ital.*, **8,** 509 (1878).

[294] Bergmann, *Chem. Revs.*, **29,** 538 (1941).

[295] Elbs, *J. prakt. Chem.*, [2] **47,** 49 (1893).

[296] Hepp, *Ber.*, **7,** 1420 (1874).

[297] Merz, *Zeit. für Chemie.*, **1868,** 395; Merz and Weith, *Ber.*, **3,** 195 (1870); Merz and Mühlhauser, *Ber.*, **3,** 710 (1870); Brande, *Quart. J. Sci.*, **8,** 289 (1819); Chamberlain, *Annals of Phil.*, **6,** 136 (1823).

[298] Fierz-David, *J. Soc. Chem. Ind.*, **42,** 421T (1923); J. R. Geigy Soc., Fr. pat. 765,771 [*C. A.*, **28,** 6726 (1934)].

[299] Landshoff and Meyer, Ger. pat. 50,411 [*Frdl.*, **2,** 241].

[300] Armstrong and Wynne, *Ber.*, **24R,** 718 (1891).

[301] Dennis, U. S. pat. 1,332,203 [*C. A.*, **14,** 1123 (1920)]; Grishin and Spruiskov, *Anilinokrasochnaya Prom.*, **2,** 19 (1932) [*C. A.*, **27,** 4791 (1933)].

[302] Schultz, *Ber.*, **23,** 77 (1890).

[303] Ewer and Pick, Brit. pat. 2,619 [*Frdl.*, **2,** 245].

[304] Corbellini, *Giorn. chim. ind. applicata*, **9,** 118 (1927) [*C. A.*, **22,** 2938 (1928)]; Armstrong, *Chem. News*, **54,** 255 (1886); Bernthsen and Semper, *Ber.*, **20,** 938 (1887).

[305] Armstrong, *Ber.*, **15,** 204 (1882).

[306] A.-G. für Anilinofabrik, Ger. pat. 45,776 [*Frdl.*, **2,** 253]; Bernthsen, *Ber.*, **22,** 3327 (1889); Armstrong and Wynne, *Chem. News*, **55,** 136 (1887).

[307] Willard, *Color Trade J.*, **15,** 40 (1924).

[308] Ewer and Pick, Ger. pat. 45,229 [*Frdl.*, **2,** 244].

[309] Baum, Ger. pat. 61,730 [*Frdl.*, **3,** 419].

[310] Dachlauer and Thiel, U. S. pat. 1,804,527 [*C. A.*, **25,** 3669 (1931)].

[311] I. G. Farbenind. A.-G., Brit. pats. 253, 118 [*C. A.*, **21,** 2477 (1927)]; 269,155 [*C. A.*, **22,** 1365 (1928)].

[312] Meyer and Bernhauer, *Monatsh.*, **53–54,** 721 (1929); *Chem. Zentr.*, **101,** I, 354 (1930).

[313] Cook and Valjavec, U. S. pat. 2,133,282 [*C. A.*, **33,** 646 (1939)].

[314] Günther and Krauch, Ger. pat. 407,240 [*Chem. Zentr.*, **96,** I, 1791 (1925)].

[315] Kimbara, Brit. pat. 502,964 [*C. A.*, **33,** 6997 (1939)].

[316] Veselý and Štursa, *Coll. Czechoslov. Chem. Commun.*, **3,** 328 (1931) [*C. A.*, **25,** 4877 (1931)].

[317] Elbs and Christ, *J. prakt. Chem.*, [2] **106,** 17 (1923).

[318] Dziewonski and Waszkowski, *Bull. intern. acad. polon. sci.*, **1929A,** 604 [*C. A.*, **25,** 1241 (1931)].

[319] Dziewonski and Otto, *Bull. intern. acad. polon. sci.*, **1935A,** 201 [*C. A.*, **30,** 2561 (1936)]; Dziewonski and Kowalczyk, *ibid.*, **1935A,** 559 [*C. A.*, **30,** 5212 (1936)].

[320] Fittig and Remsen, *Ann.*, **155,** 115 (1870).

[321] Steiger, *Helv. Chim. Acta*, **13,** 173 (1930).

[322] Veselý, Štursa, Olejníček, and Rein, *Coll. Czechoslav. Chem. Commun.*, **1,** 493 (1929) [*C. A.*, **24,** 611 (1930)].

[323] Dziewonski, Schoenówne, and Waldman, *Ber.*, **58,** 1211 (1925).

[324] (*a*) Wendt, *J. prakt. Chem.*, [2] **46,** 322 (1892); (*b*) Reingruber, *Ann.*, **206,** 377 (1881).

[325] Dziewonski and Wulffsohn, *Bull. intern. acad. polon. sci.*, **1929A,** 143 [*C. A.*, **25,** 1514 (1931)].

[326] Marchetti, *Gazz. chim. ital.*, **11,** 265, 439 (1881).

[327] Lévy, *Ann. chim.*, **9,** 5 (1938).

[328] Dziewonski and Dziecielewski, *Bull. intern. acad. polon. sci.*, **1927A**, 273 [*C. A.*, **22**, 2164 (1928)].

[329] Miquel, *Bull. soc. chim.*, [2] **26**, 5 (1876).

[330] Weissgerber and Kruber, *Ber.*, **52**, 346 (1919); Gesell. für Teerverwertung, Ger. pat. 301,079 [*Chem. Zentr.*, **88**, II, 713 (1917)].

[331] Giovannozzi, *Gazz. chim. ital.*, **12**, 147 (1882).

[332] Dziewonski and Moszew, *Bull. intern. acad. polon. sci.*, **1928**, 283 [*C. A.*, **23**, 3220 (1929)]; Dziewonski and Moszew, *Roczniki Chem.*, **9**, 361 (1929) [*C. A.*, **23**, 3923 (1929)].

[333] Armstrong and Wynne, *Chem. News*, **61**, 285 (1890).

[334] Armstrong and Williamson, *Proc. Chem. Soc.*, **1886**, 233; **1887**, 145.

[335] (*a*) Arnell, *Bull. soc. chim.*, [2] **39**, 62 (1883); (*b*) Vorozhtzow and Karlash, *Anilinokrasochnaya Prom.*, **4**, 545 (1934) [*C. A.*, **29**, 2530 (1935)].

[336] Ferrero and Bolliger, *Helv. Chim. Acta*, **11**, 1144 (1928).

[337] Oehler, Ger. pat. 76,396 [*Frdl.*, **4**, 523].

[338] Oehler, Ger. pat. 76,230 [*Frdl.*, **4**, 522].

[339] Armstrong and Wynne, *Chem. News*, **73**, 55 (1896).

[340] Armstrong and Wynne, *Chem. News*, **61**, 94 (1890).

[341] Rudolph, Ger. pat. 104,902 [*Chem. Zentr.*, **70**, II, 1038 (1899)].

[342] Arnell, *Bull. soc. chim.*, [2] **45**, 184 (1886).

[343] Armstrong and Wynne, *Chem. News*, **55**, 91 (1887); **57**, 8 (1887).

[344] Armstrong and Wynne, *Chem. News*, **62**, 164 (1890).

[345] Armstrong, *Chem. News*, **58**, 295 (1888).

[346] Armstrong and Wynne, *Chem. News*, **60**, 58 (1889).

[347] Jolin, *Bull. soc. chim.*, [2] **28**, 514 (1877).

[348] Laurent, *Ann.*, **72**, 298 (1849).

[349] Otto and Möries, *Ann.*, **147**, 183 (1868); Darmstaedter and Wichelhaus, *Ann.*, **152**, 303 (1869).

[350] Armstrong and Williamson, *Chem. News*, **54**, 256 (1886).

[351] Sindall, *Chem. News*, **60**, 58 (1889).

[352] Armstrong, *Chem. News*, **56**, 241 (1887).

[353] Houlding, *Chem. News*, **59**, 226 (1889).

[354] Armstrong and Wynne, *Chem. News*, **61**, 273 (1890).

[355] Heller, *Chem. News*, **60**, 58 (1889).

[356] Bad. Anilin- und Soda-Fabrik, Ger. pat. 229,912 [*Chem. Zentr.*, **82**, I, 358 (1911)].

[357] Arnell, dissertation, Upsala, 1889.

[358] Cleve, *Ber.*, **24**, 3477 (1891).

[359] Armstrong and Wynne, *Chem. News*, **59**, 189 (1889).

[360] Armstrong and Rossiter, *Chem. News*, **65**, 58 (1892).

[361] Salkind and Belikoff, *Ber.*, **64**, 959 (1931).

[362] Armstrong and Wynne, *Chem. News*, **71**, 254 (1895).

[363] Liebermann and Boeck, *Ber.*, **11**, 1613 (1878); Liebermann, *Ber.*, **12**, 182 (1879).

[364] Soc. St. Denis, Ger. pats. 73,961 [*Frdl.*, **3**, 196]; 76,280 [*Frdl.*, **4**, 270].

[365] I. G. Farbenind., Fr. pat. 837,855 [*C. A.*, **33**, 6349 (1939)].

[366] Bach, *Ber.*, **23**, 1570 (1890).

[367] Bad. Anilin- und Soda-Fabrik, Ger. pat. 260,562 [*Chem. Zentr.*, **84**, II, 104 (1913)].

[368] Minaev and Federov, *Bull. inst. polytech. Ivanovo-Vosniesensk*, **15**, 113 (1930) [*C. A.*, **25**, 4258 (1931)].

[369] Höchster Farbwerke, Ger. pat. 292,590 [*Chem. Zentr.*, **81**, II, 208 (1916)].

[370] Perkin, *Ann.*, **158**, 319 (1871).

[371] Ioffe and Matveeva, Russian pat. 34,550 [*C. A.*, **29**, 2977 (1935)].

[372] Bolam and Hope, *J. Chem. Soc.*, **1941**, 843.

[373] (*a*) Komppa and Wahlforss, *J. Am. Chem. Soc.*, **52**, 5009 (1930); (*b*) Fieser and Young *ibid.*, **53**, 4120 (1931).

[374] Hasselstrom and Bogert, *J. Am. Chem. Soc.*, **57**, 1579 (1935).

[375] Ekstrand, *Ann.*, **185**, 86 (1877); Fritzsche, *J. prakt. Chem.*, **82**, 333 (1861).

[376] Anschütz and Siemienski, *Ber.*, **13,** 1179 (1880); Sandqvist, *Ann.*, **398,** 125 (1913); **417,** 1, 17 (1918).

[377] Lauer, *J. prakt. Chem.*, [2] **142,** 252 (1935).

[378] I. G. Farbenind. A.-G., Brit. pat. 463,559 [*C. A.*, **31,** 5817 (1937)]; Zitscher and Kehlen, U. S. pat. 2,141,893 [*C. A.*, **33,** 2730 (1939)].

[379] Kursanoff, *Ann.*, **318,** 309 (1901).

[380] Gustavson, *Compt. rend.*, **146,** 640 (1908).

[381] Kurssanoff, *J. Russ. Phys.-Chem. Soc.*, **38,** 1304 (1907) [*Chem. Zentr.*, I, 1744 (1907)].

[382] Spilker, *Ber.*, **26,** 1538 (1893); Moschner, *Ber.* **34,** 1257 (1901).

[383] Arnold and Zaugg, *J. Am. Chem. Soc.*, **63,** 1317 (1941).

[384] Fieser and Lothrop, *J. Am. Chem. Soc.*, **58,** 2050 (1936).

[385] Bamberger and Kitschelt, *Ber.*, **23,** 1563 (1890); Schroeter and Schranth, Ger. pat. 299,603 [*Chem. Zentr.*, **90,** IV, 618 (1919)].

[386] Schroeter, Svanoe, Einbeck, Geller, and Riebensohm, *Ann.*, **426,** 83 (1922).

[387] Veselý and Štursa, *Coll. Czechoslov. Chem. Commun.*, **6,** 137 (1934) [*C. A.*, **28,** 5815 (1934)].

[388] Bogert, Davidson, and Apfelbaum, *J. Am. Chem. Soc.*, **56,** 959 (1934).

[389] Bogert and Fourman, *J. Am. Chem. Soc.*, **55,** 4676 (1933).

[390] Courtot, *Ann. chim.*, [10] **14,** 17 (1930).

[391] Courtot and Geoffrey, *Compt. rend.*, **178,** 2259 (1924).

[392] Hodgkinson and Matthews, *J. Chem. Soc.*, **43,** 166 (1883).

[393] Schmidt, Retzloff, and Haid, *Ann.*, **390,** 217 (1912); Courtot and Geoffrey, *Compt. rend.*, **180,** 1665 (1925).

[394] (*a*) Dziewoński, Galitzerówna, and Kocwa, *Bull. intern. acad. polon. sci.*, **1926A,** 209 [*C. A.*, **22,** 1154 (1928)]; (*b*) Dziewonski and Kocwa, *ibid.*, **1928,** 405 [*C. A.*, **23,** 2435 (1929)]; (*c*) Dziewonski and Stollyhwo, *Iszy. Zjazd. Chemików Polskich*, **1923,** 57 [*C. A.*, **18,** 981 (1924)]; *Ber.*, **57,** 1531 (1924).

[395] Bogert and Conklin, *Coll. Czech. Chem. Commun.*, **5,** 187 (1933) [*C. A.*, **27,** 4230 (1933)].

[396] Dziewonski and Zakrzewska-Barnaowska, *Bull. intern. acad. polon. sci.*, **1-2A,** 65 (1927) [*C. A.*, **21,** 2682 (1927)].

[397] Dziewonski, Schoen, and Glazner, *Bull. intern. acad. polon. sci.*, **1929A,** 636 [*C. A.*, **25,** 1518 (1931)]; Dziewonski, Glasnerówna, and Orzelski, *Iszy. Zjazd. Chemików Polskich*, **1923,** 57 [*C. A.*, **18,** 981 (1924)].

[398] (*a*) Schroeter, *Ber.*, **57,** 2003 (1924); (*b*) Schroeter and Götzky, *Ber.*, **60,** 2035 (1927).

[399] Schroeter, Müller, and Hwang, *Ber.*, **62,** 645 (1929).

[400] Goldschmiedt, *Monatsh.*, **1,** 227 (1880).

[401] Mellin, *Ber.*, **23,** 2533 (1890).

[402] Goldschmiedt and Wegscheider, *Monatsh.*, **4,** 242 (1883).

[403] (*a*) Smith, *J. Chem. Soc.*, **32,** 558 (1877); (*b*) Smith and Takamatsu, *ibid.*, **39,** 551 (1881).

[404] Dziewonski and Pochwalski, *Iszy. Zjazd. Chemików Polskich*, **1923,** 56 [*C. A.*, **18,** 982 (1924)].

[405] Henke and Weiland, U. S. pat. 1,853,352 [*C. A.*, **26,** 3264 (1932)].

[406] Gubelmann and Henke, U. S. pat. 1,853,348 [*C. A.*, **26,** 3264 (1932)].

CHAPTER 5

AZLACTONES

H. E. Carter

University of Illinois

CONTENTS

INTRODUCTION

Azlactones may be considered anhydrides of α-acylamino acids. It is convenient to classify them into two groups, saturated and unsaturated, as shown in formulas I and II, since the two types show characteristic differences in properties.

$$\begin{array}{c}R_2C_4\text{—}{}_5C{=}O\\ |\qquad\quad |\\ N^3\qquad {}^1O\\ \diagdown\!\!\diagdown{}^2\diagup\\ C\\ R\\ \text{I}\end{array}\qquad\qquad\begin{array}{c}R_2C{=}C_4\text{—}{}_5C{=}O\\ |\qquad\quad |\\ N^3\qquad {}^1O\\ \diagdown\!\!\diagdown{}^2\diagup\\ C\\ R\\ \text{II}\end{array}$$

Plöchl,[1] in 1883, prepared the first unsaturated azlactone by the condensation of benzaldehyde with hippuric acid in the presence of acetic anhydride. However, it remained for Erlenmeyer to determine the structure of the product,[2, 3] to extend the reaction to other aldehydes [4–10]

[1] Plöchl, *Ber.*, **16**, 2815 (1883).
[2] Erlenmeyer, *Ann.*, **275**, 1 (1893).
[3] Erlenmeyer, *Ber.*, **33**, 2036 (1900).
[4] Erlenmeyer and Halsey, *Ann.*, **307**, 138 (1899).
[5] Erlenmeyer and Kunlin, *Ann.*, **316**, 145 (1901).
[6] Erlenmeyer and Matter, *Ann.*, **337**, 271 (1904).
[7] Erlenmeyer and Stadlin, *Ann.*, **337**, 283 (1904).
[8] Erlenmeyer and Wittenberg, *Ann.*, **337**, 294 (1904).
[9] Erlenmeyer and Halsey, *Ber.*, **30**, 2981 (1897).
[10] Erlenmeyer and Kunlin, *Ber.*, **35**, 384 (1902).

(aromatic and aliphatic), and to establish the usefulness of unsaturated azlactones as intermediates in the synthesis of α-keto[11, 12, 13] and α-amino

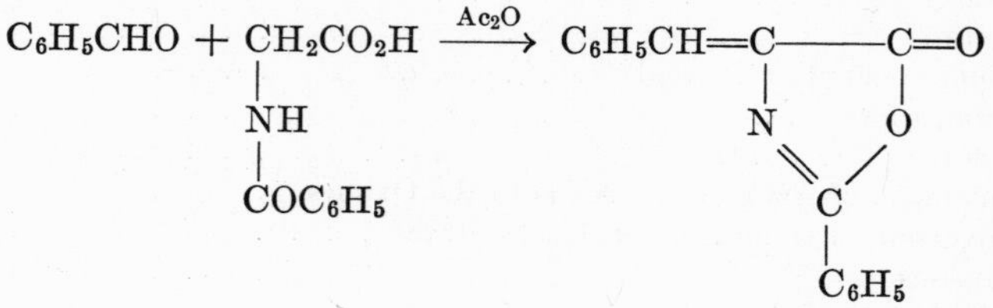

```
                            Ac2O
C6H5CHO + CH2CO2H  ─────→  C6H5CH═C────────C═O
          |                        |        |
          NH                       N        O
          |                         ╲╲     ╱
          COC6H5                       C
                                       |
                                       C6H5
```

acids.[4, 14, 15, 16] Consequently, the reaction of an aldehyde with hippuric acid usually is referred to as the Erlenmeyer azlactone synthesis.

Erlenmeyer was unable to prepare saturated azlactones,[17] probably because he failed to appreciate the ease with which they are hydrolyzed. However, Mohr and coworkers[18–24] in 1908–1910 prepared several compounds of this type by the action of acetic anhydride on α-acylamino

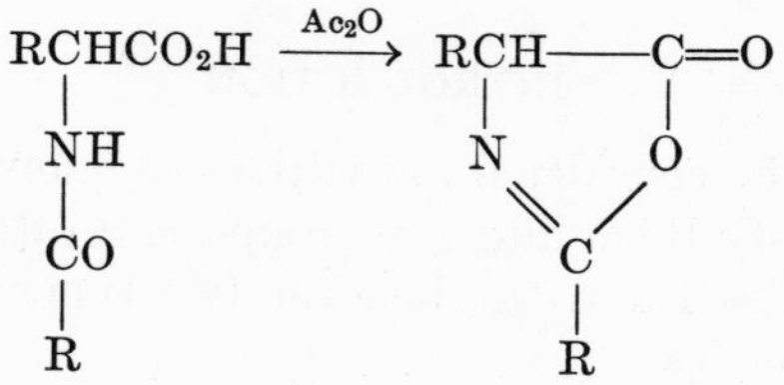

```
          Ac2O
RCHCO2H  ─────→  RCH──────C═O
|                 |        |
NH                N        O
|                  ╲╲     ╱
CO                    C
|                     |
R                     R
```

acids. This reaction has been employed in the preparation of a variety of saturated azlactones which have been used as intermediates in the synthesis of peptides.[25–28]

[11] Erlenmeyer, *Ann.*, **271,** 137 (1892).
[12] Erlenmeyer, *Ann.*, **275,** 8 (1893).
[13] Erlenmeyer and Früstück, *Ann.*, **284,** 36 (1895).
[14] Erlenmeyer, *Ann.*, **275,** 13 (1893).
[15] Erlenmeyer and Kunlin, *Ann.*, **307,** 163 (1899).
[16] Erlenmeyer, *Ann.*, **337,** 205 (1904).
[17] Erlenmeyer, *Ann.*, **307,** 70 (1899).
[18] Mohr and Geis, *Ber.*, **41,** 798 (1908).
[19] Mohr and Stroschein, *Ber.*, **42,** 2521 (1909).
[20] Mohr, *J. prakt. Chem.*, **80,** 521 (1908).
[21] Mohr, *J. prakt. Chem.*, **81,** 49 (1910).
[22] Mohr, *J. prakt. Chem.*, **81,** 473 (1910).
[23] Mohr, *J. prakt. Chem.*, **82,** 60 (1910).
[24] Mohr, *J. prakt. Chem.*, **82,** 322 (1910).
[25] Bergmann and Grafe, *Z. physiol. Chem.*, **187,** 196 (1930).
[26] Bergmann, Stern, and Witte, *Ann.*, **449,** 277 (1926).
[27] Bergmann and Koster, *Z. physiol. Chem.*, **167,** 91 (1927).
[28] Bergmann and Zervas, *Z. physiol. Chem.*, **175,** 154 (1928).

Several different structures have been suggested for the azlactones. Of these only two (formulas III and IV) have received serious considera-

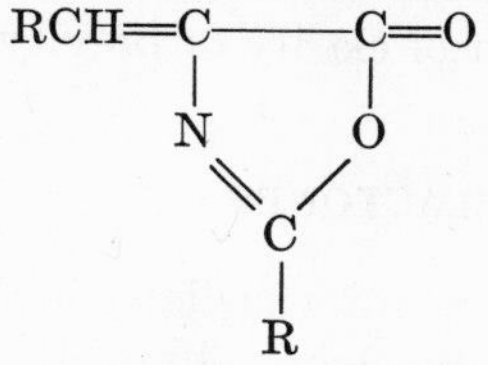

```
RCH=C———C=O          RCH=C———C=O
    |     |               \   /
    N     O                 N
     \\  /                  |
       C                   C=O
       |                    |
       R                    R
      III                   IV
```

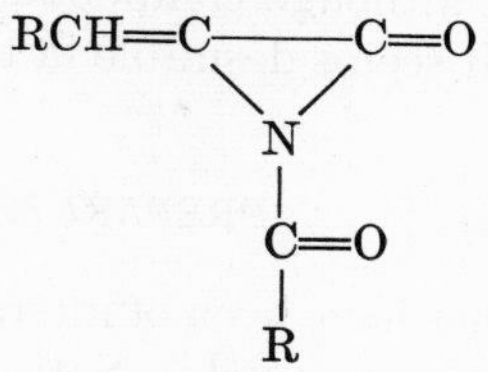

tion. The three-membered ring structure IV (called lactimide) was proposed by Rebuffat [29] in 1889 and accepted by Erlenmeyer [2] in 1893. However, in 1900 Erlenmeyer [3] abandoned this formula in favor of the five-membered ring (III) for which he later [30] proposed the term "azlactone." The term "lactimone" also has been applied to these compounds.[18, 31] Although formula III has been accepted generally, Heller and Hessel [32] as late as 1929 presented arguments in favor of the three-membered ring structure.

Geometric isomerism is possible in the unsaturated azlactones, and there has been speculation in the literature concerning the existence of the two forms.[6, 7, 10, 33] The *cis* and *trans* isomers of benzoylaminocrotonic azlactone [34] and of benzoylaminocinnamic azlactone have been isolated.[35]

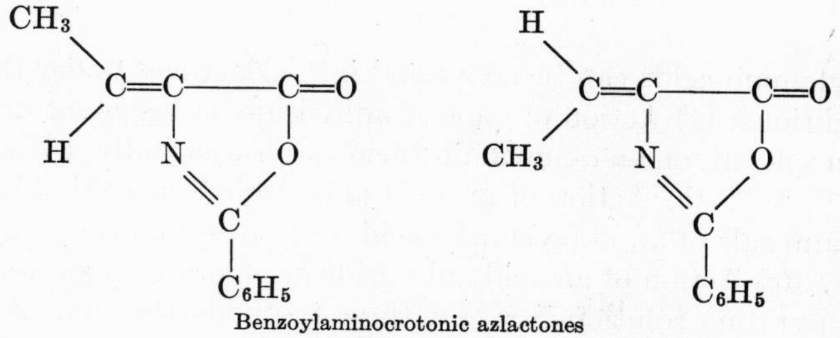

```
CH3                          H
   \                          \
    C=C———C=O                  C=C———C=O
   /  |     |                 /  |     |
  H   N     O             CH3    N     O
       \\  /                      \\  /
         C                          C
         |                          |
        C6H5                       C6H5
```

Benzoylaminocrotonic azlactones

Azlactones are named as derivatives of amino acids, of oxazolone (*Chemical Abstracts* and *Beilstein's Handbuch*), and of dihydroöxazole (British usage). Thus the condensation product of benzaldehyde with hippuric acid may be called benzoyl-α-aminocinnamic azlactone, 2-phenyl-

[29] Rebuffat, *Ber.*, **22**, 551c (1889).
[30] Erlenmeyer, *Ann.*, **337**, 265 (1904).
[31] Mohr and Köhler, *Ber.*, **40**, 997 (1907).
[32] Heller and Hessel, *J. prakt. Chem.*, **120**, 64 (1928–1929).
[33] Bergmann and Stern, *Ann.*, **448**, 20 (1926).
[34] Carter and Stevens, *J. Biol. Chem.*, **133**, 117 (1940).
[35] Carter and Risser, *J. Biol. Chem.*, **139**, 255 (1941).

4-benzal-5-oxazolone, or 5-keto-2-phenyl-4-benzylidene-4,5-dihydro-oxazole. In this chapter the *Chemical Abstracts* terminology is given preference, although compounds are named as derivatives of amino acids whenever it seems desirable in the interest of clarity or brevity.

PREPARATION OF AZLACTONES

Azlactones have been of interest mainly as intermediates in the synthesis of other compounds. Saturated azlactones are obtained most often from the corresponding amino acids and are used in preparing derivatives of those amino acids. Unsaturated azlactones, on the other hand, usually are prepared by condensing an aldehyde with an acylglycine and are used in the synthesis of the corresponding amino and keto acids. Four methods by which azlactones can be prepared are discussed in the following paragraphs.

Azlactonization of an α-Acylamino Acid

$$\underset{\substack{|\\ NH\\ |\\ COR}}{RCHCO_2H} \xrightarrow[\substack{RCOCl\\ (NaOAc)}]{(RCO)_2O} \begin{array}{c} RCH\text{---}C{=}O \\ |\qquad\quad | \\ N\qquad O \\ \diagdown\!\!\diagup \\ C \\ | \\ R \end{array}$$

α-Acylamino acids can be converted into azlactones under the following conditions: (*a*) Action of an acid anhydride, either alone or in acetic acid as a solvent, on an α-acylamino acid (or, occasionally, a free α-amino acid).[18–28, 34, 35] (*b*) Action of an acid anhydride [34] or acid chloride [36] on the sodium salt of an α-acylamino acid (or free α-amino acid) in aqueous solution. (*c*) Action of an acid anhydride or chloride on an α-acylamino acid in pyridine solution.[37, 38] Of these methods the first is the most convenient and the only one generally used; however, none of these methods is practical for the preparation of unsaturated azlactones because the unsaturated acylamino acids are not readily available.

The preparation of unsaturated azlactones is effected smoothly and quantitatively by heating the acylamino acid with an excess of acetic anhydride on a steam bath for five to fifteen minutes.[33, 34, 35, 39, 40] The

[36] Bettzieche and Menger, *Z. physiol. Chem.*, **172**, 56 (1927).

[37] Carter, Handler, and Melville, *J. Biol. Chem.*, **129**, 359 (1939).

[38] Carter, Handler, and Stevens, *J. Biol. Chem.*, **138**, 619 (1941).

[39] Bain, Perkin, and Robinson, *J. Chem. Soc.*, **105**, 2392 (1914).

[40] Gulland and Virden, *J. Chem. Soc.*, **1928**, 1478.

azlactone is isolated by pouring the reaction mixture into water, which hydrolyzes the excess acetic anhydride and causes the product to precipitate.

The lower saturated azlactones are prepared less readily by this procedure; they are liquids, unstable toward water and heat, and can be isolated only by fractional distillation. Those of low molecular weight, such as the 2,4-dimethyl-,[23] 2,4,4-trimethyl-,[21, 41] and 2,4-dimethyl-4-ethyl-oxazolone,[41] boil at about the same temperature as acetic anhydride and have not been obtained in the pure state. Higher-boiling azlactones have been prepared in good yields by this method when the distillation was effected at the lowest possible temperature. 2-Aryloxazolones are synthesized more readily since they are solids and hence can be isolated by removal of the acetic anhydride under reduced pressure and recrystallization from ether or petroleum ether.[19, 34] Acyl derivatives of glutamic acid [42] are converted to acid anhydrides rather than azlactones on treatment with acetic anhydride. Acetylaspartic acid yields either an azlactone or an anhydride, depending upon the conditions used;[43] the azlactone is formed in acetic anhydride at the reflux temperature; the anhydride, at 95°.

```
                                  HO2CCH2CH——C=O
                                          |    |
                                          N    O
                              ↗            \\ /
                                            C
HO2CCH2CHCO2H                               |
       |                                   CH3
       NH                     ↘
       |                             CH2—C=O
       CO                            |    >O
       |                      CH3CONHCH—C=O
       CH3
```

The action of acetic anhydride on an α-acylamino acid in aqueous solution yields an azlactone, provided that a basic catalyst, such as sodium acetate,*, [34] is present. Unsaturated azlactones are prepared readily by this method. Saturated azlactones are obtained in poor yields since they undergo hydrolysis rapidly in aqueous solution. Optically active α-acylamino acids are racemized under these conditions as a result of the temporary formation of the azlactone.[44]

* Sodium acetate also increases the rate of azlactone formation in glacial acetic acid solutions, but no preparative application has been made of this observation.

41 Levene and Steiger, *J. Biol. Chem.*, **93,** 581 (1931).

42 Nicolet, *J. Am. Chem. Soc.*, **52,** 1192 (1930).

43 Harington and Overhoff, *Biochem. J.*, **27,** 338 (1933).

44 duVigneaud and Meyer. *J. Biol. Chem.*, **99,** 143 (1932–1933).

Saturated α-acylamino acids are prepared by acylation of α-amino acids or, less frequently, by reduction of the corresponding unsaturated compounds. It sometimes is possible to effect both the preparation of the α-acylamino acid and the formation of the azlactone by heating the amino acid with a large excess of acetic anhydride. Leucine and phenylalanine [26] give excellent yields of azlactones under these conditions. However, this method is not satisfactory with alanine,[23] diiodotyrosine,[45] isovaline,[41] or α-aminoisobutyric acid,[41] which yield products of high molecular weight.

Unsaturated α-acylamino acids usually are obtained from the corresponding azlactones. Reconversion of the unsaturated acid to the azlactone is not, therefore, a reaction of any great preparative importance. A few α-acylaminoacrylic acids have been prepared by the reaction of an α-keto acid with an amide:

$$R'CONH_2 + RCH_2COCO_2H \rightarrow \begin{cases} (R'CONH)_2C(CO_2H)CH_2R \\ R'CONHC(CO_2H){=}CHR \end{cases}$$

However, the utilization of this reaction has been severely restricted by the unavailability of α-keto acids.

Pyruvic acid yields mainly α,α-diacetaminopropionic acid, which can be converted into α-acetaminoacrylic acid by hot acetic acid.[25, 46] Under the optimum conditions [47] a 23% yield of α-acetaminoacrylic acid is obtained. Phenylpyruvic acid gives mainly α-acetaminocinnamic acid,[48] as would be expected in view of the activating effect of the benzene ring. Benzoylformic acid [48] and α-ketoglutaric acid [49] have been employed as the acid components in this reaction, and benzamide,[50] benzylcarbamate,[51] and chloroacetamide [46] as the amide components. The preparation of α-acetaminocinnamic acid by this method is described in the next section.

Procedures

2-Phenyl-4-benzal-5-oxazolone.[35] One gram of benzoylaminocinnamic acid is heated on the steam cone for five minutes with 10 cc. of

[45] Myers, *J. Am. Chem. Soc.*, **54,** 3718 (1932).
[46] Bergmann and Grafe, *Z. physiol. Chem.*, **187,** 187 (1930).
[47] Herbst, *J. Am. Chem. Soc.*, **61,** 483 (1939).
[48] Shemin and Herbst, *J. Am. Chem. Soc.*, **60,** 1954 (1938).
[49] Shemin and Herbst, *J. Am. Chem. Soc.*, **60,** 1951 (1938).
[50] Nicolet, *J. Am. Chem. Soc.*, **57,** 1073 (1935).
[51] Herbst, *J. Org. Chem.*, **6,** 878 (1941).

acetic anhydride. The solution is poured into a mixture of ice and water and allowed to stand with occasional stirring for twenty minutes. The precipitate is removed by filtration, air-dried, and recrystallized from benzene-ethanol, yielding 0.8 g. (86%) of 2-phenyl-4-benzal-5-oxazolone; m.p. 165–166°.

2-Phenyl-4-benzyl-5-oxazolone.[19] Ten grams of benzoyl-*dl*-β-phenylalanine is heated on the steam bath for thirty minutes with 100 cc. of acetic anhydride. The solution is concentrated in vacuum, and the syrupy residue is dissolved in 100 cc. of petroleum ether, b.p. 60–110°. The solution is decanted from a small amount of insoluble material and is cooled. Practically pure 2-phenyl-4-benzyl-5-oxazolone crystallizes in long needles, m.p. 69–71°; yield 7.5 g. (80%).

2-Methyl-4-benzyl-5-oxazolone.[26] Five grams of powdered *dl*-β-phenylalanine is heated at 100° for five minutes with 50 cc. of acetic anhydride. The mixture is shaken vigorously during the heating. Acetic acid and acetic anhydride are removed under reduced pressure, and the residue is fractionated, yielding 3.1 g. (54%) of 2-methyl-4-benzyl-5-oxazolone, b.p. 118°/0.8 mm.

α-Acetaminocinnamic Acid.[48] A mixture of 12 g. of phenylpyruvic acid and 12 g. of acetamide is heated for three hours at 110–115° under 10–15 mm. pressure. The residue is dissolved in boiling water, and the solution is treated with Norit and allowed to cool, yielding 7.1 g. (47%) of α-acetaminocinnamic acid, m.p. 193°.

Reaction of an Aldehyde with an Acylglycine in the Presence of Acetic Anhydride

```
ArCHO + CH2CO2H  --Ac2O-->  ArCH=C------C=O
        |        (NaOAc)          |      |
        NH                        N      O
        |                          \\   /
        COR                          C
                                     |
                                     R
```

The Erlenmeyer azlactone synthesis consists in the condensation of an aldehyde with an acylglycine in the presence of acetic anhydride (and usually sodium acetate). It is a special case of the Perkin condensation and as such has been discussed briefly by Johnson.[52]

Mechanism. Erlenmeyer believed that the reaction proceeds in two steps as shown in the equations.[13, 17] However, convincing evidence has accumulated that the actual condensation takes place between the alde-

[52] Johnson, *Org. Reactions*, I, 231 (1942).

hyde and the azlactone formed by the action of acetic anhydride on the acylglycine. The strongest support for this mechanism is the fact that

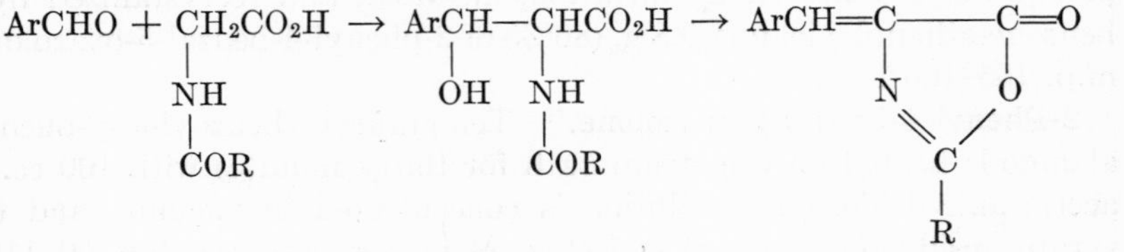

$$\text{ArCHO} + \underset{\underset{\text{COR}}{|}}{\underset{\text{NH}}{|}}\!\!\text{CH}_2\text{CO}_2\text{H} \rightarrow \text{ArCH}(\text{OH})\text{—CH}(\text{NHCOR})\text{CO}_2\text{H} \rightarrow \text{ArCH{=}C—C{=}O (N, O ring, C—R)}$$

the condensation occurs under much milder conditions than those required in the Perkin condensation. In the azlactone synthesis uniformly high yields are obtained from aldehydes which give poor results or fail to react (4-imidazolealdehyde)[53] in the Perkin condensation. Furthermore,

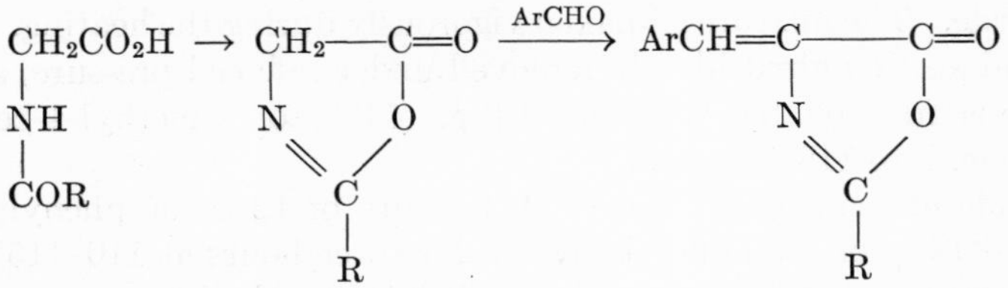

$$\text{CH}_2(\text{NHCOR})\text{CO}_2\text{H} \rightarrow \text{CH}_2\text{—C{=}O (N, O ring, C—R)} \xrightarrow{\text{ArCHO}} \text{ArCH{=}C—C{=}O (N, O ring, C—R)}$$

the yields from substituted aldehydes do not vary as they do in Perkin reactions,[52] which suggests that the condensation reaction is not the limiting step in the azlactone synthesis. All these data indicate that the intermediate contains an extremely active methylene group and therefore is the azlactone rather than the acylglycine. Furthermore, benzoylsarcosine (benzoyl-N-methylglycine), which cannot form an azlactone, condenses with aldehydes much less readily than does hippuric acid.[54, 55] Similarly, benzenesulfonylglycine [54] fails to condense with piperonal.

Scope and Limitations. *Carbonyl Component.* For practical purposes this reaction is limited to aromatic aldehydes, of which a wide variety has been studied, and to α,β-unsaturated aliphatic aldehydes. The substitutents on the ring of the aromatic aldehydes include alkyl, fluoro, chloro, bromo, iodo, hydroxyl, alkoxy, acyloxy, carbethoxy, nitro, and various combinations of two or more of these groups. Aldehydes of the naphthalene, pyrene, biphenyl, thiophene, furan, pyrrole, indole, chromane, coumarane, and thiazole series also have been employed.

No generalizations can be made concerning the effect of the structure of the aldehyde on the yield of azlactone. In several preparations the

[53] Pyman, *J. Chem. Soc.*, **109**, 186 (1916).
[54] Heard, *Biochem. J.*, **27**, 54 (1933).
[55] Deulofeu, *Ber.*, **67**, 1542 (1934).

yields are not reported, and in others the reaction conditions have not been comparable. The yields in this azlactone synthesis are uniformly good, ranging from 60 to 80%, with a few as high as 95%. The few lower yields reported were obtained from aldehydes belonging to no particular type and may have resulted from poor reaction conditions.

The presence of an *o*-nitro group appears to hinder some reactions but not others. Thus, 2-nitro-3,4-methylenedioxybenzaldehyde gives a 35% yield of azlactone,[56] and 2-nitro-3-methoxy-4-hydroxybenzaldehyde gives a 42% yield.[57] However, 2-nitro-3,4-dimethoxybenzaldehyde gives a 75% yield of azlactone,[58] and 2-nitro-5-methoxybenzaldehyde gives an 84% yield.[59] In general, no substituent group has a specific or consistent effect on the yield. In this respect the azlactone synthesis differs markedly from the Perkin condensation.

When salicylaldehyde is heated with hippuric acid, acetic anhydride, and sodium acetate, benzoylaminocoumarin is obtained along with the acetoxyazlactone.[7, 29, 60–62] Similar results are obtained with 2,4-dihy-

OH, CHO + CH_2—CO_2H / NH / CO—C_6H_5 $\xrightarrow[NaOAc]{Ac_2O}$

OAc, CH=C——C=O / N O / C / C_6H_5 + O, CO, CNHCOC$_6$H$_5$, CH

droxybenzaldehyde [63] and 2,5-dihydroxybenzaldehyde.[64] It is interesting to note that only the azlactone is obtained by heating salicylaldehyde with acetylglycine, acetic anhydride, and sodium acetate.[65]

56 Narang and Ray, *J. Chem. Soc.*, **1931**, 976.
57 Gulland, Ross, and Smellie, *J. Chem. Soc.*, **1931**, 2885.
58 Gulland, Robinson, Scott, and Thornley, *J. Chem. Soc.*, **1929**, 2924.
59 Burton, *J. Chem. Soc.*, **1935**, 1265.
60 Asahina, *Bull. Chem. Soc. Japan*, **5**, 354 (1930).
61 Rebuffat, *Gazz. chim. ital.*, **15**, 527 (1885).
62 Plöchl and Wolfrum, *Ber.*, **18**, 1183 (1885).
63 Deulofeu, *Ber.*, **69**, 2456 (1936).
64 Neubauer and Flatow, *Z. physiol. Chem.*, **52**, 375 (1907).
65 Dakin, *J. Biol. Chem.*, **82**, 439 (1929).

Phthalic anhydride [2] and pyruvic acid [66] condense with hippuric acid to give products which have been assigned the following structures.

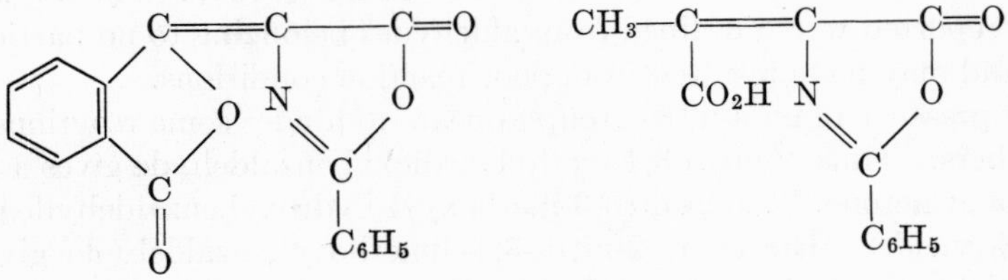

```
      C═════C────C=O        CH3─C════C────C=O
     / \    |    |              |    |    |
    ⬡   O   N    O            CO2H   N    O
     \ /     \\ /                     \\ /
      C       C                         C
      ‖       |                         |
      O      C6H5                      C6H5
```

Saturated aliphatic aldehydes generally give low yields in the azlactone synthesis.[5, 37] α,β-Unsaturated aldehydes such as cinnamaldehyde,[6] α-n-amylcinnamaldehyde,[67] and perilla aldehyde,[67] which cannot undergo an aldol condensation, react satisfactorily (65–80% yields). 2-Thiophenealdehyde diethylacetal gives yields as satisfactory as those from the

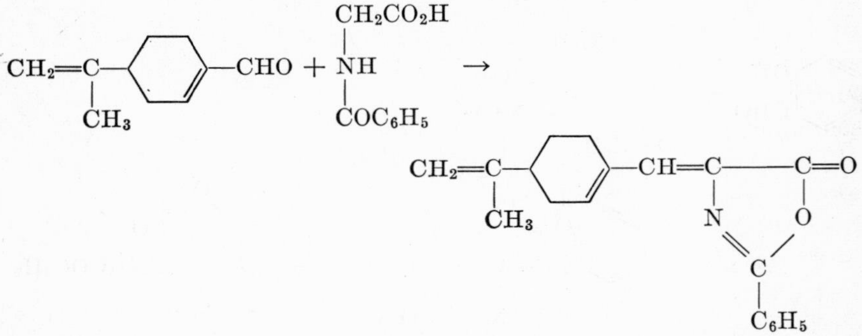

```
                                  CH2CO2H
                                  |
CH2=C─⟨cyclohexenyl⟩─CHO   +   NH              →
    |                             |
    CH3                           COC6H5

          CH2=C─⟨cyclohexenyl⟩─CH=C────C=O
              |                    |    |
              CH3                  N    O
                                    \\ /
                                     C
                                     |
                                    C6H5
```

free aldehyde, an observation which has led to the suggestion that acetals might be used generally in the condensation with hippuric acid.[68] This possibility should be investigated further since certain aldehydes may be destroyed slowly under the usual reaction conditions. Thioaldehydes can be condensed with hippuric acid if either cupric acetate or lead oxide is added to the reaction mixture.[69] Acetone gives a 45% yield of azlactone.[70] No other simple ketone has been tested.

Acylglycines. Several acylglycines (acetyl, benzoyl, phenylacetyl, galloyl, etc.) have been used in the azlactone synthesis. Of these, benzoylglycine and acetylglycine have been studied most. Each has certain

[66] Erlenmeyer and Arbenz, *Ann.*, **337,** 302 (1904).
[67] Rodionow and Korolew, *Z. angew. Chem.*, **42,** 1091 (1929).
[68] Yuan and Li, *J. Chinese Chem. Soc.*, **5,** 214 (1937).
[69] Fischer and Hofmann, *Z. physiol. Chem.*, **245,** 139 (1936–1937).
[70] Ramage and Simonsen. *J. Chem. Soc.*, **1935,** 532.

advantages. Generally the yields with hippuric acid are somewhat higher, and the resulting azlactones are more stable. If the azlactone is to be used in preparing the α-keto acid the acetyl derivative is to be preferred since it is hydrolyzed to the keto acid under milder conditions and the acetic acid produced is separated from the α-keto acid more readily than is benzoic acid.

Experimental Conditions and Procedures. 2-Phenyloxazolones usually are prepared by heating a mixture of 1 mole each of aldehyde, hippuric acid, and freshly fused sodium acetate with 3 moles of acetic anhydride on the water bath for varying lengths of time. In many instances a larger proportion of sodium acetate and/or acetic anhydride has been used, although there is no direct evidence that such alterations improve the yield. Indeed, some doubt exists whether sodium acetate is necessary. Originally, this component was omitted [1] and an 80% yield of 2-phenyl-4-benzal-5-oxazolone was obtained. Dimethylethylpyrrolealdehyde [69] and *m*-benzyloxybenzaldehyde [71] give 83 and 74% yields, respectively, of azlactone without the use of sodium acetate. No other such experiments have been reported. This point should be investigated further since it seems possible that in certain cases the addition of sodium acetate may actually decrease the yield.

The length of heating has varied from six minutes to ten hours, but usually it is from fifteen minutes to one hour. This matter also deserves a more careful scrutiny. In several preparations excellent yields have been obtained with very short reaction times (six to fifteen minutes). It seems probable that in other preparations a shorter reaction period might give as good or better results, since even unsaturated azlactones decompose slowly on heating. Thus, 3-ethoxy-4-methoxybenzaldehyde is reported to yield 82% of the azlactone when the reaction mixture is heated for twenty minutes,[72] and 78% when the heating period is one hour.[73] 3,4,5-Trimethoxybenzaldehyde gives a 65% yield in six minutes [74] and an 85% yield in ninety minutes; [75] this reaction must have been practically complete in ten minutes. With 2-nitro-3-methoxy-4-hydroxybenzaldehyde, extensive decomposition occurs if the heating is prolonged beyond ten minutes.[57] The fact that hippuric acid azlactone is unstable and will not exist in the reaction mixture for an appreciable length of time also argues against a prolonged reaction time.

[71] Rapson and Robinson, *J. Chem. Soc.*, **1935**, 1533.

[72] Späth and Tharrer, *Ber.*, **66**, 583 (1933).

[73] Barger, Eisenbrand, and Eisenbrand, *Ber.*, **66**, 450 (1933).

[74] Baker and Robinson, *J. Chem. Soc.*, **1929**, 152.

[75] Mauthner, *Ber.*, **41**, 3662 (1908).

Better results have been claimed [76] in preparations effected by mixing the aldehyde, acetic anhydride, and sodium acetate in one flask, hippuric acid and acetic anhydride in another, and combining the warm solutions. However, the yields reported are little, if any, better than those obtained in the usual manner. Another variation of doubtful value is the addition of sodium acetate to a hot mixture of the other reactants.[77]

2-Methyloxazolones are best prepared by the method of Dakin.[65] In this procedure acetylglycine is produced by heating glycine in acetic acid with 1 mole of acetic anhydride. The aldehyde, sodium acetate, and more acetic anhydride are then added, and the heating is continued two to ten hours. This procedure has the advantage over the hippuric acid synthesis that it is not necessary to prepare the acetylglycine separately. The 2-methyloxazolones can be obtained also by heating a mixture of glycine, acetic anhydride, sodium acetate, and aldehyde,[33] but the yields are somewhat lower, probably owing to condensation of the aldehyde with the amino group of the glycine.[65]

The reaction times reported with acetylglycine are longer than those with hippuric acid, and temperatures have been higher (120–135°). Although no direct comparison has been made, it would appear that 2-methyloxazolone either condenses less readily with aldehydes than does 2-phenyloxazolone or is formed more slowly. Even so, it seems doubtful that heating longer than two hours or at a temperature above 100° is desirable, since under those conditions Dakin obtained yields as high as any reported. Furthermore, he indicated that more severe conditions led to lower yields.

The azlactones usually are isolated either by cooling the reaction mixture and removing the azlactone by filtration or by pouring the cold reaction mixture into water, allowing the excess acetic anhydride to hydrolyze, and collecting the crude azlactone. The product can be purified by recrystallization from ethanol (with the exception of a few which undergo alcoholysis), benzene, petroleum ether, or ethyl acetate.

Detailed descriptions of the preparations of three azlactones by condensations of aldehydes with acylglycines are given in *Organic Syntheses*. These include the syntheses of 2-methyl-4-benzal-5-oxazolone from benzaldehyde and acetylglycine,[78] 2-phenyl-4-benzal-5-oxazolone from benzaldehyde and hippuric acid,[79] and 2-phenyl-4-(3′,4′-dimethoxybenzal)-5-oxazolone from veratraldehyde and hippuric acid.[80]

[76] Oliverio, *Gazz. chim. ital.*, **65**, 143 (1935).
[77] Douglas and Gulland, *J. Chem. Soc.*, **1931**, 2893.
[78] Herbst and Shemin, *Org. Syntheses*, *Coll. Vol.* **2**, 1 (1943).
[79] Gillespie and Snyder, *Org. Syntheses*, *Coll. Vol.* **2**, 489 (1943).
[80] Buck and Ide, *Org. Syntheses*, *Coll. Vol.* **2**, 55 (1943).

Reaction of an α-Acylamino-β-hydroxy Acid with an Acid Anhydride or Acid Chloride

$$RCH(OR')\text{—}CH(NHCOR'')CO_2H \xrightarrow[\text{(NaOAc)}]{Ac_2O \text{ or } R'''COCl} \left[RCH(OR')\text{—}CH\text{—}CO \ (\text{ring: } N{=}C(R'')\text{—}O) \right] \rightarrow RCH{=}C\text{—}C{=}O \ (\text{ring: } N{=}C(R'')\text{—}O) + R'OH$$

$R' = H, CH_3, CH_3CO$

The action of acetic anhydride on an α-acylamino-β-hydroxy (alkoxy or acyloxy) acid produces an unsaturated azlactone.[13, 34–37, 81–86] The first step in this transformation is the conversion of the acyl derivative into the corresponding saturated azlactone. This saturated azlactone possesses an extremely active α-hydrogen atom which splits out with the β-substituent under very mild conditions.

The *cis* and *trans* isomers of an unsaturated azlactone were obtained for the first time by this method. α-Benzoylamino-β-methoxybutyric acid on heating for ten minutes with acetic anhydride yields a mixture of the isomeric benzoylaminocrotonic azlactones.[34] The labile isomer is less soluble and hence readily isolated in the pure state. It is rapidly converted into the stable isomer by heat or by the action of cold pyridine. The two isomeric benzoylaminocinnamic azlactones have been prepared in a similar manner.[35]

Procedures. *α-Benzoylaminocinnamic Azlactones I and II.*[35] Fifteen grams (0.05 mole) of α-benzoylamino-β-methoxy-β-phenylpropionic acid is suspended in 75 cc. of acetic anhydride, and the mixture is heated on a steam bath until the benzoyl derivative has dissolved completely (ten to fifteen minutes). The solution is cooled in an ice bath and filtered; 6.0–7.0 g. (48–56%) of almost pure α-benzoylaminocinnamic azlactone I, m.p. 164–166°, is collected. The filtrate is poured into water with vigorous stirring. A light yellow solid separates as the acetic anhydride is hydrolyzed. This material is collected, washed with water, air-dried, and recrystallized from benzene, yielding 4.0–4.5 g. (32–36%) of crude azlactone II, m.p. 124–140°. The total yield is 10.0–11.5 g. (80–92%).

[81] Botvinnik, Prokof'ev, and Zelinskii, *Compt. rend. acad. sci. U.R.S.S.*, **30,** 129 (1941).
[82] Erlenmeyer and Bade, *Ann.*, **337,** 222 (1904).
[83] Bergmann and Delis, *Ann.*, **458,** 76 (1927).
[84] Dakin and West, *J. Biol. Chem.*, **78,** 745 (1928).
[85] Forster and Rao, *J. Chem. Soc.*, **1926,** 1943.
[86] Bergmann, Schmitt, and Miekeley, *Z. physiol. Chem.*, **187,** 264 (1930).

Pure benzoylaminocinnamic azlactone I, m.p. 167–168°, is obtained by recrystallizing the crude material from 2 volumes of benzene. Recrystallization of crude azlactone II from benzene or ethanol does not raise the melting point appreciably. A preparation melting at 146–148° can be obtained by hydrolyzing the crude material to the corresponding acid, recrystallizing the acid from a benzene-ethanol-petroleum ether mixture, and reconverting the purified acid to the azlactone with acetic anhydride.

An 80–90% yield of α-benzoylaminocinnamic azlactone I is obtained in the above preparation if 1 cc. of pyridine is added to the reaction mixture.

Reaction of an α-(α′-Haloacyl)-amino Acid with Acetic Anhydride

```
RCH2CH——CO2H    Ac2O     RCH2C———C=O  →  RCH=C———C=O
    |         ————————→      ||     |         |     |
    HN         (C5H5N)       N      O         N     O
      \                       \    /           \\  /
       CO                       C                C
       |                        ||               |
    X—CHR                      CHR              CH2R
```

The conversion of an α-(α′-haloacyl)-amino acid into an unsaturated azlactone [33] has not been studied extensively. A proposed mechanism [33] is shown in the above equations. On treatment with acetic anhydride and pyridine at room temperature, N-chloroacetyl-*dl*-β-phenylalanine is converted into α-acetaminocinnamic azlactone (yield, 80%) [87] and N-chloroacetyl-*l*-tyrosine into 2-methyl-4-*p*-acetoxybenzal-5-oxazolone.[87] This reaction has been applied in the synthesis of an α-keto acid from the corresponding α-amino acid. α-Bromopropionyl-*dl*-methionine was converted into the unsaturated azlactone by the action of acetic anhydride and sodium acetate. Dilute hydrochloric acid was added, and the reaction mixture was heated in a water bath for five minutes, yielding α-keto-γ-methiolbutyric acid, which was isolated as the phenylhydrazone.[88]

```
CH3SCH2CH=C———CO    HCl
          |    |   ————→ CH3SCH2CH2COCO2H + CH3CH2CO2H + NH4Cl
          N    O
           \\ /
            C
            |
           C2H5
```

[87] Bergmann, Zervas, and Lebrecht, *Ber.*, **64**, 2315 (1931).
[88] Cahill and Rudolph, *J. Biol. Chem.*, **145**, 201 (1942).

PROPERTIES AND REACTIONS OF AZLACTONES

General Discussion

Saturated azlactones are colorless liquids or low-melting solids. Unsaturated azlactones are solids, often high-melting, and the majority have colors ranging from light yellow to dark red. The color is most intense in 2-aryl-4-aralkylidene-5-oxazolones; the 2-alkyl-4-alkylidene-5-oxazolones are colorless.

The azlactones behave in many respects like acid anhydrides and react with a wide variety of compounds, such as water, alcohols, amines, and hydrogen halides, which contain active hydrogen atoms. As with acid anhydrides, reaction occurs most readily with amines, less readily with alcohols, and least readily with water.

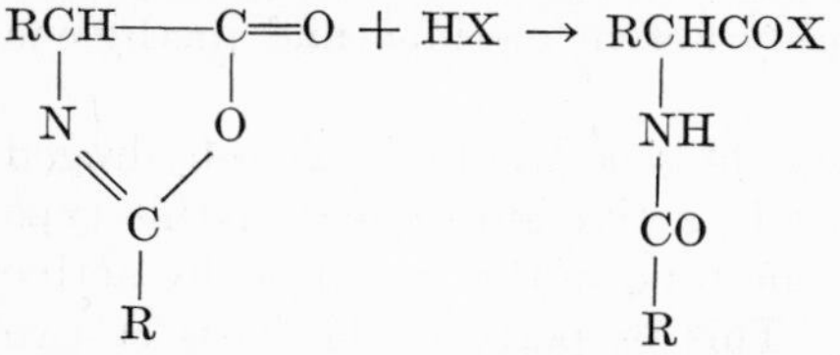

```
RCH——C=O + HX → RCHCOX        (X = —NH2, —NHR, —NR2,
 |      |         |                —OR, —OH, and halogen)
 N      O         NH
  \\   /          |
    C             CO
    |             |
    R             R
```

The saturated azlactones are much more reactive than the unsaturated compounds. The unsaturated azlactones can be recrystallized from boiling ethanol (with one known exception, see p. 215) and are not altered by long contact with water, whereas the saturated compounds are slowly hydrolyzed by water at room temperature and react even more rapidly with ethanol. Saturated azlactones are converted into thiohydantoins by ammonium thiocyanate,[42, 89–91] whereas unsaturated azlactones do not react with this reagent.[89]

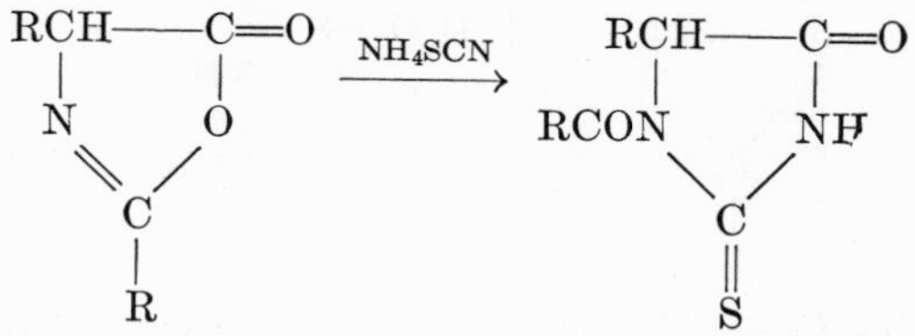

```
RCH——C=O    NH4SCN        RCH——C=O
 |      |   ———————→        |      |
 N      O               RCON      NH
  \\   /                    \    /
    C                         C
    |                         ||
    R                         S
```

Unsaturated azlactones are relatively stable to heat, whereas saturated azlactones undergo condensation reactions, often at room temperature. During this process liquid azlactones are converted into clear semi-solid waxes. The nature of the substituents has a marked effect on this reaction. 2-Phenyl-4,4-dialkyl-5-oxazolones are relatively stable, 2-phenyl-

[89] Johnson and Scott, *J. Am. Chem. Soc.*, **35**, 1136 (1913).

[90] Johnson and Scott, *J. Am. Chem. Soc.*, **35**, 1130 (1913).

[91] Csonka and Nicolet, *J. Biol. Chem.*, **99**, 213 (1932).

4-alkyl-5-oxazolones are less stable, and hippuric azlactone is quite unstable, and only recently was prepared by heating hippuric acid with acetic anhydride.*

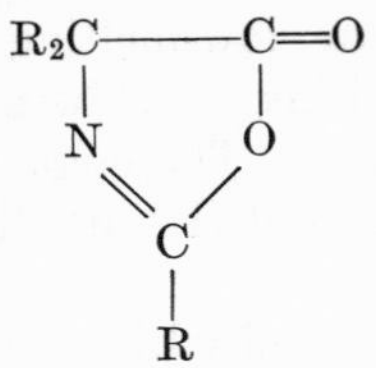

```
R2C———C=O        RCH———C=O        CH2———C=O
 |     |          |     |          |     |
 N     O          N     O          N     O
  \\  /            \\  /            \\  /
    C                C                C
    |                |                |
    R                R                R

    V                VI               VII
```

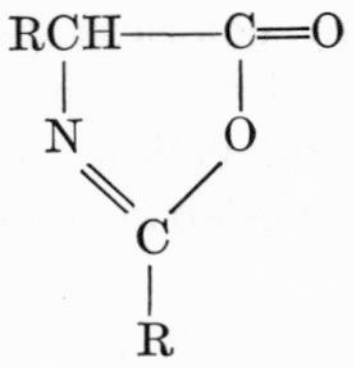

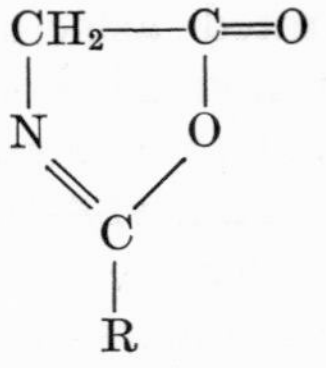

The difference in stability between V and VII suggests that the condensation reactions brought about by heating may be of the aldol type, and it will be noted that in VI and VII the two unsaturated linkages flanking the 4-position produce highly active methine and methylene groups, respectively.

In view of the presence in azlactones of type VI of a labile α-hydrogen atom it is not surprising that optically active substances of this type racemize very readily. So rapid is the process that an optically active azlactone never has been isolated. This property is the basis of two effective methods for the racemization of amino acids.[44, 92, 93] In one, the amino acid is heated in glacial acetic acid with 2 moles of acetic anhydride. In the other, the sodium salt of the amino acid in aqueous solution is treated with a large excess of acetic anhydride at room temperature. The racemic acetyl derivative of the amino acid is produced by either procedure.

Hydrolysis

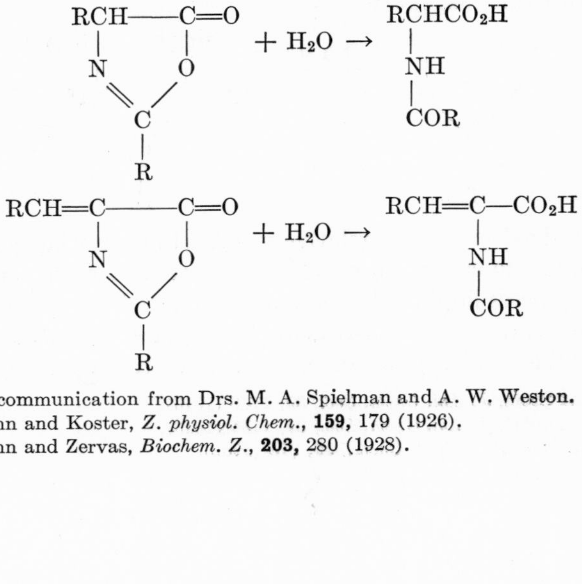

```
RCH———C=O                   RCHCO2H
 |     |                     |
 |     |      + H2O  →       |
 N     O                     NH
  \\  /                      |
    C                        COR
    |
    R

RCH=C———C=O                 RCH=C—CO2H
    |    |                       |
    |    |    + H2O  →           |
    N    O                       NH
     \\ /                        |
      C                          COR
      |
      R
```

* Private communication from Drs. M. A. Spielman and A. W. Weston.

[92] Bergmann and Koster, *Z. physiol. Chem.*, **159**, 179 (1926).

[93] Bergmann and Zervas, *Biochem. Z.*, **203**, 280 (1928).

Azlactones can be hydrolyzed to the corresponding acids with either alkaline or acidic [37] reagents, the alkalies being considerably more effective. The ease of the reaction depends to a marked extent upon the nature of the substituents on the oxazolone ring. Unsaturation in the 4-position or an aryl group in the 2-position stabilizes the molecule. Thus 2-methyl-4-benzyl-5-oxazolone is hydrolyzed by water at room temperature,[26] 2-methyl-4-benzal-5-oxazolone by boiling aqueous acetone,[78] and 2-phenyl-4-benzal-5-oxazolone by boiling 1% aqueous sodium hydroxide.[12]

A solution of sodium hydroxide in aqueous methanol is an effective reagent for hydrolyzing azlactones.[35, 94–96] It converts an azlactone into the α-acylamino ester, which is saponified. The reaction proceeds rapidly and under less drastic conditions than those required when aqueous alkali is used. In this connection it should be noted that prolonged action of alkali may hydrolyze the α-acylaminoacrylic acid to the α-keto acid.

Alcoholysis

Unsaturated azlactones ordinarily do not react readily with hot alcohols.* However, if either an acid [12, 97] or a base is added to the ethanol, the oxazolone ring is opened rapidly with the formation of an α-acylaminoacrylic ester. With sodium hydroxide or alkoxide the reaction is complete in three to five minutes at room temperature.[6, 7, 35, 69, 98] With sodium carbonate as catalyst a short period of refluxing is required.[99, 100] Azlactones also react rapidly with higher alcohols in the presence of the sodium alkoxide.[69]

```
RCH——C=O
 |   |
 N   O          + C4H9OH  --C4H9ONa-->  RCHCO2C4H9
  \\ /                                    |
   C                                      NH
   |                                      |
   R                                      COR
```

* 2-Phenyl-4-(2′-nitro-3′-methoxy-4′-acetoxybenzal)-5-oxazolone is an exception to this rule (see ref. 57).

[94] Schmalfusz and Peschke, *Ber.*, **62**, 2591 (1929).

[95] Lamb and Robson, *Biochem. J.*, **25**, 1231 (1931).

[96] Slotta and Soremba, *Ber.*, **69**, 566 (1936).

[97] Harington and Barger, *Biochem. J.*, **21**, 169 (1927).

[98] Posner and Sichert, *Ber.*, **63**, 3078 (1930).

[99] Kropp and Decker, *Ber.*, **42**, 1184 (1909).

[100] King and Stiller, *J. Chem. Soc.*, **1937**, 466.

Aminolysis, Synthesis of Peptides

No systematic study has been made of the reaction of azlactones with amines. Conditions of a widely varying nature have been reported, and many of them obviously are far from optimum. However, the yields of amide or substituted amide are usually excellent, and many are practically quantitative.

```
RCH——C=O
 |     |     + R'NH2 → RCHCONHR'
 N     O                |
  \\  /                 NH
    C                   |
    |                   COR
    R
```

Saturated azlactones react quite vigorously with ammonia and amines.[18, 21, 26, 34, 101] The reaction usually is effected by treating the azlactone with the pure amine or with an aqueous or ethanolic solution of the amine at room temperature. The rate of reaction of a saturated azlactone with aniline is markedly accelerated by the presence of a trace of an amine hydrochloride.[38] Unsaturated azlactones react somewhat less readily with amines, and warming at 50–100° has been employed in many instances.[7, 8, 102] Occasionally the reaction has been effected at room temperature but with a longer reaction time.[103] Much more drastic conditions have been employed, but there is no evidence that the severe conditions were essential.[56, 104]

Acyldipeptides are produced by the reaction of an azlactone with an amino acid, and many have been synthesized in this way.[26, 103, 105, 106] The method consists in the addition of the azlactone to a solution of the amino acid in aqueous acetone containing an equivalent amount of sodium hydroxide. Excellent results are obtained with unsaturated

```
RCH——C=O
 |     |     + R''CHCO2Na → RCHCONHCHCO2Na
 N     O         |            |      |
  \\  /          NH2          NH     R''
    C                         |
    |                         COR'
    R'
```

[101] Lettre and Fernholz, *Z. physiol. Chem.*, **266**, 37 (1940).
[102] Granächer and Gulbas, *Helv. Chim. Acta*, **10**, 819 (1927).
[103] Bergmann and Fruton, *J. Biol. Chem.*, **124**, 321 (1938).
[104] Banerjee, *J. Indian Chem. Soc.*, **9**, 479 (1932).
[105] Bergmann and Miekeley, *Ann.*, **458**, 40 (1927).
[106] Behrens and Bergmann, *J. Biol. Chem.*, **129**, 587 (1939).

azlactones and with many saturated azlactones. With certain saturated azlactones better yields are obtained [107] by heating the azlactone and the amino acid in acetic acid. Occasionally the ester of the amino acid has been employed [103, 108] and the reaction carried out in ether, ethanol, or ethyl acetate.

TYPES OF COMPOUNDS WHICH CAN BE PREPARED FROM AZLACTONES

General Discussion

Unsaturated azlactones furnish a convenient starting point in the synthesis of a variety of compounds, some of which are indicated below.

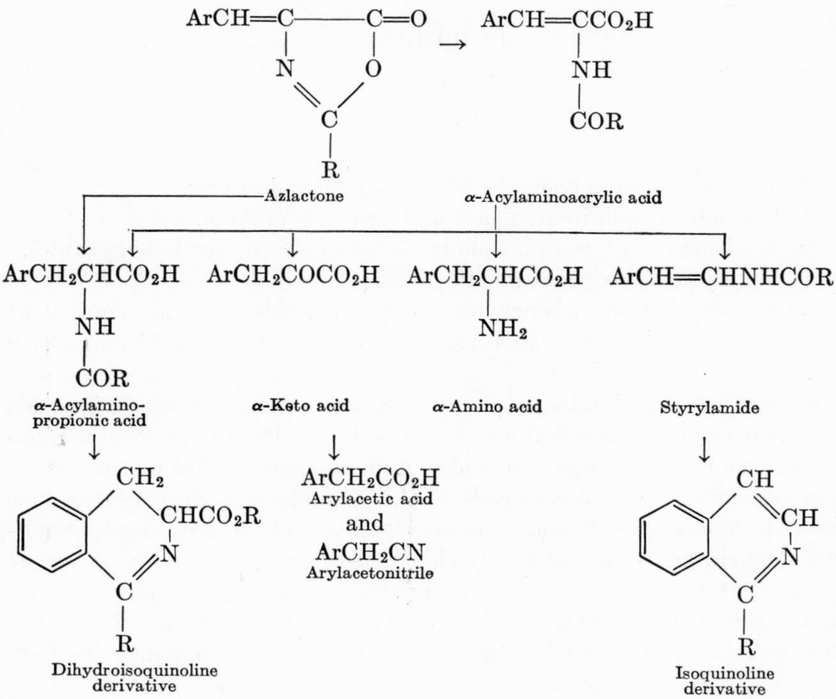

Azlactone ($ArCH{=}C$—$C{=}O$, ring N, O, C—R) → α-Acylaminoacrylic acid ($ArCH{=}CCO_2H$, NH, COR)

$ArCH_2CHCO_2H$ (NH, COR)
α-Acylamino-propionic acid

$ArCH_2COCO_2H$
α-Keto acid

$ArCH_2CHCO_2H$ (NH_2)
α-Amino acid

$ArCH{=}CHNHCOR$
Styrylamide

α-Acylaminopropionic acid ↓ Dihydroisoquinoline derivative (CH_2, $CHCO_2R$, N, C—R)

α-Keto acid ↓ $ArCH_2CO_2H$
Arylacetic acid
and
$ArCH_2CN$
Arylacetonitrile

Styrylamide ↓ Isoquinoline derivative (CH, CH, N, C—R)

Most of the reactions involve the intermediate formation of an α-acylaminoacrylic acid and hence are not strictly azlactone reactions.

[107] Steiger, *Helv. Chim. Acta*, **17**, 563 (1934).
[108] Granächer and Mahler, *Helv. Chim. Acta*, **10**, 246 (1927).

α-Amino Acids

Unsaturated azlactones and acylaminoacrylic acids are converted to α-amino acids by reduction and hydrolysis. Three general methods of

$$\text{RCH=C—C=O (azlactone: N, O, C–R ring)} \rightarrow \text{RCH=C(NHCOR)CO}_2\text{H} \rightarrow \text{RCH}_2\text{CH(NH}_2\text{)CO}_2\text{H}$$

$$\text{azlactone} \rightarrow \text{RCH}_2\text{CH(NHCOR)CO}_2\text{H} \rightarrow \text{RCH}_2\text{CH(NH}_2\text{)CO}_2\text{H}; \quad \text{RCH=C(NHCOR)CO}_2\text{H} \rightarrow \text{RCH}_2\text{CH(NHCOR)CO}_2\text{H}$$

reduction which have been used for this conversion are:

1. Sodium or sodium amalgam and water or ethanol.
2. Hydriodic acid, red phosphorus, acetic acid (or acetic anhydride).
3. Catalytic hydrogenation (Pt or Pd).

The reduction of α-benzoylaminoacrylic acids with an equivalent amount of 3% sodium amalgam as originally described by Erlenmeyer [14] has been improved in several ways.[109, 110] In a modification of the procedure,[110] α-benzoylaminopropionic acids are obtained in 62–80% yields by treating aqueous solutions of the sodium salts of α-benzoylaminoacrylic acids with a large excess of sodium amalgam. This method is not always satisfactory; 2-phenyl-4-(3′,4′,5′-trimethoxybenzal)-5-oxazolone is not reduced,[111, 112] and α-benzoylamino-β-(4-methoxy-1-naphthyl)-acrylic acid gives only a 10% yield.[113] α-Benzoylamino-β-indoleacrylic acids [114–116] and α-benzoylamino-β-pyrroleacrylic acids [117] also are not reduced satisfactorily by sodium amalgam. However, reduction of the former is effected readily by the action of sodium and ethanol,[115, 116, 118, 119]

[109] Fischer, *Ber.*, **32,** 3638 (1899).
[110] Deulofeu, *Anales soc. españ. fís. quím.*, **32,** 152 (1934).
[111] Sonn, Müller, Bülow, and Meyer, *Ber.*, **58,** 1103 (1925).
[112] Schaaf and Labouchere, *Helv. Chim. Acta*, **7,** 357 (1924).
[113] Dey and Rajagopalan, *Arch. Pharm.*, **277,** 359, 377 (1939).
[114] Restelli, *Anales asoc. quím. argentina*, **23,** 58 (1935).
[115] Ellinger and Flamand, *Ber.*, **40,** 3029 (1907).
[116] Ellinger and Flamand, *Z. physiol. Chem.*, **55,** 8 (1908).
[117] Fischer and Zerweck, *Ber.*, **56,** 519 (1923).
[118] Barger and Ewins, *Biochem. J.*, **11,** 58 (1917).
[119] Ellinger and Matsuoka, *Z. physiol. Chem.*, **91,** 45 (1914).

which also hydrolyzes a considerable proportion of the reduction product to the free amino acid. Tryptophane has been synthesized by this procedure.[115] α-Phenylacetaminocinnamic acid is reduced to phenylacetylphenylalanine in 90–95% yield by sodium amalgam.[15, 120] Sufficient data are not available to show whether this result is unusual or whether phenylacetyl and perhaps other aliphatic derivatives also may give better results than the benzoyl derivatives in this reaction.

The use of a mixture of hydriodic acid and red phosphorus as a reducing agent for benzoylaminoacrylic acids was first reported [97] in the synthesis of thyroxine, in which an alkaline agent could not be employed. The yields were improved markedly by adding acetic acid [95] or acetic anhydride [121] to the reaction mixture. With the acetic anhydride-containing reagent the free amino acid is produced directly and alkylphenyl ether linkages are cleaved at the same time. The best results are obtained from the acrylic acid or ester, although the azlactone can be used satisfactorily. Hydroxybenzaloxazolones, which are destroyed by alkalies, are smoothly reduced by phosphorus, hydriodic acid, and acetic anhydride. This reagent has been applied successfully to a variety of compounds, the following amino acids being obtained in the yields indicated: phenylalanine, 65%;[79] several methyl and dimethyl tyrosines, 61–78%;[94] *o*-, *m*-, and *p*-fluorophenylalanines, 37, 78, and 41%, respectively;[122] dibromo- and dichloro-thyronines, 70–80%.[123] In the reduction of α-benzoylamino-β-[4-(4′-nitrophenoxy)phenyl]-acrylic acid, the nitro group and the double bond are reduced and the benzoyl group is removed to give α-amino-β-[4-(4′-aminophenoxy)phenyl]-propionic acid (yield 62%).[96]

Catalytic reduction has been used to a limited extent only.[26, 37, 124, 125] It seems likely that this method would be most satisfactory, except where other reducible or catalyst-poisoning groups may be present. Catalytic hydrogenation could not be used in the preparation of thyroxine [121] or for the reduction of pyrrole azlactones.[69] Benzoylaminocrotonic azlactone is reduced smoothly over platinum catalyst in glacial acetic acid containing 1 mole of water; the saturated azlactone first formed hydrolyzes immediately since it is much more reactive than the original compound.[37]

The conversion of an aldehyde to an amino acid containing two more carbon atoms can be effected in at least three other ways. These involve condensation of the aldehyde with hydantoin and its derivatives, with diketopiperazine, or with rhodanine. Since these methods have been

[120] Erlenmeyer, *Ber.*, **31**, 2238 (1898).

[121] Harington and McCartney, *Biochem. J.*, **21**, 852 (1927).

[122] Schiemann and Roselius, *Ber.*, **65**, 1439 (1932).

[123] Schuegraf, *Helv. Chim. Acta*, **12**, 405 (1929).

[124] Harwood and Johnson, *J. Am. Chem. Soc.*, **56**, 468 (1934).

[125] Herbst and Shemin, *Org. Syntheses*, *Coll. Vol.* **2**, 491 (1943).

reviewed elsewhere,[52, 126, 127] they will not be discussed here. In general the azlactone synthesis is most satisfactory although in certain instances one or both of the other methods is preferable to it.[128–131]

Procedures. The preparation of *dl*-β-phenylalanine by the reduction and cleavage of α-benzoylaminocinnamic azlactone with phosphorus, hydriodic acid, and acetic anhydride, and the preparation of the same amino acid from α-acetaminocinnamic acid by catalytic reduction and hydrolysis, are described in *Organic Syntheses*.[79, 125]

Reduction of α-Benzoylaminoacrylic Acids with Sodium Amalgam.[110] Ten grams of the acrylic acid is suspended in 100 cc. of water and reduced with 30–100 times the calculated amount of 3% sodium amalgam. The amalgam is added in 4 portions at fifteen-minute intervals. The reaction mixture is stirred vigorously for a period of two hours beginning with the first addition of the sodium amalgam. The mercury then is separated and the solution is filtered (if necessary), cooled in an ice bath, and acidified with 10% hydrochloric acid. The saturated benzoyl derivative precipitates. It is filtered, washed with water, and recrystallized from acetic acid or water. The following α-benzoylaminoacrylic acids have been reduced to the saturated derivative in the yield indicated: α-benzoylaminocinnamic acid (82%); α-benzoylamino-*p*-methoxycinnamic acid (78%); α-benzoylamino-β-furylacrylic acid (80%); α-benzoylamino-β-(2,4-dimethoxyphenyl)-acrylic acid (62%); α-benzoylamino-β-(3,4-methylenedioxyphenyl)-acrylic acid (74%).

The saturated benzoyl derivatives are converted into amino acids in excellent yields by heating under reflux with 10–20% hydrochloric acid.

α-Keto Acids

Unsaturated azlactones and α-acylaminoacrylic acids are converted into α-keto acids by strong mineral acids or alkalies.

$$\begin{array}{ccccc}
\mathrm{RCH{=}C\text{——}C{=}O} & & \mathrm{RCH{=}CCO_2H} & & \\
\mathrm{\quad\ |\qquad\ \ |} & \rightarrow & \mathrm{|} & \rightarrow & \mathrm{RCH_2COCO_2H} + \\
\mathrm{\quad\ N\qquad\ O} & & \mathrm{NH} & & \mathrm{C_6H_5CO_2H + NH_3} \\
\mathrm{\quad\ \ \diagdown\!\!\diagdown\ \diagup} & & \mathrm{|} & & \\
\mathrm{C} & & \mathrm{COC_6H_5} & & \\
\mathrm{|} & & & & \\
\mathrm{C_6H_5} & & & &
\end{array}$$

[126] Dunn in Schmidt, "Chemistry of the Amino Acids and Proteins," p. 51, Charles C. Thomas, Springfield, 1944.

[127] Clarke in Gilman, "Organic Chemistry," 2nd ed., p. 1108, John Wiley & Sons, New York, 1943.

[128] Deulofeu and Repetto, *Anales soc. españ. fís. quím.*, **32**, 159 (1934).

[129] Deulofeu, *Z. physiol. Chem.*, **204**, 214 (1932).

[130] Deulofeu and Mendive, *Z. physiol. Chem.*, **211**, 1 (1932).

[131] Deulofeu and Mendivelzua, *Z. physiol. Chem.*, **219**, 233 (1933).

The initial cleavage may occur between the acrylic acid residue and the nitrogen atom yielding an α-keto acid and benzamide, or between the benzoyl group and nitrogen yielding an α-aminoacrylic acid and benzoic acid. In either case further hydrolysis of the nitrogen-containing fragment yields the final products. There is direct evidence favoring the first path. If the alkaline hydrolysis of 2-phenyl-4-benzal-5-oxazolone is stopped when the odor of ammonia is first evident, benzamide is obtained from the reaction mixture in 30% yield.[11, 132] However, there is one case in which the nitrogen remains in the hydrolysis product[39, 100, 133] as shown in the following equation. It is possible, of course, that both

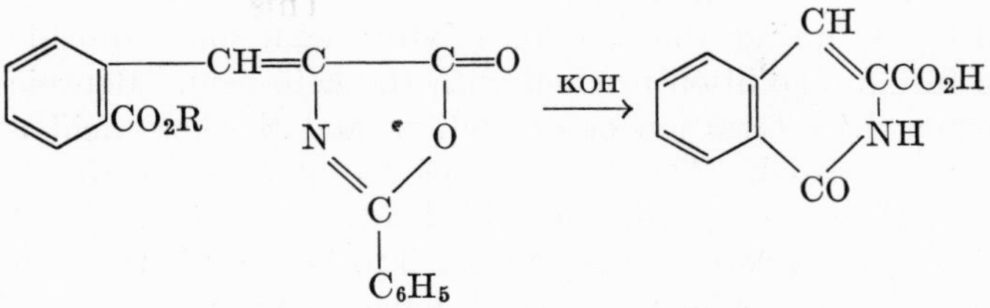

CH=C—C=O ; CO_2R ; N O ; C ; C_6H_5 $\xrightarrow{\text{KOH}}$ CH ; CCO_2H ; NH ; CO

reactions occur simultaneously and that various substituents may affect the relative rates.

The conversion of unsaturated azlactones into α-keto acids can be effected by either strong alkalies (sodium, potassium, or barium hydroxide) or strong acids (usually hydrochloric) in aqueous or alcoholic solutions. Alkalies are much more effective and generally are used. The azlactone (or acylaminoacrylic acid) is refluxed with 10 volumes of 10% sodium or potassium hydroxide for four to six hours.[8, 40, 71, 134–137] Occasionally 30–40% alkali is used with a shorter reaction time.[138–140] Barium hydroxide in aqueous ethanol gives excellent results in a few cases but is unsatisfactory in others.[77] This reagent has one advantage, namely, that the barium salts of α-keto acids often are insoluble in the reaction mixture. *p*-Hydroxybenzaloxazolones are hydrolyzed in an atmosphere of hydrogen in order to prevent oxidation of the pyruvic acids.

Acids generally are less effective than bases as hydrolytic agents. They are used for aliphatic azlactones, which are more easily hydrolyzed,

[132] Plöchl, *Ber.*, **17,** 1616 (1884).
[133] Stiller, *J. Chem. Soc.*, **1937,** 473.
[134] Gulland and Virden, *J. Chem. Soc.*, **1928,** 921.
[135] Hill and Short, *J. Chem. Soc.*, **1937,** 260.
[136] Birch and Robertson, *J. Chem. Soc.*, **1938,** 306.
[137] Foster, Robertson, and Healy, *J. Chem. Soc.*, **1939,** 1594.
[138] Henze, Whitney, and Eppright, *J. Am. Chem. Soc.*, **62,** 565 (1940).
[139] Canzanelli, Guild, and Harington, *Biochem. J.*, **29,** 1617 (1935).
[140] Späth and Land, *Monatsh.*, **42,** 273 (1921).

or for aromatic azlactones which, because of the nature of substituent groups, are unstable toward alkalies. Aqueous hydrochloric acid has been used for 2-phenyl-4-ethylidene-[37] and 2-phenyl-4-isopropylidene-5-oxazolone.[70] Sulfuric acid (50%) or boiling ethanolic hydrochloric acid merely opens the azlactone ring of 2-phenyl-4-(2′-nitro-3′-methoxy-4′-acetoxybenzal)-5-oxazolone. However, the last reagent under pressure at 100° gives a 55% yield of α-keto ester.[57] The conversion of nitrobenzaloxazolones into α-keto esters has been effected by the action of aqueous-ethanolic hydrochloric acid.[141]

In the preparation of α-keto acids from 2-phenyloxazolones, benzoic acid must be separated from the product. This separation has been effected by saturating the reaction mixture with sulfur dioxide, which forms a bisulfite addition product with the keto acid. Benzoic acid is then removed by filtration or extraction, and the keto acid is subsequently regenerated. These operations are avoided by the use of 2-methyloxazolones,[65, 142] with the added advantage that the 2-methyl derivatives are converted more readily into keto acids than are the 2-phenyl derivatives. Thus, 90% yields have been reported [143] in the conversion of a series of 2-methyloxazolones to α-keto acids by alkaline hydrolysis to the acetaminoacrylic acids and conversion of these acids to α-keto acids with dilute hydrochloric acid.

Abnormal Hydrolytic Products. 1. *o-Nitrobenzaloxazolones.* o-Nitrobenzaloxazolones undergo extensive decomposition when treated with alkali. The reactions are of two types, depending on the nature and position of other substituents. Unsubstituted o-nitrobenzaloxazolone yields o-nitrotoluene. The following mechanism has been suggested for this reaction.[144] o-Nitrophenylpyruvic acids are known to undergo a reaction of this type,[144] presumably due to vinylogous activation of the methylene

$$o\text{-}NO_2C_6H_4\text{—}CH\text{=}C\text{—}C\text{=}O \ (\text{ring: } N, O, C\text{—}C_6H_5) \rightarrow \left[o\text{-}NO_2C_6H_4CH_2COCO_2H \right] \rightarrow o\text{-}NO_2C_6H_4CH_3 + \begin{matrix} CO_2H \\ | \\ CO_2H \end{matrix}$$

group by the o-nitro substituent. The fact that m-nitrobenzaloxazolones give no nitrotoluene under the same conditions [59] supports this interpretation. o-Nitrobenzaloxazolones with no substituents adjacent to the

[141] Avenarius and Pschorr, *Ber.*, **62,** 321 (1929).

[142] Sugasawa and Tsuda, *J. Pharm. Soc. Japan*, **55,** 1050 (1935).

[143] Niederl and Ziering, *J. Am. Chem. Soc.*, **64,** 885 (1942).

[144] Burton and Stoves, *J. Chem. Soc.*, **1937,** 402.

nitro group also decompose into toluene derivatives. However, the presence of an alkoxy group next to the nitro group leads to a different reaction as shown in the following equation.[58] 2-Phenyl-4-(2′-nitro-3′-

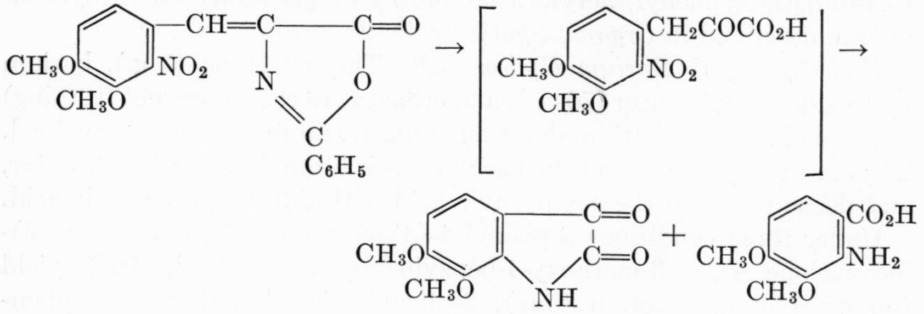

CH_3O, CH_3O, NO_2 —CH=C——C=O, N, O, C, C_6H_5 → [CH_3O, CH_3O, CH_2COCO_2H, NO_2] →

CH_3O, CH_3O, C=O, C=O, NH + CH_3O, CH_3O, CO_2H, NH_2

methoxy-4′-acetoxybenzal)-5-oxazolone gives the isatin derivative but no aminovanillic acid.[144] Several *o*-nitrobenzaloxazolones which decompose with alkali have been converted into the corresponding α-keto acids or esters by the use of ethanolic hydrochloric acid.[141]

2. *o-Carboalkoxybenzaloxazolones.* *o*-Carboalkoxybenzaloxazolones are converted into derivatives of isocarbostyril-3-carboxylic acid by refluxing

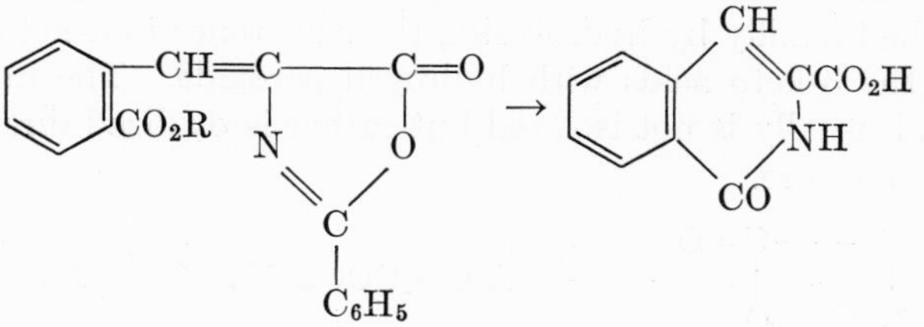

—CH=C——C=O, CO_2R, N, O, C, C_6H_5 → CH, CCO_2H, NH, CO

10% aqueous potassium hydroxide.[39, 100, 133] If the reaction is carried out in methanol or ethanol the main product is an orthoester [133] of the following structure.

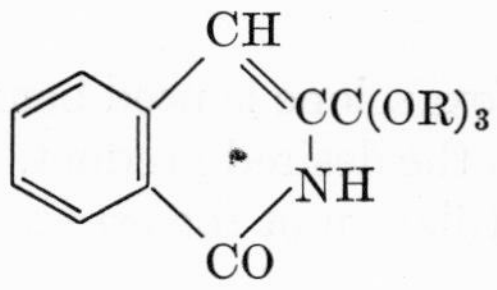

CH, $CC(OR)_3$, NH, CO

3. *Miscellaneous Reactions.* (*a*) The decomposition of azlactones to toluene derivatives, noted for *o*-nitrobenzaloxazolones, also has been reported for *p*-methoxybenzal-,[138] 2-methoxy-1-naphthal-,[145] and 6-methoxy-3,7-dimethylcoumarilal-2-phenyl-5-oxazolones.[137]

(*b*) Cinnamaloxazolone on treatment with hydrochloric acid yields naphthalene and α-naphthoic acid.[6, 10]

[145] Mauthner, *J. prakt. Chem.*, **95**, 55 (1917).

Procedures. The preparations of phenylpyruvic acid by the hydrolysis of α-acetaminocinnamic acid with 1 *N* hydrochloric acid and of 3,4-dimethoxyphenylpyruvic acid by the hydrolysis of α-benzoylamino-β-(3,4-dimethoxyphenyl)-acrylic azlactone by 10% aqueous sodium hydroxide are described in *Organic Syntheses*.[146, 147]

Hydrolysis with Barium Hydroxide.[77] The azlactone (5 g.), barium hydroxide (20 g.), water (70 cc.), and ethanol (10 cc., to prevent frothing) are heated in an oil bath under reflux until no more ammonia is evolved. The mixture is cooled, and the barium salt is filtered, washed with water, and decomposed to the arylpyruvic acid with dilute hydrochloric acid.

Under these conditions 2-phenyl-4-(3′-methoxy-4′-benzyloxybenzal)-5-oxazolone gives 3-methoxy-4-benzyloxypyruvic acid in 90% yield (ninety-six-hour reaction time); 2-phenyl-4-(3′,4′-methylenedioxybenzal)-5-oxazolone gives the pyruvic acid in 85% yield (reaction time not given); the azlactones derived from vanillin, *m*-hydroxybenzaldehyde, and *p*-hydroxybenzaldehyde give no arylpyruvic acid.

Arylacetic Acids

The conversion of substituted 4-benzaloxazolones to arylacetic acids is accomplished readily by hydrolyzing the azlactones to α-keto acids and oxidizing the α-keto acids with hydrogen peroxide. The intermediate α-keto acid usually is not isolated but rather is oxidized directly in the hydrolysis mixture.

$$\text{ArCH=C—C=O (ring: C–N=C(R)–O–C=O)} \xrightarrow{\text{NaOH}} \text{ArCH}_2\text{COCO}_2\text{Na} \xrightarrow{\text{H}_2\text{O}_2} \text{ArCH}_2\text{CO}_2\text{Na}$$

If a substituted 2-phenyloxazolone is used benzoic acid is produced, and it must be separated from the desired product. This separation has been effected by fractional distillation of the esters[146, 148] or by steam distillation of the benzoic acid.

At least two other methods are available for preparing arylacetic acids from aromatic aldehydes. One involves the condensation of the aldehyde with rhodanine,[52, 149] and the other[150] involves the formation of the

[146] Snyder, Buck, and Ide, *Org. Syntheses, Coll. Vol.* **2**, 333 (1943).
[147] Herbst and Shemin, *Org. Syntheses, Coll. Vol.* **2**, 519 (1943).
[148] Cain, Simonsen, and Smith, *J. Chem. Soc.*, **103**, 1035 (1913).
[149] Julian and Sturgis, *J. Am. Chem. Soc.*, **57**, 1126 (1935).
[150] Kindler, Metzendorf, and Dschi-yin-Kwok, *Ber.*, **76**, 308 (1943).

cyanohydrin, which may be converted into the arylacetic acid in several ways.[150, 151]

Procedures. The preparation of 3,4-dimethoxyphenylacetic acid (homoveratric acid) is described in *Organic Syntheses*.[146]

4-Chlorophenylacetic Acid.[145] Five grams of 2-phenyl-4-(4′-chlorobenzal)-5-oxazolone is heated under reflux for five hours with 50 cc. of 10% aqueous sodium hydroxide. The solution is cooled in an ice bath and shaken vigorously while 25 cc. of 10% hydrogen peroxide is added slowly. The reaction mixture is allowed to stand overnight at room temperature and is acidified with dilute hydrochloric acid. The benzoic acid is removed by steam distillation, and the crude 4-chlorophenylacetic acid separates when the residual solution is cooled. The crude product is recrystallized from petroleum ether, giving 1.8 g. (60%) of the pure material, m.p. 104–105°.

Arylacetonitriles

Arylacetonitriles also can be prepared from the α-keto acids obtained from azlactones. The α-keto acids are isolated from the hydrolysis mixture and converted into the oximes, from which the nitriles are obtained by reaction with acetic anhydride. Good yields have been obtained with a variety of compounds.[74, 141, 143, 152–156]

$$ArCH_2COCO_2H \rightarrow ArCH_2\underset{\underset{NOH}{\|}}{C}CO_2H \xrightarrow{Ac_2O} ArCH_2CN$$

Procedures. 1. *Conversion of Arylpyruvic Acids to the Oximes.*[143] Approximately 1 mole of the arylpyruvic acid is dissolved in 800 cc. of a solution containing 2 mole equivalents of sodium hydroxide, and 1.5 moles of hydroxylamine is added. The solution is allowed to stand for thirty-six hours, and the oxime is precipitated by acidification with dilute hydrochloric acid. The yield of oxime is 95%.

2. *Conversion of Oximes to Arylacetonitriles.*[143] The oxime is dehydrated by warming with 4 parts of acetic anhydride. Since the reaction is violent the oxime is added in 3 portions to the warm reagent, the reaction being allowed to subside between additions. The nitriles are separated from the reaction mixture by fractional distillation in vacuum. The yields vary from 50 to 70%.

[151] Krannichfeldt, *Ber.*, **46**, 4023 (1913).
[152] Mitter and Maitra, *J. Indian Chem. Soc.*, **13**, 236 (1936).
[153] Pfeiffer, Quehl, and Tappermann, *Ber.*, **63**, 1301 (1930).
[154] Buck, Baltzly, and Ide, *J. Am. Chem. Soc.*, **60**, 1789 (1938).
[155] Robertson, *J. Chem. Soc.*, **1933**, 489.
[156] Haworth, Mavin, and Sheldrick, *J. Chem. Soc.*, **1934**, 1423.

4-Methoxy-, 3,4-dimethoxy-, and 3,4-methylenedioxy-phenylacetonitriles have been prepared by the above methods.

Miscellaneous

Isoquinoline Derivatives. The preparation of derivatives of isocarbostyryl from 2-carboalkoxybenzaloxazolones already has been discussed. Derivatives of dihydroisoquinoline have been obtained indirectly from azlactones as shown in the following equations.

(*a*) [124]

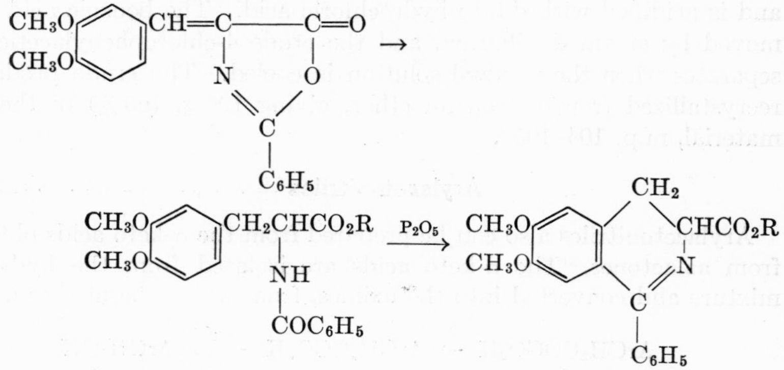

CH_3O, CH_3O — $CH{=}C$—$C{=}O$, N, O, C, C_6H_5 →

CH_3O, CH_3O — CH_2CHCO_2R, NH, COC_6H_5 $\xrightarrow{P_2O_5}$ CH_3O, CH_3O — CH_2, $CHCO_2R$, N, C, C_6H_5

(*b*) [157]

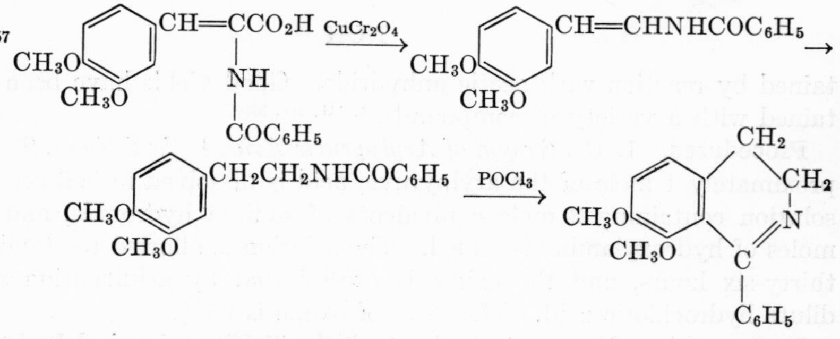

CH_3O, CH_3O — $CH{=}CCO_2H$, NH, COC_6H_5 $\xrightarrow{CuCr_2O_4}$ CH_3O, CH_3O — $CH{=}CHNHCOC_6H_5$ →

CH_3O, CH_3O — $CH_2CH_2NHCOC_6H_5$ $\xrightarrow{POCl_3}$ CH_3O, CH_3O — CH_2, CH_2, N, C, C_6H_5

Quinoline Derivatives. Imidazolones obtained from *o*-nitrobenzaloxazolones give substituted diaminoquinolines on reduction.[56]

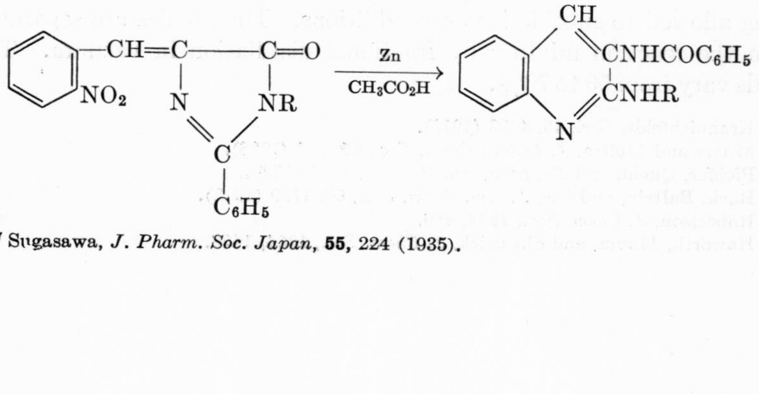

NO_2 — $CH{=}C$—$C{=}O$, N, NR, C, C_6H_5 $\xrightarrow[CH_3CO_2H]{Zn}$ CH, $CNHCOC_6H_5$, CNHR, N

[157] Sugasawa, *J. Pharm. Soc. Japan*, **55**, 224 (1935).

Imidazolone (Glyoxalone) Derivatives. Amides of α-acylaminoacrylic acids can be converted into imidazolone derivatives as shown in the equations:

```
                                           O
                                          //
RCH=C————C=O  R'NH2  RCH=C—C—NHR'     →   RCH=C————C=O
    |    |    ————→      |                    |    |
    N    O               NH                   N    NR'
     \\ /                |                     \\ /
      C                  CO                     C
      |                  |                      |
      R                  R                      R
```

The ring closure can be effected under a variety of conditions. When $R' = H$ the action of sodium hydroxide alone converts the amide into the imidazolone;[6, 8] when $R' = —CH_2R$, heating above the melting point is required.[108] Substituted anilides ($R' = —C_6H_4R$) have been converted into imidazolone derivatives by the action of phosphorus oxychloride.[56] The conversion of amides of saturated α-acylamino acids into imidazolones has not been studied extensively.[21–24] Benzoylphenylalanine amide [24] gives a poor yield; benzoylaminoisobutyric acid amide, a good yield.[21]

Certain imidazolone derivatives can be converted into dipeptides as follows.[108]

```
C6H5CH=C————C=O           Na·Hg   C6H5CH2CH————C=O              H+
       |    |             ————→            |    |               ——→
       N    NCH2CO2C2H5                    NH   NCH2CO2C2H5
        \\ /                                 \ /
         C                                    CH
         |                                    |
         C6H5                                 C6H5

                          C6H5CH2CHCONHCH2CO2H + C6H5CHO
                                 |
                                 NH2
```

Indole Derivatives. An indole derivative has been obtained from a substituted azlactone as shown in the following equation.[158] This reaction has not been applied to other compounds.

```
O2N(C6H2)—CH=C————C=O    CH3OH     O2N(C6H3)————CH
    |  OCH3   |    |     ————→         |         ||
   NO2        N    O      NH3         NO2  \    CCONH2
               \\ /                         N  /
                C                           H
                |
                C6H5
```

158 Hill and Robinson, *J. Chem. Soc.*, **1933**, 486.

Styrylamides. Benzoylaminocinnamic acids can be decarboxylated to styrylamides by heating with copper chromite in quinoline at 120–180°.[157, 159]

$$\begin{array}{l} C_6H_5CH{=}CCO_2H \\ \qquad\quad\;\; | \\ \qquad\quad\; NH \qquad \rightarrow C_6H_5CH{=}CHNHCOC_6H_5 \\ \qquad\quad\;\; | \\ \qquad\quad\; COC_6H_5 \end{array}$$

TABLES OF AZLACTONES AND DERIVED SUBSTANCES

Those azlactones reported in the literature up to and including the 1944 *Chemical Abstracts* are listed in the following tables. Many of them were prepared as intermediates, and the substances to which they were converted are listed along with them.

[159] Sugasawa and Kakemi, *J. Pharm. Soc. Japan*, **55**, 1283 (1935).

TABLE I

Unsaturated Azlactones

A. *2-Phenyl-4-benzal-5-oxazolones*

Substituted Benzaldehyde	Azlactone References and Yields	Derived Acids		
		Pyruvic	Acetic	Amino
Unsubstituted	79 (*64%*), 1 (*80%*), 2, 3, 12–14, 35, 36, 69, 77, 85, 95, 102, 103, 108, 110, 121, 132, 133, 160–166	12, 77, 147 (*90%*)	160 (*55%*)	14, 79 (*65%*), 95 (*82%*), 110, 121 (*88%*), 161, 164
3-Methyl	167			167 (*50%*)
4-Methyl	168 (*80%*), 166			168
4-Isopropyl	6 (*80%*), 169			
2-Styryl	170 (*42%*)			
2-Fluoro	122 (*35%*)			122 (*37%*)
3-Fluoro	122 (*70%*)			122 (*78%*)
4-Fluoro	122 (*75%*), 171			122 (*41%*)
2-Chloro	145		145	
3-Chloro	172 (*75%*), 173	173 (*77%*)	173 (*57%*)	172
4-Chloro	174 (*79%*), 145	174	145 (*60%*)	174
3-Bromo	145		145	
3-Fluoro-4-methoxy	175 (*95%*), 176–178			175–178,* 177 * (*77%*)
3-Fluoro-4-ethoxy	178 (*65%*), 176			176,* 178 * (*88%*)
3,5-Difluoro-4-methoxy	177 (*50%*), 175			175,* 177 * (*77%*)
3-Chloro-4,5-dimethoxy	179			
2-Bromo-4,5-dimethoxy	156	156	156	
4-(4′-Iodophenoxy)	96 (*70%*)			96
2-Fluoro-4-(4′-methoxyphenoxy)	178 (*39%*), 176			176,* 178 * (*85%*)
3,5-Dichloro-4-(4′-methoxyphenoxy)	123 (*80–85%*)			123 * (*80%*)
3,5-Dibromo-4-(4′-methoxyphenoxy)	123 (*80%*)			123 * (*70–80%*)
3,5-Diiodo-4-(2′-methoxyphenoxy)	180 (*95%*)			180 * (*12%*)
3,5-Diiodo-4-(3′-methoxyphenoxy)	181 (*95%*)			181 * (*39%*)
3,5-Diiodo-4-(4′-methoxyphenoxy)	97 (*90%*), 121, 182			97,* 121 * (*82%*)
3,5-Diiodo-4-(3′-fluoro-4′-methoxyphenoxy)	183 (*90%*)			183 * (*42%*)
3,5-Diiodo-4-(3′,5′-difluoro-4′-methoxyphenoxy)	177 (*60–65%*)			177 * (*55%*)
5-Chloro-3-methoxy-4-hydroxy	184 † (*80%*)	184 (*49%*)		

References 160–248 appear on pp. 238–239.

* Alkoxyl group replaced by hydroxyl.

† Hydroxyl group acetylated during azlactonization.

TABLE I—*Continued*

UNSATURATED AZLACTONES

Substituted Benzaldehyde	Azlactone References and Yields	Derived Acids		
		Pyruvic	Acetic	Amino
6-Chloro-3-methoxy-4-hydroxy	184 † (*68%*)			
5,6-Dichloro-3-methoxy-4-hydroxy	184 † (*62%*)			
5-Bromo-3-methoxy-4-hydroxy	184 † (*70%*)	184 (*47%*)		
6-Bromo-3-methoxy-4-hydroxy	184 † (*71%*)			
5,6-Dibromo-3-methoxy-4-hydroxy	184 † (*51%*)			
2,5,6-Tribromo-3-methoxy-4-hydroxy	184 † (*72%*)			
5-Bromo-3,4-dimethoxy	184 (*62%*)	184 (*37%*)		
5-Iodo-3-methoxy-4-hydroxy	184 †	184 (*43%*)		
2-Methoxy	60, 160, 185		160, 185	
3-Methoxy	186 (*53%*), 60		186 (*60%*)	
4-Methoxy	187 (*80%*), 8, 60, 77, 95, 102, 110, 121, 138, 148, 160, 188	8, 77 (*23%*) 138, 148	148, 160 (*80%*)	95,* 110, 121 * (*60%*), 187
2,3-Dimethoxy	189 (*60%*), 185, 190	190	189 (*66%*), 185, 190	
2,4-Dimethoxy	110 (*71%*), 152, 191	152	152, 191 (*60%*)	110 (*62%*)
2,5-Dimethoxy	40 (*75%*), 112	40 (*76%*)	40 (*80%*)	112 *
3,4-Dimethoxy	80 (*69–73%*), 76, 99, 124, 131, 153, 156, 157, 192, 193	99, 146 (*80%*) 153, 156, 192	146 (*51%*), 153, 156, 192	124, 131, 193
3,4-Methylenedioxy	76 (*70%*), 56, 77, 99, 110, 160, 193–198	77 (*85%*), 99, 194, 195	160 (*90%*), 195	110 (*74%*), 193, 196
3,4-Carbonyldioxy	199 (*74%*)			199 ‡ (*76%*)
2,3,5-Trimethoxy	200 (*95%*)		200	
2,4,5-Trimethoxy	201	201	201	
2,4,6-Trimethoxy	202		202 (*61%*)	
3,4,5-Trimethoxy	75 (*85%*), 74, 111	74, 75	74, 75	
4,5-Dimethoxy-2-methoxymethoxy	203 (*79%*)		203 (*57%*)	
2-Methoxy-3-methyl	135 (*100%*)	135	135	
4-Methoxy-3-methyl	204 (*70%*)			204 * (*65%*)
2-Methoxy-5-ethyl	134	134 (*70%*)	134 (*85%*)	
4,5-Dimethoxy-2-ethyl	205 (*66%*)	205 (*71%*)	205 (*78%*)	
2,3-Dimethoxy-5-*n*-propyl	206 (*61%*)	206	206 (*83%*)	

References 160–248 appear on pp. 238–239.
* Alkoxyl group replaced by hydroxyl.
† Hydroxyl group acetylated during azlactonization.
‡ Carbonyldioxy group hydrolyzed.

TABLE I—*Continued*

UNSATURATED AZLACTONES

Substituted Benzaldehyde	Azlactone References and Yields	Derived Acids		
		Pyruvic	Acetic	Amino
2-Ethoxy	154 (*65%*)	154 (*55%*)	154	
3-Ethoxy	154 (*65%*)	154 (*55%*)	154	
4-Ethoxy	154 (*65%*)	154 (*55%*)	154	
2-Ethoxy-3-methoxy	154 (*65%*)	154 (*55%*)	154	
3-Ethoxy-4-methoxy	72 (*82%*), 73	73 (*71%*)	72, 73 (*98%*)	
4-Ethoxy-3-methoxy	73 (*67%*)	73 (*71%*)	73 (*98%*)	
3,4-Diethoxy	154 (*65%*)	154 (*55%*)	154	
4-Phenoxy	96 (*85%*)			96 (*70%*)
3-Phenoxy-4-hydroxy	207 ‡ (*75%*)			207 (*50%*)
3-Benzyloxy	71 (*74%*)	71 (*65%*)	71 (*90%*)	
2-Benzyloxy	185 (*63%*)	185	185	
3-Benzyloxy-4-methoxy	208 (*72%*), 194, 209	194 (*61%*), 208, 209	208, 209 (*86%*),	
4-Benzyloxy-3-methoxy	77 (*80%*)	77 (*90%*)	77	
3,4-Dibenzyloxy	194 (*60%*)	194 (*0%*)		
4-(4′-Methoxyphenoxy)	121 (*70%*)			121 * (*61%*)
2-Carbethoxymethoxy	155 (*54%*)	155 †	155 †	
2-Carbethoxymethoxy-4-methoxy	155 (*63%*)	155 † (*83%*)	155 †	
2-Carbomethoxy-3,4-dimethoxy	39			
2-Carbomethoxy	39, 133			
2-Hydroxy-4-methoxy	155 ‡			
3-Hydroxy-4-methoxy	140 ‡ (*76%*), 128 ‡	140 (*24%*)	140	128 (*85%*)
4-Hydroxy-3-methoxy	121 ‡ (*75%*), 160,‡ 204,‡ 210,‡ 211 ‡		160	121 * (*50%*), 204,* 210,* 211
5-Hydroxy-3,4-dimethoxy	212 ‡ (*38%*)		212 (*36%*)	
2-Hydroxy	7,‡ 29,‡ 60–62,‡ 213 ‡	7		213 (*85%*)
3-Hydroxy	8,‡ 60,‡ 172,‡ 213 ‡			213 (*65%*)
4-Hydroxy	4 ‡ (*85%*), 9,‡ 60,‡ 69,‡ 103,‡ 109,‡ 160,‡ 214 ‡	214 (*36%*)	160 (*80%*)	4, 103, 109 (*67%*)
2,4-Dihydroxy	63,‡ 155 ‡			
2,5-Dihydroxy	64 ‡ (*43%*)	64		
3,4-Dihydroxy	131 ‡ (*65%*), 210 †			131
4-Hydroxy-2-methyl	94 ‡ (*73%*)			94 (*61%*)
4-Hydroxy-3-methyl	94 ‡			94
4-Hydroxy-2,3-dimethyl	94 ‡ (*77%*)			94 (*78%*)
4-Hydroxy-3,5-dimethyl	94 ‡ (*95%*)			94 (*65%*)
4-Hydroxy-2,5-dimethyl	94 ‡ (*71%*)			94 (*72%*)

References 160–248 appear on pp. 238–239.
* Alkoxyl group replaced by hydroxyl.
† Carbethoxy group hydrolyzed.
‡ Hydroxyl group acetylated during azlactonization.

TABLE I—*Continued*

UNSATURATED AZLACTONES

Substituted Benzaldehyde	Azlactone References and Yields	Derived Acids		
		Pyruvic	Acetic	Amino
2-Nitro	59 (*61%*), 56, 166, 169	59 (*0%*), 169		
3-Nitro	77 (*76%*), 59, 166			
4-Nitro	59, 77, 166	77 (*0%*)		
2-Nitro-5-methoxy	59 (*84%*)	59 (*0%*)		
3-Nitro-4-methoxy	215			
2-Nitro-3,4-dimethoxy	58 (*75%*), 39, 141	58 (*0%*), 141	141	
2-Nitro-4,5-dimethoxy	76 (*89%*), 169	76 (*0%*), 169		
2-Nitro-3,4-methylenedioxy	56 (*35%*), 39			
2-Nitro-5-benzyloxy	59 (*59%*)	59 (*0%*)		
2-Nitro-5-hydroxy	59 * (*65%*)	59 (*0%*)		
5-Nitro-3-methoxy-4-hydroxy	111 * (*32%*)			
2-Nitro-3-methoxy-4-hydroxy	57 * (*42%*), 39, 144	57 (*53%*) 144 (*0%*)		
3,5-Dinitro-2-methoxy	158 (*66%*)			
3,5-Dinitro-2-hydroxy	158 (*85%*)			
4-(4′-Nitrophenoxy)	96 (*82%*)			96 † (*62%*)

B. *2-Phenyl-4-indolal-5-oxazolones*

Carbonyl Component	Azlactone References and Yields	Derived Acids		
		Pyruvic	Acetic	Amino
2-Indolealdehyde	114 (1-acetyl)			
3-Indolealdehyde	116 (*80%*), 114, 115, 133; 1-acetyl 216 (*83%*), 69, 114	216 (*90%?*)		114 (*0%*), 115, 116
3-Oxindolealdehyde	217, 218 ‡			
1-Methyl-3-oxindolealdehyde	217 ‡ (*50%*)			
Ethyl 3-oxindoleglyoxylate	218			
Substituted 3-indolealdehyde				
2-Carbethoxy (methoxy)	100 (*80%*), 219			
2-Methyl	119 (*89%*), 118			118 (*40%*), 119
5-Methyl	220 (*0%*)			
1-Methyl	221			221

References 160–248 appear on pp. 238–239.

* Hydroxyl group acetylated during azlactonization.

† Nitro group reduced to amino.

‡ The structures of these azlactones have not been established completely.

TABLE I—*Continued*

UNSATURATED AZLACTONES

C. *2–Phenyl-4-pyrrolal-5-oxazolones*

Carbonyl Component	Azlactone References and Yields	Derived Acids		
		Pyruvic	Acetic	Amino
2-Pyrrolealdehyde	222			
Substituted 2-pyrrole-aldehyde				
3,5-Dimethyl-4-ethyl	69 (*83%*)			
3,5-Dimethyl-4 (2′-carbethoxy-2′-cyano)-vinyl	223			
Substituted 3-pyrrole-aldehyde				
2,4,5-Trimethyl	117			
2,5-Dimethyl-4-carbethoxy-1-phenyl	217			
2,5-Dimethyl-4-carbethoxy-1-*p*-tolyl	217			
2,4-Dimethyl-5-carboalkoxy	224 (*62%*), 69			

D. *2-Phenyl-4-substituted-5-oxazolones Derived from Other Aromatic Ring Systems*

Carbonyl Component	Azlactone References and Yields	Pyruvic	Acetic	Amino
1-Naphthaldehyde	145 (*38%*), 160a (*67%*)		145	160a (*33%*)
2-Methoxy-1-naphthaldehyde	145 (*28%*)		145	
4-Methoxy-1-naphthaldehyde	113 (*43%*), 145		145	113
3-Pyrenealdehyde	225 (*77%*)			225 (*Good*)
Furfural	172 (*70%*), 7, 98, 110, 226			110 (*Good*), 172, 226
Phthalic anhydride	2, 227			
3-Methyl-6-methoxy-2-benzofuranaldehyde	137 (*86%*)	137 (*50%*)	137 (*69%*)	
3,7-Dimethyl-6-methoxy-2-benzofuranaldehyde	137 (*89%*)	137 (*50%*)		
3-Methyl-4,6-dimethoxy-2-benzofuranaldehyde	136	136 (*83%*)	136 (*95%*)	
3,5-Dimethyl-4,6-dimethoxy-2-benzofuranaldehyde	136 (*73%*)	136	136	
6-Formylcoumarin	104 (*60%*)	104		
2-Thiophenealdehyde	228 (*70%*), 68			68 (*65%*), 228
4-Methyl-5-thiazolealdehyde	229 (*70%*), 230			229 (*70%*), 230
4-Imidazolealdehyde	53 (*72%*) (1-acetyl)			53

References 160–248 appear on pp. 238–239.

TABLE I—*Continued*

Unsaturated Azlactones

E. *bis-2-Phenyl-5-oxazolones*

Carbonyl Component	Azlactone References and Yields	Derived Acids		
		Pyruvic	Acetic	Amino
Terephthalaldehyde	231 (*97%*)			
Isophthalaldehyde	231	231 (*0%*)		
Dinitroisophthalaldehyde	231 (*65%*)			
2,2′-Dimethoxy-5,5′-diformyldiphenylether	232			

F. *2-Phenyl-4-alkylidene-5-oxazolones*

Carbonyl Component	Azlactone References and Yields	Pyruvic	Acetic	Amino
Acetaldehyde	37 (*20%*), 34, 81			37 (*80%*)
Acetone	70 (*40%*), 81	70, 81		
Isobutyraldehyde	5			5
Perilla aldehyde	67 (*67%*)			
Cinnamaldehyde	6, 10	10 (*0%*)		
α-*n*-Amylcinnamaldehyde	67 (*80%*), 233			

G. *2-Methyl-4-benzal-5-oxazolones*

Substituted Benzaldehyde	Azlactone References and Yields	Derived Acids		
		Pyruvic	Acetic	Amino
Unsubstituted	78 (*75%*), 13, 26, 27, 33, 65, 83–85, 87, 105–108, 125, 162, 165, 184, 234	13, 65, 147 (*90%*)		125 (*94%*)
5-Chloro-3-methoxy-4-hydroxy	184 * (*55%*)			
5-Chloro-3,4-dimethoxy	184			
5-Bromo-3-methoxy-4-hydroxy	184 * (*72%*)			
5-Bromo-3,4-dimethoxy	184 (*70%*)			
6-Bromo-3-methoxy-4-hydroxy	184 *			
5-Iodo-3-methoxy-4-hydroxy	184 * (*27%*)			

References 160–248 appear on pp. 238–239.

* Hydroxyl group acetylated during azlactonization.

TABLE I—*Continued*

UNSATURATED AZLACTONES

Substituted Benzaldehyde	Azlactone References and Yields	Derived Acids		
		Pyruvic	Acetic	Amino
3,5-Diiodo-4-(4′-methoxyphenoxy)	139 (*92%*)	139		
3,5-Diiodo-4-[3′,5′-diiodo-4′-(4″-methoxyphenoxy)-phenoxy]	235 (*80%*)			235 * (*Poor*)
4-Nitro	65 (*96%*)			
2-Methoxy	82			
4-Methoxy	143 (*35%*), 142	142, 143 (*90%*)	142, 143	
3,4-Dimethoxy	143 (*35%*), 142	142, 143 (*90%*)	142, 143	
3,4-Methylenedioxy	65 (*57%*), 54, 142, 143	142, 143 (*90%*)	142, 143	
2-Hydroxy	65 † (*50%*)			
4-Hydroxy	65 † (*72%*), 33, 87			

H. *Miscellaneous Unsaturated Azlactones*

5-Oxazolone ‡	References and Yields	Derived Acids		
		Pyruvic	Acetic	Amino
4-(4′-Methyl-5′-thiazolylmethylene)-2-methyl	236 (*27%*)			
4-Formal-2-methyl	83	83		
4-Formal-2-ethyl	33			
4-Isobutylidene-2-methyl	165 (*70%*)			
4-Benzal-2-chloromethyl	86 (*56%*)			86
4-Benzal-2-benzyl	15 (*37%*), 120			15 (*90%*), 120
4-(3′-Methoxy-4′-hydroxybenzal-2-*o*-bromophenyl	184 † (*61%*)			

References 160–248 appear on pp. 238–239.

* Alkoxy group replaced by hydroxyl.

† Hydroxyl group acetylated during azlactonization.

‡ A group of azlactones derived from acylated peptides of α-aminocinnamic acid has been described. (See refs. 165 and 237.) These compounds are of the general type:

$$R[CONHC(=CHC_6H_5)]_x—C=N—C(=CHC_6H_5)—CO$$

(with C and CO joined through —O—)

$$R = CH_3,\ C_6H_5 \text{ and } x = 0, 1, 2, 3$$

TABLE I—*Continued*

UNSATURATED AZLACTONES

5-Oxazolone	References and Yields	Derived Acids		
		Pyruvic	Acetic	Amino
4-(3′-Methoxy-4′-hydroxy-5′-bromobenzal)-2-*o*-bromophenyl	184 * (*65%*)			
4-(3′-Methoxy-4′-hydroxy-6′-bromobenzal)-2-*o*-bromophenyl	184 * (*62%*)			
4-(3′-Methoxy-4′-hydroxy-5′,6′-dibromobenzal)-2-*o*-bromophenyl	184 * (*62%*)			
4-(3′-Methoxy-4′-hydroxy-2′,5′,6′-tribromobenzal)-2-*o*-bromophenyl	184 * (*28%*)			
4-(3′,4′-Diethoxybenzal)-2-(3′,4′,5′-trimethoxyphenyl)	157 (*60%*)			
4-(3′-Isopropoxy-4′-methoxybenzal)-2-(3′,4′,5′-trimethoxyphenyl)	159			
4-(3′-*n*-Propoxy-4′-methoxybenzal)-2-(3′,4′,5′-trimethoxyphenyl)	159			

References 160–248 appear on pp. 238–239.

* Hydroxyl group acetylated during azlactonization.

TABLE II

SATURATED AZLACTONES

A. *2-Phenyl-4-substituted 5-oxazolones*

4-Substituents	Azlactone References and Yields	Dipeptides
None	238, 239	
Methyl	22 (*95%*), 19, 89, 101, 240	19, 22, 101, 240
Dimethyl	21 (*95%*), 18, 108, 162	21, 108
Benzyl	19, 24, 38	19, 24
4′-Methoxybenzyl	34 (*65%*)	
Methyl, benzamido	50	50
3-Pyrenylmethyl	225	

B. *2-Methyl-4-substituted 5-oxazolones*

4-Substituents	Azlactone References and Yields	Dipeptides
Methyl	23, 91	
Isobutyl	26, 84	26
Dimethyl	21, 41	
Methyl, ethyl	41	
Methyl, acetamido	25 (*85%*), 241	25
Methyl, phenyl	41 (*72%*), 107	41, 107
Benzyl	26 (*54%*), 38, 84, 107	26, 107
3′,5′-Diiodo-4′-acetoxybenzyl	45	

C. *Miscellaneous Saturated Azlactones*

5-Oxazolone	References	
2-CH_3CO-NH-CH_2-4,4-CH_3,CH_3	107	
2-$CH_3CONHCH(CH_3)$-4,4-CH_3,CH_3	107	
2-$CH_3CONHCH(C_6H_5CH_2)$-4,4-CH_3,CH_3	107	
2-$C_6H_5CONHCH(CH_3)$-4,4-CH_3,CH_3	19, 22	
2-$CH_3CONHC(C_6H_5)(CH_3)$-	107	
2-$CH_3CONHC(C_6H_5)(CH_3)$-4-CH_3	107	
2-$CH_3CONHC(C_6H_5)(CH_3)$-4,4-CH_3,CH_3	107	
2-Pyrenyl-4-methyl	225	
2-(*p*-Nitrophenyl)-4-isobutyl	242	
2-(*p*-Phenylazophenyl)-4-isopropyl	243	
2-(*p*-Phenylazophenyl)-4-isobutyl	243	

References 160–248 appear on pp. 238–239.

TABLE III

COMPOUNDS NOT DEFINITELY ESTABLISHED AS AZLACTONES

5-Oxazolone	References
2-Methyl-4-carboxymethyl	26, 43, 84
2-Phenyl-4-carboxymethyl	244
2-CH_3-4-$HO_2CCH_2CH_2$-	42, 93
2-Methyl-4-N-acetylimidazolemethyl	28
2-Phenyl-4-imidazolemethyl	245
2-Phenyl-4-*m*-benzoylphenyl	246
2-CH_3CH_2-4-HO_2CCH=	247
2-C_6H_5-4-$CH_3C(CO_2H)$=	66, 248

REFERENCES TO TABLES

[160] Mauthner, *Ann.*, **370**, 368 (1909).
[160a] Kikkoji, *Biochem. Zeit.*, **35**, 68 (1911).
[161] Erlenmeyer, *Ber.*, **30**, 2976 (1897).
[162] Heller and Lauth, *Ber.*, **52**, 2295 (1919).
[163] Nicolet, *J. Biol. Chem.*, **95**, 389 (1932).
[164] Erlenmeyer and Kunlin, *Ann.*, **307**, 146 (1899).
[165] Doherty, Tietzman, and Bergmann, *J. Biol. Chem.*, **147**, 617 (1943).
[166] Vanghelovici and Stefanescu, *C. A.*, **38**, 5501 (1944).
[167] Bohm, *Z. physiol. Chem.*, **89**, 101 (1914).
[168] Dakin, *J. Biol. Chem.*, **9**, 151 (1911).
[169] Red'kin and Shemyakin, *J. Gen. Chem. U.S.S.R.*, **11**, 1175 (1941).
[170] Natelson and Gottfried, *J. Am. Chem. Soc.*, **63**, 487 (1941).
[171] Schiemann, Winkelmüller, and Roselius, Ger. pat. 621,862, Nov. 14, 1935.
[172] Flatow, *Z. physiol. Chem.*, **64**, 367 (1910).
[173] Buck and Ide, *J. Am. Chem. Soc.*, **54**, 3302 (1932).
[174] Friedmann and Maase, *Biochem. Z.*, **27**, 97 (1910).
[175] English, Mead, and Niemann, *J. Am. Chem. Soc.*, **62**, 350 (1940).
[176] Schiemann, Winkelmüller, and Roselius, *Ber.*, **65**, 1435 (1932).
[177] Niemann, Benson, and Mead, *J. Am. Chem. Soc.*, **63**, 2204 (1941).
[178] Schiemann and Winkelmüller, *J. prakt. Chem.*, **135**, 101 (1932–1933).
[179] Hann, *J. Wash. Acad. Sci.*, **24**, 464 (1934).
[180] Niemann and Mead, *J. Am. Chem. Soc.*, **63**, 2685 (1941).
[181] Niemann and Redemann, *J. Am. Chem. Soc.*, **63**, 1549 (1941).
[182] Savitzkii, *Méd. exptl. Ukraine*, No. 1, 39 (1934).
[183] Niemann, Mead, and Benson, *J. Am. Chem. Soc.*, **63**, 609 (1941).
[184] Raiford and Buurman, *J. Org. Chem.*, **8**, 466 (1943).
[185] Bergel, Haworth, Morrison, and Rinderknecht, *J. Chem. Soc.*, **1944**, 261.
[186] Pschorr, *Ann.*, **391**, 40 (1912).
[187] Dakin, *J. Biol. Chem.*, **8**, 11 (1910).
[188] Vanghelovici and Moise, *C. A.*, **38**, 5500 (1944).
[189] Späth and Mosettig, *Ann.*, **433**, 138 (1923).
[190] Chakravarti and Swaninathan, *J. Indian Chem. Soc.*, **11**, 107 (1934).
[191] Pschorr and Knöffler, *Ann.*, **382**, 50 (1911).
[192] Haworth, Perkin, and Rankin, *J. Chem. Soc.*, **125**, 1686 (1924).

[193] Narang, Ray, and Sachdeva, *J. Indian Chem. Soc.*, **13,** 260 (1936).
[194] Schopf, Brass, Jacobi, Jordl, Macnik, Neuroth, and Slazer, *Ann.*, **544,** 30 (1940).
[195] Buck and Perkin, *J. Chem. Soc.*, **125,** 1675 (1924).
[196] Deulofeu and Mendive, *Anales asoc. quím. argentina*, **21,** 100 (1933).
[197] Labruto and Irrera, *Gazz. chim. ital.*, **64,** 136 (1934).
[198] Labruto and Irrera, *Gazz. chim. ital.*, **65,** 1201 (1935).
[199] Funk, *J. Chem. Soc.*, **99,** 554 (1911).
[200] Smith and LaForge, *J. Am. Chem. Soc.*, **53,** 3072 (1931).
[201] Sugasawa and Sigehara, *Ber.*, **74,** 459 (1941).
[202] Freudenburg and Harder, *Ann.*, **451,** 213 (1926–1927).
[203] Smith and LaForge, *J. Am. Chem. Soc.*, **56,** 2431 (1934).
[204] Fromherz and Hermanns, *Z. physiol. Chem.*, **91,** 194 (1914).
[205] Barger and Silberschmidt, *J. Chem. Soc.*, **1928,** 2919.
[206] Freudenberg and Richtzenhain, *Ann.*, **552,** 126 (1942).
[207] Ungnade and Orwoll, *J. Am. Chem. Soc.*, **65,** 1736 (1943).
[208] Robinson and Sugasawa, *J. Chem. Soc.*, **1931,** 3163.
[209] Schöpf, Perrey, and Jäckl, *Ann.*, **497,** 47 (1932).
[210] Sugii, *J. Pharm. Soc. Japan*, **468,** 130 (1921).
[211] Waser, *Helv. Chim. Acta*, **8,** 117 (1925).
[212] Mauthner, *Ann.*, **449,** 102 (1926).
[213] Blum, *Arch. exptl. Pathol. Pharmakol.*, **59,** 269 (1908).
[214] Neubauer and Fromherz, *Z. physiol. Chem.*, **70,** 326 (1910–1911).
[215] McRae and Hopkins, *Can. J. Research*, **7,** 248 (1932).
[216] Ellinger and Matsuoka, *Z. physiol. Chem.*, **109,** 259 (1920).
[217] Fischer and Smeykal, *Ber.*, **56,** 2368 (1923).
[218] Horner, *Ann.*, **548,** 117 (1941).
[219] Fischer and Pistor, *Ber.*, **56,** 2313 (1923).
[220] Robson, *J. Biol. Chem.*, **62,** 495 (1924).
[221] Wieland, Konz, and Mittasch, *Ann.*, **513,** 1 (1934).
[222] Asahina and Mitsunaga, *J. Pharm. Soc. Japan*, **1917,** No. 429, 986.
[223] Fischer and Wasenegger, *Ann.*, **461,** 277 (1928).
[224] Fischer, Weisz, and Schubert, *Ber.*, **56,** 1194 (1923).
[225] Lettre, Buchholz, and Fernholz, *Z. physiol. Chem.*, **267,** 108 (1941).
[226] Deulofeu, *Anales asoc. quím. argentina*, **20,** 190 (1932).
[227] Erlenmeyer, *Ber.*, **22,** 792 (1889).
[228] Barger and Easson, *J. Chem. Soc.*, **1938,** 2100.
[229] Buchman and Richardson, *J. Am. Chem. Soc.*, **61,** 891 (1939).
[230] Harington and Moggridge, *J. Chem. Soc.*, **1939,** 443.
[231] Ruggli and Schetly, *Helv. Chim. Acta*, **23,** 718 (1940).
[232] Robinson and Sugasawa, *J. Chem. Soc.*, **1931,** 3173.
[233] Rutowski and Korolew, *J. prakt. Chem.*, **119,** 272 (1928).
[234] Behrens, *J. Biol. Chem.*, **136,** 61 (1940).
[235] Bovarnick, Bloch, and Foster, *J. Am. Chem. Soc.*, **61,** 2472 (1939).
[236] Harington and Moggridge, *Biochem. J.*, **34,** 685 (1940).
[237] Tietzman, Doherty, and Bergmann, *J. Biol. Chem.*, **151,** 387 (1943).
[238] Karrer and Widmer, *Helv. Chim. Acta*, **8,** 203 (1925).
[239] Karrer and Bussmann, *Helv. Chim. Acta*, **24,** 645 (1941).
[240] Lettre and Haas, *Z. physiol. Chem.*, **266,** 31 (1940).
[241] Bergmann and Grafe, *Z. physiol. Chem.*, **187,** 183 (1930).
[242] Karrer and Keller, *Helv. Chim. Acta*, **26,** 50 (1943).
[243] Karrer, Keller, and Szonyi, *Helv. Chim. Acta*, **26,** 38 (1943).
[244] Pauly and Weir, *Ber.*, **43,** 661 (1910).
[245] Kuster and Irion, *Z. physiol. Chem.*, **184,** 225 (1929).
[246] Minovice and Thuringer, *Bul. Soc. Chim. România*, **2,** 13 (1920).
[247] Bergmann, Kann, and Miekeley, *Ann.*, **449,** 135 (1926).
[248] Hoffmann, *Ber.*, **19,** 2554 (1886).

CHAPTER 6

SUBSTITUTION AND ADDITION REACTIONS OF THIOCYANOGEN

JOHN L. WOOD *

Cornell University Medical College

CONTENTS

* Present address, School of Biological Sciences, The Medical School, University of Tennessee, Memphis, Tenn.

INTRODUCTION

The direct replacement of a hydrogen atom by a thiocyano group through the use of thiocyanogen, $(SCN)_2$, is commonly termed thiocyanation. This replacement reaction is limited practically to aromatic

$$RH + (SCN)_2 \rightarrow RSCN + HSCN$$

amines and phenols, although a few particularly reactive aromatic hydrocarbons can be thiocyanated. Thiocyanogen reacts with olefinic and acetylenic linkages, the reagent adding to the unsaturated linkage.

$$R_2C{=}CR_2 + (SCN)_2 \rightarrow \begin{array}{cc} R_2C\text{—} & CR_2 \\ | & | \\ NCS & SCN \end{array}$$

Thiocyanogen reacts also with compounds of other types; it can replace a hydrogen atom attached to sulfur or nitrogen, it can replace the heavy-metal atom of certain organometallic compounds, and it can add to the triaryl derivatives of arsenic, antimony, and bismuth.

$$ArSH + (SCN)_2 \rightarrow ArSSCN + HSCN$$

$$2R_2NH + (SCN)_2 \rightarrow R_2NSCN + R_2NH_2SCN$$

$$2RONHR + (SCN)_2 \rightarrow RONRSCN + RONH_2RSCN$$

$$R_2Zn + 2(SCN)_2 \rightarrow 2RSCN + Zn(SCN)_2$$

$$Ar_2Hg + (SCN)_2 \rightarrow ArSCN + ArHgSCN$$

$$Ar_3Sb + (SCN)_2 \rightarrow Ar_3Sb(SCN)_2$$

The reagent is used in synthesis in essentially the same way as the halogens, with the exception that certain precautions must be observed owing to the instability of thiocyanogen. Thiocyanogen is a liquid which on cooling forms a colorless, crystalline solid melting between -3 and $-2°$.[1] At room temperature it polymerizes rapidly to a reddish orange, amorphous mass of indefinite composition known as pseudo- or para-thiocyanogen. Although relatively stable in inert, dry solvents, thiocyanogen may polymerize in solution, especially under the catalytic influence of heat, light, moisture, or oxygen. Thiocyanogen is readily hydrolyzed to produce thiocyanic acid and hypothiocyanous acid.

$$(SCN)_2 + H_2O \rightarrow HSCN + HOSCN$$

The latter acid is unstable and is converted into hydrocyanic acid and sulfuric acid, both of which occur as end products of the overall hydroly-

$$3(SCN)_2 + 4H_2O \rightarrow 5HSCN + HCN + H_2SO_4$$

[1] Söderbäck, *Ann.*, **419**, 217 (1919).

sis. The quantitative relationships of the process are complicated by side reactions.

The extreme sensitivity of thiocyanogen toward hydrolysis and polymerization probably accounts for the long interval between its formulation by Berzelius and its preparation by Bjerrum and Kirshner [2] and by Söderbäck.[1, *] For this same reason, when thiocyanogen is employed in chemical reactions, it is prepared in solution and more commonly is produced *in situ*.

Thiocyanogen is often classified as a pseudohalogen because of its resemblance to halogens in its chemical behavior.[1, 3] It attacks even noble metals like gold and mercury;[2] it reacts with nitric oxide,[1] aqueous hydrogen sulfide,[4] hydrazoic acid,[5] ammonia,[6] and hydrochloric acid.[1, 7] It is released from metal thiocyanates by the action of chlorine, bromine, and other oxidizing agents. Halogen-thiocyanogen combinations are formed with chlorine [8, 9, 10] and with iodine.[11, 12] Thiocyanogen is similar to iodine in its chemical reactivity but is slightly less electronegative: $E°$, SCN°, SCN^- = 0.769; $E°$, I°, I^- = 0.54.[1, 2]

The properties and uses of thiocyano compounds have been reviewed.[13] Many show toxic effects, mainly dermatitis, which vary considerably in different individuals;[14] in addition, the alkyl thiocyanates produce degenerative changes in various organs of experimental animals.

SCOPE AND LIMITATIONS

Thiocyanogen reacts with aromatic compounds that are highly susceptible to substitution with the introduction of a thiocyano group. Reactions reported thus far are mainly with phenols of the benzene and naphthalene series and with primary, secondary, or tertiary amines of the

* An historical review of the attempts to prepare thiocyanogen may be found in Goldberg, *J. prakt. Chem.*, [2] **63,** 465 (1901); Kaufmann, *Arch. Pharm.*, **263,** 675 (1925).

[2] Bjerrum and Kirshner, "Die Rhodanide des Goldes und das frei Rhodan," Verlag Horst und Sohn, Copenhagen, 1918; *Kgl. Danske Videnskab. Selskab*, [8] **5,** 76 (1918) [*C. A.*, **13,** 1057 (1919)].

[3] Birckenbach and Kellerman, *Ber.*, **58,** 786 (1925); Walden and Audrieth, *Chem. Revs.*, **5,** 339 (1928).

[4] Kaufmann and Gaertner, *Ber.*, **57,** 928 (1924).

[5] Wilcoxon, McKinney, and Browne, *J. Am. Chem. Soc.*, **47,** 1917 (1925).

[6] Lecher, Wittwer, and Speer, *Ber.*, **56,** 1104 (1923).

[7] Söderbäck, *Ann.*, **465,** 184 (1928).

[8] Kaufmann and Liepe, *Ber.*, **57,** 923 (1924).

[9] Kaufmann, *Ber.*, **60,** 58 (1927).

[10] Lecher and Joseph, *Ber.*, **59,** 2603 (1926).

[11] Kaufmann and Grosse-Oetringhaus, *Ber.*, **69,** 2670 (1936).

[12] Birckenbach and Goubeau, *Ber.*, **70,** 171 (1937).

[13] Kaufmann, *Angew. Chem.*, **54,** 168 (1941).

[14] Oettingen, Hueper, and Deichmann-Gruebler, *J. Ind. Hyg. Toxicol.*, **18,** 310 (1936).

benzene, naphthalene, and anthracene series. Apparently the presence of other substituents, such as nitro, chloro, bromo, alkoxy, carboxyl, or carbethoxy groups, does not interfere with the reaction provided that an active position is still available; however, the presence of a sulfonic acid group may prevent the reaction, since it is reported that *p*-amino- and *p*-hydroxy-benzenesulfonic acids do not undergo thiocyanation.

Anthracene, benzanthracene and certain of its derivatives, and 3,4-benzpyrene also react with thiocyanogen. Anthracene yields a 9,10-dithiocyano derivative; but the other hydrocarbons, which are characterized by the presence of one very easily substituted hydrogen atom, give only products of monosubstitution. The powerfully carcinogenic benzpyrene and methylcholanthrene both react in this manner with particular ease, although the point of attack with benzpyrene is the aromatic nucleus and with methylcholanthrene the reactive methylene group.

Ethylene and a variety of substituted ethylenes react with thiocyanogen to give addition products containing two thiocyano groups. The reaction appears to be fairly general in its application as indicated by addition to such compounds as amylene, cyclohexene, allyl alcohol, pinene, styrene, stilbene, anethole, isosafrole, and oleic and other unsaturated acids. The yields, when given, nearly always are high. Thiocyanogen adds to α,β-unsaturated ketones, but not to α,β-unsaturated acids. The addition to other α,β-unsaturated carbonyl or related systems has not been explored. Conjugated diene systems react, as they do with halogen, to add two thiocyano groups, probably in the 1,4-positions. The reactions with butadiene, isoprene, and dimethylbutadiene have been described. The acetylenic compounds that have been investigated in this reaction, acetylene, phenylacetylene, and tolan, add one molecule of thiocyanogen to give a dithiocyanoethylene. The yields are lower than with the olefinic substances.

Miscellaneous reactions of thiocyanogen have been reported, but their study has been too limited for a proper evaluation of their usefulness. Thiocyanogen has been shown to react with a variety of organometallic compounds and to replace the hydrogen on sulfur in mercaptans and thiophenols and the hydrogen on nitrogen of aliphatic amines and disubstituted hydroxylamines. These reactions doubtless are capable of further development.

Thiocyanation of Aromatic Amines. The thiocyano group is introduced into aromatic amines with rapidity; it enters a free *para* position if available, otherwise an *ortho* position. For example, aniline is converted into 4-thiocyanoaniline (97% yield),[15, 16] *o*-toluidine into 4-thio-

[15] Kaufmann and Weber, *Arch. Pharm.*, **267**, 192 (1929).

[16] Kaufmann, *Ber.*, **62**, 390 (1929).

cyano-*o*-toluidine (80% yield),[17] and anthranilic acid into 5-thiocyanoanthranilic acid (80% yield).[18] The reaction when carried out in neutral solvents almost always gives a monosubstitution product, but in an acid medium and in the presence of excess reagent the reaction often leads to a disubstitution product, though in lower yield.[19] For example, the dithiocyano derivatives of aniline,[18, 20, 21] *p*-toluidine,[17, 18, 22] and 2,5-xylidine [22] have been prepared. Acetylation of the amino group prevents thiocyanation.[23]

When thiocyanation takes place in the position *ortho* to a primary amino group, as in *p*-toluidine, *p*-chloroaniline, *p*-nitroaniline, or *p*-aminobenzoic acid, the final product is often an aminobenzothiazole, formed by a secondary reaction between the amino and the thiocyano groups. 2-Amino-4,6-dimethylbenzothiazole is formed from 2,4-xylidine in 79%

$$\text{2,4-}(CH_3)_2C_6H_3NH_2 \xrightarrow{(SCN)_2} \text{2-}NH_2\text{-3-}CH_3\text{-5-}CH_3\text{-}C_6H_2SCN \longrightarrow \text{2-Amino-4,6-dimethylbenzothiazole}$$

yield,[23] 2-amino-6-chlorobenzothiazole from *p*-chloroaniline in 75% yield,[22] and 2-amino-6-ethoxybenzothiazole from phenetidine in 95% yield.[24] The ease of formation of the thiazole derivative varies with the substituents in the primary product; thiocyanophenetidine rearranges spontaneously, whereas 1-thiocyano-2-naphthylamine rearranges when warmed with ethanolic hydrogen chloride.[22] The *ortho* thiocyano derivative often can be isolated if a low temperature is maintained and if acid is excluded. The *ortho* thiocyano derivatives of monoalkylamines rearrange readily into 2-iminobenzothiazolines.[23]

$$R'C_6H_3(NHR)(SCN) \longrightarrow R'C_6H_3\langle{}^{NR}_{S}\rangle C{=}NH$$

[17] Likhosherstov and Petrov, *J. Gen. Chem. U.S.S.R.*, **3**, 759 (1933) [*C. A.*, **28**, 2690 (1934)].

[18] Likhosherstov and Petrov, *J. Gen. Chem. U.S.S.R.*, **3**, 183 (1933) [*C. A.*, **28**, 1677 (1934)].

[19] Kaufmann and Oehring, *Ber.*, **59**, 187 (1926).

[20] U. S. pat., 1,790,097 [*C. A.*, **25**, 1258 (1931)]; Brit. pat., 257,619 [*C. A.*, **21**, 3507 (1927)]; Ger. pat., 484,360 [*C. A.*, **24**, 1119 (1930)].

[21] U. S. pat., 1,787,315; U. S. pat., 1,787,316.

[22] Kaufmann, Oehring, and Clauberg, *Arch. Pharm.*, **266**, 197 (1928).

[23] Brewster and Dains, *J. Am. Chem. Soc.*, **58**, 1364 (1936).

[24] Neu, *Ber.*, **72**, 1505 (1939).

Aromatic secondary and tertiary amines undergo thiocyanation, often more readily than primary amines. N,N-Dimethylaniline gives N,N-dimethyl-4-thiocyanoaniline (92% yield),[25] and N,N-dimethyl-*p*-toluidine gives N,N-dimethyl-2-thiocyano-*p*-toluidine (21% yield).[25] Diphenylamine and triphenylamine are converted into dithiocyano derivatives, each with two of the phenyl rings substituted in the *para* positions.[1]

Two positions are potentially reactive in aminophenols, but the amino group directs the orientation of the entering group in thiocyanation.[24] An example is the conversion of *o*-aminophenol into 4-thiocyano-2-hydroxyaniline in 50% yield.

Thiocyanation of Phenols. The reaction of phenols with thiocyanogen has not been studied so extensively as that of amines. Phenol is converted into 4-thiocyanophenol in 69% yield,[26, 27] *o*-cresol into 4-thiocyano-*o*-cresol in 90% yield,[15] thymol into 4-thiocyanothymol in 95% yield,[15] and α-naphthol into 4-thiocyano-1-naphthol in 83% yield.[28] The point of attack is again the *para* position if free; *ortho* substitution occurs when this position is blocked, as in the reaction of *p*-cresol and β-naphthol (100% yield).[28] In general the yields do not appear to be quite so high as in the reaction of amines. The effect of a substituent other than an alkyl group in the position *ortho* to the hydroxyl group has been examined to only a limited extent; the yield of the thiocyano product is lowered in the case of an alkoxyl (guaiacol, 21% yield [25]), hydroxyl (pyrocatechol, 48% yield [29]), or carboxyl group (salicylic acid, 30% yield [30]). Dithiocyanation has been reported only in the reaction of α-naphthol; the reaction can be controlled to give the monosubstitution product or disubstitution product (2,4-dithiocyano-1-naphthol, 60% yield [19]).

Ortho thiocyanophenols rearrange similarly to the corresponding amines to yield 2-iminobenzothioxoles.[15, 31] The imino group is readily hydrolyzed to a keto group on hydrolysis with acid.

R–C$_6$H$_4$–OH $\xrightarrow{(SCN)_2}$ R–C$_6$H$_3$(OH)SCN → R–C$_6$H$_3$<(O$_1$)(S$_3$)>$_2$C=NH

[25] Fichter and Schönmann, *Helv. Chim. Acta*, **19**, 1411 (1936).

[26] Zaboev and Kudryavtzev, *J. Gen. Chem. U.S.S.R.*, **5**, 1607 (1935) [*C. A.*, **30**, 2182 (1936)].

[27] Melinikov, Sklyarenko, and Cherkasova, *J. Gen. Chem. U.S.S.R.*, **9**, 1819 (1939) [*C. A.*, **34**, 3699 (1940); *Chem. Zentr.*, **1940**, I, 641].

[28] Kaufmann and Liepe, *Ber. deut. pharm. Ges.*, **33**, 139 (1923).

[29] Machek, *Monatsh.*, **63**, 216 (1933).

[30] Kaufmann and Liepe, *Ber.*, **56**, 2514 (1923).

[31] French pat., 852,020 [*C. A.*, **36**, 1951 (1942)].

Thiocyanation of Polynuclear Hydrocarbons. Aromatic hydrocarbons of the benzene and naphthalene series do not undergo thiocyanation, but certain hydrocarbons with several condensed benzene rings do.[32] Anthracene reacts with the reagent to yield the 9,10-dithiocyano derivative. Benzpyrene is substituted in the 5-position (82% yield); 1,2-benzanthracene in the two *meso* positions (9-derivative, 5%; 10-derivative, 57%); 9-methyl- and 10-methyl-1,2-benzanthracene in the free *meso* position (43% and 66%, respectively); and methylcholanthrene in the 15-position. Benzpyrene and benzanthracene and its alkyl derivtives also react with aromatic diazo compounds and with lead tetra-acetate, and thus are substituted far more readily than benzene or naphthalene.

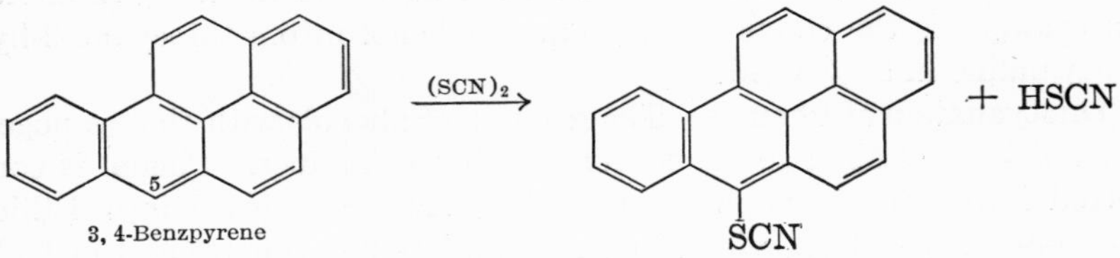

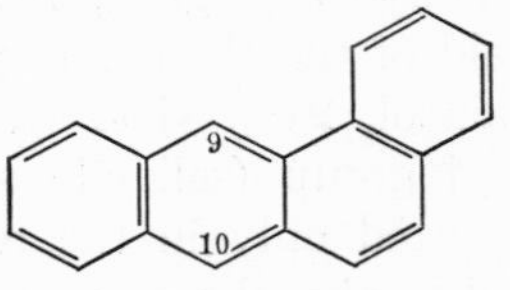

3, 4-Benzpyrene $\xrightarrow{(SCN)_2}$ (5-SCN derivative) + HSCN

1, 2-Benzanthracene

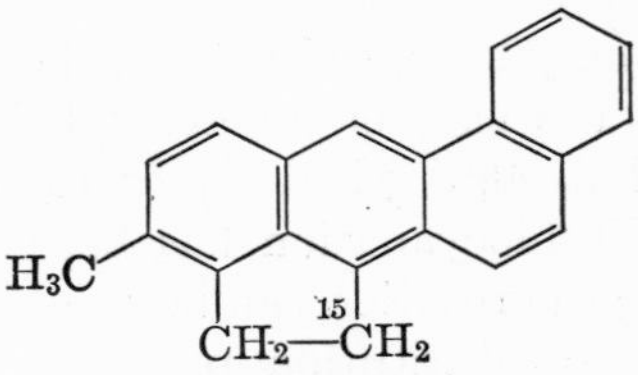

Methylcholanthrene

Addition of Thiocyanogen to Olefins and Acetylenes. Thiocyanogen resembles iodine in its addition to double and triple bonds. The yields are usually excellent; ethylene dithiocyanate,[33] styrene dithiocyanate,[28] and 1-(*p*-methoxyphenyl)-1,2-dithiocyanopropane [28] are reported to be formed in quantitative yield from the corresponding olefin, ethylene, styrene, or anethole. Pinene, allyl alcohol, isosafrole, terpineol, and stilbene are examples of other unsaturated compounds to which thiocyanogen has been added, but in unspecified yield. Conjugated dienes, illustrated by isoprene [20, 34] and butadiene,[35] add two thiocyano groups in the 1,4-positions, after which no further addition takes place. The yields of the dithiocyano derivative are 19% and 80%, respectively.

[32] Wood and Fieser, *J. Am. Chem. Soc.*, **63**, 2323 (1941).
[33] Söderbäck, *Ann.*, **443**, 142 (1925).
[34] Bruson and Calvert, *J. Am. Chem. Soc.*, **50**, 1735 (1928).
[35] Müller and Freytag, *J. prakt Chem.*, [2] **146**, 58 (1936).

The addition of thiocyanogen to an olefin is a slow reaction but can be catalyzed by light and metals. Ethylene adds only traces of the reagent in the dark in nine days, but in sunlight the reaction is complete in two hours.[33, 34] Sunlight also promotes polymerization of the reagent, but the rate of this reaction in benzene is not so rapid as to interfere with the addition reaction.

The reaction of thiocyanogen with unsaturated fatty acids [36] has been introduced as a method of analysis. Excess of a standardized thiocyanogen solution is used, and the amount of unreacted reagent is titrated. Thiocyanogen reacts quantitatively with oleic acid but with only one of the two double bonds of linoleic acid and with two of the three double bonds of linolenic acid.

Methyl styryl ketone and distyryl ketone, typical α,β-unsaturated ketones, add thiocyanogen in unstated yields.[37] Few other substances of the α,β-unsaturated carbonyl type have been examined. It is reported, however, that maleic, fumaric, acrylic, crotonic, and cinnamic acids do not react with thiocyanogen.[38]

Substances containing a triple bond add only one mole of thiocyanogen. Acetylene reacts under the catalytic influence of light to give dithiocyanoethylene (20% yield).[33] Phenylacetylene [33] and tolan [33] react in the dark; the yields of the products are 50% and 20%, respectively. Acetylene diiodide yields the same product as acetylene, dithiocyanoethylene,[33] formed as a result of replacement of the iodine groups by the reagent. Dibromoethylene and thiocyanogen form an equilibrium system containing dithiocyanoethylene and bromothiocyanoethylene.

$$C_2H_2Br_2 + (SCN)_2 \rightleftarrows C_2H_2(SCN)_2 + Br_2$$
$$\downarrow\uparrow$$
$$C_2H_2(SCN)Br + BrSCN$$

Miscellaneous Syntheses with Thiocyanogen. Aliphatic primary and secondary amines react with thiocyanogen with replacement of the hydrogen atom attached to nitrogen to form thiocyanoamines.[1, 6] The

$$2RNH_2 + (SCN)_2 \rightarrow RNHSCN + RNH_3SCN$$

$$2R_2NH + (SCN)_2 \rightarrow R_2NSCN + R_2NH_2SCN$$

reaction is represented for primary amines by benzylamine [39] and triphenylmethylamine (55% yield),[39] and for secondary amines by diethylamine.[6]

[36] Kaufmann, "Studien auf dem Fettgebiet," Verlag Chemie, Berlin, 1935; Kaufmann and Grosse-Oetringhaus, *Ber.*, **70**, 911 (1937).

[37] Challenger and Bott, *J. Chem. Soc.*, **127**, 1039 (1925).

[38] Kaufmann, *Angew. Chem.*, **54**, 195 (1941).

[39] Jones and Fleck, *J. Am. Chem. Soc.*, **50**, 2018 (1928).

O,N-Disubstituted hydroxylamines react similarly to aliphatic amines to yield N-thiocyanohydroxylamines. O,N-Dibenzyl- and O,N-diethylhydroxylamine yield the corresponding N-thiocyano derivatives in 47% and 40% yields, respectively.[39]

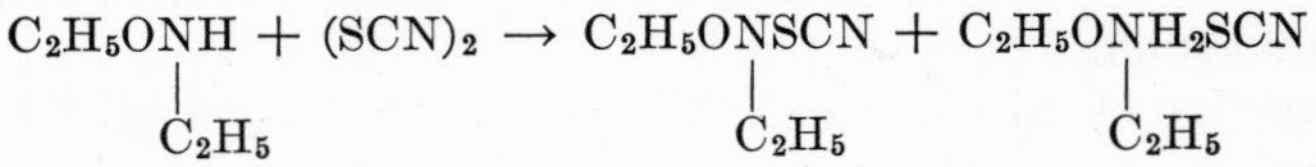

$$C_2H_5ONH(C_2H_5) + (SCN)_2 \rightarrow C_2H_5ON(C_2H_5)SCN + C_2H_5ONH_2(C_2H_5)SCN$$

N-Acyl- and N-aroyl-diphenylhydrazines behave like diarylamines, forming N-acyl- and N-aroyl-bis-(*p*-thiocyanophenyl)-hydrazines in 65–75% yields.[15]

$$(C_6H_5)_2NNHCOR + 2(SCN)_2 \rightarrow (p\text{-}NCSC_6H_4)_2NNHCOR + 2HSCN$$

Only a few heterocyclic substances have been investigated. Antipyrine is converted into the 4-thiocyano derivative.

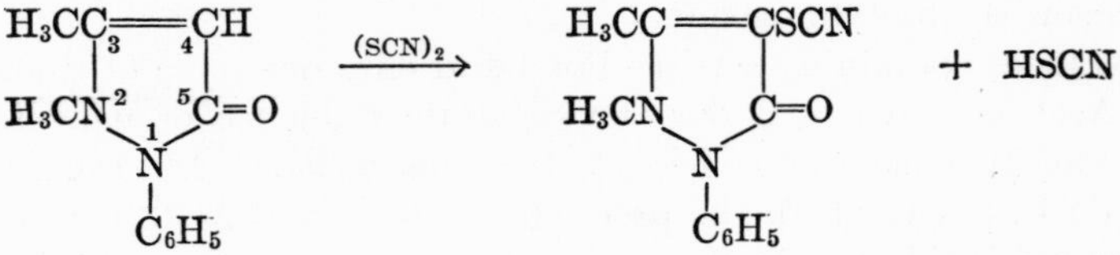

$$\text{Antipyrine } (H_3C\overset{3}{C}{=}\overset{4}{C}H,\ H_3C\overset{2}{N},\ \overset{5}{C}{=}O,\ \overset{1}{N}C_6H_5) \xrightarrow{(SCN)_2} H_3CC{=}CSCN,\ H_3CN,\ C{=}O,\ NC_6H_5 \text{ (4-thiocyanoantipyrine)} + HSCN$$

Both 2-hydroxyquinoline (carbostyryl) and 8-hydroxyquinoline react in the 4-position, *para* to the nitrogen atom.

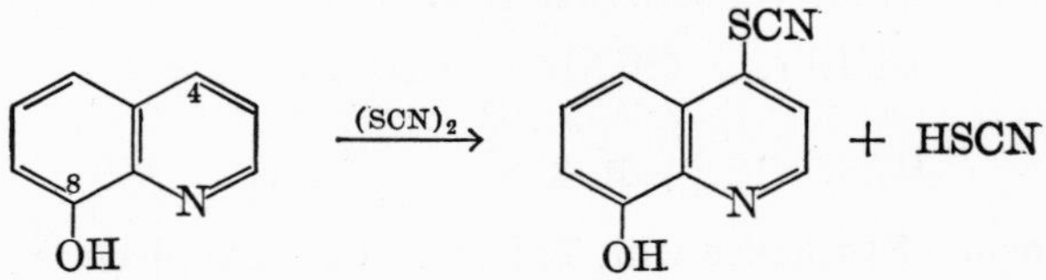

$$\text{8-Hydroxyquinoline} \xrightarrow{(SCN)_2} \text{4-SCN-8-hydroxyquinoline} + HSCN$$

Ethyl acetoacetate has been thiocyanated,[28] but the primary thiocyano derivative has not been isolated owing to hydrolysis to ethyl 2-hydroxy-4-methylthiazole-5-carboxylate (19% yield).[28]

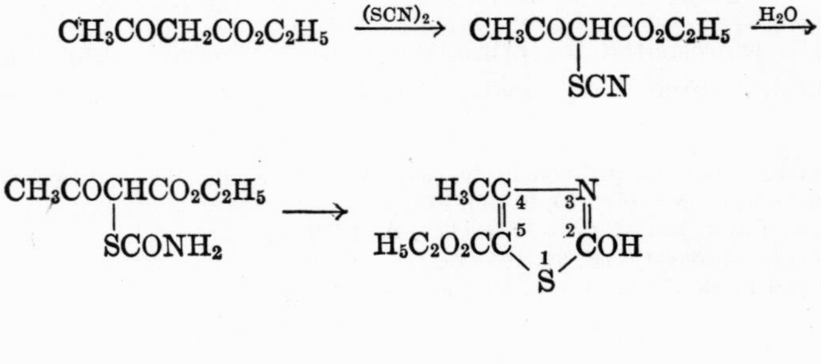

$$CH_3COCH_2CO_2C_2H_5 \xrightarrow{(SCN)_2} CH_3COCH(SCN)CO_2C_2H_5 \xrightarrow{H_2O}$$

$$CH_3COCH(SCONH_2)CO_2C_2H_5 \longrightarrow \text{thiazole: } H_3C\overset{4}{C}{=}\overset{3}{N},\ H_5C_2O_2C\overset{5}{C},\ \overset{2}{C}OH,\ \overset{1}{S}$$

Treatment of ethyl mercaptan with thiocyanogen affords ethyl thiothiocyanate (50% yield),[40] a compound similar to a sulfenyl chloride (RSCl) but somewhat more stable toward hydrolysis. Thiophenols

$$C_2H_5SH + (SCN)_2 \rightarrow C_2H_5SSCN + HSCN$$

yield analogous substances; the reaction has been applied to thiophenol (70% yield),[40] to *p*-nitrothiophenol (75% yield),[41] and to *β*-thionaphthol.[40]

On thiocyanation, mercury diphenyl is converted into phenyl thiocyanate in 66% yield, and similarly zinc diethyl yields ethyl thiocyanate in small yield.[1]

$$(C_6H_5)_2Hg + (SCN)_2 \rightarrow C_6H_5SCN + C_6H_5HgSCN$$

$$(C_2H_5)_2Zn + 2(SCN)_2 \rightarrow 2C_2H_5SCN + Zn(SCN)_2$$

The triaryl derivatives of phosphorus, arsenic, antimony, and bismuth add thiocyanogen,[42, 43] with decreasing reactivity in the order indicated. The primary products are sufficiently stable to hydrolysis to be isolable

$$(C_6H_5)_3Sb + (SCN)_2 \rightarrow (C_6H_5)_3Sb(SCN)_2$$

only in the reactions of triphenylstibine and triphenylbismuthine; but there is no substitution in the phenyl ring of any of these compounds, as in the reaction of triphenylamine.[1] Small amounts of phenyl and *α*-naphthyl thiocyanate are formed as secondary products in the reaction of triphenyl- and tri-*α*-naphthyl-bismuthine.[43]

$$(C_6H_5)_3Bi(SCN)_2 \rightarrow C_6H_5SCN + (C_6H_5)_2BiSCN$$

OTHER METHODS OF SYNTHESIS OF THIOCYANO COMPOUNDS

The use of thiocyanogen for the introduction of a thiocyano group is limited to substances containing either a hydrogen atom particularly sensitive to substitution or an unsaturated carbon-carbon linkage, and consequently does not have such a wide application for the preparation of aryl thiocyanates as the Gattermann and Sandmeyer reaction,[44, 45] in which a diazonium salt group is replaced on treatment with cuprous thiocyanate. Furthermore, the yields are usually higher in the Gattermann and Sandmeyer reaction; for example, 4-thiocyanosalicylic acid is

[40] Lecher and Wittwer, *Ber.*, **55**, 1474 (1922).

[41] Lecher and Simon, *Ber.*, **54**, 632 (1921).

[42] Challenger, Smith, and Paton, *J. Chem. Soc.*, **123**, 1046 (1923).

[43] Challenger and Wilkinson, *J. Chem. Soc.*, **121**, 91 (1922).

[44] Gattermann and Haussknecht, *Ber.*, **23**, 738 (1890); Hantzch and Hirsch, *Ber.*, **29**, 947 (1896); Korczynski, Kniatowna, and Kaminski, *Bull. soc. chim.*, **31**, 1179 (1922).

[45] Dienske, *Rec. trav. chim.*, **50**, 407 (1931).

available in 73% yield by the diazotization method[45] and in only 30% yield by thiocyanation.[30] Aryl thiocyanates can also be made by the action of alkali cyanides on thiosulfates[46] or arylsulfenyl chlorides,[47] and by treating lead mercaptides with cyanogen chloride or iodide.[48]

There are numerous instances of the reaction of alkali metal thiocyanates with alkyl halides or sulfates[49, 50] for the preparation of alkyl mono- and poly-thiocyanates. Another method for the preparation of an alkyl thiocyanate involves cleavage of a dialkyl sulfide by treatment with cyanogen bromide;[51] the second product is an alkyl bromide. When the two alkyl groups are different, the larger radical generally remains attached to sulfur; an example is the conversion of *n*-propyl *n*-butyl sulfide into *n*-propyl bromide and *n*-butyl thiocyanate. Thiocyano compounds are also available from the reaction of metal mercaptides with cyanogen halides.[52]

USE OF THIOCYANATES IN SYNTHESIS

Thiocyanates can often be utilized as intermediates in the preparation of other sulfur-containing compounds, alkylthiocarbonic acid amides, disulfides, mercaptans, sulfides, and sulfonic acids. Typical reactions are as follows:

$$\mathrm{RSCN + R'OH \rightarrow RSC\begin{cases}OR' \\ NH_2Cl\end{cases} \rightarrow RSC\begin{cases}O \\ NH_2\end{cases} + R'Cl}\ ^{53}$$

$$\mathrm{2RSCN + NaOH \longrightarrow RSSR + NaCN + NaOCN + H_2O}\ ^{1,\,8,\,53}$$

$$\mathrm{RSCN + H_2 \longrightarrow RSH + HCN}\ ^{1,\,54,\,55,\,56}$$

$$\mathrm{RSCN + R'MgBr \longrightarrow RSR' + MgBrCN}\ ^{57}$$

$$\mathrm{RSCN + R'MgBr \xrightarrow{HBr} RSH + R'CN + MgBr_2}\ ^{57}$$

$$\mathrm{RSCN + [O] \longrightarrow RSO_3H}\ ^{54,\,58}$$

[46] Footner and Smiles, *J. Chem. Soc.*, **127**, 2887 (1925).

[47] Zinke and Eismayer, *Ber.*, **51**, 751 (1918).

[48] Billeter, *Ber.*, **7**, 1753 (1874); Gabriel, *Ber.*, **10**, 184 (1877); Gabriel and Deutsch, *Ber.*, **13**, 386 (1880).

[49] Kaufler and Pomeranz, *Monatsh.*, **22**, 492 (1901).

[50] Walden, *Ber.*, **40**, 3214 (1907).

[51] von Braun and Englebertz, *Ber.*, **56**, 1573 (1923); von Braun, May, and Michaelis, *Ann.*, **490**, 189 (1931).

[52] Brit. pat., 431,064 [*C. A.*, **29**, 8220 (1935)].

[53] Knorr, *Ber.*, **49**, 1735 (1936).

[54] Fichter and Schonlau, *Ber.*, **48**, 1150 (1915).

[55] Kaufmann and Rossbach, *Ber.*, **58**, 1556 (1925).

[56] Fichter and Beck, *Ber.*, **44**, 3636 (1911).

[57] Adams, Bramlet, and Tendick, *J. Am. Chem. Soc.*, **42**, 2369 (1920).

[58] Fichter and Wenk, *Ber.*, **45**, 1373 (1912).

EXPERIMENTAL CONDITIONS

Three general methods have been described for the use of thiocyanogen in substitution and addition reactions: free thiocyanogen in organic solvents; thiocyanogen evolved by electrolysis of concentrated aqueous solutions of alkali metal thiocyanates; and thiocyanogen liberated gradually in an organic solvent from a metal thiocyanate by various reagents.

Free Thiocyanogen. This method was the first to be employed and is still a useful procedure when the reaction involved is slow, as in addition reactions, or when the product is difficult to purify. Usually the only contaminant of the product other than starting material is polythiocyanogen, which is entirely insoluble in water and in organic solvents.

The reagent is prepared by the action of an oxidizing agent upon thiocyanic acid or a metal thiocyanate. The oxidation of thiocyanic acid in an organic solvent is accomplished by means of such reagents as lead tetraacetate, lead peroxide, or manganese dioxide,[59] but the yield is so low that the preparation from metal thiocyanates is much to be preferred. Lead thiocyanate reacts rapidly and quantitatively with bromine to form thiocyanogen and lead bromide, which is removed readily by filtration. Halogen carriers, such as phenyl iodochloride,[25] sulfuryl chloride,[60] or certain N-chloroamides,[17, 18, 61] can also be used, but do not appear to possess any advantages over bromine or chlorine. Chloroamides usually cannot be used in the thiocyanation of a phenol owing to their oxidizing action.

Solvents that have been used with thiocyanogen include benzene, bromobenzene, carbon tetrachloride, chloroform, ether, ethylene bromide, carbon disulfide, petroleum ether, methyl acetate, nitromethane, and anhydrous formic and acetic acids. At low temperatures such solvents as saturated solutions of alkali thiocyanates in methanol [16, 62] or acetone [63] can be used. The yield in the thiocyanation of amines is 20–30% higher when the reaction is carried out in a neutral medium like methanol rather than in acetic acid. The formation of a thiazole is also inhibited in a neutral solvent. Ether is usually not satisfactory because the solvent is attacked and because some of the amine is precipitated as the thiocyanate.[1, 19] On the other hand, thiocyanation of phenols appears to give better yields in acetic acid solution than in neutral solvents.

[59] Kaufmann and Kögler, *Ber.*, **58**, 1553 (1925).

[60] Spangler and Müller, U. S. pat., 1,687,596 [*C. A.*, **23**, 154 (1929)].

[61] Likhosherstov and Aldoshin, *J. Gen. Chem. U.S.S.R.*, **5**, 981 (1935) [*C. A.*, **30**, 1033 (1936)].

[62] Kaufmann and Hansen-Schmidt, *Arch. Pharm.*, **263**, 692 (1923).

[63] Fialkov and Kleiner, *J. Gen. Chem. U.S.S.R.*, **11**, 671 (1941) [*C. A.*, **35**, 7307 (1941)].

Moisture must be excluded from thiocyanation solutions in order to prevent hydrolysis. Another troublesome side reaction, particularly in concentrated solutions, is polymerization, which is induced by light, heat, and the presence of hydrolysis products. Polymerization is reported to be dependent upon the dielectric constant of the solvent.[1, 62, 64] The limiting concentration of stable solutions of thiocyanogen depends upon the temperature and the exposure to light. Tenth normal solutions in the dark at 21° show 10% decomposition as follows: carbon tetrachloride, thirty-eight days; carbon disulfide, fourteen days; ethylene chloride, fourteen days. Four per cent decomposition occurs in acetic acid in ten days.[62] A normal solution in carbon tetrachloride at the boiling point is polymerized to the extent of 90% after three hours in the sunlight as compared with 24% in the dark. At room temperature 50% polymerization occurs in twenty-four hours in the sunlight compared with 5% when the solution is kept in the dark throughout the period.[30] Tenth normal solutions in carbon tetrachloride or acetic acid-acetic anhydride have been reported to be stable from one week to several months when kept in the refrigerator. Stirring is said to retard polymerization.[1]

In this modification of the synthesis, the organic compound is mixed with a solution containing from 1 to 4 equivalents of thiocyanogen at room temperature. The end of the reaction, which may be slow, is often determined by the disappearance or polymerization of all the reagent. Frequently a significant yield depends upon successful initiation of the process, but the usual methods of forcing a reaction cannot be employed owing to the instability of the reagent.

Free thiocyanogen is used in determining the thiocyanogen number of fats and oils,[36, 65] of resins,[66] and of hydrocarbons;[38, 67, 68] but for the usual synthetic reaction the preferred procedure is to generate thiocyanogen in a solution of the substance to be thiocyanated at a rate equal to the rate of the removal by reaction. The low concentration of reagent maintained in this way minimizes polymerization. The reagent is generated from thiocyanate salts either by electrolysis or by a chemical reaction.

Thiocyanogen Generated from Salts by Electrolysis. Thiocyanogen is produced when concentrated solutions of alkali thiocyanates are electrolyzed.[19, 24, 27, 69] Ammonium thiocyanate is most commonly used, and the electrolyzed solution is stabilized by maintaining it at tempera-

[64] Bhatnagar, Kapur, and Khosla, *J. Indian Chem. Soc.*, **17**, 529 (1940).

[65] McKinney, *J. Assoc. Official Agr. Chem.*, **21**, 87, 443 (1938).

[66] Gardner, Pribyl, and Weinberger, *Ind. Eng. Chem., Anal. Ed.*, **6**, 259 (1934).

[67] Stavely and Bergmann, *J. Org. Chem.*, **1**, 580 (1937).

[68] Pummerer and Stärk, *Ber.*, **64**, 825 (1931).

[69] Kerstein and Hoffman, *Ber.*, **57**, 491 (1924).

tures below $-8°$. The stability is satisfactory provided that the concentration of thiocyanogen does not become greater than that corresponding to the complex $NH_4(SCN)_3$. An amine or a phenol is dissolved in the concentrated alkali thiocyanate solution; it is usually desirable to add enough ethanol to lower the freezing point of the mixture below $-8°$. A cathode of copper, aluminum, nickel, or iron and a rotating graphite anode are introduced, and a current of 0.02 to 0.03 ampere per square centimeter is used for the electrolysis. If either the compound to be treated or the thiocyanation product is reduced readily, a divided compartment cell is employed. The yields usually vary from 50 to 90%.

Thiocyanogen Generated from Salts by Chemical Reagents. The compound is placed in a solution of a metal thiocyanate in acetic or formic acid,[19, 26] or, better, in a neutral solvent like methyl acetate, acetone, or methanol.[15, 16] Bromine or chlorine is added to the cooled solution at such a rate that the thiocyanogen reacts as fast as it is liberated. A neutral solvent that is susceptible to attack by halogen is protected by saturating the solution with an appropriate alkali metal halide or by using a large excess of an alkali metal thiocyanate in the reaction mixture. Other reagents for producing thiocyanogen from ammonium thiocyanate have been described; N,N-dichlorourea,[18] N-chloroacetamide,[17] and N-dichloropentamethylenetetramine [61] in acetic acid, acetone, or methanol solution. The addition of a drop of concentrated sulfuric acid is reported to improve the yield. The results that have been obtained do not clearly justify substitution of these reagents for the halogens.

By the action of the oxidizing agent phenyl iodochloride [24] on lead thiocyanate, phenyl iodothiocyanate is formed. It has been suggested that this substance is the thiocyanating agent.

$$C_6H_5ICl_2 + Pb(SCN)_2 \rightarrow C_6H_5I(SCN)_2 + PbCl_2$$

Cupric thiocyanate,[70] the use of which may be considered still another modification of this general procedure, shows promise of being very effective. It releases thiocyanogen merely by the dissociation of the cupric to cuprous salt.

$$2Cu(SCN)_2 \rightarrow 2CuSCN + (SCN)_2$$

Cupric thiocyanate, prepared in advance, or a paste of copper sulfate and sodium thiocyanate in equivalent proportions is added to a solution of the compound in methanol or acetic acid, and the mixture is warmed to 35–80° until the black cupric thiocyanate has changed completely to the white cuprous thiocyanate. The product is isolated by dilution with

[70] Kaufmann and Küchler, *Ber.*, **67**, 944 (1934).

water, followed by extraction with ether. This procedure has the advantage over the others previously described of permitting higher temperatures for thiocyanation. The preferential thiocyanation of aromatic amines with susceptible olefinic linkages in side chains has been accomplished with this reagent.[71] Still further improvement [70, 72] of the above method is reported to consist in the addition of a cupric salt to a solution of the amine or phenol and an inorganic thiocyanate in water, dilute acid, or 30% ethanol. Organic compounds that are insoluble in the solvents to be used can be thiocyanated successfully by this method after dispersal with commercial detergents. The presence of oxalic acid is reported to decrease color formation. Resorcinol [31] and olefins [73] as well as amines have been found to react with thiocyanogen generated by this method.

Detection of Thiocyano Compounds. The characterization of the products of thiocyanation does not present many difficulties. Aryl thiocyanates do not rearrange readily upon heating into isothiocyanates (ArN=C=S), and alkyl thiocyanates rearrange only when heated to high temperatures. Allyl thiocyanates and analogous compounds, however, rearrange very readily at elevated temperatures into isothiocyanates.[74]

The reaction with thiol acids serves to differentiate thiocyano from isothiocyano compounds. [75]

$$\mathrm{RSCN + HSCOAr \rightarrow RSCSHNCOAr}$$

$$\mathrm{RNCS + HSCOAr \rightarrow RNHCOAr + CS_2}$$

A simple test for aliphatic dithiocyanates consists in the development of a red color on the addition of ferric chloride to a solution formed by heating the thiocyanate with aqueous sodium hydroxide followed by acidification.[76] A few instances have been reported in which a monothiocyano compound produces a red color with ferric chloride alone.[32] A more general test involves heating a thiocyanate with alkaline lead tartrate, which results in the formation of a yellow precipitate.[1] The reaction with sodium malonic ester to produce a disulfide has been suggested as a qualitative test.[77] A method for the quantitative determination involves heating the compound under reflux with an ethanolic solution of sodium

[71] Arnold, *Arch. Pharm.*, **279**, 181 (1941).

[72] U. S. pat., 2,212,175 [*C. A.*, **35**, 466 (1941)]; Brit. pat., 513,473 [*C. A.*, **35**, 1804 (1941)]; Brit. pat., 514,203 [*C. A.*, **35**, 4041 (1941)]; Ger. pat., 579,818 [*C. A.*, **28**, 1053 (1934)].

[73] Dermer and Dysinger, *J. Am. Chem. Soc.*, **61**, 750 (1939).

[74] Bergmann, *J. Chem. Soc.*, 1361 (1935); Mumm and Richter, *Ber.*, **73**, 843 (1940).

[75] Wheeler and Merriam, *J. Am. Chem. Soc.*, **23**, 283 (1901).

[76] Hagelberg, *Ber.*, **23**, 1083 (1890).

[77] Whitmore, "Organic Chemistry," p. 542, Van Nostrand, New York, 1937.

sulfide.[78] After removal of the excess sulfide, silver thiocyanate is precipitated by the addition of standard silver nitrate and the excess silver ion is determined by the Volhard method.

$$2RSCN + Na_2S \rightarrow R_2S + 2NaSCN$$

It has been noted that 20 to 30% of the nitrogen of the thiocyano ion escapes conversion to ammonia in the regular Kjeldahl digestion.[79]

EXPERIMENTAL PROCEDURES

Thiocyanogen Solutions. Lead thiocyanate, used advantageously in the formation of thiocyanogen, is prepared from lead nitrate and sodium thiocyanate. To an ice-cold solution of 45 g. of lead nitrate in 100 cc. of water is added a cold solution of 25 g. of sodium thiocyanate in 100 cc. of water. Lead thiocyanate precipitates as a fine, white powder. It is collected on a filter, washed free of nitrates with ice water, and then dried in vacuum over phosphorus pentoxide in the dark. The product should remain perfectly white.

One part by weight (in grams) of lead thiocyanate is suspended in 5 to 10 parts by volume (in cubic centimeters) of the desired solvent in a glass-stoppered flask. The solution is cooled to 5–10°, and a small portion of 10% bromine in the same solvent is added. The mixture is shaken vigorously until the color due to the bromine disappears. The process of addition and shaking is repeated until the calculated amount of bromine has been used. The suspended solids are allowed to settle, the thiocyanogen solution is decanted, and the residual solids are washed by decantation with small portions of the solvent.

Decoloration of the bromine solution by lead thiocyanate is usually immediate; if a protracted induction period appears to be indicated, it can be terminated readily by exposure of the solution to direct sunlight. As heat is evolved by the reaction, the flask must be cooled regularly during the preparation to maintain the low temperature necessary to stabilize the thiocyanogen. At the end of the reaction lead thiocyanate should remain in about 10% excess. Solutions of pure thiocyanogen are water-clear and colorless. Filtration of the solution is of little advantage and is not easily accomplished without the appearance of a pink coloration indicative of the presence of moisture.

Since the reaction between bromine and lead thiocyanate is quantitative, the amount of thiocyanogen present can be taken as equivalent to the amount of bromine added to the solution provided that the reagent is used immediately. A quantitative estimate is furnished by titration

[78] Panchenko and Smirnov, *J. Gen. Chem. U.S.S.R.*, **2,** 193 (1932) [*C. A.*, **27,** 245 (1933)].

[79] Valdiguié, *Bull. soc. chim. biol.*, **21,** 609 (1939).

of the iodine released when an aliquot of the solution is shaken with aqueous potassium iodide.[4] In most syntheses it is desirable that free thiocyanogen remain in excess until the end of the reaction. The presence of the free halogenoid may be determined by the formation of a red color when a few drops of the solution are shaken with iron powder and ether.

Styrene Dithiocyanate [33] **(Use of Free Thiocyanogen).** To a solution of 11.6 g. (0.1 mole) of thiocyanogen in 150 cc. of benzene is added 10.4 g. (0.1 mole) of styrene. The flask is set in direct sunlight. In about one-half hour a mass of fine yellow crystals forms. When the test for thiocyanogen is negative (about two hours), the solids are filtered, washed with cold benzene, and dried in air. The yield is 17.5 g. (80%). For purification the product is crystallized from hot benzene and then from ethanol. The melting point is 101–102°.

***p*-Thiocyanoaniline** [16] **(Use of Sodium Thiocyanate and Bromine).** A solution of 14 g. (0.14 mole) of freshly distilled aniline and 37 g. (0.45 mole) of sodium thiocyanate in 90 cc. of methanol is cooled to 5°, and 8.5 cc. (0.155 mole) of bromine in 30 cc. of methanol saturated with sodium bromide is added with stirring. The reaction mixture is poured into 1 l. of water. The solution is neutralized with sodium carbonate. *p*-Thiocyanoaniline separates in colorless crystals, which after recrystallization from water melt at 97°; yield, 20.4 g. (97%).

9,10-Dithiocyanostearic Acid [80] **(Use of Sodium Thiocyanate and Bromine).** A solution of 2.8 g. (0.01 mole) of elaidic acid in 60 cc. of glacial acetic acid containing 5 g. (0.06 mole) of sodium thiocyanate is warmed to 40°, and 1.5 cc. (0.29 mole) of bromine in 10 cc. of acetic acid is dropped in. The mixture is poured into water, and the product, which precipitates, is collected on a filter and washed with water to free it of thiocyanic acid. It is recrystallized from a small amount of warm ethanol and then washed with a little petroleum ether; m.p. 79°. The mother liquor is concentrated for a second crop. The total yield of product is 2.78 g. (70%).

2-Amino-4,6-dimethylbenzothiazole [23] **(Use of Sodium Thiocyanate and Bromine).** A solution of 12.1 g. (0.1 mole) of 2,4-xylidine and 1.6 g. (0.2 mole) of sodium thiocyanate in 150 cc. of glacial acetic acid is cooled in ice and stirred mechanically while a solution of 16 g. (0.2 mole) of bromine in 25 cc. of acetic acid is added dropwise. The temperature is kept below 10° by external cooling throughout the addition and for thirty minutes thereafter. The product, 2-amino-4,6-dimethylbenzothiazole hydrobromide, is collected by filtration. It is dissolved in warm water, and the base is precipitated by alkali and recrystallized from ethanol or ligroin; m.p. 140°. The yield is 13 g. (79%) of free base.

[80] Kaufmann, *Chem. Umschau Fette Öle Wachse Harze*, **37**, 113 (1930).

N,N-Dimethyl-4-thiocyanoaniline [25] **(Use of Ammonium Thiocyanate and Electrolysis).** A solution of 21.5 g. of dimethylaniline (0.18 mole) and 55.5 g. (0.73 mole) of ammonium thiocyanate in 48 cc. of water, 25 cc. of 95% ethanol, and 19 cc. of 35% hydrochloric acid is cooled to 0° and electrolyzed. A cathode of copper or platinum gauze and a rotating graphite anode are used to produce a current of 0.02–0.03 ampere per square centimeter. When 0.5 faraday (140% of the theoretical amount) has been consumed the precipitated product is collected by filtration. It is dissolved in hydrochloric acid, reprecipitated with ammonia, and recrystallized from 90% ethanol. The yield of N,N-dimethyl-4-thiocyanoaniline is 29 g. (92%); m.p. 73°.

4-Thiocyano-1-naphthol [70] **(Use of Preformed Cupric Thiocyanate).** The cupric thiocyanate is prepared by treating an aqueous solution of copper sulfate with an equivalent amount of aqueous sodium thiocyanate. The precipitate is filtered and washed with ethanol and ether.

A solution of 3.6 g. (0.025 mole) of α-naphthol in 30 cc. of acetic acid is warmed gently with 19 g. (0.105 mole) of cupric thiocyanate until decoloration of the copper salt is complete. The solution is filtered and diluted with water. An oil separates but soon crystallizes. Recrystallization from carbon disulfide yields 3.6 g. (72%) of 4-thiocyano-1-naphthol, m.p. 112°.

2-Amino-6-ethoxybenzothiazole [70] **(Use of Copper Chloride and Sodium Thiocyanate).** To a solution of 3.5 g. (0.025 mole) of *p*-phenetidine and 7.6 g. (0.094 mole) of sodium thiocyanate in 40 cc. of glacial acetic acid is added a solution of 12 g. (0.090 mole) of cupric chloride in 25 cc. of ethanol. The mixture is stirred for half an hour at 70°, and then the temperature is raised to 100°. Approximately 80 cc. of hot, dilute hydrochloric acid is added, and the solution is filtered. The residue is washed on the funnel with hot water. The combined filtrates are decolorized with carbon and then are neutralized with sodium carbonate. The product, 2-amino-6-ethoxybenzothiazole, separates as crystals which have a melting point of 161°. The yield is 3.5 g. (71%).

SURVEY OF SYNTHESES WITH THIOCYANOGEN

The following tables record organic compounds and the products of their reaction with thiocyanogen that were reported prior to January, 1945. Many organic compounds have been shown to react with thiocyanogen by titration data in terms of a "thiocyanogen number." Such compounds are included in the tables only if a product was isolated from the reaction mixture. An omission of the yield in the table indicates that the information was not given in the original paper. Many of the yields reported probably can be increased by application of the improved techniques illustrated in the more recent papers.

TABLE I

AROMATIC AMINES SUBSTITUTED BY THIOCYANOGEN

Amine	Product	Method*	Yield	Reference
Aniline	p-Thiocyanoaniline	C	97%	15, 16
		C	87%	19
		C	80%	18
		C	78%	70
		C	50%	17, 24
		A	27%	1
		C		20, 72
	2,4-Dithiocyanoaniline	C	80%	18
	2-Amino-6-thiocyanobenzothiazole	C	15%	19
		C		20, 21, 22
o-Toluidine	4-Thiocyano-o-toluidine	C	80%	17
		B	75%	82
		B	44%	27
		C	39%	26
		C		81
p-Toluidine	2-Amino-6-methylbenzothiazole	C	81%	70, 72
		C		17, 18, 22
	2,6-Dithiocyano-p-toluidine	C	45%	22
m-Toluidine	4-Thiocyano-m-toluidine	B	62%	27
		C		17
	4,6-Dithiocyano-m-toluidine	C		17
2,4-Xylidine	2-Amino-4,6-dimethylbenzothiazole	C	79%	23
2,5-Xylidine	4-Thiocyano-2,5-xylidine	C	47%	22
		C		72, 83
	2-Amino-4,7-dimethyl-6-thiocyanobenzothiazole	C		22
o-Chloroaniline	2-Chloro-4-thiocyanoaniline	B		37, 72, 84
p-Chloroaniline	2-Amino-6-chlorobenzothiazole	C	75%	22
		C	69%	70, 72
		C		21
4-Chloro-o-toluidine	5-Chloro-2-thiocyano-o-toluidine	C		84
	2-Amino-6-chloro-4-methylbenzothiazole	C		21
4-Chloro-2,5-xylidine	2-Amino-6-chloro-4,7-dimethylbenzothiazole	C		21
2-Bromo-p-toluidine	2-Amino-4-bromo-6-methylbenzothiazole	C		23
p-Nitroaniline	2-Amino-6-nitrobenzothiazole	C		23

* A refers to free thiocyanogen, B to thiocyanogen generated from salts by electrolysis, and C to thiocyanogen generated from salts by chemical reagents.

TABLE I—*Continued*

AROMATIC AMINES SUBSTITUTED BY THIOCYANOGEN

Amine	Product	Method*	Yield	Reference
3-Nitro-*p*-toluidine	2-Amino-6-methyl-5-nitrobenzothiazole	C		23
4-Nitro-*o*-toluidine	2-Amino-4-methyl-6-nitrobenzothiazole	C		23
2-Hydroxyaniline	2-Hydroxy-4-thiocyanoaniline	C	50%	24
3-Hydroxyaniline	3-Hydroxy-4-thiocyanoaniline	C	55%	24
o-Anisidine	2-Methoxy-4-thiocyanoaniline	C		72, 84
Phenetidine	4-Ethoxy-2-thiocyanoaniline	C		15, 84
	2-Amino-6-ethoxybenzothiazole	C	95%	24
		C	65%	70
		C	60%	22
		C	54%	72
		C		15, 21
Anthranilic acid	4(5)-Thiocyanoanthranilic acid	C	80%	18
		B	60%	82
		B	54%	85
		C	50%	24
		C		72
p-Aminobenzoic acid	2-Amino-6-carboxybenzothiazole	C	67%	72
Ethyl *p*-aminobenzoate	Ethyl 4-amino-3-thiocyanobenzoate	C	85%	22
m-Aminobenzoic acid	3-Amino-4-thiocyanobenzoic acid	C		18
α-Naphthylamine	4-Thiocyano-1-naphthylamine	C	80%	18
		C	71%	8
	2,4-Dithiocyano-1-naphthylamine	B	55%	82
		C	50%	10, 19
		C		18, 20
	2-Amino-5-thiocyanonaphtho-[1′,2′ : 4,5]-thiazole	C		22
4-Chloro-1-naphthylamine	2-Amino-5-chloronaphtho-[1′,2′ : 4,5]-thiazole	C		21
β-Naphthylamine	1-Thiocyano-2-naphthylamine	C	94%	70, 72
		C	55%	19
		C		20, 24, 84, 86
	2-Aminonaphtho-[2′,1′ : 4,5]-thiazole	C		21, 22, 72
7-Methoxy-2-naphthylamine	7-Methoxy-1-thiocyano-2-naphthylamine	C		84

* A refers to free thiocyanogen, B to thiocyanogen generated from salts by electrolysis, and C to thiocyanogen generated from salts by chemical reagents.

TABLE I—*Continued*

Aromatic Amines Substituted by Thiocyanogen

Amine	Product	Method*	Yield	Reference
7-Methoxy-2-naphthylamine—*Cont.*	2-Amino-8-methoxynaphtho-[2′,1′ : 4,5]-thiazole	C		21
β-Anthrylamine	1-Thiocyano-2-anthrylamine	C		84
	2-Aminoanthra-[2′,1′ : 4,5]-thiazole	C		21
2,6-Diaminoanthracene	2,6-Diamino-1-thiocyanoanthracene	C		84
	2,6-Diamino-1,5-dithiocyanoanthracene	C		84
N-Methylaniline	N-Methyl-4-thiocyanoaniline	C		85
N-Ethylaniline	N-Ethyl-4-thiocyanoaniline	C		27, 85
N-Propylaniline	N-Propyl-4-thiocyanoaniline	C		85
N-Butylaniline	N-Butyl-4-thiocyanoaniline	C		85
N-Benzylaniline	N-Benzyl-4-thiocyanoaniline	C		85, 87
N-Cetylaniline	N-Cetyl-4-thiocyanoaniline	A		71
N-Oleylaniline	N-Oleyl-4-thiocyanoaniline	C		71
N-Chaulmoogrylaniline	N-Chaulmoogryl-4-thiocyanoaniline	C	65%	71
N-Ethyl-*m*-toluidine	N-Ethyl-4-thiocyano-*m*-toluidine	C	84%	85
N-Methyl-*p*-toluidine	2-Imino-3,6-dimethylbenzothiazoline	C		23
N-Ethyl-*p*-toluidine	2-Imino-3-ethyl-6-methylbenzothiazoline	C		23
N-Benzyl-*p*-toluidine	2-Imino-3-benzyl-6-methylbenzothiazoline	C		23
N-Methylanthranilic acid	N-Methyl-4(5)-thiocyanoanthranilic acid	C	64%	85
Diphenylamine	Di-(4-thiocyanophenyl)-amine	A		1
		C		19, 20, 61, 72
N,N-Dimethylaniline	N,N-Dimethyl-4-thiocyanoaniline	B	92%	25
		C	79%	26
		B	75%	82
		C	65%	88
		C	45%	24
		A		1, 60
		C		18, 72
N,N-Diethylaniline	N,N-Diethyl-4-thiocyanoaniline	C	84%	85
		B	81%	25
N,N-Dimethyl-*p*-toluidine	N,N-Dimethyl-2-thiocyano-*p*-toluidine	B	21%	25

* A refers to free thiocyanogen, B to thiocyanogen generated from salts by electrolysis, and C to thiocyanogen generated from salts by chemical reagents.

TABLE I—*Continued*

AROMATIC AMINES SUBSTITUTED BY THIOCYANOGEN

Amine	Product	Method*	Yield	Reference
N-Benzyl-N-methylaniline	N-Benzyl-N-methyl-4-thiocyanoaniline	C	70%	87
N-Benzyl-N-ethylaniline	N-Benzyl-N-ethyl-4-thiocyanoaniline	B C	84% 70%	85 87
Triphenylamine	Di-(4-thiocyanophenyl)-phenylamine	A		1
m-Phenylenediamine	4-Thiocyano-*m*-phenylenediamine	A		1
	4,6-Dithiocyano-*m*-phenylenediamine	C		18
Benzidine	Dithiocyanobenzidine	C		18, 24
Sulfanilamide	4-Amino-3-thiocyanobenzenesulfonamide	C	75%	89
	2-Amino-6-sulfamylbenzothiazole	C C	58%	89 71
N^1,N^1-Dimethylsulfanilamide	2-Amino-6-(N,N-dimethylsulfamyl)-benzothiazole	C	70%	89
N^1,N^1-Diethylsulfanilamide	2-Amino-6-(N,N-diethylsulfamyl)-benzothiazole	C	80%	89
N^4-Acetylsulfanilamide	2-Amino-6-(N-acetylsulfamyl)-benzothiazole	C		71
4′-Sulfamylsulfanilanilide	N^4-(2-Amino-6-benzothiazolylsulfonyl)-sulfanilamide	C	65%	89
N,N′-Disulfanilyl-*p*-phenylenediamine	N-(Sulfanilyl)-N′-(2-amino-6-benzothiazolylsulfonyl)-*p*-phenylenediamine	C	40%	89
N-Sulfanilyl-*p*-nitroaniline	N-(2-Amino-6-benzothiazolylsulfonyl)-*p*-nitroaniline	C	68%	89
N-Sulfanilyl-*p*-toluidine	N-(2-Amino-6-benzothiazolylsulfonyl)-*p*-toluidine	C	75%	89

* A refers to free thiocyanogen, B to thiocyanogen generated from salts by electrolysis, and C to thiocyanogen generated from salts by chemical reagents.

[81] Horii, *J. Pharm. Soc. Japan*, **55**, 6 (1935) [*C. A.*, **29**, 3317 (1935)].

[82] U. S. pat., 1,816,848 [*C. A.*, **25**, 5355 (1931)]; Brit. pat., 364,060; Fr. pat., 702,829 [*C. A.*, **25**, 4284 (1931)].

[83] Brit. pat., 299,327.

[84] U. S. pat., 1,765,678 [*C. A.*, **24**, 4307 (1930)]; Brit. pat., 303,813 [*C. A.*, **23**, 4482 (1929)]; Ger. pat., 491,225 [*C. A.*, **24**, 2138 (1930)].

[85] Cherkasova, Sklyarenko, and Melinikov, *J. Gen. Chem. U.S.S.R.*, **10**, 1373 (1940) [*C. A.*, **35**, 3615 (1941)].

[86] Ger. pat., 493,025 [*C. A.*, **24**, 2754 (1930)].

[87] Kaufmann and Ritter, *Arch. Pharm.*, **267**, 212 (1929).

[88] Brewster and Schroeder, *Org. Syntheses*, **19**, 79 (1939).

[89] Kaufmann and Bückmann, *Arch. Pharm.*, **279**, 194 (1941).

TABLE II

PHENOLS SUBSTITUTED BY THIOCYANOGEN

Phenol	Product	Method*	Yield	Reference
Phenol	4-Thiocyanophenol	A	69%	1
		C	68%	26
		B	67%	27
		B	25%	82
		C	20%	24
		C		72, 84
m-Cresol	4-Thiocyano-*m*-cresol	B		27
		C		15
o-Cresol	4-Thiocyano-*o*-cresol	C	90%	15
		B	72%	27
		B	40%	82
p-Cresol	2-Thiocyano-*p*-cresol	B		27
		C		15
Guaiacol	4-Thiocyanoguaiacol	B	21%	25
Diethylphenol	Thiocyanodiethylphenol	B		27
Thymol	4-Thiocyanothymol	C	95%	15
		C	77%	25
		B	76%	27
		A		7
		C		4, 19
Carvacrol	Thiocyanocarvacrol	B	50%	27
Salicylic acid	5-Thiocyanosalicylic acid	A	30%	30
		C	10%	19
		C		20
α-Naphthol	4-Thiocyano-1-naphthol	A	83%	28
		C	72%	18, 19, 70
		A	50%	59
		C		20, 84
	2,4-Dithiocyano-1-naphthol	C	60%	19
		C		18, 20
β-Naphthol	1-Thiocyano-2-naphthol	A	100%	28
		C	90%	24
		C	72%	72
		C		18
Nerolin	2-Methoxy-1-thiocyanonaphthalene	A	65%	28
Resorcinol	4-Thiocyanoresorcinol	B	60%	82
Pyrocatechol	4-Thiocyanopyrocatechol	C	48%	29
		C		24

* A refers to free thiocyanogen, B to thiocyanogen generated from salts by electrolysis, and C to thiocyanogen generated from salts by chemical reagents.

TABLE III

POLYNUCLEAR HYDROCARBONS SUBSTITUTED BY THIOCYANOGEN

Hydrocarbon	Product	Method*	Yield	Reference
Anthracene	9,10-Dithiocyanoanthracene	A	45%	32
3,4-Benzpyrene	5-Thiocyano-3,4-benzpyrene	A	82%	32
20-Methylcholanthrene	20-Methyl-15-thiocyanocholanthrene	A	89%	32
1,2-Benzanthracene	9-Thiocyano-1,2-benzanthracene	A	5%	32
	10-Thiocyano-1,2-benzanthracene	A	57%	32
9-Methyl-1,2-benzanthracene	9-Methyl-10-thiocyano-1,2-benzanthracene	A	43%	32
10-Methyl-1,2-benzanthracene	10-Methyl-9-thiocyano-1,2-benzanthracene	A	66%	32

* A refers to free thiocyanogen, B to thiocyanogen generated from salts by electrolysis, and C to thiocyanogen generated from salts by chemical reagents.

TABLE IV

UNSATURATED COMPOUNDS THAT ADD THIOCYANOGEN

Compound	Product	Method*	Yield	Reference
Ethylene	1,2-Dithiocyanoethane	A	100%	33
		A	75%	28
		C	15%	20
Amylene	Dithiocyanopentane	A		42
		C		20, 90
Acetylene	1,2-Dithiocyanoethylene	A	20%	33
Acetylene diiodide	1,2-Dithiocyanoethylene	A		33
Phenylacetylene	1,2-Dithiocyano-1-phenylethylene	A	50%	33
Tolan	1,2-Diphenyl-1,2-dithiocyanoethylene	A	26%	33
Styrene	α,β-Dithiocyanoethylbenzene	A	100%	28
		A	80%	33
		C	65%	19
		C		20
Stilbene	1,2-Diphenyl-1,2-dithiocyanoethane	A	83%	33
Butadiene	1,4-Dithiocyanobutene-2	A	80%	35

* A refers to free thiocyanogen, B to thiocyanogen generated from salts by electrolysis, and C to thiocyanogen generated from salts by chemical reagents.

TABLE IV—*Continued*

UNSATURATED COMPOUNDS THAT ADD THIOCYANOGEN

Compound	Product	Method*	Yield	Reference
Isoprene	1,4-Dithiocyano-2-methyl-butene-2	C	19%	34
		C		20
Dimethylbutadiene	2,3-Dimethyl-1,4-dithiocyano-butene-2	C	11%	34
Allyl alcohol	2,3-Dithiocyanopropanol	A		28
Anethole	1,2-Dithiocyano-1-(*p*-methoxy-phenyl)-propane	A	100%	28
		C	75%	19
		A		20
Isosafrole	4-(Dithiocyanopropyl)-1,2-methylenedioxybenzene	A		28
Carvone	Dihydrodithiocyanocarvone	A		37
Pinene	Dithiocyanopinane	A		91
Terpineol	Dithiocyanomenthanol	A		91
Terpineol methyl ether	Dithiocyanomenthanol methyl ether	A		91
Alloöcimene	Dihydrodithiocyanoalloöcimene	A		91
Cyclohexene	1,2-Dithiocyanocyclohexane	C		73
3-Methylcyclo-hexene	1,2-Dithiocyano-3-methyl-cyclohexane	C		73
Methyl styryl ketone	Methyl α-thiocyanostyryl ketone	A		37
Distyryl ketone	Dithiocyanodistyryl ketone	A		37
Oleic acid	9,10-Dithiocyanostearic acid	A		80, 93
		C		92
Elaidic acid	9,10-Dithiocyanostearic acid	C	70%	80
		A	62%	93
		C	60%	92
		C		94
Erucic acid	13,14-Dithiocyanobehenic acid	C	57%	70, 72
		C	49%	80
		A	45%	94
		A		80
		C		92
Brassidic acid	13,14-Dithiocyanobehenic acid	A	75%	93
		A		94
		C		92
Petroselenic acid	6,7-Dithiocyanostearic acid	A		80
Linolic acid	Dihydrodithiocyanolinolic acid	A	96%	94
Ethyl linolate	Ethyl dihydrodithiocyanolino-late	A	93%	95

* A refers to free thiocyanogen, B to thiocyanogen generated from salts by electrolysis, and C to thiocyanogen generated from salts by chemical reagents.

TABLE IV—*Continued*

UNSATURATED COMPOUNDS THAT ADD THIOCYANOGEN

Compound	Product	Method*	Yield	Reference
β-Oleostearin	β-Oleostearin hexathiocyanate	A		80
Hydnocarpic acid	Dihydrodithiocyanohydnocarpic acid	A		96
Chaulmoogric acid	Dihydrodithiocyanochaulmoogric acid	A		96

* A refers to free thiocyanogen, B to thiocyanogen generated from salts by electrolysis, and C to thiocyanogen generated from salts by chemical reagents.

TABLE V

MISCELLANEOUS COMPOUNDS SUBSTITUTED BY THIOCYANOGEN

Compound	Product	Method*	Yield	Reference
Antipyrine	2,3-Dimethyl-1-phenyl-4-thiocyanopyrazolone	A	56%	30
	Bis-(2,3-dimethyl-1-phenyl-5-pyrazolone-4)-1-disulfide	C C	61%	70 20, 72
Carbostyryl	2-Hydroxy-4-thiocyanoquinoline	C		15
8-Hydroxyquinoline	8-Hydroxy-4-thiocyanoquinoline	C		15, 27
N-Acetyldiphenylhydrazine	N-Acetyl-di-(4-thiocyanophenyl)-hydrazine	C	75%	15
N-Benzoyldiphenylhydrazine	N-Benzoyl-di-(4-thiocyanophenyl)-hydrazine	C	64%	15
N-Formyldiphenylhydrazine	N-Formyl-di-(4-thiocyanophenyl)-hydrazine	C	68%	15
N-Phthalyldiphenylhydrazine	N-Phthalyl-di-(4-thiocyanophenyl)-hydrazine	C	73%	15
O,N-Dibenzylhydroxylamine	O,N-Dibenzyl-N-thiocyanohydroxylamine	C	47%	39
O,N-Diethylhydroxylamine	O,N-Diethyl-N-thiocyanohydroxylamine	C	40%	39

* A refers to free thiocyanogen, B to thiocyanogen generated from salts by electrolysis, and C to thiocyanogen generated from salts by chemical reagents.

[90] U. S. pat., 1,859,399 [*C. A.*, **26,** 3804 (1932)].

[91] U. S. pat., 2,188,495 [*C. A.*, **34,** 3763 (1940)].

[92] Kaufmann, Gindsberg, Rottig, and Salchow, *Ber.*, **70*B*,** 2519 (1937).

[93] Kimura, *Chem. Umschau Fette Öle Wachse Harze*, **37,** 72 (1930).

[94] Holde, *Chem. Umschau Fette Öle Wachse Harze*, **37,** 173 (1930).

[95] Kimura, *Ber.*, **69,** 786 (1936).

[96] Arnold, *Arch. Pharm.*, **277,** 206 (1939).

TABLE V—*Continued*

MISCELLANEOUS COMPOUNDS SUBSTITUTED BY THIOCYANOGEN

Compound	Product	Method*	Yield	Reference
Benzylamine	Benzylthiocyanoamine	C		39
Diethylamine	Diethylthiocyanoamine	A		6
Triphenylmethylamine	Triphenylmethylthiocyanoamine	C	55%	39
Diphenylmercury	Phenyl thiocyanate	A	66%	1
Diethylzinc	Ethyl thiocyanate	A		1
Ethyl mercaptan	Ethyl thiothiocyanate	A	50%	40
Thiophenol	Phenyl thiothiocyanate	A	70%	40
β-Thionaphthol	β-Naphthylthiothiocyanate	A		40
p-Nitrothiophenol	*p*-Nitrophenylthiothiocyanate	A	75%	41
Triphenylphosphine	Triphenylphosphine sulfide	A		42
Triphenylarsine	Triphenylarsinehydroxy thiocyanate	A		42
Triphenylstibine	Triphenylstibine dithiocyanate	A		42
Triphenylbismuthine	Diphenylbismuthine dithiocyanate	A		42, 43
	Phenyl thiocyanate	A		42
Tri-α-naphthylbismuthine	α-Naphthyl thiocyanate	A		43
Ethyl acetoacetate	Ethyl 2-hydroxy-4-methylthiazole-5-carboxylate	A	19%	28
Diethyl hydrocollidine dicarboxylate	Diethyl hydrocollidine dicarboxylate dithiocyanate	A	30%	30
Ammonium lignosulfonate	Ammonium thiocyanolignosulfonate	B		97
		C		97

* A refers to free thiocyanogen, B to thiocyanogen generated from salts by electrolysis, and C to thiocyanogen generated from salts by chemical reagents.

[97] Schwabe and Preu, *Cellulosechem.*, **21**, 1 (1943).

CHAPTER 7

THE HOFMANN REACTION

EVERETT S. WALLIS and JOHN F. LANE *

Princeton University

CONTENTS

* Present address, Rutgers University, New Brunswick, N. J.

THE NATURE OF THE REACTION

In the Hofmann reaction an amide is converted to an amine of one less carbon atom by treatment with bromine (or chlorine) and alkali.[1] In effect the carbonyl group of the amide is eliminated. The reaction is

$$RCONH_2 + Br_2 + 4OH^- \rightarrow RNH_2 + CO_3^= + 2Br^- + 2H_2O$$

applicable to the preparation of amines from amides of aliphatic, aromatic, arylaliphatic, and heterocyclic acids.

The Hofmann reaction generally is carried out by dissolving the amide in a very slight excess of cold aqueous hypohalite solution, followed by rapid warming (with steam distillation if the amine produced is volatile).[2] A valuable modification (p. 282) consists in carrying out the reaction in an alcoholic (usually methanolic) solution, with subsequent hydrolysis of the urethan so obtained.

$$RCONH_2 + Br_2 + 2OH^- + R'OH \rightarrow RNHCO_2R' + 2Br^- + 2H_2O$$

$$RNHCO_2R' + H_2O \rightarrow RNH_2 + CO_2 + ROH$$

THE MECHANISM OF THE REACTION

Hofmann found that the reaction of acetamide with equimolecular quantities of bromine and alkali yielded N-bromoacetamide.

$$CH_3CONH_2 + Br_2 + OH^- \rightarrow CH_3CONHBr + Br^- + H_2O$$

Investigation of the behavior of this and other N-haloamides showed that they react with alkali to give unstable salts.[3]

$$RCONHX + OH^- \rightarrow [RCONX]^- + H_2O$$

In the dry state these salts undergo a decomposition wherein the organic residue migrates from the carbon atom to the nitrogen atom, the products being isocyanates and alkali metal halides.

$$[RCONX]^- \rightarrow RN{=}C{=}O + X^-$$

In the presence of water and an excess of alkali, the isocyanates are hydrolyzed to amines.

$$OH^- + RN{=}C{=}O \rightarrow [RNHCO_2]^- \xrightarrow{OH^-} RNH_2 + CO_3^=$$

In alcoholic solution they are converted to urethans.

$$RN{=}C{=}O + R'OH \rightarrow RNHCO_2R'$$

[1] Hofmann, *Ber.*, (*a*) **14,** 2725 (1881); (*b*) **15,** 407 (1882); (*c*) **15,** 762 (1882); (*d*) **17,** 1406 (1884); (*e*) **18,** 2734 (1885); (*f*) **15,** 752 (1882).

[2] Hoogewerff and van Dorp, *Rec. trav. chim.*, (*a*) **5,** 252 (1886); (*b*) **6,** 373 (1887); (*c*) **10,** 5 (1891); (*d*) **10,** 145 (1891); (*e*) **15,** 107 (1896).

[3] Mauguin, *Ann. chim.*, [8] **22,** 297 (1911).

When one-half of the usual quantities of bromine and alkali are employed, alkyl acyl ureas are obtained. The isocyanates, in the absence of excess alkali, react with the sodium salts of the haloamides to give salts of the alkyl acyl ureas from which the ureas themselves result on hydrolysis.[4]

$$[\mathrm{RCONX}]^- + \mathrm{RN{=}C{=}O} \rightarrow [\mathrm{RN}\overset{\overset{\mathrm{O}}{/\!/}}{\mathrm{C}}\text{—}\mathrm{NX}\overset{\overset{\mathrm{O}}{/\!/}}{\mathrm{C}}\text{—}\mathrm{R}]^- + \mathrm{H_2O}$$

$$\rightarrow \mathrm{RNH}\overset{\overset{\mathrm{O}}{/\!/}}{\mathrm{C}}\text{—}\mathrm{NH}\overset{\overset{\mathrm{O}}{/\!/}}{\mathrm{C}}\text{—}\mathrm{R} + \mathrm{OX}^-$$

Isocyanates derived from the higher aliphatic amides react more rapidly with the haloamide salts than with water and alkali, so that, when these amides are subjected to the Hofmann reaction in aqueous medium, only small amounts of the expected amines are formed. Although amines arise from the hydrolysis of the alkyl acyl ureas, they are largely oxidized to nitriles by the excess of hypobromite present.

$$\mathrm{RNHCONHCOR} + \mathrm{H_2O} \rightarrow \mathrm{RNH_2} + \mathrm{RCONH_2} + \mathrm{CO_2}$$

$$\mathrm{RCH_2NH_2} + 2\,\mathrm{OX}^- \rightarrow \mathrm{RCN} + 2\mathrm{X}^- + 2\mathrm{H_2O}$$

However, amides of this type usually may be converted in good yield to the urethans by reaction in methanol (p. 282).

In addition it may be noted that amides of α,β-unsaturated acids and of α-hydroxyacids yield aldehydes when allowed to undergo this rearrangement. Aryl-substituted semicarbazides yield azides, and aryl-substituted ureas yield aryl-substituted hydrazines. These reactions are discussed more fully in a subsequent section of this chapter (p. 273).

The Hofmann reaction involves a rearrangement quite similar to the Curtius rearrangement and to the Lossen rearrangement, as indicated by the following equations.[5, 6]

$$[\mathrm{R}\overset{\overset{\mathrm{O}}{/\!/}}{\mathrm{C}}\text{—}\mathrm{NX}]^- \rightarrow \mathrm{RN{=}C{=}O} + \mathrm{X}^- \qquad \text{(Hofmann)}$$

$$\mathrm{R}\overset{\overset{\mathrm{O}}{/\!/}}{\mathrm{C}}\text{—}\mathrm{N_3} \rightarrow \mathrm{RN{=}C{=}O} + \mathrm{N_2} \qquad \text{(Curtius)}$$

$$[\mathrm{R}\overset{\overset{\mathrm{O}}{/\!/}}{\mathrm{C}}\text{—}\mathrm{NOCOR'}]^- \rightarrow \mathrm{RN{=}C{=}O} + \mathrm{RCO_2}^- \qquad \text{(Lossen).}$$

[4] (*a*) Stieglitz and Earle, *Am. Chem. J.*, **30** 412 (1903); (*b*) Jeffreys, *ibid.*, **22** 14 (1899).

[5] Stieglitz and Slosson, *Ber.*, **34**, 1613 (1901); Stieglitz, *J. Am. Chem. Soc.*, **30**, 1797 (1908); Stieglitz and Peterson, *Ber.*, **43**, 782 (1910); Peterson, *Am. Chem. J.*, **46**, 325 (1911); Stieglitz and Vosburgh, *Ber.*, **46**, 2151 (1913); Stieglitz, *Proc. Natl. Acad. Sci.*, **1**, 196 (1915).

[6] Tiemann, *Ber.*, **24**, 4163 (1891).

Any of these reactions may be formulated by the general equation [7, 8]

$$R\!:\!\overset{\displaystyle :\ddot{O}:}{\ddot{C}}\!:\!\underset{\displaystyle B}{\ddot{\underset{\cdot\cdot}{N}}}\!:\!A \rightarrow A\!:\!B + \underset{\text{I}}{R\!:\!\overset{\displaystyle :\ddot{O}:}{\ddot{C}}\!:\!\ddot{\underset{\cdot\cdot}{N}}} \rightarrow R\!:\!\ddot{N}\!::\!C\!::\!O$$

and the driving force of rearrangement may be presumed to arise from the tendency of the electronically deficient nitrogen atom of the fragment (I) to acquire electrons from the neighboring carbon atom.

The rate-determining step in the Hofmann rearrangement apparently is the release of the halide ion from the haloamide anion. This follows from a quantitative study of the effect of *m*- and *p*-substituents on the rates of rearrangement of benzamide derivatives.[9] Thus, substituents Y that promote electron release through the carbonyl group (like methyl and methoxyl, which decrease the acidic strength of the corresponding benzoic acids) facilitate the rearrangement.

$$\left[\text{Y}\!-\!\text{C}_6\text{H}_4(\text{Y})\!-\!\overset{\displaystyle :\ddot{O}:}{\ddot{C}}\!:\!\underset{\displaystyle Br}{\ddot{\underset{\cdot\cdot}{N}}}: \right]^- K^+$$

Conversely, substituents that withdraw electrons (like nitro and cyano groups, which increase the acidity of the corresponding benzoic acids) retard the rearrangement. The same effects are observed with substituents Y in the salts of O-aroylbenzohydroxamic acids, while for substituents Z the inverse effects obtain.

$$\left[\text{Y}\!-\!\text{C}_6\text{H}_4(\text{Y})\!-\!\overset{\displaystyle :\ddot{O}:}{\ddot{C}}\!:\!\ddot{\underset{\cdot\cdot}{N}}\!:\!\text{OCO}\!-\!\text{C}_6\text{H}_4(\text{Z})\!-\!\text{Z} \right]^- K^+$$

Studies have been made on the mechanism of isomerization of the transient intermediate (I). It is now definitely established that in this isomerization the group R never becomes free during its migration from carbon to nitrogen. Thus the action of bromine and alkali on (+) 2-methyl-3-phenylpropionamide gives optically pure (+)2-amino-3-phenylpropane.[10] The same optically pure amine may be obtained from (+)2-methyl-3-phenylpropionazide by the Curtius rearrangement [11] as

[7] Jones, *Am. Chem. J.*, **50**, 414 (1913).

[8] Whitmore, *J. Am. Chem. Soc.*, **54**, 3274 (1932).

[9] Hauser and coworkers, *J. Am. Chem. Soc.*, (*a*) **59**, 121 (1937); (*b*) **60**, 2308 (1937); **61**, 618 (1939).

[10] Wallis and Nagel, *J. Am. Chem. Soc.*, **53**, 2787 (1931).

[11] Jones and Wallis, *J. Am. Chem. Soc.*, **48**, 169 (1926).

well as from derivatives of (+)2-methyl-3-phenylpropionylhydroxamic acid by the Lossen rearrangement. Moreover, the Hofmann rearrangement of (+)3,5-dinitro-2-α-naphthylbenzamide leads to optically pure (+)3,5-dinitro-2-α-naphthylaniline.[12] Here optical activity is due to restriction of rotation about the pivot bond between the benzene and naphthalene nuclei. If at any time during migration the migrating group had been free, the restriction would have been removed, and at least partial racemization would have occurred. Similar results have been observed in the Curtius rearrangement.[13] Thus, in the rearrangement of *o*-(2-methyl-6-nitrophenyl)-benzazide, the amine obtained is optically pure.

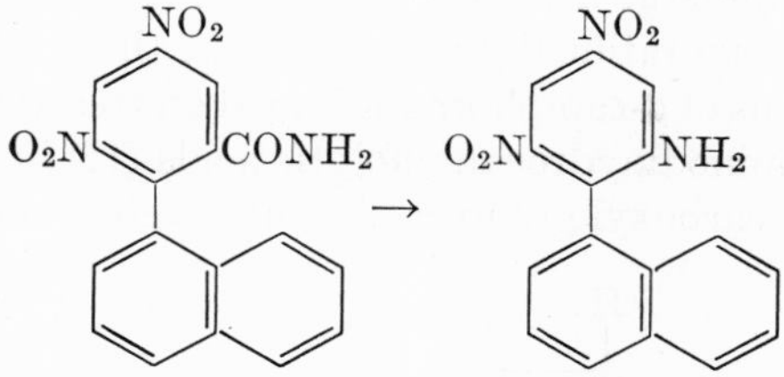

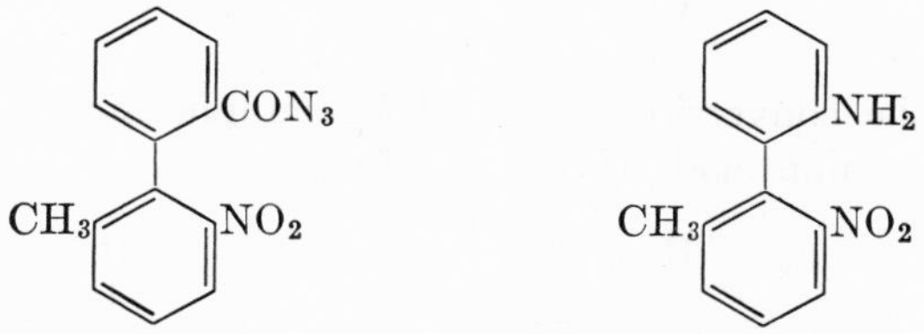

Further support for this conclusion is found in the results of studies on the Hofmann reaction of amides such as β,β,β-triphenylpropionamide [14] and β,β-dimethylbutyramide.[15] Here the migrating groups R_3CCH_2, if free, are extremely susceptible of rearrangement. From these amides, however, only the expected amines, i.e., β,β,β-triphenylethylamine and neopentylamine, are obtained.

The absence of interference of triphenylmethyl radicals in the Curtius rearrangement of acid azides [16] also is in agreement with this conclusion. In fact, experimental evidence indicates that this latter rearrangement is also unimolecular.[17] Unfortunately, no quantitative studies have

[12] Wallis and Moyer, *J. Am. Chem. Soc.*, **55**, 2598 (1933).

[13] Bell, *J. Chem. Soc.*, **1934**, 835.

[14] Hellermann, *J. Am. Chem. Soc.*, **49**, 1735 (1927).

[15] Whitmore and Homeyer, *J. Am. Chem. Soc.*, **54**, 3435 (1932).

[16] Powell, *J. Am. Chem. Soc.*, **51**, 2436 (1929); Wallis, *ibid.*, **51**, 2982 (1929).

[17] Barrett and Porter, *J. Am. Chem. Soc.*, **63**, 3434 (1941); Jones and Wallis, *ibid.*, **48**, 169 (1926); Porter and Young, *ibid.*, **60**, 1497 (1938).

been made, as of the Hofmann rearrangement, to show the rate-determining step in this process, and hence its true mechanism is still not clearly defined.

It has been established also that in rearrangements of this type the group R does not undergo a Walden inversion. Amines so obtained may be regarded as configurationally identical with the parent acids. Thus, the *d*, *l*, and *dl* forms of β-camphoramidic acid on treatment with bromine and alkali yield aminodihydrocampholytic acids (II) in which the amino group is *cis* to the carboxyl group.[18] A similar retention of configuration

H, CH_3, CO_2H, CH_3, CH_3, $CONH_2$ → H, CH_3, CO_2H, CH_3, CH_3, NH_2

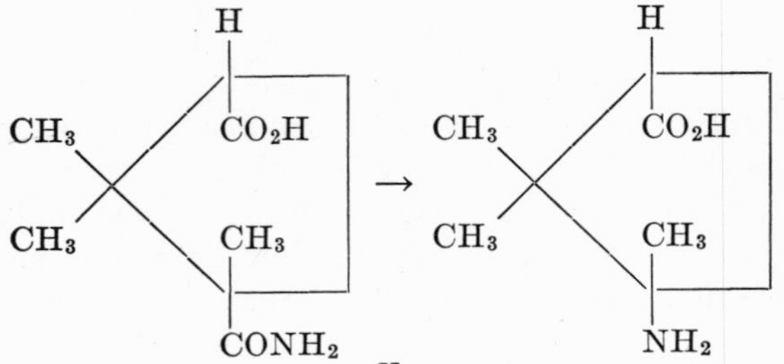

II

accompanies the conversion of *d* and *l*-α-camphoramidic acids to the corresponding amino acids (III).[19] A further, though somewhat indi-

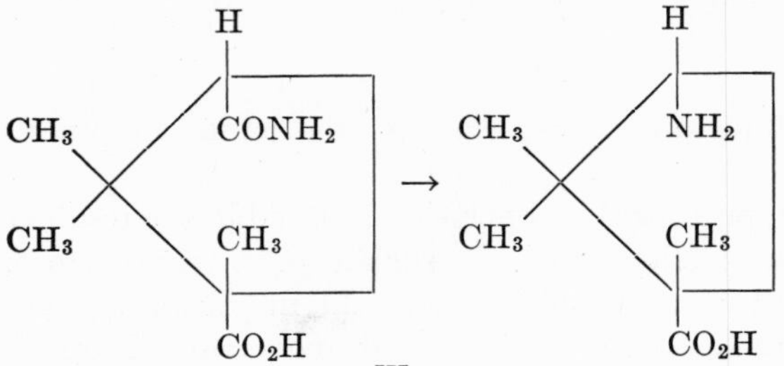

H, CH_3, $CONH_2$, CH_3, CH_3, CO_2H → H, CH_3, NH_2, CH_3, CH_3, CO_2H

III

rect, proof of the retention of configuration in the Hofmann reaction has been reported in connection with studies of replacement reactions occurring at a bridgehead in derivatives of apocamphane,[20] while retention of configuration in the Curtius rearrangements of the azides of 1-methylquinic and of dihydroshikimic acids has been observed.[21] Although

[18] Noyes, *Am. Chem. J.*, **24,** 290 (1900); **27,** 432 (1902); Noyes and Knight, *J. Am. Chem. Soc.*, **32,** 1672 (1910); Noyes and Nickell, *ibid.*, **36,** 124 (1914).

[19] (*a*) Noyes, *Am. Chem. J.*, **16,** 506 (1894); Noyes and Littleton, *J. Am. Chem. Soc.*, **39,** 2699 (1917); (*b*) Weir, *J. Chem. Soc.*, **99,** 1273 (1911).

[20] Bartlett and Knox, *J. Am. Chem. Soc.*, **61,** 3184 (1939).

[21] H. O. L. Fischer and coworkers, *Ber.*, **65,** 1009 (1932); *Helv. Chim. Acta*, **17,** 1200 (1934).

the difficulty of relating rotation to configuration has as yet prevented extensive confirmation of the absence of Walden inversion in the Hofmann rearrangement of aliphatic amides, the point in question has been studied in the Curtius rearrangement of optically active azides of the type, $R_1R_2R_3C\overset{O}{\overset{\|}{C}}—N_3$[22] and has been conclusively proved for the closely analogous Wolff rearrangement. Thus (+)1-diazo-3-phenyl-3-methylheptanone-2 rearranges to the configurationally identical (optically pure) (−)β-phenyl-β-methylenanthic acid.[23] This fact, in conjunction with the results obtained in cyclic systems, leaves no doubt that the Hofmann reaction also always involves retention of configuration. Any doubts incurred from conflicting or inconclusive results of studies of this type of rearrangement on geometrical isomers need not be taken too seriously. No one has submitted any evidence to show that *cis,trans* isomeric changes do not precede rearrangement of this type.[24]

$$(+)R\overset{O}{\overset{\|}{C}}:\overset{H}{\overset{\cdot\cdot}{\underset{\cdot\cdot}{C}}}:N_2 \rightarrow R\overset{O}{\overset{\|}{C}}:\overset{H}{\overset{\cdot\cdot}{C}}: \xrightarrow{H_2O} (-)RCH_2CO_2H$$

$$\left(R = n\text{-}C_4H_9\overset{C_6H_5}{\underset{CH_3}{C}}—\right)$$

THE SCOPE OF THE REACTION

Aliphatic, Alicyclic, and Arylaliphatic Amides

Monoamides. Good yields of the corresponding monoamines are obtained from aliphatic monoamides unless the latter contain more than eight carbon atoms, and with such amides a modification of the usual procedure[4b, 25] (p. 282) using methanol gives satisfactory results. Lauramide on treatment with aqueous alkaline hypobromite solution gives largely N-undecyl-N′-lauryl urea,[26] but treatment of the amide in methanol with sodium methoxide and bromine gives a 90% yield of methyl

[22] Kenyon and Young, *J. Chem. Soc.*, **1941**, 263.

[23] Lane and Wallis, *J. Am. Chem. Soc.*, **63**, 1674 (1942).

[24] Jones and Mason, *J. Am. Chem. Soc.*, **49**, 2528 (1927); Alder and coworkers, *Ann.*, **514**, 211 (1934); Skita and Rössler, *Ber.*, **72**, 416 (1939).

[25] Jeffreys, *Ber.*, **30**, 898 (1897).

[26] Ehestädt, dissertation, Freiburg i.B., 1886.

undecylcarbamate which may be converted with negligible loss to the desired undecylamine.

$$2C_{11}H_{23}CONH_2 \xrightarrow[H_2O]{NaOBr} C_{11}H_{23}CONHCONHC_{11}H_{23}$$

$$C_{11}H_{23}CONH_2 \xrightarrow[Br_2]{NaOCH_3} C_{11}H_{23}NHCO_2CH_3 \xrightarrow[H_2O]{OH^-} C_{11}H_{23}NH_2$$

This method also has been applied with advantage to the production of alicyclic monoamines from monoamides. The isomeric *o*-, *m*-, and *p*-hexahydrotoluamides have been converted through the urethans to the corresponding aminomethylcyclohexanes in approximately 70% yield.[27] Similarly camphane-4-carboxamide has been converted to 4-aminocamphane (56% yield). Although many conversions of alicyclic monoamides to alicyclic amines have been carried out by the usual procedure (aqueous alkaline hypobromite) the yields have not been reported.

No special difficulties are encountered with arylaliphatic amides unless the aromatic ring contains hydroxyl or a derived function, in which event low yields may result from side reactions involving halogenation of the ring. β-(*p*-Methoxyphenyl)-propionamide gives on treatment with aqueous alkaline hypobromite only 35% of the desired β-*p*-methoxyphenethylamine,[28] while *p*-hydroxybenzamide yields exclusively 2,6-dibromo-4-aminophenol.[29] β-(3-Benzyloxy-4-methoxyphenyl)propionamide [30] and β-(*m*-benzyloxyphenyl)propionamide [31] give none of the amines. Sodium hypochlorite, which leads to a more rapid rearrangement, may be used to advantage in the treatment of many amides containing phenolic or aromatic ether functions (p. 281). Thus, piperonylacetamide on treatment with aqueous alkaline hypochlorite gives a 50% yield of homopiperonylamine.[32]

Diamides. Diamides of adipic acid and its higher homologs are converted to diamines by aqueous alkaline hypobromite or hypochlorite solutions.[33]

$$H_2NCO(CH_2)_nCONH_2 \rightarrow H_2N(CH_2)_nNH_2 \qquad (n \geq 6)$$

Application of the reaction to glutaramide has not been reported. Succinamide is converted not to ethylene diamine but to dihydrouracil (IV),

[27] Gut, *Ber.*, **40**, 2065 (1907).

[28] Barger and Walpole, *J. Chem. Soc.*, **95**, 1724 (1909).

[29] Van Dam, *Rec. trav. chim.*, **18**, 418 (1899).

[30] Robinson and Sugasawa, *J. Chem. Soc.*, **1931**, 3166.

[31] Schöpf, Perrey, and Jäckh, *Ann.*, **497**, 49 (1932).

[32] Decker, *Ann.*, **395**, 291 (1913); Haworth, Perkin, and Rankin, *J. Chem. Soc.*, **125**, 1694 (1924).

[33] (*a*) von Braun and Jostes, *Ber.*, **59**, 1091 (1926); (*b*) von Brenkeleveen, *Rev. trav. chim.*, **13**, 34 (1894); (*c*) Ssolonina, *Bull. soc. chim.*, [3] **16**, 1878 (1896); (*d*) Bayer and Co., Ger. pats. 216,808, 232,072 [*Chem. Zentr.*, I, 311 (1910); I, 938 (1911)]; (*e*) von Braun and Lemke, *Ber.*, **55**, 3529 (1922).

which evidently is formed by the reaction (p. 269) leading to alkyl acyl ureas.[34] If an excess of alkali is employed at higher temperature β-alanine is produced. The action of aqueous alkaline sodium hypochlorite on diethyl malonamide leads, in analogous fashion, to C,C-diethylhydantoin (V). Similarly maleinamide is converted to uracil (VI).[35]

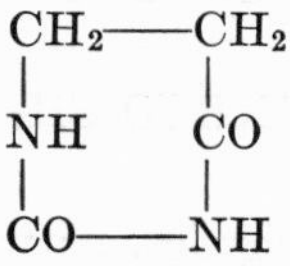

```
CH2——CH2        (C2H5)2C———NH          CH══CH
|      |               |     |          |     |
NH     CO              CO    CO         NH    CO
|      |                \   /           |     |
CO——NH                   N              CO——NH
                         H
   IV                    V                 VI
```

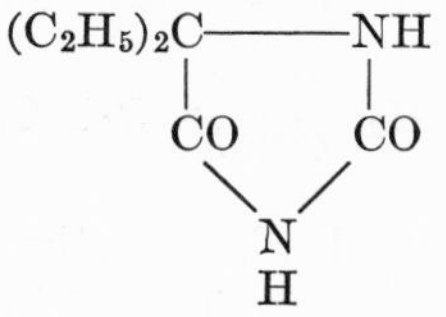

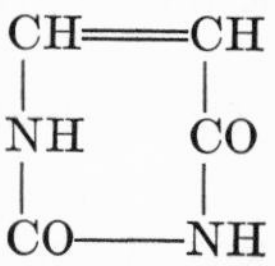

Aliphatic Monoacid-Monoamides. The action of a dilute solution of barium hydroxide and barium hypobromite converts *l*-β-malamidic acid to *l*-isoserine [36] (45% yield), and the same reagent converts *l*-acetylasparagine to *l*-2-imidazolidone-5-carboxylic acid (15% yield) from which *l*(+) β-aminoalanine (60% yield) is obtained on acid hydrolysis.[37]

Higher amidic acids, like the higher monoamides, are best treated with sodium methoxide and bromine in methanol solution instead of with aqueous hypochlorite or hypobromite. Sebacamidic acid, for example, can be converted to ω-carbomethoxyaminopelargonic acid in 74% yield.[38]

The alicyclic amidic acids are converted easily to amino acids. With aqueous alkaline hypochlorite the isomeric truxillamidic and truxinamidic acids give the corresponding truxillamic and truxinamic acids in yields of 70–85%.[39]

α-Camphoramidic acid is converted by aqueous alkaline hypobromite to 3^c-amino-1^t,2,2-trimethylcyclopentane-1-carboxylic acid (formula III, p. 272) in 70% yield,[19] while the conversion of β-camphoramidic acid by this reagent to 3^c-amino-2,2,3^t-trimethylcyclopentane-1^c-carboxylic acid (formula II, p. 272) is quantitative.[18]

α-Hydroxy Amides. Aldehydes are obtained when aqueous sodium hypochlorite acts on amides of α-hydroxyacids.

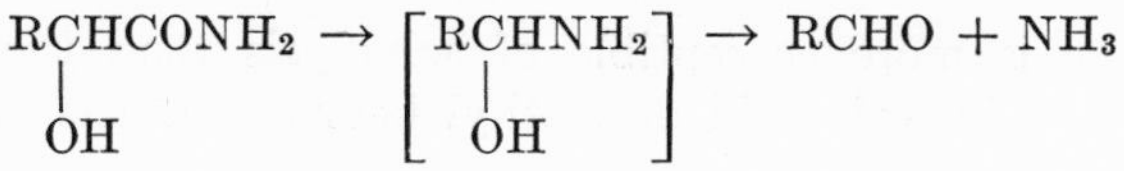

$$\begin{array}{l}\mathrm{RCHCONH_2}\\ \;|\\ \mathrm{OH}\end{array} \rightarrow \left[\begin{array}{l}\mathrm{RCHNH_2}\\ \;|\\ \mathrm{OH}\end{array}\right] \rightarrow \mathrm{RCHO + NH_3}$$

[34] Weidel and Roithner, *Monatsh.*, **17**, 183 (1896).

[35] Rinkes, *Rec. trav. chim.*, **46**, 268 (1927).

[36] Freudenberg, *Ber.*, **47**, 2027 (1914).

[37] Karrer, *Helv. Chim. Acta*, **6**, 415 (1923).

[38] Flaschentrager and Gebhart, *Z. physiol. Chem.*, **192**, 250 (1930).

[39] (*a*) Stoermer and Schmidt, *Ber.*, **58**, 2716 (1925); (*b*) Stoermer and Schenk, *Ber.*, **60**, 2575 (1927); (*c*) Stoermer and Schenk, *Ber.*, **61**, 2312 (1928); (*d*) Stoermer and Keller *Ber.*, **64**, 2783 (1931); (*e*) Stoermer and Asbrand, *Ber.*, **64**, 2793 (1931).

From *d*-gluconamide, *d*-arabinose results in 50% yield. *l*-Arabinonamide gives a 30% yield of *l*-erythrose. Similarly, benzaldehyde has been obtained from mandelamide.[40]

Ethylenic Amides. α,β-Unsaturated amides give satisfactory yields of urethans when treated with methanolic sodium hypochlorite.[41] Thus, cinnamic amide gives a 70% yield of methylstyrylcarbamate

$$C_6H_5CH{=}CHCONH_2 \xrightarrow[CH_3OH]{NaOCl} C_6H_5CH{=}CHNHCO_2CH_3$$

Hydrolysis of these urethans leads directly to aldehydes, as would be expected, and therefore is best carried out in an acid medium.

Poor yields attend the conversion of β,γ- and γ,δ-unsaturated amides to the corresponding unsaturated amines. Only 20% of the theoretical amount of 1-amino-2-cycloheptene was obtained from 2-cycloheptene-1-carboxamide.[42] A yield of less than 15% is reported in the preparation of 2,3,3-trimethyl-1-cyclopentenylcarbinylamine from 2,3,3-trimethyl-1-cyclopentenylacetamide.[43] In the conversion of 2,2-dimethyl-3-methylenecyclopentanecarboxamide to the corresponding amine, the amine was isolated in a yield of only 40%.[44]

α,β-Acetylenic Amides. With α,β-acetylenic amides the Hofmann reaction leads to the formation of nitriles.[45]

$$RC{\equiv}CCONH_2 \rightarrow [RC{\equiv}CNH_2] \rightarrow RCH_2C{\equiv}N$$

N-Chloro-2-octynamide, for example, on treatment with barium hydroxide gives a 70% yield of enanthonitrile.

α-Keto Amides. The expected products of the Hofmann reaction of α-keto amides ($RCOCONH_2$) would be amides ($RCONH_2$). For the only amide of this type investigated (benzoylformamide), however, it appears that in the intermediate aroyl isocyanate ($C_6H_5C({=}O){-}N{=}C{=}O$) the $C({=}O){-}N$ linkage is more susceptible of solvolysis than the $-N{=}C-$ linkage, so that benzoic acid or methyl benzoate is the only product isolated.[46]

[40] Weerman, *Rec. trav. chim.*, **37,** 16 (1918).

[41] Weerman, (*a*) *Ann.*, **401,** 1 (1913); (*b*) *Rec. trav. chim.*, **37,** 2 (1918).

[42] Willstätter, *Ann.*, **317,** 243 (1901).

[43] Blaise and Blanc, *Bull. soc. chim.*, [3] **21,** 973 (1899).

[44] Forster, *J. Chem. Soc.*, **79,** 119 (1901).

[45] Rinkes, *Rec. trav. chim.*, **39,** 704 (1920).

[46] Rinkes, *Rec. trav. chim.*, (*a*) **39,** 200 (1920); (*b*) **45,** 819 (1926); (*c*) **48,** 960 (1929).

Aromatic and Heterocyclic Amides

Aromatic Amides and Phthalimides. Benzamide, naphthamide, and their homologs are converted smoothly by aqueous alkaline hypobromite solutions to the corresponding aromatic amines. If free or methylated phenolic hydroxyl groups are present in aromatic amides, however, halogenation of the ring is likely to occur with serious lowering of the yield. This effect is minimized by the use of hypochlorite and a large excess of alkali, the rearrangement then being rapid enough to compete favorably with the side reaction of halogenation. Thus veratric amide is converted by alkaline hypochlorite to 4-aminoveratrole in 80% yield.[47] With the same reagent salicylamide gives an 80% yield of 4,5-benzoxazolone, from which *o*-aminophenol results in 90% yield on acid hydrolysis.[48]

Extensive application of the reaction has been made in the production of anthranilic acid from phthalimide and of substituted anthranilic acids from substituted phthalimides. While isomeric anthranilic acids theoretically are derivable from certain phthalimides, one usually predominates or forms exclusively. Generally it is possible to correlate the predominance of one product over the other with the known electronic and vicinal effects of the substituents. Formation of an N-haloimide is followed by hydrolytic fission of one of the $\overset{\text{O}}{\overset{\|}{\text{C}}}\text{—N}$ bonds in the alkaline medium to generate a carboxylate ion and an N-haloamide ion. Ejection of a halide ion X^- and rearrangement lead to the ultimate production of the anion of the amino acid.

$$\begin{array}{l}>\text{C—CO}\\ \;\;|\qquad\quad>\text{NH}\\ >\text{C—CO}\end{array} \rightarrow \begin{array}{l}>\text{C—CO}\\ \;\;|\qquad\quad>\text{NX}\\ >\text{C—CO}\end{array} \rightarrow \begin{array}{l}>\text{CCO}_2^-\\ \;\;|\\ >\text{CCONX}^-\end{array} \rightarrow \begin{array}{l}>\text{CCO}_2^-\\ \;\;|\\ >\text{CNH}_2\end{array}$$

Since it is known that the hydrolysis of benzamides is facilitated by substituents which withdraw electrons from the $\overset{\text{O}}{\overset{\|}{\text{C}}}\text{—N}$ linkage into the ring,[49] it is evident that in the Hofmann reaction of 4-nitrophthalimide,

[47] Buck and Ide, *Org. Syntheses, Coll. Vol.* **2,** 44 (1943).

[48] Graebe and Rostowzev, *Ber.*, **35,** 2747 (1902).

[49] Hammett, "Physical Organic Chemistry," McGraw-Hill Book Co., New York, 1940, p. 188.

for example, the nitro group by withdrawing electrons at position 1 will cause preferential hydrolysis of the $-\overset{O}{\overset{\|}{C}}-N$ linkage at this point, with

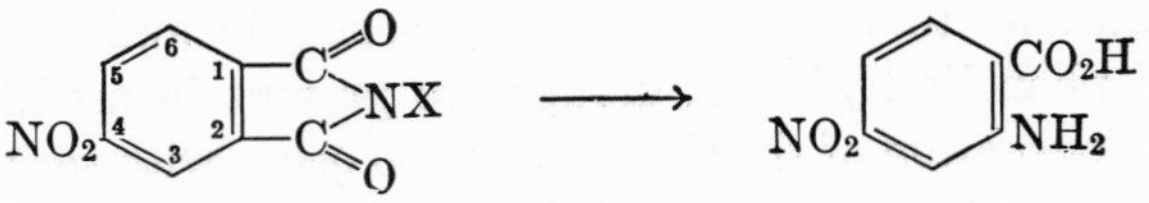

NO₂ (4) phthalimide ring (positions 1–6) C=O, NX, C=O ⟶ NO₂ ring CO₂H, NH₂

subsequent rearrangement at position 2. Actually, 70% of the theoretical amount of the expected 4-nitroanthranilic acid is formed.[50, 51] Similarly, the expected product from 3-nitrophthalic acid, 6-nitroan-

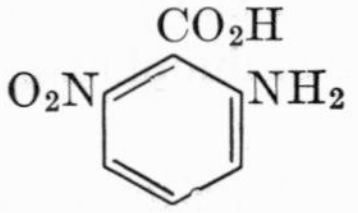

CO_2H, O_2N, NH_2

thranilic acid (i.e., hydrolysis at position 2), is obtained in 80% yield. Furthermore, it is known that a methoxyl group in the *ortho* position to the $\overset{O}{\overset{\|}{C}}-N$ linkage in a substituted benzamide is much less effective in promoting hydrolysis than the same substituent in the *para*-position. In the Hofmann reaction of 3,4-dimethoxyphthalimide, hydrolysis of the $\overset{O}{\overset{\|}{C}}-N$ linkage should occur preferentially at the 1-position. Only the ex-

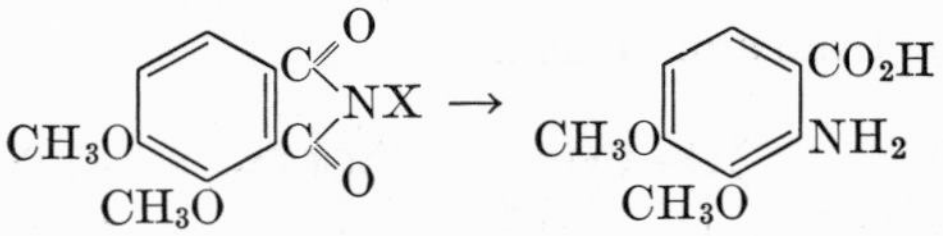

CH_3O, CH_3O ring C=O, NX, C=O → CH_3O, CH_3O ring CO_2H, NH_2

pected 3,4-dimethoxyanthranilic acid is formed (35% yield).[52]

Successful application of the reaction has also been made to the half-amides of aromatic dicarboxylic acids. For example, 2-carboxy-4,5-dichlorobenzamide is converted readily by the action of alkaline sodium hypochlorite to 4,5-dichloroanthranilic acid.[53]

Aryl Semicarbazides and Ureas. An interesting application of the Hofmann reaction has been made to aryl semicarbazides

[50] Seidel and Bittner, *Monatsh.*, **23**, 418 (1902).

[51] Kahn, *Ber.*, **35**, 471 (1902).

[52] Kuhn, *Ber.*, **28**, 809 (1905).

[53] Villiger, *Ber.*, **42**, 3547 (1909).

$(ArNHNHCONH_2)$.[54] These compounds are first oxidized by hypochlorite to aryl diazocarboxamides

$$ArNHNHCONH_2 + OCl^- \rightarrow ArN{=}NCONH_2 + H_2O + Cl^-$$

which apparently undergo the usual rearrangement, the expected product $(ArN{=}N{-}NH_2)$, however, being immediately oxidized by hypochlorite to an aryl azide (ArN_3). The overall reaction thus consumes three molecules of hypochlorite.

$$ArNHNHCONH_2 + 3\,OCl^- + 2\,OH^- \rightarrow ArN_3 + 3H_2O + CO_2^{=} + 3Cl^-$$

Phenyl semicarbazide may be converted to phenyl azide in 30% yield. Further examples are included in the tables at the end of the chapter.

A limited application of the reaction has been made to aryl ureas. N-Chloro-N′-2,4,6-trichlorophenylurea gives 2,4,6-trichlorophenylhydrazine on treatment with alkali. N-Chloro-N′-phenylurea, however, gives *p*-chlorophenylhydrazine as the only isolable product. The yields in these reactions are reported as very poor.[55]

Heterocyclic Amides. Little use has been made of the reaction in the degradation of amides containing a five-membered heterocyclic ring attached to the carbonyl group. 1,2,2,5,5-Pentamethylpyrrolidine-3-carboxamide has been converted to 1,2,2,5,5-pentamethyl-3-aminopyrrolidine by the action of alkaline potassium hypobromite, but the yield is not stated.[56] An unsuccessful attempt to convert isoxazole-5-carboxamide to the corresponding amine also has been reported.[57]

The action of alkaline hypobromite, however, converts the isomeric picolinamides to aminopyridines,[58] and 3- and 4-quinolinecarboxamides to the corresponding aminoquinolines.[59] Pyridine-3,4-dicarboxamide has also been converted to 3-amino-4-picolinic acid.[60] The yields in these reactions, however, rarely have been given (see table).

SIDE REACTIONS

With higher aliphatic amides as well as with many alicyclic amides the most serious side reaction is that leading to the formation of alkyl acyl ureas (p. 269). As noted elsewhere (pp. 282, 269), this reaction is sup-

[54] Darapsky, *J. prakt. Chem.*, **76,** 433 (1907).

[55] Elliott, *J. Chem. Soc.*, **123,** 804 (1923).

[56] Pauli and Schaum, *Ber.*, **34,** 2289 (1901).

[57] Freri, *Gazz. chim. ital.*, **62,** 459 (1932).

[58] (*a*) Pollak, *Monatsh.*, **16,** 54 (1895); Phillips, *Ann.*, **288,** 263 (1895); (*b*) Camps, *Arch. Pharm.*, **240,** 354.

[59] Claus and Howitz, *J. prakt. Chem.*, [2] **50,** 237 (1894); Claus and Frobenius, *ibid.*, [2] **56,** 187 (1897); Wenzel, *Monatsh.*, **15,** 457 (1894).

[60] Gabriel and Coleman, *Ber.*, **35,** 2844, 3847 (1902).

pressed practically completely when the aqueous alkaline hypobromite solution customarily employed is replaced by methanolic sodium methoxide and bromine.

The low yields attending the rearrangement of unsaturated amides have been attributed [41a] to interference by the reaction just discussed coupled with oxidation of the double bond by the hypobromite present. The products of oxidation have not been isolated and characterized, however. Such reactions may be avoided with α,β-unsaturated amides by employing methanolic sodium hypochlorite (p. 282), but the action of this reagent on other types of unsaturated amides has yet to be investigated.

With aromatic amides, hydrolysis prior to rearrangement may occur to such an extent that the yield is lowered seriously. Amides like *p*-nitrobenzamide, having a substituent which withdraws electrons from the $\overset{O}{\overset{/\!/}{\mathrm{C}}}\text{—N}$ linkage, are particularly susceptible, since the withdrawal of electrons facilitates hydrolysis and inhibits rearrangement. The rearrangement, however, has a higher temperature coefficient than the hydrolysis, so that a high reaction temperature (90–100°) reduces the interference to negligible proportions.[9]

Substituents like hydroxyl or methoxyl facilitate rearrangement but also promote the halogenation of the ring, particularly by hypobromite. The use of sodium hypochlorite to circumvent such interfering ring halogenation has been discussed (pp. 274, 277).

THE CHOICE OF EXPERIMENTAL CONDITIONS AND PROCEDURES

The Use of Alkaline Sodium Hypobromite. The procedure most commonly adopted in carrying out the Hofmann reaction is essentially that developed by Hoogewerff and van Dorp,[2] in which the amide is first dissolved in a cold alkaline solution of sodium or potassium hypobromite. Rearrangement to the amine then occurs when the resulting solution is warmed to about 70°. A generally satisfactory procedure is the following: A solution of sodium hypobromite is prepared at 0° by adding bromine (0.6 cc.; 0.012 mole) to a solution of sodium hydroxide (2.4 g., 0.06 mole) in 20 cc. of water. To the cold solution is added the finely divided amide (0.01 mole), and the mixture is stirred until solution is complete. The solution is warmed to 70–80° to effect rearrangement, and after a short time (usually fifteen to twenty minutes) it is subjected to distillation with steam, the product being collected in a slight excess of dilute hydrochloric acid. Evaporation of the distillate gives the hydrochloride of the desired amine, which is freed from impurities by washing with ether. If the amine is not volatile with steam, it may be removed from the reaction mixture by extraction with ether and precipitated as the hydrochloride from a dry ethereal solution with gaseous hydrogen chloride. If the amine solidifies readily, it frequently can be removed from the reaction mixture by filtration and purified by recrystallization from a suitable solvent. Alternatively, if the benzoyl derivative of the amine is desired, as for example when the amine is to be used in the von Braun reaction, it can be prepared directly by stirring benzoyl chloride and sodium hydroxide into the reaction mixture after the rearrangement has been completed.[33a]

An excess of bromine amounting to 10–20% is advisable, since even with the most carefully prepared hypobromite solutions only 80 to 90% of the expected activity is realized.[61] A larger excess is usually to be avoided, however; otherwise the yield of amine may be seriously reduced by the side reactions discussed earlier. Occasionally, if the resulting amine is relatively unreactive toward the reagent, a considerable excess of both alkali and bromine may be employed without adverse consequences, sometimes, indeed, to considerable advantage when the amide is also unreactive. Thus 3,5-dinitro-2-α-naphthylbenzamide is converted most smoothly to 3,5-dinitro-2-α-naphthylaniline when the amide (0.01 mole) is treated with a hypobromite solution prepared from 0.16 mole (8 cc.) of bromine and 1.5 mole (60 g.) of sodium hydroxide in 100 cc. of water.[12] In addition, it must be emphasized that only hypobromite solutions which have been freshly prepared are satisfactory. Serious loss of activity always occurs on standing, even in the dark.[61]

The Use of Alkaline Sodium Hypochlorite. Although alkaline hypobromite solutions have been used more generally in the Hofmann reaction (primarily because bromine is easily weighed or measured volumetrically), sodium hypochlorite has certain advantages. The use of this reagent permits a lower reaction temperature and in many instances results in a distinctly higher yield of the desired amine, particularly when the amide possesses either protected or unprotected aromatic hydroxyl groups.[48, 62] The maximum yields obtainable with hypobromite and with hypochlorite in the conversion of some phthalimides to the corresponding anthranilic acids, summarized in the accompanying table, clearly show the advantage of using sodium hypochlorite. Distinctly better results with hypochlorite are reported also in the conversion of *o*-benzylbenzamide to *o*-benzylaniline. A 0.5 *N* solution of sodium hypochlorite, suitable for use in the Hofmann reaction, may be prepared by

[61] Graebe, *Ber.*, **35**, 2753 (1902).

[62] Cf. also Bayer and Co., Ger. pat. 233,551 [*Chem. Zentr.*, I, 1263, 1334 (1911)].

allowing 210 g. of concentrated hydrochloric acid (sp. gr. 1.17) to flow through a dropping funnel onto 16.15 g. of potassium permanganate in an ordinary distilling flask and collecting the chlorine so produced in 1 l. of cold 10% sodium hydroxide. When γ-truxillamidic acid is treated

Maximum Yields of Anthranilic Acids Obtainable from Phthalimides by the Hofmann Reaction with Alkaline Hypochlorite and Hypobromite [48]

	Hypochlorite	*Hypobromite*
Phthalimide	95%	75%
3,6-Dichlorophthalimide	90	73
Trichlorophthalimide	90	76
Tetrachlorophthalimide	98	95

with the theoretical quantity of this solution at 40° for two hours, γ-truxillamic acid is produced in 68% yield.[39b, 63] The concentration of sodium hypochlorite in the solution, which is reasonably stable in the dark, may be determined directly from the weight of permanganate used (10 g. $KMnO_4 \approx 11$ g. Cl_2).

Special Conditions for the Hofmann Reaction of Higher Aliphatic Amides and of α,β-Unsaturated Amides. As mentioned earlier, amides of the higher aliphatic acids are converted to the corresponding amines in poor yield by the usual technique. Such amides, however, are smoothly converted to methyl carbamates if bromine (1 mole) is added rapidly with thorough mixing to a methanolic solution of the amide (1 mole) containing sodium methoxide (2 moles).

$$RCONH_2 + Br_2 + 2NaOCH_3 \rightarrow RNHCO_2CH_3 + 2NaBr + CH_3OH$$

Warming the solution completes the reaction in a few minutes. The urethan is isolated easily from the reaction mixture, and the amine may be obtained in good yield by saponification with sodium, potassium, or calcium hydroxide (p. 283).[4b, 25]

A somewhat similar procedure is recommended for the degradation of amides of α,β-unsaturated acids. The amide, dissolved in methanol, is treated with the theoretical amount of a solution 0.8 *M* in both sodium hypochlorite and sodium hydroxide. The conversion of the α,β-unsaturated amide to the urethan (which in many instances crystallizes directly from the reaction mixture) occurs rapidly when the solution is warmed on the water bath. Hydrolysis of the urethan in acid medium then gives the corresponding aldehyde in good yield. This method has been applied successfully to the amides of several types of α,β-unsaturated acids.[41, 42]

[63] Bernstein and Wallis, *J. Org. Chem.*, **7**, 261 (1942).

EXPERIMENTAL PROCEDURES

Neopentylamine.[15] Two and four-tenths cubic centimeters of bromine is added dropwise to a solution of 7.2 g. of sodium hydroxide in 60 cc. of water cooled to 0°. To the clear yellow solution is added immediately 3.50 g. (0.0304 mole) of β,β-dimethylbutyramide (m.p. 131°), and stirring is continued for one hour after the amide dissolves. The reaction mixture is then warmed slowly. At room temperature a yellow turbidity appears; at about 50° the solution becomes colorless and an oily layer separates. One hundred cubic centimeters of water is added, and the mixture is distilled until no more oil comes over. The distillate is collected in dilute hydrochloric acid. The yellow solution becomes colorless on heating and on evaporation yields neopentylamine hydrochloride as a white crystalline residue. The residue is dissolved in absolute ethanol, and the solution is evaporated to dryness and washed with ether. The product is dried to constant weight (3.60 g., 94%) in vacuum; m.p. (dec.) 273°.

Pentadecylamine.[4b] A solution of 25.5 g. (0.10 mole) of palmitamide in 90 cc. of methanol is mixed with a solution of 4.6 g. (0.20 atom) of sodium in 145 cc. of methanol. To this solution is added with thorough mixing 16 g. (0.10 mole) of bromine. The resulting solution is heated for ten minutes on the water bath, after which it is rendered just acid with acetic acid. The methanol is then removed. The product is washed with water to remove sodium bromide. It is then dissolved in ligroin. The ligroin solution is filtered to remove traces of palmitamide, the ligroin is removed by evaporation, and the product is recrystallized twice from ethanol. The yield of pure methyl pentadecylcarbamate (m.p. 61–62°) is 24–27 g. (84–94%).

The urethan (20 g.) is thoroughly mixed with 70 g. of calcium oxide to which 30 cc. of water has been added. The mixture is distilled, and the distillate is taken up in ligroin. The ligroin solution is first dried over potassium hydroxide, then over sodium. Finally the solvent is removed by evaporation, and the product is distilled twice over sodium. The yield of pure pentadecylamine (m.p. 36.5°; b.p. 298–301°) is almost quantitative.

2-Methyl-1,4-diaminobutane.[33a] Fifty-one grams of bromine is stirred into a mixture of 71 g. of sodium hydroxide, 142 cc. of water, and 200 g. of ice. To the resulting solution 25 g. (0.16 mole) of β-methyladipamide is added in small portions with stirring. The mixture is warmed on the water bath until clear, and heating is continued until four hours in all have elapsed. The solution is then cooled, filtered, and shaken with 60 g. of benzoyl chloride. The crude dibenzoyl derivative is removed by filtration and recrystallized twice from 95% ethanol. The yield of pure product is 35 g. (72%).

The hydrochloride of 2-methyl-1,4-diaminobutane is obtained readily by heating the dibenzoyl derivative in a sealed tube for three hours at 130° with an excess of concentrated hydrochloric acid.

***l*-Isoserine.**[36] To a solution of 20 g. (0.15 mole) of *l*-β-malamidic acid in 530 cc. of 0.0286 *N* barium hydroxide is added a solution of 25 g. of bromine in 650 cc. of water. After five minutes the clear, reddish brown solution is poured into 2400 cc. of 0.0286 *N* barium hydroxide. The color disappears. Over a period of one hour the temperature of the reaction mixture is gradually raised to 90°, at which temperature it is kept for an additional hour. It is then boiled for a short time, saturated with carbon dioxide, and the solution finally decanted from the precipitate. The hot solution is treated with a slight excess of sulfuric acid and then boiled for one hour with a large amount of lead dioxide until the evolution of ammonia ceases and the hydrobromic acid is destroyed. The filtered solution is freed from lead with hydrogen sulfide and evaporated to a volume of 50 cc. Hot ethanol is then added until a slight turbidity appears, and the mixture is finally poured cautiously into 500 cc. of boiling ethanol. *l*-Isoserine precipitates immediately. Eight grams of a crude product is obtained which on recrystallization from water gives 7 g. (45%) of pure *l*-isoserine; m.p. (dec.) 200°.

γ-Truxillamic Acid.[39b, 63] A 0.5 *N* solution of sodium hypochlorite is prepared by allowing 21.0 g. of hydrochloric acid (sp. gr. 1.17) to flow through a dropping funnel onto 1.62 g. of potassium permanganate in an ordinary distilling flask. The chlorine so produced is collected in 100 cc. of cold aqueous 10% sodium hydroxide. To 2.95 g. (0.010 mole) of γ-truxillamidic acid is added 40 cc. of this solution. The mixture is then kept at 35–40° for two hours. At the end of this time it is cooled to room temperature, neutralized with dilute hydrochloric acid, and finally made just basic to litmus with dilute sodium hydroxide solution. The solution is filtered to remove a small amount of insoluble material, and carbon dioxide is passed through the filtrate until a precipitate begins to form (at this point, if too much sodium hydroxide solution has been added, it is sometimes necessary to add a few drops of hydrochloric acid to induce precipitation). Carbon dioxide is then passed through the solution for an additional hour, at the end of which time 2.18 g. (68% of pure γ-truxillamic acid trihydrate has separated. The dried product is insoluble in most solvents; it can be characterized as the methyl ester, m.p. 83.5–84°. By acidification of the aqueous mother liquor, unchanged γ-truxillamidic acid may be recovered.

***m*-Bromoaniline.**[64] A solution of 10.2 g. of potassium hydroxide and 10.8 g. of bromine in 100 cc. of water is poured on 12 g. (0.060 mole) of *m*-bromobenzamide. The mixture is then added to a solution of 14.4 g. of potassium hydroxide in 25 cc. of water. The temperature is maintained at 70–75° for about forty-five minutes. Finally the amine is distilled with steam. The yield of crude *m*-bromoaniline so obtained is 8.9 g. (87%); it distils without decomposition at 250°.

Phenylacetaldehyde.[41] An alkaline solution of sodium hypochlorite is prepared by passing 55 g. of chlorine into a mixture of 600 g. of cracked ice and a cold solution of 100 g. of sodium hydroxide (95%) in 150 cc. of water. Water is then added until the total volume of the solution is 1 l. (The solution is best kept in the dark until used.) To a solution of 14.7 g. (0.1 mole) of cinnamic amide (m.p. 147°) in 125 cc. of methanol is added 130 cc. of the stock solution of sodium hypochlorite. The mixture is warmed on the water bath. A thick sludge of crystals soon forms. The mixture is cooled rapidly and filtered, and the crystals are washed with dilute ethanol and with water. The yield of methyl styrylcarbamate so obtained is 13 g. (70%), m.p. 117–118°.

Twenty-five grams of the urethan is dissolved in 100 cc. of warm ethanol, and to the solution is added gradually 48 cc. of 6 *N* sulfuric acid. Carbon dioxide is evolved, and some urethan precipitates, but redissolves quickly when the solution is warmed. When all the sulfuric acid has been added, the aldehyde is distilled at once with steam. The product so obtained is a colorless oil, b.p. 90–92°/20 mm. The yield is good.

TABULAR SURVEY OF PRODUCTS AND YIELDS OBTAINED IN THE HOFMANN REACTION OF AMIDES

The following table summarizes examples of the Hofmann reaction reported prior to September 1942. The amides are listed by their molecular formulas in the order of increasing number of carbon atoms. Within a group having the same number of carbon atoms, the listing is arranged so that amides having one oxygen and one nitrogen atom appear first in the order of increasing hydrogen content, next those having two or more oxygen atoms and one nitrogen atom in the same order, then those having one oxygen atom and two nitrogen atoms and so on, until finally the list is concluded with amides containing other elements besides carbon, hydrogen, oxygen, and nitrogen. An exception to this order is to be found in the listing of N-bromoamides which have first been prepared in a pure state and then treated with aqueous or alcoholic

[64] Beckmann and Correns, *Ber.*, **55**, 850 (1922).

alkali to effect the rearrangement. These are listed in parentheses under the parent amides. The second column lists the name of the amide, and the third column describes the hypohalite used. Unless otherwise noted, water is the solvent, and the requisite amount of the appropriate alkali metal hydroxide is present in the reaction mixture. For the N-bromoamides, the hydroxide or alkoxide used to effect rearrangement is listed in this column, the solvent being water for hydroxides or the appropriate alcohol for alkoxides.

The name of the product is given in the fourth column. The product is usually an amine or its hydrochloride, between which no differentiation is made in this table. Occasionally the reaction affords first a urethan or urea, which is then hydrolyzed to an amine or an aldehyde. When hydrolysis has occurred the initial and final products are listed in the column under subdivisions (*a*) and (*b*).

The yields reported in the fifth column, based upon the weight of amide initially taken, are given to the nearest 5% or are reported only as good (G) or poor (P). A dash indicates that no yield was reported. If the reaction was conducted in two stages, subdivisions (*a*) and (*b*) are again employed: under (*a*) is given the yield of urethan (or urea) based on the amount of amide taken; under (*b*), the yield of amine (or aldehyde) based on product (*a*).

PRODUCTS AND YIELDS OBTAINED IN HOFMANN REACTIONS OF AMIDES

Amide: Formula	Amide: Name or Structural Formula	Reagent	Product	Yield	Reference *
		C_1–C_3			
CH_4ON_2	Urea	NaOCl, NaOH	Hydrazine	60%	65
C_2H_5ON	Acetamide	KOBr; $Ca(OBr)_2$; NaOBr	Methylamine	70–80%	1*c*, 66
		NaOBr(CH_3OH)	Methyl methylcarbamate	—	67
(C_2H_4ONBr)	N-Bromoacetamide	$NaOC_2H_5$	Ethyl methylcarbamate	—	3
($C_2H_3ONBrNa$)	N-Bromoacetamide, sodium salt	NH_3	Methylurea	80%	3
C_2H_4ONCl	Chloroacetamide	KOBr	N-Chloromethyl-N′-chloroacetylurea	—	1*e*
C_3H_7ON	Propionamide	KOBr	Ethylamine	85%	1*c*
(C_3H_6ONBr)	N-Bromopropionamide	$NaOC_2H_5$	Ethyl ethylcarbamate	80%	3
($C_3H_6ONBrNa$)	N-Bromopropionamide, sodium salt	NH_3	Ethylurea	30%	3
		C_4–C_5			
C_4H_7ON	Cyclopropanecarboxamide	KOBr	Cyclopropylamine	—	68
C_4H_9ON	*n*-Butyramide	KOBr	*n*-Propylamine	90%	1*c*
	Isobutyramide	KOBr	Isopropylamine	90%	1*c*
(C_4H_8ONBr)	N-Bromoisobutyramide	$NaOC_2H_5$	Ethyl isopropylcarbamate	—	3
($C_4H_7ONBrNa$)	N-Bromoisobutyramide, sodium salt	—	Isopropyl isocyanate	—	3
C_4H_8ONBr	α-Bromoisobutyramide	NaOBr	Acetone	55%	170

$C_4H_3O_2N$	Maleinimide	NaOCl	CH═CH O═C NH O—C═O	40–45%	35
$C_4H_5O_2N$	Succinimide	KOBr	β-Alanine	40–45%	69, 70, 71, 72
$(C_4H_4O_2NBr)$	N-Bromosuccinimide	$NaOCH_3$	$CH_3OCONHCH_2CH_2CO_2CH_3$	40%	70
$C_4H_9O_2N$	Ethoxyacetamide	KOBr	N-Ethoxymethyl-N′-ethoxy-acetylurea	—	1*e*
$C_4H_5O_3N$	Maleinamidic acid	NaOCl	Formylacetic acid	85% †	35
$C_4H_7O_4N$	*l*-β-Malamidic acid	$Ba(OBr)_2$, $Ba(OH)_2$	*l*-Isoserine	50%	36
	Ethyloxamate	KOBr	Ethyl carbamate	P	73
$C_4H_6O_2N_2$	Maleinamide	NaOCl	Uracil	55%	35
$C_4H_8O_2N_2$	Succinamide	KOBr	(*a*) Dihydrouracil (*b*)β-Alanine	(*a*) — (*b*) —	34
C_5H_9ON	2-Pentenoamide	$NaOCl(CH_3OH)$	(*a*) Methyl 1-butenylcarbamate (*b*) Butyraldehyde	(*a*) — (*b*) —	46*c*
	Cyclobutanecarboxamide	KOBr	Cyclobutylamine	—	74, 75
		$NaOCl(CH_3OH)$	(*a*) Methyl cyclobutylcarbamate (*b*) Cyclobutylamine	(*a*) — (*b*) 20%	76
		$NaOBr(CH_3OH)$	(*a*) Methyl cyclobutylcarbamate (*b*) Cyclobutylamine	(*a*) 90% (*b*) —	77
C_5H_8ONBr	α-Bromocyclobutanecarboxamide	NaOBr	Cyclobutanone	P	171
$C_5H_{11}ON$	Isovaleramide	KOBr	Isobutylamine	90%	1*c*
	Trimethylacetamide	KOBr	*tert*-Butylamine	45–65%	20, 78
$C_5H_{11}O_5N$	*l*-Arabinonamide	NaOCl	*l*-Erythrose	30% ‡	40
$C_5H_{10}O_2N_2$	Methylsuccinamide	KOBr	α-Methyl-β-alanine	—	34
$C_5H_9O_3N_2Br$	N-Bromo-β-carbomethoxyamino-propionic acid	$NaOCH_3$	1,2-Dicarbomethoxyaminoethane	—	79

* References 65–173 are listed on pp. 305–306. † As semicarbazone. ‡ As benzylphenylhydrazone.

PRODUCTS AND YIELDS OBTAINED IN HOFMANN REACTIONS OF AMIDES—*Continued*

C_6

Amide		Reagent	Product	Yield	Reference *
Formula	Name or Structural Formula				
$C_6H_{13}ON$	Caproamide	KOBr	*n*-Amylamine	90%	1*c*
	Isocaproamide	KOBr	Isoamylamine	90%	1*c*
	β,β-Dimethylbutyramide	NaOBr	Neopentylamine	90%	15
($C_6H_{12}ONBr$)	N-Bromo-2-ethylbutyramide	NaOH	3-Aminopentane	6%	80
$C_6H_{13}O_6N$	*d*-Gluconamide	NaOCl	*d*-Arabinose	50% †	40
	d-Galactonamide	NaOCl	*d*-Lyxose	30% ‡	40
	l-Mannonamide	NaOCl	*l*-Arabinose	60% †	40
$C_6H_6ON_2$	α-Picolinamide	KOBr	2-Aminopyridine	—	58*b*, 81
	Nicotinamide	KOBr	3-Aminopyridine	—	58
	γ-Picolinamide	KOBr	4-Aminopyridine	—	58*b*
$C_6H_{12}O_2N_2$	Adipamide	NaOCl	1,4-Diaminobutane	—	33*d*
		NaOBr	1,4-Diaminobutane	60%	33*e*
$C_6H_9O_2N_2$	*l*(−)Acetylasparagine	$Ba(OBr)_2$	(*a*) *l*(−)2-Imidazolidone-5-carboxylic acid	(*a*) 15%	37
			(*b*) *l*(+)β-Aminoalanine	(*b*) 60%	
$C_6H_5ON_2Cl$	6-Chloronicotinamide	KOBr	3-Amino-6-chloropyridine	50%	82
$C_6H_4ON_2Cl_2$	3,5-Dichloro-α-picolinamide	NaOBr	2-Amino-3,5-dichloropyridine	—	83
$C_6H_3ON_2Cl_3$	3,4,5-Trichloro-α-picolinamide	NaOBr	2-Amino-3,4,5-trichloropyridine	—	84

		C_7			
C_7H_7ON	Benzamide				
(C_7H_6ONCl)	N-Chlorobenzamide	NaOH	(*a*) Diphenylurea (*b*) Aniline	(*a*) 90% (*b*) 90%	48
(C_7H_6ONBr)	N-Bromobenzamide	KOH	Aniline	95	9*a*
$C_7H_{11}ON$	1-Cyclohexenecarboxamide	NaOCl(CH_3OH)	Cyclohexanone	—	46*b*
$C_7H_{13}ON$	2-Methylcyclopentanecarboxamide	NaOBr	2-Methyl-1-aminocyclopentane	—	85
$C_7H_{13}ON$	Cyclopentylacetamide	NaOBr	Cyclopentylcarbinylamine	—	86
$C_7H_{15}ON$	Enanthamide	KOBr	*n*-Hexylamine	70%	1*c*, 2*b*
	2-Methylcapramide	KOBr	2-Methyl-*n*-amylamine	—	87
$C_7H_7O_2N$	*o*-Salicylamide	NaOCl	(*a*) 4,5-Benzoxazolone-2 (*b*) *o*-Aminophenol	(*a*) 80% (*b*) 70%	48
	p-Hydroxybenzamide	NaOBr	7,9-Dibromo-4,5-benzoxazolone-2	35%	29
		Ba(OBr)$_2$	2,6-Dibromo-4-aminophenol	70%	29
		KOBr	2,4,6-Tribromo-3-aminophenol	—	29
	2-Furanacrylamide	NaOCl(CH_3OH)	(*a*) Methyl furfurylcarbamate (*b*) 2-Furanacetaldehyde	(*a*) 50% (*b*) 40%	46*a*
$C_7H_8ON_2$	6-Methylnicotinamide	NaOCl	2-Methyl-5-aminopyridine	55%	89
$C_7H_{14}ON_2$	Hexahydroanthranilamide	KOBr	1,2-Cyclohexanediamine	—	88
$C_7H_4O_2N_2$	Pyridine-3,4-dicarboximide	NaOBr	β-Amino-γ-picolinic acid	—	90
$C_7H_{14}O_2N_2$	β-Methyladipamide	NaOBr	2-Methyl-1,4-diaminobutane	70%	33*a*, *d*
	Diethylmalonamide	NaOCl	C,C-Diethylhydantoin	—	36
$C_7H_6O_3N_2$	2-Carboxypyridine-3-carboxamide	NaOBr	β-Amino-α-picolinic acid	—	91
	3-Carboxypyridine-2-carboxamide	NaOBr	2-Aminonicotinic acid	—	92
	3-Carboxypyridine-4-carboxamide	NaOBr	4-Aminonicotinic acid	—	93
	4-Carboxypyridine-3-carboxamide	NaOBr	β-Amino-γ-picolinic acid	—	60

* References 65–173 are listed on pp. 305–306. † As diphenylhydrazone. ‡ As *p*-bromophenylhydrazone.

Products and Yields Obtained in Hofmann Reactions of Amides—*Continued*

Amide		Reagent	Product	Yield	Reference *
Formula	Name or Structural Formula				
	Nitrobenzamide				
($C_7H_5O_3N_2Br$)	N-Bromo-*o*-nitrobenzamide	KOH	*o*-Nitraniline	—	9*a*
	N-Bromo-*m*-nitrobenzamide	KOH	*m*-Nitraniline	70%	9*a*
		$NaOCH_3$	Methyl *m*-nitrophenylcarbamate	90%	79, 94
		$NaOC_2H_5$	(*a*) Ethyl *m*-nitrophenylcarbamate (*b*) *m*-Nitraniline	(*a*) — (*b*) 55%	94
	N-Bromo-*p*-nitrobenzamide	KOH	*p*-Nitraniline	50–90%	9*a*
		$NaOC_2H_5$	Methyl *p*-nitrophenylcarbamate	—	94
$C_7H_9ON_3$	Phenylsemicarbazide	NaOCl	Phenyl azide	55%	
$C_7H_7O_2N_3$	Pyridine-3,4-dicarboxamide	KOBr	*β*-Amino-*γ*-picolinic acid	—	60
$C_7H_8O_3N_4$	*p*-Nitrophenylsemicarbazide	NaOCl	*p*-Nitrophenyl azide	35%	
C_7H_6ONBr	*m*-Bromobenzamide	KOBr	*m*-Bromoaniline	90%	64
	p-Bromobenzamide	KOBr	*p*-Bromoaniline	G	64
($C_7H_5ONBr_2$)	N-Bromo-*m*-bromobenzamide	KOH	*m*-Bromoaniline	90%	9*a*
		$NaOCH_3$	Methyl *m*-bromophenylcarbamate	90%	79
C_7H_6ONCl	Chlorobenzamide				
($C_7H_5ONBrCl$)	N-Bromo-*o*-chlorobenzamide	KOH	*o*-Chloroaniline	—	9*a*
	N-Bromo-*m*-chlorobenzamide	KOH	*m*-Chloroaniline	90%	9*a*
	N-Bromo-*p*-chlorobenzamide	KOH	*p*-Chloroaniline	95%	9*a*
C_7H_6ONF	Fluorobenzamide				
(C_7H_5ONClF)	N-Chloro-*o*-fluorobenzamide	$Ba(OH)_2$	*o*-Fluoroaniline	89%	95
$C_7H_5ONBr_2$	2,6-Dibromobenzamide	KOBr	2,6-Dibromoaniline	—	96
$C_7H_4ONBr_3$	2,4,6-Tribromobenzamide	KOBr	2,4,6-Tribromoaniline	—	96

$C_7H_7O_4N_5$	*o*-Sulfobenzamide	NaOBr	*o*-Sulfanilic acid	—	97
$C_7H_7ON_2Cl$	N-Chloro-N′-phenylurea	NaOH	*p*-Chlorophenylhydrazine	P	55
$C_7H_4ON_2Cl_4$	N-Chloro-N′-2,4,6-trichlorophenylurea	NaOH	2,4,6-Trichlorophenylhydrazine	P	55
$C_7H_8ON_3Br$	*p*-Bromophenylsemicarbazide	NaOCl	*p*-Bromophenyl azide	75%	54
		C_8			
C_8H_9ON	Phenylacetamide	KOBr	Benzylamine	60–85%	1*e*, 2*a*
(C_8H_8ONBr)	N-Bromo-*p*-toluamide	KOH	*p*-Toluidine	98%	9*a*
$C_8H_{\ 3}ON$	2-Cycloheptenecarboxamide	KOBr	1-Amino-2-cycloheptene	20%	42
	2,5-*Endo*methylenecyclohexane-1-carboxamide		1-Amino-2,5-*endo*methylenecyclohexane	—	98
$(C_8H_{12}ONCl)$	N-Chloro-2-octynamide	$Ba(OH)_2$	Enanthonitrile	70%	35
$C_8H_{15}ON$	1-Methylcyclohexanecarboxamide	$NaOBr(CH_3OH)$	(*a*) Methyl 1-methylcyclohexylcarbamate (*b*) 1-Methyl-1-aminocyclohexane	(*a*) — (*b*) —	27
	Hexahydro-*o*-toluamide	$NaOBr(CH_3OH)$	(*a*) Methyl 2-methylcyclohexylcarbamate (*b*) 2-Methyl-1-aminocyclohexane	(*a*) 95% (*b*) 75%	27
	Hexahydro-*m*-toluamide	$NaOBr(CH_3OH)$	(*a*) Methyl 3-methylcyclohexylcarbamate (*b*) 3-Methyl-1-aminocyclohexane	(*a*) 95% (*b*) 70%	27
	Hexahydro-*p*-toluamide	$NaOBr(CH_3OH)$	(*a*) Methyl 4-methylcyclohexylcarbamate (*b*) 4-Methyl-1-aminocyclohexane	(*a*) — (*b*) 90%	27

* References 65–173 are listed on pp. 305–306.

Products and Yields Obtained in Hofmann Reactions of Amides—*Continued*

Amide		Reagent	Product	Yield	Reference *
Formula	Name or Structural Formula				
	Cyclohexylacetamide	$NaOBr(CH_3OH)$	(*a*) Methyl hexahydrobenzylcarbamate	(*a*) —	27
			(*b*) Hexahydrobenzylamine	(*b*) 70%	
		NaOBr	Hexahydrobenzylamine	—	99
	Cycloheptanecarboxamide	NaOBr	Cycloheptylamine	95%	172
$C_8H_{17}ON$	Caprylamide	KOBr	*n*-Heptylamine	30–65%	1*c*, 2*b*
	β-Methylenanthamide	KOBr	2-Methyl-1-aminohexane	—	100
	α-Ethylcaproamide	NaOBr	3-Aminoheptane	—	101
$(C_8H_{16}ONBr)$	N-Bromo-α-propylvaleramide	NaOH	4-Aminoheptane	85%	80
$C_8H_5O_2N$	Phthalimide	KOBr	Anthranilic acid	75–85%	2*c*, 48
		NaOCl	Anthranilic acid	95%	48
		$NaOCl(C_2H_5OH)$	Methyl anthranilate	70%	102
$C_8H_7O_2N$	Benzoylformamide	NaOCl	Benzoic acid	—	46*c*
		$NaOCl(CH_3OH)$	Methyl benzoate	—	46*c*
$C_8H_9O_2N$	Mandelamide	NaOCl	Benzaldehyde	—	40
	o-Methoxybenzamide †	NaOCl	*o*-Methoxyaniline †	G	48
$(C_8H_8O_2NBr)$	N-Bromoanisamide	KOH	*p*-Anisidine	—	9*a*
$C_8H_7O_3N$	Piperonylamide	NaOBr	*nor*-Piperonylamine	30–40%	103
$C_8H_{16}O_2N_2$	Suberamide	NaOBr	1,6-Diaminohexane	—	33*c*
$C_8H_8O_2N_2$	Benzoylurea	NaOCl	Benzoylhydrazine	—	173

$C_8H_4O_4N_2$	3-Nitrophthalimide	NaOCl; $Ca(OCl)_2$	6-Nitroanthranilic acid	80%	50
		KOBr	6-Nitroanthranilic acid	—	51
			3-Nitroanthranilic acid	P	
	4-Nitrophthalimide	NaOCl	4-Nitroanthranilic acid	70%	50
			5-Nitroanthranilic acid	20%	50
$C_8H_6O_5N_2$	2-Carboxy-3-nitrobenzamide	KOBr	6-Nitroanthranilic acid	85%	51, 104
$C_8H_{11}ON_3$	*p*-Tolylsemicarbazide	NaOCl	*p*-Tolyl azide	75%	54
$C_8H_7ONBr_2$	2,6-Dibromo-4-methylbenzamide	NaOBr	2,6-Dibromo-4-methylaniline	—	96
$C_8H_4O_2NCl$	4-Chlorophthalimide	NaOCl	4-Chloroanthranilic acid	70%	105
			3-Chloroanthranilic acid	25%	105
$C_8H_3O_2NBr_2$	4,5-Dibromophthalimide	NaOCl	4,5-Dibromoanthranilic acid	—	106
$C_8H_3O_2NCl_2$	3,6-Dichlorophthalimide	NaOBr	3,6-Dichloroanthranilic acid	75%	48, 107
		NaOCl	3,6-Dichloroanthranilic acid	90%	53, 48
$C_8H_5O_3NCl$	4,5-Dichloro-2-carboxybenzamide	NaOCl	4,5-Dichloroanthranilic acid	—	53
$C_8H_2O_2NCl_3$	3,4,6-Trichlorophthalimide	NaOBr	3,4,6-Trichloroanthranilic acid	75%	48
		NaOCl	3,4,6-Trichloroanthranilic acid	90%	48, 108
$C_8HO_2NBr_4$	Tetrabromophthalimide	KOCl	Tetrabromoanthranilic acid	—	106
$C_8HO_2NBr_2Cl_2$	4,5-Dibromo-3,6-dichlorophthalimide	NaOCl	4,5-Dibromo-3,6-dichloroanthranilic acid	—	106
$C_8HO_2NCl_4$	Tetrachlorophthalimide	NaOBr; NaOCl	Tetrachloroanthranilic acid	95–100%	48, 109
		C_9			
C_9H_7ON	Phenylpropiolamide	$NaOCl(CH_3OH)$	Phenylacetonitrile	—	45
(C_9H_6ONCl)	N-Chlorophenylpropiolamide	$Ba(OH)_2$	Phenylacetonitrile	—	45
C_9H_9ON	Cinnamic amide	$NaOCl(CH_3OH)$	(*a*) Methyl styrylcarbamate	(*a*) 70%	41*a*
			(*b*) Phenylacetaldehyde	(*b*) G	41*a*
		$NaOCl(C_2H_5OH)$	N-Styryl-N-cinnamoylurea	—	41*a*

* References 65–173 are listed on pp. 305–306.

† Conversions of this amide and the *o*- and *p*- isomers to the amines (in unspecified yields) with NaOBr are reported in ref. 29.

PRODUCTS AND YIELDS OBTAINED IN HOFMANN REACTIONS OF AMIDES—*Continued*

Amide		Reagent	Product	Yield	Reference *
Formula	Name or Structural Formula				
$C_9H_{11}ON$	β-Phenylpropionamide	KOBr	β-Phenethylamine	30–60%	1*e*, 2*a*
		NaOCl	β-Phenethylamine	—	110
		NaOBr(CH_3OH)	Methyl α-phenethylcarbamate	—	110
		NaOBr(C_2H_5OH)	Ethyl β-phenethylcarbamate	—	110
	Hydratropamide	NaOBr	α-Phenethylamine	60%	111
$C_9H_{15}ON$	2,2-Dimethyl-3-methylenecyclopentanecarboxamide	NaOBr	1-Amino-2,2-dimethyl-3-methylenecyclopentane	40%	44
$C_9H_{17}ON$	2,3,3-Trimethylcyclopentanecarboxamide	NaOBr	1-Amino-2,3,3-trimethylcyclopentane	—	112
	3-Isopropylcyclopentanecarboxamide	NaOBr(CH_3OH)	(*a*) Methyl 3-isopropylcyclopentylcarbamate (*b*) 1-Amino-3-isopropylcyclopentane	(*a*) — (*b*) —	113
	Cycloheptylacetamide	KOBr	Cycloheptylcarbinylamine	40%	99
	2-Nonenamide	NaOCl(CH_3OH)	(*a*) Methyl 1-octenylcarbamate (*b*) Caprylaldehyde	(*a*) 50% (*b*) G	46*b*
$C_9H_{19}ON$	Pelargonamide	NaOBr	Octylamine	45%	1*c*, 2*b*
$C_9H_{11}O_2N$	β-(*o*-Hydroxyphenyl)-propionamide	NaOCl	*o*-Hydroxy-β-phenethylamine	—	114
	β-(*p*-Hydroxyphenyl)-propionamide	NaOCl	*p*-Hydroxy-β-phenethylamine	—	114
$C_9H_9O_3N$	2-Carboxy-α-toluamide	KOBr	*o*-Carboxybenzylamine	—	115
$C_9H_{11}O_3N$	Veratric amide	NaOCl	4-Aminoveratrol	80%	47
$C_9H_9O_4N$	5-Methoxypiperonylamide	NaOCl	5-Methoxy-*nor*-piperonylamine	—	116

Formula	Amide	Reagent	Product	Yield	Reference*
$C_9H_6O_5N$	3,6-Dicarboxybenzamide	KOBr	3,6-Dicarboxyaniline	—	117
	2,4-Dicarboxybenzamide	KOBr	2,4-Dicarboxyaniline	—	117
$C_9H_{16}ON_2$	1-Methyl-2,6-*endo*methylene-3-piperidinecarboxamide	KOBr	1-Methyl-2,6-*endo*methylene-3-aminopiperidine	—	118
$C_9H_{18}ON_2$	2,2,5,5-Tetramethylpyrollidine-3-carboxamide	KOBr	2,2,5,5-Tetramethyl-3-amino-pyrrolidine	60%	119
$C_9H_{18}O_2N_2$	Azelaic amide	NaOBr	1,7-Diaminoheptane	—	33*c*
$C_9H_8O_3N_2$	*o*-Nitrocinnamic amide	NaOCl (CH_3OH)	(*a*) Methyl *o*-nitrostyrylcarbamate (*b*) *o*-Nitrophenylacetaldehyde	(*a*) — (*b*) —	41*a*
	m-Nitrocinnamic amide	NaOCl(CH_3OH)	(*a*) Methyl *m*-nitrostyrylcarbamate (*b*) *m*-Nitrophenylacetaldehyde	(*a*) — (*b*) P	41*a*
	p-Nitrocinnamic amide	NaOCl(CH_3OH)	(*a*) Methyl *p*-nitrostyrylcarbamate (*b*) *m*-Nitrophenylacetaldehyde	(*a*) — (*b*) P	41*a*
$C_9H_{10}O_5N_2$	2-Nitro-3,4-dimethoxybenzamide	NaOBr	2-Nitro-3,4-dimethoxyaniline	85%	120
		C_{10}–C_{11}			
$C_{10}OH_{13}ON$	*o*-*n*-Propylbenzamide	NaOBr	*o*-*n*-Propylaniline	—	121
	α-Methyl-β-phenylpropionamide	KOBr	1-Phenyl-2-aminopropane	65–95%	10, 122
	β-Phenylbutyramide	KOBr	2-Phenyl-1-aminopropane	60%	123
	α,α-Dimethyl-α-toluamide	NaOBr	2-Phenyl-2-aminopropane	35%	124
$C_{10}H_{17}ON$	2,2,3-Trimethyl-2-cyclopentenyl-acetamide	KOBr	2,2,3-Trimethyl-2-cyclopentenyl-carbinylamine	15%	43, 125
	2,3,3-Trimethyl-1-cyclopentenyl-acetamide	KOBr	2,3,3-Trimethyl-1-cyclopentenyl-carbinylamine	P	43
	1-Apocamphanecarboxamide	NaOBr(CH_3OH)	(*a*) Methyl 1-apocamphylcarbamate (*b*) 1-Aminoapocamphane	(*a*) 60% (*b*) 85%	20

* References 65–173 are listed on pp. 305–306.

PRODUCTS AND YIELDS OBTAINED IN HOFMANN REACTIONS OF AMIDES—*Continued*

Amide		Reagent	Product	Yield	Reference *
Formula	Name or Structural Formula				
$C_{10}H_{19}ON$	1,2,2,3-Tetramethylcyclopentanecarboxamide	KOBr	1,2,2,3-Tetramethyl-1-aminocyclopentane	—	126
	1-Methyl-3-isopropylcyclopentanecarboxamide	NaOBr	1-Methyl-3-isopropyl-1-aminocyclopentane	—	127
	2-Methyl-2-isopropylcyclopentanecarboxamide	KOBr	2-Methyl-2-isopropyl-1-aminocyclopentane	—	128*b*
		NaOBr(CH_3OH)	(*a*) Methyl 2-methyl-2-isopropylcyclopentylcarbamate (*b*) 2-Methyl-2-isopropyl-1-aminocyclopentane	(*a*) 90% (*b*) 80%	129
	2,2,3-Trimethylcyclopentylacetamide	KOBr	2,2,3-Trimethylcyclopentylcarbinylamine	—	130
	3,5-Dimethylcyclohexylacetamide	NaOBr	3,5-Dimethylhexahydrobenzylamine	—	128*a*
$C_{10}H_{21}ON$	Capramide	KOBr	*n*-Nonylamine	P	1*c*
$C_{10}H_{11}O_2N$	*o*-Methoxycinnamic amide	NaOCl(CH_3OH)	(*a*) Methyl *o*-methoxystyrylcarbamate (*b*) *o*-Methoxyphenylacetaldehyde	(*a*) — (*b*) —	41*b*
	p-Methoxycinnamic amide	NaOCl(CH_3OH)	(*a*) Methyl *p*-methoxystyrylcarbamate (*b*) *p*-Methoxyphenylacetaldehyde	(*a*) 65% (*b*) —	41*b*
$C_{10}H_{13}O_2N$	β-(*p*-Methoxyphenyl)propionamide	NaOBr	*p*-Methoxy-β-phenethylamine	35%	114, 28

$C_{10}H_{11}O_3N$	Piperonylacetamide	NaOCl	Homopiperonylamine	50%	32
	3,5-Dimethyl-4-carboxybenzamide	NaOBr	2,6-Dimethyl-4-aminobenzoic acid	—	131
$C_{10}H_{17}O_3N$	α-Camphoramidic acid	NaOBr; NaOCl	1^t,2,2-Trimethyl-3^c-aminocyclopentanecarboxylic acid	70%	19
	β-Camphoramidic acid	NaOBr	2,2,3^t-Trimethyl-3^c-aminocyclopentanecarboxylic acid	100%	18
$C_{10}H_{19}O_3N$	Sebacamidic acid	$NaOCH_3$; Br_2	(*a*) ω-Carbomethoxyaminopelargonic acid (*b*) ω-Aminopelargonic acid	(*a*) 75% (*b*) 100%	38
$C_{10}H_9O_4N$	3,4-Dimethoxyphthalimide	NaOCl	3,4-Dimethoxyanthranilic acid	35%	52
$C_{10}H_{13}O_4N$	2,3,4-Trimethoxybenzamide	NaOCl	2,3,4-Trimethoxyaniline	—	132
	3,4,5-Trimethoxybenzamide	NaOCl	3,4,5-Trimethoxyaniline	75%	132
$C_{10}H_8ON_2$	3-Quinolinecarboxamide	KOBr	3-Aminoquinoline	75%	133
	4-Quinolinecarboxamide	KOBr	4-Aminoquinoline	—	2*d*, 59
$C_{10}H_{16}ON_2$	2,2,3^t-Trimethyl-3^c-cyanocyclopentanecarboxamide	NaOBr	1^c-Amino-2,2,3^t-trimethyl-3^c-cyanocyclopentane	—	134
$C_{10}H_{20}ON_2$	1,2,2,5,5-Pentamethylpyrrolidine-4-carboxamide	KOBr	1,2,2,5,5-Pentamethyl-4-aminopyrrolidine	—	56
$C_{10}H_{18}O_2N_2$	Cyclopentanecarboxamide-1-[α-isobutyramide]-3	NaOBr(CH_3OH)	3,1′-*bis*[Carbomethoxyamino]-1-methylcyclopentane	—	135
$C_{10}H_{20}O_2N_2$	Sebacamide	NaOBr	1,8-Diaminoöctane	—	33*b*, 136
$C_{10}H_8O_3N_2$	3-Acetaminophthalimide	NaOCl	6-Aminoanthranilic acid	35% 20%	105
$C_{10}H_{10}O_5N_2$	4,6-Dimethyl-3,5-dicarboxypyridine-2-carboxamide	NaOBr	4,6-Dimethyl-2-amino-pyridine-dicarboxylic acid-(3,5)	—	137
$C_{10}H_7ON_2Cl$	2-Chloro-3-quinolinecarboxamide	NaOBr	2-Chloro-3-aminoquinoline	85	133
$C_{11}H_{10}ON$	3-Aminonaphthalene-2-carboxamide	NaOCl	4,5-β,β′-Naphthimidazol-2-one		138
$C_{11}H_{11}ON$	Cinnamalacetamide	NaOCl(CH_3OH)	(*a*) Methyl styrylvinylcarbamate (*b*) Styrylacetaldehyde	(*a*) 70% (*b*) 70%	46*a*

* References 65–173 are listed on pp. 305–306.

PRODUCTS AND YIELDS OBTAINED IN HOFMANN REACTIONS OF AMIDES—*Continued*

Amide		Reagent	Product	Yield	Reference *
Formula	Name or Structural Formula				
$C_{11}H_{13}ON$	1-Methyl-2-indancarboxamide	NaOBr	1-Methyl-2-aminoindan	15%	139
	1-Indanacetamide	NaOBr	1-Indylcarbinylamine	15%	139
$C_{11}H_{19}ON$	Camphane-4-carboxamide	NaOBr(CH_3OH)	(*a*) Methyl 4-camphanylcarbamate	(*a*) 80%	140
			(*b*) 4-Aminocamphane	(*b*) 70%	
$C_{11}H_{23}ON$	Undecanoamide	NaOBr	(*a*) N-Decyl-N′-undecanoylurea	(*a*) —	26
			(*b*) *n*-Decylamine	(*b*) —	
$C_{11}H_{15}O_2N$	β-(*o*-Ethoxyphenyl)propionamide	NaOCl	*o*-Ethoxy-β-phenethylamine	—	114
	β-(*m*-Ethoxyphenyl)propionamide	NaOCl	*m*-Ethoxy-β-phenethylamine	75%	132
$C_{11}H_{17}O_2N$	2-Ketocamphane-4-carboxamide	NaOBr(CH_3OH)	(*a*) Methyl 4-camphorylcarbamate	(*a*) 75%	140
			(*b*) 4-Aminocamphor	(*b*) 65%	
$C_{11}H_{15}O_3N$	β-(3,4-Dimethoxyphenyl)propionamide	NaOCl	3,4-Dimethoxy-β-phenethylamine	—	141
	β-(3,5-Dimethoxyphenyl)propionamide	NaOCl	3,5-Dimethoxy-β-phenethylamine	—	142
$C_{11}H_{19}O_3N$	α-Camphoramidic acid methyl ester	NaOBr	$2^c,2^t,3^t$-Trimethyl-3^c-aminocyclopentanecarboxylic acid methyl ester	—	19
$C_{11}H_{13}O_4N$	5-Methoxypiperonylacetamide	NaOCl	5-Methoxyhomopiperonylamine	—	143
$C_{11}H_{15}O_4N$	3,5-Dimethoxy-4-ethoxybenzamide	NaOCl	3,5-Dimethoxy-4-ethoxyaniline	85%	144

$C_{11}H_{10}O_2N_2$	2-Methyl-4-quinolinecarboxamide	NaOBr	2-Methyl-4-aminoquinoline	—	145
$C_{11}H_{10}O_2N_2$	6-Methoxy-4-quinolinecarboxamide	KOBr	6-Methoxy-4-aminoquinoline	—	146
$C_{11}H_{11}ON_3$	β-Naphthylsemicarbazide	NaOCl	β-Naphthyl azide	—	54
$C_{11}H_{18}ONCl$	2-Chloro-4-camphanecarboxamide	NaOBr(CH_3OH)	(*a*) Methyl 2-chloro-4-camphanylcarbamate (*b*) 4-Aminocamphene	(*a*) 75% (*b*) —	140
		C_{12}–C_{13}			
$C_{12}H_{21}ON$	CH_2, CH_3, CH_3, CH_2, $CHCONH_2$	NaOBr	CH_2, CH_3, CH_3, CH_2, $CHNH_2$	—	147
$C_{12}H_{25}ON$	Lauramide	NaOBr	(*a*) N-Undecyl-N′-laurylurea (*b*) Undecylamine	(*a*) — (*b*) —	26
		NaOBr(CH_3OH)	(*a*) Methyl undecylcarbamate (*b*) Undecylamine	(*a*) 90% (*b*) G	4*b*
$C_{12}H_7O_2N$	*peri*-Naphthalenedicarboximide	NaOBr	8-Amino-1-naphthoic acid	—	148
$C_{12}H_{11}O_2N$	3-Methoxynaphthalene-2-carboxamide	KOBr	2-Amino-3-methoxynaphthalene	—	149
$C_{12}H_{10}O_2N_2$	β-Benzoyl-α-picolinamide	NaOBr	2-Amino-3-benzoylpyridine	—	150
$C_{13}H_{11}ON$	2-Phenylbenzamide	NaOBr	2-Phenylaniline	—	151
$C_{13}H_{27}ON$	Tridecanamide	NaOBr	(*a*) N-dodecyl-N′-tridecanoylurea (*b*) Dodecylamine	(*a*) — (*b*) —	152

* References 65–173 are listed on pp. 305–306.

PRODUCTS AND YIELDS OBTAINED IN HOFMANN REACTIONS OF AMIDES—*Continued*

Amide		Reagent	Product	Yield	Reference *
Formula	Name or Structural Formula				
	C_{14}				
$C_{14}H_{13}ON$	*o*-Benzylbenzamide	NaOCl	*o*-Benzylaniline	45%	48
$C_{14}H_{25}ON$	Tetradecanamide	KOBr	(*a*) N-Tridecyl-N′-tetradecanoylurea	(*a*) G	152, 153
			(*b*) Tridecylamine	(*b*) —	
		NaOBr(CH_3OH)	(*a*) Methyl tridecylcarbamate	(*a*) 95%	154
			(*b*) Tridecylamine	(*b*) 70%	
$C_{14}H_9O_2N$	9-Keto-1-fluorenecarboxamide	KOBr	1-Amino-9-fluorenone	—	155
	9-Keto-4-fluorenecarboxamide	KOBr	4-Amino-9-fluorenone	80%	156
$C_{14}H_{11}O_2N$	*o*-Benzoylbenzamide	NaOBr	*o*-Benzoylaniline	40%	157
$C_{14}H_{12}O_3N_2$	*o*-(2-Methyl-6-nitrophenyl)benzamide	NaOBr	*o*-(2-Methyl-6-nitrophenyl)-aniline	—	158
	C_{15}				
$C_{15}H_{13}O_2N$	*o*-(*p*-Toluyl)benzamide	NaOBr	*o*-(*p*-Toluyl)aniline	70%	159
$C_{15}H_9O_3N$	1-Anthraquinonecarboxamide	KOBr	1-Aminoanthraquinone	—	160
$C_{15}H_9O_5N$	1,8-Dihydroxy-3-anthraquinonecarboxamide	NaOCl	1,8-Dihydroxy-3-aminoanthraquinone	—	161
$C_{15}H_8O_5N_2$	1-Nitro-2-anthraquinonecarboxamide	KOBr	1-Nitro-2-aminoanthraquinone	60%	162

Formula	Amide	Reagent	Product	Yield	Reference*
		C_{16}–C_{17}			
$C_{16}H_{12}ON$	2-Phenylquinoline-4′-carboxamide	KOBr	2-Phenyl-4′-aminoquinoline	80%	163
$C_{16}H_{33}ON$	Palmitamide	NaOBr(CH_3OH)	(*a*) Methyl pentadecylcarbamate	(*a*) 80%	4*b*
			(*b*) Pentadecylamine	(*b*) G	
		NaOBr(C_2H_5OH)	(*a*) Ethyl pentadecylcarbamate	(*a*) 50%	4*b*
			(*b*) Pentadecylamine	(*b*) G	
($C_{16}H_{32}ONCl$)	N-Chloropalmitamide	$NaOCH_3$	(*a*) Methyl pentadecylcarbamate	(*a*) —	4*b*, 25
			(*b*) Pentadecylamine	(*b*) G	
$C_{16}H_{15}O_2N$	*o*-(2,4-Dimethylbenzoyl)benzamide	NaOBr	*o*-(2,4-Dimethylbenzoyl)aniline	—	164
$C_{17}H_{13}ON$	*o*-α-Naphthylbenzamide	NaOBr	*o*-α-Naphthylaniline	15%	165
$C_{17}H_{14}ON$	2-Phenyl-3-methylquinoline-4-carboxamide	KOBr	2-Phenyl-3-methyl-4-aminoquinoline	25%	166
$C_{17}H_{11}O_5N$	3,5-Dinitro-2-α-naphthylbenzamide	NaOBr	3,5-Dinitro-2-α-naphthylaniline	—	12
		C_{18}			
$C_{18}H_{37}ON$	Stearamide	NaOBr	(*a*) N-Heptadecyl-N′-stearylurea	(*a*) —	1*c*
			(*b*) Heptadecylamine	(*b*) —	
		NaOBr(CH_3OH)	(*a*) Methyl heptadecylcarbamate	(*a*) 90%	4*b*
			(*b*) Heptadecylamine	(*b*) G	
$C_{18}H_{13}O_2N$	*o*-α-Naphthoylbenzamide	NaOBr	*o*-α-Naphthoylaniline	—	167
$C_{18}H_{17}O_3N$	α-Truxillamidic acid	NaOCl	α-Truxillamic acid	85%	39*d*
	γ-Truxillamidic acid	NaOCl	γ-Truxillamic acid	70%	39*b*

* References 65–173 are listed on pp. 305–306.

PRODUCTS AND YIELDS OBTAINED IN HOFMANN REACTIONS OF AMIDES—*Continued*

Amide		Reagent	Product	Yield	Reference *
Formula	Name or Structural Formula				
	ε-Truxillamidic acid	NaOCl	ε-Truxillamic acid	—	39*a*, *c*
	β-Truxinamidic acid	NaOCl	β-Truxinamic acid	80%	39*b*
	δ-Truxinamidic acid	NaOCl	δ-Truxinamic acid	70%	39*e*
$C_{18}H_{20}O_2N_2$	3-Methyl-4′-isopropyl-2,2′-biphenyldicarboxamide	KOBr	3-Methyl-4′-isopropyl-2,2′-diaminobiphenyl	25%	168
		C_{21}–C_{28}			
$C_{21}H_{19}ON$	β,β,β-Triphenylpropionamide				
($C_{21}H_{18}ONBr$)	N-Bromo-β,β,β-triphenylpropionamide	$NaOC_2H_5$	(*a*) Ethyl β,β,β-triphenylethylcarbamate (*b*) β,β,β-Triphenylethylamine	(*a*) — (*b*) —	14
$C_{28}H_{57}ON$	$C_{27}H_{55}CONH_2$ (montanamide)	$NaOBr(CH_3OH)$	$C_{27}H_{55}NHCO_2CH_3$	—	169

* References 65–173 are listed on pp. 305–306.

REFERENCES TO TABLE

[65] Schestakov, *Chem. Zentr.*, I, 1227 (1905).
[66] François, *Compt. rend.*, **147**, 430, 680 (1908).
[67] Lengfeld and Stieglitz, *Am. Chem. J.*, **16**, 370 (1894).
[68] Kishner, *J. Russ. Phys. Chem. Soc.*, **37**, 308 (1905) [*Chem. Zentr.*, I, 1703 (1905)].
[69] Clarke and Behr, *Org. Syntheses, Coll. Vol.* **2**, 19 (1943).
[70] Lengfeld and Stieglitz, *Am. Chem. J.*, **15**, 508 (1893).
[71] Holm, *Arch. Pharm.*, **242**, 597 (1904).
[72] Hale and Honan, *J. Am. Chem. Soc.*, **41**, 774 (1920).
[73] Miliotis, *Bull. soc. chim.*, [5] **3**, 2367 (1936).
[74] Freund and Gudeman, *Ber.*, **21**, 2695 (1888).
[75] Perkin, *J. Chem. Soc.*, **65**, 959 (1894).
[76] Böeseken, *Rec. trav. chim.*, **37**, 262 (1918).
[77] Zelinsky and Gutt, *Ber.*, **40**, 4745 (1907).
[78] Van Erp, *Rec. trav. chim.*, **14**, 17 (1895).
[79] Folin, *Am. Chem. J.*, **19**, 335 (1897).
[80] Pyman, *J. Chem. Soc.*, **103**, 859 (1913).
[81] Meyer, *Monatsh.*, **15**, 173 (1894).
[82] Mills and Widdows, *J. Chem. Soc.*, **93**, 1379 (1908).
[83] Sell, *J. Chem. Soc.*, **93**, 2002 (1908).
[84] Sell, *J. Chem. Soc.*, **87**, 804 (1905).
[85] Markonikow, *Ber.*, **30**, 1224 (1897); *Ann.*, **307**, 371 (1899).
[86] Wallach and Fleischer, *Ann.*, **353**, 305 (1907).
[87] Levene and Marker, *J. Biol. Chem.*, **98**, 1 (1932).
[88] Einhorn and Bull, *Ann.*, **295**, 211 (1897).
[89] Graf, *J. prakt. Chem.*, **133**, 19 (1932).
[90] Kirpal, *Monatsh.*, **23**, 243 (1902).
[91] Kirpal, *Monatsh.*, **29**, 228 (1908).
[92] Phillips, *Ber.*, **27**, 840 (1894); *Ann.*, **288**, 259 (1895).
[93] Kirpal, *Monatsh.*, **23**, 243 (1902).
[94] Swartz, *Am. Chem. J.*, **19**, 304 (1897).
[95] Rinkes, *Chem. Zentr.*, I, 822 (1919).
[96] Holleman, den Holländer, and van Hoeften, *Rec. trav. chim.*, **40**, 327 (1921).
[97] Bradshaw, *Am. Chem. J.*, **35**, 339 (1906).
[98] Komppa and Beckmann, *Ann.*, **512**, 172 (1934).
[99] Wallach, *Ann.*, **353**, 298 (1907).
[100] Levene and Marker, *J. Biol. Chem.*, **95**, 153 (1932).
[101] Kenyon and Young, *J. Chem. Soc.*, **1941**, 263.
[102] Basler Chemische Fabrik, Ger. pat., 139,218 [*Frdl.*, **7**, 118; *Chem. Zentr.*, I, 745 (1903)].
[103] Rupe and von Majewski, *Ber.*, **33**, 3403 (1900); van Linge, *Rec. trav. chim.*, **16**, 50 (1897).
[104] Bogert and Chambers, *J. Am. Chem. Soc.*, **27**, 652 (1905).
[105] Moore, Marrach, and Proud, *J. Chem. Soc.*, **119**, 1786 (1921).
[106] Lesser and Weiss, *Ber.*, **46**, 3943 (1913).
[107] Graebe and Gourewitz, *Ber.*, **33**, 2025 (1900).
[108] Graebe and Rostowzew, *Ber.*, **34**, 2110 (1901).
[109] Villiger and Blangey, *Ber.*, **42**, 3550 (1909).
[110] Weerman and Jonkers, *Rec. trav. chim.*, **25**, 243 (1906).
[111] Arcus and Kenyon, *J. Chem. Soc.*, **1939**, 916.
[112] Noyes and Harris, *Am. Chem. J.*, **18**, 692 (1896).
[113] Bouveault and Blanc, *Compt. rend.*, **146**, 235 (1908).
[114] Bayer and Co., Ger. pat., 233,551 [*Frdl.*, **10**, 1231; *Chem. Zentr.*, I, 1334 (1911)].
[115] Wegscheider and Glogau, *Monatsh.*, **24**, 953 (1903).
[116] Salway, *J. Chem. Soc.*, **95**, 1162 (1909).
[117] Wegscheider, Perndonner, and Auspitzer, *Monatsh.*, **31**, 1297 (1910).
[118] Willstätter and Müller, *Ber.*, **31**, 2661 (1878).

[119] Pauly and Rossbach, *Ber.*, **32**, 2005 (1899); Pauly, *Ann.*, **322**, 97 (1902).
[120] Pisovschi, *Ber.*, **43**, 2142 (1910).
[121] Gottlieb, *Ber.*, **32**, 962 (1898).
[122] Edeleanu, *Ber.*, **20**, 618 (1887).
[123] von Braun, Grabowski, and Kirschbaum, *Ber.*, **46**, 1280 (1913).
[124] Brander, *Rec. trav. chim.*, **37**, 68 (1918).
[125] Blanc and Desfontaines, *Compt. rend.*, **138**, 697 (1904); *Bull. soc. chim.*, [3] **31**, 385 (1904).
[126] Errera, *Gazz. chim. ital.*, **22**, (I) 221 (1892).
[127] Wallach, *Ann.*, **369**, 79 (1909).
[128] Wallach, (*a*) *Ann.*, **414**, 232 (1918); (*b*) **414**, 239 (1918).
[129] Bouveault and Lavallois, *Bull. soc. chim.*, [4] **7**, 685 (1916).
[130] Blaise and Blanc, *Bull. soc. chim.*, [3] **27**, 74 (1902); Blanc and Desfontaines, *Compt. rend.*, **136**, 1143 (1903).
[131] Noyes, *Am. Chem. J.*, **20**, 812 (1898).
[132] Graebe and Suter, *Ann.*, **340**, 227 (1905).
[133] Mills and Watson, *J. Chem. Soc.*, **97**, 746 (1910).
[134] Tiemann and Tigges, *Ber.*, **33**, 2962 (1900).
[135] Moycho and Zienkowski, *Ann.*, **340**, 49 (1905).
[136] Loeble, *Monatsh.*, **24**, 393 (1903).
[137] Kirpal and Reimann, *Monatsh.*, **38**, 254 (1917).
[138] Fries, Walter, and Schilling, *Ann.*, **516**, 279 (1935).
[139] von Braun, Danziger, and Koehler, *Ber.*, **50**, 63 (1917).
[140] Houben and Pfankuch, *Ann.*, **489**, 193 (1931).
[141] Pictet and Finkelstein, *Compt. rend.*, **148**, 926 (1909); *Ber.*, **42**, 1986 (1909).
[142] Salway, *J. Chem. Soc.*, **99**, 1322 (1911).
[143] Salway, *J. Chem. Soc.*, **97**, 1212 (1910).
[144] Bogert and Erlich, *J. Am. Chem. Soc.*, **41**, 803 (1919).
[145] Meyer, *Monatsh.*, **28**, 52 (1907).
[146] Hirsch, *Monatsh.*, **17**, 333 (1896).
[147] Buchner and Weigand, *Ber.*, **46**, 765 (1913).
[148] Francesconi and Recchi, *Atti accad. Lincei*, [5] **18**, (II) 667 (1909).
[149] Jambuserwala, Holt, and Mason, *J. Chem. Soc.*, **1931**, 373.
[150] Kirpal, *Monatsh.*, **27**, 375 (1907).
[151] Graebe and Rateanu, *Ann.*, **279**, 266 (1894).
[152] Lutz, *Ber.*, **19**, 1440 (1886).
[153] Reiner and Will, *Ber.*, **18**, 2016 (1885).
[154] Blau, *Monatsh.*, **26**, 99 (1906).
[155] Goldschmidt, *Monatsh.*, **23**, 893 (1902).
[156] Graebe and Schestakow, *Ann.*, **284**, 311 (1895).
[157] Graebe and Ullmann, *Ann.*, **291**, 13 (1896).
[158] Bell, *J. Chem. Soc.*, **1934**, 835.
[159] Kippenberg, *Ber.*, **30**, 1133 (1897).
[160] Graebe and Blumenfeld, *Ber.*, **30**, 1116 (1897).
[161] Oesterle, *Chem. Zentr.*, I, 142 (1912).
[162] Tierres, *Ber.*, **46**, 1641 (1913).
[163] John and Ottawa, *J. prakt. Chem.*, **133**, 13 (1932).
[164] Drawert, *Ber.*, **32**, 1260 (1899).
[165] Graebe and Honigsberger, *Ann.*, **311**, 271 (1900).
[166] John and Ottawa, *J. prakt. Chem.*, **131**, 310 (1931).
[167] Graebe, *Ber.*, **29**, 827 (1896).
[168] Lux, *Monatsh.*, **31**, 945 (1910).
[169] Ryan and Algar, *Proc. Roy. Irish Acad.*, **30**, B, 97 (1913) [*Chem. Zentr.* II, 2051 (1913)].
[170] Kishner, *Chem. Zentr.*, I, 1219 (1905).
[171] Kishner, *Chem. Zentr.*, I, 1220 (1905).
[172] Willstätter, *Ann.*, **317**, 219 (1901).
[173] Schestakov, *Chem. Zentr.*, II, 1703 (1905).

CHAPTER 8

THE SCHMIDT REACTION

HANS WOLFF

A. E. Staley Manufacturing Company
Decatur, Illinois

CONTENTS

INTRODUCTION

The reaction between equimolar quantities of hydrazoic acid and carbonyl compounds in the presence of strong mineral acid has become known as the Schmidt reaction. It affords a convenient method for the preparation of amines from acids according to the following scheme.

$$RCO_2H + HN_3 \xrightarrow{H_2SO_4} RNH_2 + CO_2 + N_2$$

Aldehydes yield nitriles and formyl derivatives of amines, and ketones yield amides.

$$RCHO + HN_3 \xrightarrow{H_2SO_4} RCN \text{ and } RNHCHO$$

$$RCOR + HN_3 \xrightarrow{H_2SO_4} RCONHR + N_2$$

With hydrazoic acid in large excess (two or more moles), aldehydes and ketones yield substituted tetrazoles.

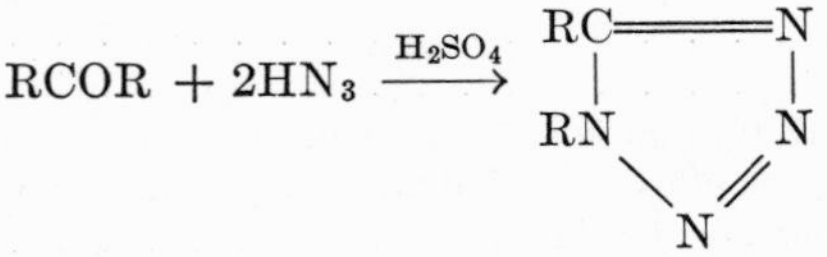

$$RCOR + 2HN_3 \xrightarrow{H_2SO_4} \begin{array}{ccc} RC & = & N \\ | & & | \\ RN & & N \\ & \diagdown \; N \; \diagup\!\!\diagup & \end{array}$$

The reaction of carbonyl compounds with hydrazoic acid was first reported by Karl Friedrich Schmidt in 1923 in a study of the decomposition of hydrazoic acid by sulfuric acid. He observed that benzene had an accelerating effect on the decomposition [1, 2] and that the products obtained differed according to the temperature at which the reaction was carried out; at room temperature hydrazine sulfate was the main product, but at a temperature of 60–70° aniline sulfate was formed in high

[1] Schmidt, *Z. angew. Chem.*, **36**, 511 (1923).

[2] Schmidt, *Acta Acad. Aboensis, Math. et Phys.*, [2] **38** (1924) [*C. A.*, **19**, 3248 (1925); *Ber.*, **57**, 704 (1924)].

yields. Acting on the hypothesis that during the decomposition of hydrazoic acid a free imide radical (NH) is formed which is capable of adding to a reactive group, Schmidt added benzophenone to the reaction mixture. A very fast reaction occurred, and a quantitative yield of benzanilide was obtained.[1, 2, 3]

MECHANISM OF THE REACTION

The mechanism of the Schmidt reaction has not been established with certainty. Schmidt proposed a mechanism in which the hydrazoic acid is cleaved by the strong mineral acid to nitrogen and the imide radical (NH). This radical is supposed to add to the carbonyl group, followed by a rearrangement either directly or by a Beckmann transformation of an intermediate oxime to the amide.[2, 4]

$$R_2C{=}O + [NH] \nearrow \left[R_2C(OH){-}N(-){-} \right], \searrow \left[RC(=NOH)R \right] \rightarrow RCONHR$$

Oliveri-Mandalà advanced a mechanism involving addition of the hydrazoic acid molecule to the carbonyl group.[5] This mechanism was elaborated by Hurd [6] and shown by Briggs and Lyttleton [7] to be more acceptable in the light of later evidence. Hurd proposed the activation of hydrazoic acid (I) by concentrated sulfuric acid to an active form (II); this adds to the carbonyl forming III. The transient adduct (III) loses nitrogen to yield an unstable immo derivative (IV) which immediately undergoes a Beckmann type rearrangement and yields the amide (V)

$$\underset{\text{I}}{H\ddot{N}{=}\overset{+}{N}{=}\overset{-}{\ddot{N}}{:}} \xrightarrow{H_2SO_4} \underset{\text{II}}{H\ddot{\ddot{N}}{-}\overset{+}{N}{\equiv}N{:}}$$

$$R_2C{=}O \rightarrow [R_2\overset{+}{C}{-}\overset{-}{O}] + \text{II} \rightarrow$$

$$\underset{\text{III}}{\left[R_2C(O^-){-}\overset{..+}{N}(H)N{\equiv}N{:} \right]} \xrightarrow{-N_2} \underset{\text{IV}}{\left[R_2C(O^-){-}\overset{+}{N}(H){:} \right]} \rightarrow \underset{\text{V}}{RCONHR}$$

[3] Ger. pat., 427,858 [*Frdl.*, **15,** 221 (1928)]; U. S. pat., 1,564,631 [*C. A.*, **20,** 423 (1926)].
[4] Schmidt, *Ber.*, **58,** 2413 (1925).
[5] Oliveri-Mandalà, *Gazz. chim. ital.*, **55,** I, 271 (1925).
[6] Hurd, in Gilman, "Organic Chemistry," *I*, 699, 1st ed., John Wiley & Sons, 1938.
[7] Briggs and Lyttleton, *J. Chem. Soc.*, **1943,** 421.

This mechanism also accounts for the formation of amines from acids. If one of the R groups in IV is hydroxyl, the intermediate carbamic acid VI decomposes to an amine and carbon dioxide.

$$RCO_2H \rightarrow \left[\begin{array}{c} O^- \\ | \\ RC\text{—}\overset{+}{N}_3H \\ | \\ OH \end{array} \right] \xrightarrow{-N_2} \left[\begin{array}{c} O^- \\ | \\ RC\text{—}\overset{+}{N}H \\ | \\ OH \end{array} \right] \rightarrow$$

$$\underset{\text{VI}}{[RNHCO_2H]} \rightarrow RNH_2 + CO_2$$

The formation of tetrazoles can be accounted for by further action of hydrazoic acid on the intermediate IV, before completion of the rearrangement.

Although aromatic amination by hydrazoic acid could be explained by a similar mechanism,[6] evidence has been presented that it proceeds in a different fashion.[8] It appears that this reaction proceeds through an (NH) or $(NH_2)^+$ radical. The aromatic amination requires higher temperatures than the carbonyl reaction, a fact that lends support to the view that the two reactions proceed by different mechanisms.

SCOPE AND LIMITATIONS

The Reaction of Hydrazoic Acid with Organic Acids

Aliphatic and Alicyclic Acids. The Schmidt reaction has found its most extensive application in the preparation of amines from acids. With straight-chain aliphatic acids the yield of amine generally increases with the length of the chain.[9, 10] Thus, *n*-caproic acid yields 70% of amylamine [9] and stearic acid, 96% of heptadecylamine.[11] This generalization does not hold for acids of more complicated structure. In the naphthenic acid series, where the lower members contain one and the higher members two cyclopentane rings, the yields drop with the increase of molecular complexity.[10] Dibasic acids, in general, react bifunctionally to give diamines, and the yields improve as the distance between carboxyl groups increases. Thus, succinic acid gives ethylenediamine (8%),[12] adipic acid yields tetramethylenediamine (83%),[13] and dodecamethylenedicarboxylic acid gives dodecamethylenediamine

[8] Keller and Smith, *J. Am. Chem. Soc.*, **66**, 1122 (1944).

[9] Adamson and Kenner, *J. Chem. Soc.*, **1934**, 838.

[10] v. Braun, *Ann.*, **490**, 100 (1931).

[11] Briggs, De Ath, and Ellis, *J. Chem. Soc.*, **1942**, 61.

[12] Oesterlin, *Z. angew. Chem.*, **45**, 536 (1932).

[13] Ger. pat., 500,435 [*Frdl.*, **17**, 2612 (1932); U. S. pat., 1,926,756 [*C. A.*, **27**, 5752 (1933)].

(90%).[14] Malonic acids, however, yield α-amino acids which do not react further with hydrazoic acid.[11, 15] No acid containing three or more carboxyl groups has been studied.

The reaction proceeds quite smoothly even with acids in which the carboxyl group is inert to many reagents. Thus, carboxyl groups attached to tertiary carbon atoms as in campholic acid (VII),[10, 16] podocarpic acid (VIII),[11] and the isobutyric acid derivative (IX)[17] are replaced by amino groups in good yields.

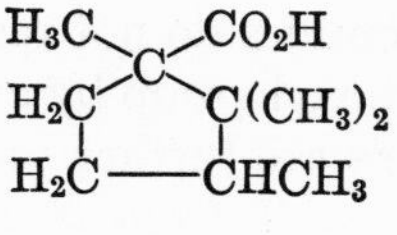

H_3C, CO_2H, H_2C, $C(CH_3)_2$, H_2C—$CHCH_3$
VII

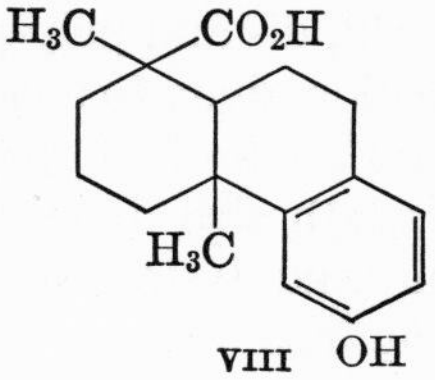

H_3C, CO_2H, H_3C, OH
VIII

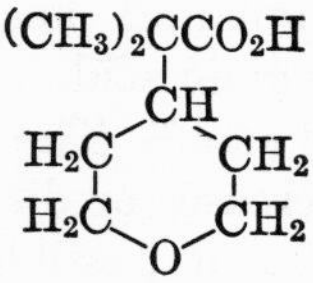

$(CH_3)_2CCO_2H$, CH, H_2C, CH_2, H_2C, CH_2, O
IX

A good yield (70%) of β-phenylethylamine is obtained from β-phenylpropionic acid, but the introduction of methoxyl groups in the benzene ring causes a sharp drop in the yields of the amines.[12]

Cinnamic acid yields phenylacetaldehyde, probably through formation of styrylamine (X), rearrangement to the aldimine (XI), and hydrolysis.[12] Aniline is obtained as a by-product, and no explanation has been given for its formation.

$$C_6H_5CH{=}CHCO_2H + HN_3 \rightarrow \underset{X}{[C_6H_5CH{=}CHNH_2]} \rightarrow$$

$$\underset{XI}{[C_6H_5CH_2CH{=}NH]} \rightarrow C_6H_5CH_2CHO$$

The Schmidt reaction cannot be applied to acids which are unstable toward concentrated sulfuric acid. Thus, α-halo acids are dehydrohalogenated under the reaction conditions.[18, 18a]

The replacement of a carboxyl group attached to an asymmetric carbon atom in an optically active molecule has been studied. No racemization occurs in the transformation of active methylbenzylacetic acid to α-benzylethylamine, or of fencholic acid to fenchelylamine.[19] A dimethylcampholic acid, however, yields a dimethylcamphelylamine of

[14] v. Braun and Anton, *Ber.*, **64**, 2865 (1931).
[15] Adamson, *J. Chem. Soc.*, **1939**, 1564.
[16] Ger. pat., 544,890 [*Frdl.*, **18**, 3054 (1933)].
[17] Prelog, Heimbach, and Režek, *Ann.*, **545**, 231 (1940).
[18] v. Braun, *Ber.*, **67**, 218 (1934).
[18a] Gilman and Jones, *J. Am. Chem. Soc.*, **65**, 1458 (1943).
[19] v. Braun and Friehmelt, *Ber.*, **66**, 684 (1933).

lower rotation than that of the amine obtained by a Hofmann degradation.[20]

An amino group alpha to a carboxyl group in aliphatic amino acids has an inhibiting effect upon the reactivity of the carboxyl group. Thus, the following aliphatic amino acids and their derivatives are reported to be unreactive toward hydrazoic acid:[12] glycine, hippuric and nitrohippuric acids, α- and β-alanine, phenylalanine, acetylalanine, phenylaminoacetic acid, N-(*p*-toluenesulfonyl)phenylalanine, β-phenyl-β-aminohydrocinnamic acid, and N-(*p*-toluenesulfonyl)β-phenyl-β-aminohydrocinnamic acid. Similarly, di- and poly-peptides do not react with hydrazoic acid.[21] The protection given to a carboxyl group by an amino group decreases or disappears as the two groups are further separated. This makes it possible to synthesize diamino acids from α-amino-dicarboxylic acids. Ornithine and lysine have been prepared in very satisfactory yields from α-aminoadipic acid and α-aminopimelic acid, respectively.[15]

$$H_2OC(CH_2)_3\underset{\displaystyle NH_2}{\underset{|}{C}}HCO_2H + HN_3 \xrightarrow{H_2SO_4} H_2N(CH_2)_3\underset{\displaystyle NH_2}{\underset{|}{C}}HCO_2H$$

Similarly, 1-phenylpiperidine-4-carboxylic acid has been converted to 4-amino-1-phenylpiperidine.[22]

Aromatic Acids. The position and type of ring substitution in aromatic acids have a marked effect on the reaction rates and yields of amines.[7, 11, 12] *p*-Toluic acid yields 70% of *p*-toluidine, but from *m*-toluic acid only 24% of *m*-toluidine is obtained.[11] If the time at which half of the total volume of nitrogen is evolved can be considered a measure of the reaction rate, the general conclusion can be drawn that in *meta*-substituted benzoic acids the reaction rates are in reverse order of the acidities as measured by dissociation constants.[7] This generalization applies to the reaction rates but not to the yields of amines obtained from different *meta*-substituted benzoic acids.

Of the aromatic dibasic acids, the three phthalic acids on treatment with hydrazoic acid yield the corresponding aminobenzoic acids with mere traces of the diaminobenzenes.[7, 12] Anthranilic acid and its derivatives in which one hydrogen on the amino group is replaced by acetyl, benzoyl, or *p*-toluyl are inert to hydrazoic acid.[12] These compounds thus resemble in activity α-amino acids and their derivatives in the aliphatic series. The following pyridine and quinoline acids resemble α-amino acids and also do not react: pyridine-2-carboxylic acid, pyridine-2,3-

[20] v. Braun and Kurtz, *Ber.*, **67**, 225 (1934).

[21] Nelles, *Ber.*, **65**, 1345 (1932).

[22] Cerkovnikov and Prelog, *Ber.*, **74**, 1648 (1941) [*C. A.*, **37**, 125 (1943)].

dicarboxylic acid, 2,6-dimethylpyridine-3,5-dicarboxylic acid, quinoline-6-carboxylic acid, and quinoline-8-carboxylic acid.[12] Similarly, very little 2,2′-diaminobiphenyl is obtained from diphenic acid, the main product being phenanthridone.[23]

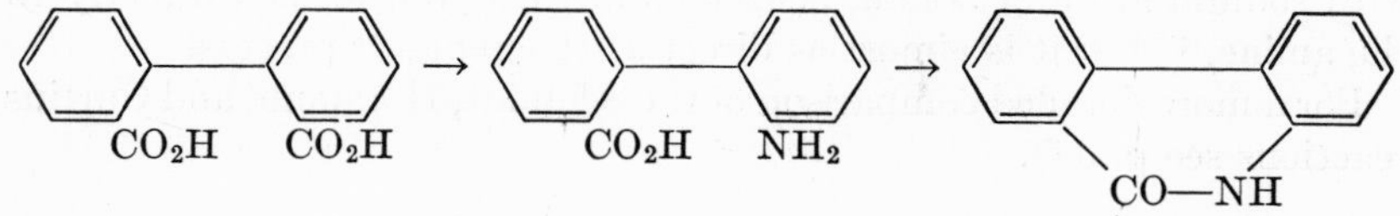

CO_2H CO_2H → CO_2H NH_2 → CO—NH

Highly substituted or hindered aromatic dibasic acids like tetrachlorophthalic acid and naphthalic acid fail to undergo the Schmidt reaction.[23]

Application of the Schmidt Reaction to Acids. The Schmidt reaction affords an additional method to the Hofmann and Curtius degradation of acids to amines having one less carbon atom. Schmidt's method presents two advantages over the older methods: it is a one-step reaction and thus avoids the isolation of intermediates; the yields often are higher than those from either the Hofmann or Curtius degradation. Thus, the naphthenic acids are degraded in 70–90% yields to the corresponding amines by the Schmidt reaction and in yields of only 25–35% by the Hofmann degradation.[10] From cyclobutane-1,2-dicarboxylic acid the *cis*- and *trans*-1,2-diaminocyclobutanes are obtained in 35% and 55% yields by the hydrazoic acid method and in only 17% and 12% yields by the Curtius degradation.[24] In general, it may be advantageous to use the Schmidt reaction for the preparation of amines if the free acids are the available raw materials; if, however, the esters or amides are more accessible, the Curtius or Hofmann degradations may be preferred. The use of hydrazoic acid requires precaution on account of the toxicity of the reagent; its explosiveness presents no special hazards under controlled laboratory conditions. Large-scale reactions with hydrazoic acid proceed with generation of much heat and great violence, thus involving the dangers of explosion.[25] The hydrazoic acid degradation of naphthenic acids was an invaluable aid in von Braun's investigation of mixtures of naphthenic acids.[10, 26] In his studies on alkaloids Prelog used the Schmidt reaction extensively.[17, 27–33]

[23] Caronna, *Gazz. chim. ital.*, **71,** 475 (1941) [*C. A.*, **37,** 118 (1943)].

[24] Buchman, Reims, Skei, and Schlatter, *J. Am. Chem. Soc.*, **64,** 2696 (1942).

[25] Ger. pat., 455,585 [*Frdl.*, **16,** 2862 (1931)]; U. S. pat., 1,637,661 [*C. A.*, **21,** 3057 (1927)]

[26] v. Braun and Wittmeyer, *Ber.*, **67,** 1739 (1934).

[27] Prelog and Božičevič, *Ber.*, **72,** 1103 (1939).

[28] Prelog, Cerkovnikov, and Ustricev, *Ann.*, **535,** 37 (1938).

[29] Prelog and Heimbach, *Ber.*, **72,** 1101 (1939).

[30] Prelog, Heimbach, and Seiwerth, *Ber.*, **72,** 1319 (1939).

[31] Prelog and Schönbaum, *Ann.*, **545,** 256 (1940).

[32] Prelog and Seiwerth, *Ber.*, **72,** 1638 (1939).

[33] Prelog, Šoštarič, and Guštac, *Ann.*, **545,** 247 (1940).

The Schmidt reaction cannot be used on acids unstable towards sulfuric acid or on acids containing aromatic rings that are readily sulfonated. The Curtius reaction can be used on such compounds; in one of its modifications (see p. 339), in which an acid chloride is treated with sodium azide in boiling benzene and thus transformed directly to the amine,[34, 35, 36] it is almost as direct as the Schmidt process.

For a more detailed comparison of the Schmidt, Hofmann, and Curtius reactions see p. 363.

The Reactions of Hydrazoic Acid with Lactones, Anhydrides, Esters, and Acid Halides

Phthalide and phenolphthalein appear to be the only lactones which have been subjected to the Schmidt reaction,[37] and both proved to be unreactive. Acetic anhydride gives a yield of 85% of methyl amine.[13] Phthalic anhydride yields isatoic anhydride, benzimidazolone, and anthranilic acid.[37]

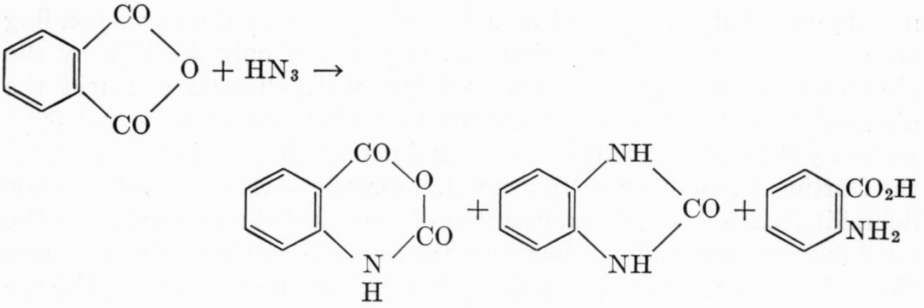

CO O CO + HN_3 →

CO O CO N H + NH CO NH + CO_2H NH_2

From methyl or ethyl benzoate a small amount of aniline is obtained, the bulk of the ester being recovered.[11, 13] Benzoyl chloride also yields aniline.[13] It would appear from the limited number of experiments performed that the reaction products from acid derivatives and hydrazoic acid are identical with those obtained directly by use of the corresponding acid but that the yields are lower.

The Reactions of Hydrazoic Acid with Aldehydes and Ketones

Aldehydes and ketones are more reactive towards hydrazoic acid than acids. Therefore it is possible to control the reaction of a keto acid or

[34] Forster, *J. Chem. Soc.*, **95**, 433 (1909).

[35] Naegeli and Stefanovitsch, *Helv. Chim. Acta*, **11**, 609 (1928); Naegeli, Gruntuch, and Lendorff, *ibid.*, **12**, 227 (1929); Naegeli and Lendorff, *ibid.*, **15**, 49 (1932); Naegeli and Vogt-Markus, *ibid.*, **15**, 60 (1932); Naegeli and Tyabji, *ibid.*, **16**, 349 (1933).

[36] Schroeter, *Ber.*, **42**, 3356 (1909).

[37] Caronna, *Gazz. chim. ital.*, **71**, 189 (1941) [*C. A.*, **36**, 3173 (1942)].

keto ester, by using a molar quantity of hydrazoic acid, in such a manner that only the ketone group enters the reaction. It is to be expected that molecules containing both carboxyl and aldehyde groups will react exclusively on the aldehyde although no experiments with compounds of this type have been reported.

Aldehydes. Acetaldehyde is the only aliphatic aldehyde whose behavior towards hydrazoic acid has been reported; it yields acetonitrile.[3]

From benzaldehyde two reaction products, benzonitrile and formanilide, are obtained.[2, 3, 25]

$$C_6H_5CHO + HN_3 \rightarrow C_6H_5CN + C_6H_5NHCHO$$

The relative yields of the two products depend upon the amount of sulfuric acid added to the reaction mixture. In an experiment in which 4 cc. of the acid was added to a solution of 10.6 g. of benzaldehyde and 4.8 g. of hydrazoic acid in 150 cc. of benzene, the yields of the nitrile and anilide were 70% and 13%, respectively; when 30 cc. of sulfuric acid was added the yields were 5% and 50%, respectively.[3]

Ketones. With symmetrical ketones the Schmidt reaction yields the corresponding substituted acid amides.

$$RCOR + HN_3 \rightarrow RCONHR$$

Thus methylacetamide and benzanilide are obtained from acetone and benzophenone, respectively, in quantitative yields.[1, 2, 3] Symmetrical ketones of a more complex structure have not yet been investigated. Unsymmetrical ketones can react in two different ways.

$$RCOR' + HN_3 \rightarrow RCONHR' \text{ and } RNHCOR'$$

Both reactions have been shown to occur when levulinic acid is treated with an equimolar amount of hydrazoic acid,[38] hydrolysis of the reaction mixture yielding β-alanine, acetic acid, methylamine, and succinic acid.[12, 38]

$$CH_3COCH_2CH_2CO_2H + HN_3 \nearrow CH_3CONHCH_2CH_2CO_2H \rightarrow CH_3CO_2H + NH_2CH_2CH_2CO_2H$$

$$CH_3COCH_2CH_2CO_2H + HN_3 \searrow CH_3NHCOCH_2CH_2CO_2H \rightarrow CH_3NH_2 + CO_2HCH_2CH_2CO_2H$$

[38] Moyer and Wolff, unpublished observation.

Since the main reaction product is β-alanine, the propionic acid group evidently migrates more readily than the methyl group. It appears that in aliphatic and alicyclic β-keto esters the acetic or substituted acetic ester residue migrates in preference to the hydrocarbon residue; thus the reaction of substituted acetoacetic esters with hydrazoic acid affords a convenient way to synthesize α-amino acids in excellent yields.[2, 25]

$$CH_3COC(R)(R')—CO_2C_2H_5 + HN_3 \rightarrow$$

$$CH_3CONHC(R)(R')—CO_2C_2H_5 + H_2O \rightarrow$$

$$H_2NC(R)(R')—CO_2H + C_2H_5OH + CH_3CO_2H$$

This reaction is particularly useful for the preparation of α-disubstituted α-amino acids, $R_2C(NH_2)—CO_2H$, which cannot be prepared by the more conventional condensation syntheses.

By the same scheme, β-amino acids should result from substituted levulinic acids. An exception to the preferential formation of acylamino acids is found in the α-,β-unsaturated ketone, benzalacetone, from which only N-methylcinnamamide has been isolated.[11]

$$C_6H_5CH{=}CHCOCH_3 + HN_3 \rightarrow C_6H_5CH{=}CHCONHCH_3$$

Apparently there is no tendency to form an N-vinyl acetamide in this instance.

The only diketone that has been brought into reaction with hydrazoic acid is benzil.[39] A careful investigation of the products of reaction with 2 moles of hydrazoic acid revealed that 1 mole reacted to form phenylglyoxanilide, which in turn reacted in two different ways with the second

[39] Spielman and Austin, *J. Am. Chem. Soc.*, **59**, 2658 (1937).

mole of hydrazoic acid, yielding mainly N-benzoyl-N′-phenylurea and some oxanilide.

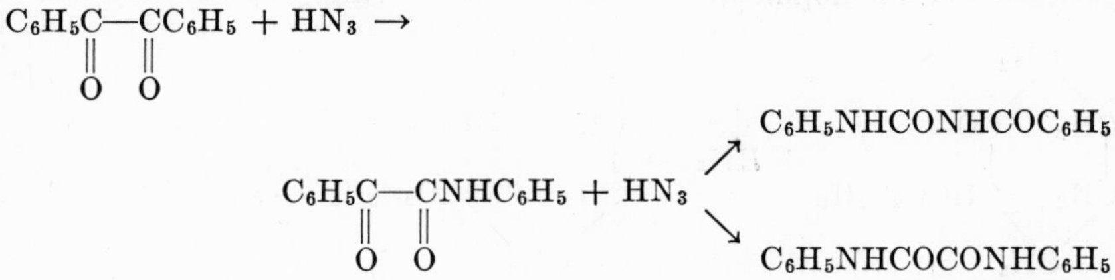

$$C_6H_5C(=O)—C(=O)C_6H_5 + HN_3 \rightarrow$$

$$C_6H_5C(=O)—C(=O)NHC_6H_5 + HN_3 \begin{cases} \nearrow C_6H_5NHCONHCOC_6H_5 \\ \searrow C_6H_5NHCOCONHC_6H_5 \end{cases}$$

Benzoic acid, aniline, and several tetrazole derivatives also have been isolated as by-products of this reaction. Essentially the same reaction products have been obtained from phenylglyoxylic anhydride.[40]

Hydrazoic acid reacts with cyclic ketones in the same way as with open-chain ketones, yielding cyclic amides (lactams) by ring enlargement.[2, 3, 4, 41–43]

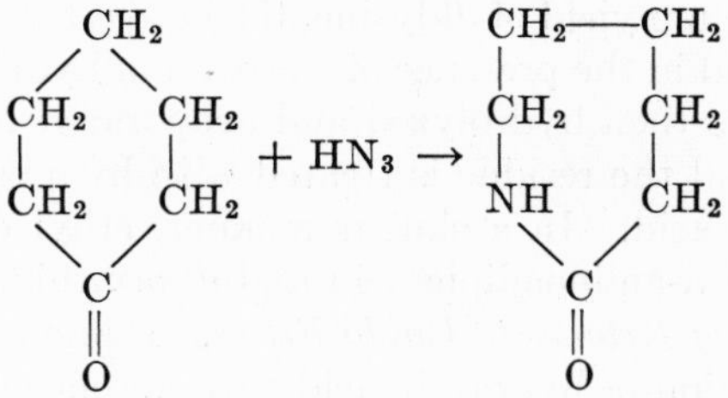

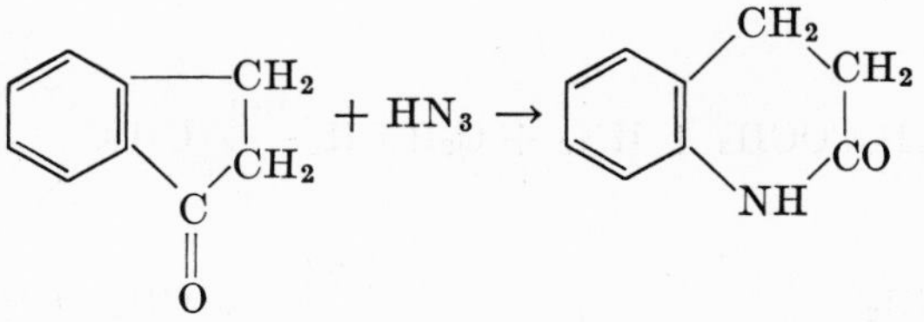

$$\text{cyclo-}(CH_2CH_2CH_2CH_2CH_2C{=}O) + HN_3 \rightarrow \text{cyclo-}(CH_2CH_2CH_2CH_2NHC{=}O)$$

$$C_6H_4\text{-}CH_2\text{-}CH_2\text{-}C{=}O\ (\alpha\text{-hydrindone}) + HN_3 \rightarrow C_6H_4\text{-}CH_2\text{-}CH_2\text{-}CO\text{-}NH$$

In the alkyl aryl ketones which have been investigated (acetophenone, α-hydrindone, etc.) the aryl groups migrate preferentially, yielding N-aryl amides.

From the reaction product of ethyl cyclohexanone-2-carboxylate and hydrazoic acid, α-aminopimelic acid is obtained by hydrolysis.[15, 25] This is the sole product when concentrated sulfuric acid is used as catalyst.

[40] Caronna, *Gazz. chim. ital.*, **71**, 585 (1941) [*C. A.*, **37**, 118 (1943)].
[41] Adamson and Kenner, *J. Chem. Soc.*, **1939**, 181.
[42] Briggs and De Ath, *J. Chem. Soc.*, **1937**, 456.
[43] Ruzicka, Goldberg, Hurbin, and Boeckenoogen, *Helv. Chim. Acta*, **16**, 1323 (1933).

If, however, traces of water are present in the reaction mixture and gaseous hydrogen chloride is the catalyst, the intermediate lactam hydrolyzes partially to α-aminopimelic acid which reacts further to yield *dl*-lysine.[15]

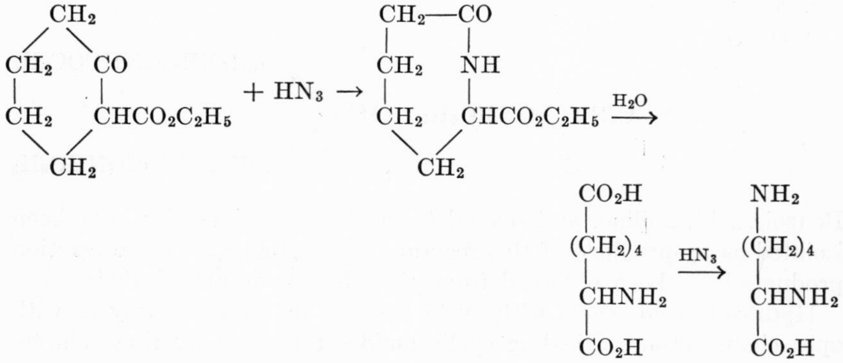

$$\begin{array}{c} CH_2 \\ / \quad \backslash \\ CH_2 \quad CO \\ | \qquad | \\ CH_2 \quad CHCO_2C_2H_5 \\ \backslash \quad / \\ CH_2 \end{array} + HN_3 \rightarrow \begin{array}{c} CH_2—CO \\ | \qquad | \\ CH_2 \quad NH \\ | \qquad | \\ CH_2 \quad CHCO_2C_2H_5 \\ \backslash \quad / \\ CH_2 \end{array} \xrightarrow{H_2O} \begin{array}{c} CO_2H \\ | \\ (CH_2)_4 \\ | \\ CHNH_2 \\ | \\ CO_2H \end{array} \xrightarrow{HN_3} \begin{array}{c} NH_2 \\ | \\ (CH_2)_4 \\ | \\ CHNH_2 \\ | \\ CO_2H \end{array}$$

To obtain a maximum yield of *dl*-lysine, the keto ester is allowed to react with hydrazoic acid in the presence of a stream of hydrogen chloride; the reaction mixture is then hydrolyzed and evaporated to remove the hydrochloric acid, and the residue is treated with hydrazoic acid and concentrated sulfuric acid. In a similar manner, ethyl cyclopentanone-2-carboxylate yields α-aminoadipic acid and *dl*-ornithine.

The Conversion of Ketones to Imido Esters. Imino esters may be prepared by the reaction of hydrazoic acid with ketones in the presence of alcohol.[44, 45]

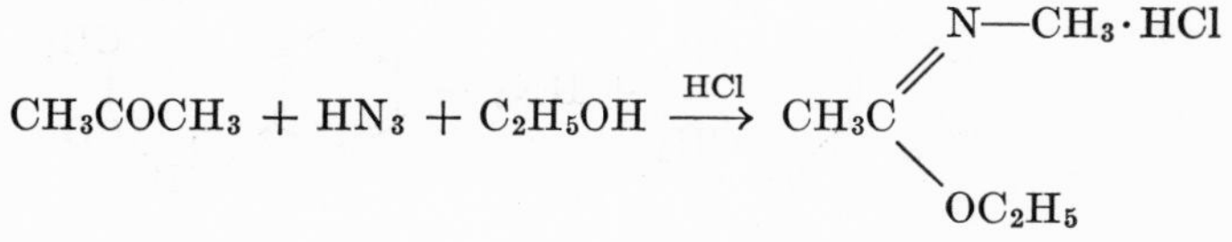

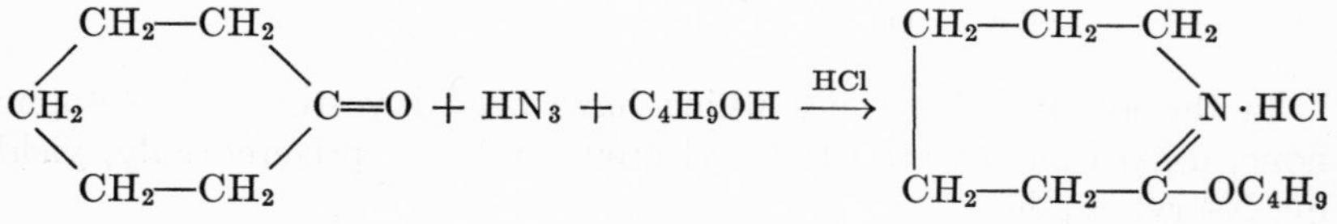

$$CH_3COCH_3 + HN_3 + C_2H_5OH \xrightarrow{HCl} CH_3C\begin{array}{l} \nearrow\!\!\!\!= N—CH_3 \cdot HCl \\ \searrow OC_2H_5 \end{array}$$

$$\begin{array}{c} CH_2—CH_2 \\ CH_2 \qquad\qquad C{=}O \\ CH_2—CH_2 \end{array} + HN_3 + C_4H_9OH \xrightarrow{HCl} \begin{array}{l} CH_2—CH_2—CH_2 \\ | \qquad\qquad\qquad\quad \backslash \\ | \qquad\qquad\qquad\quad N \cdot HCl \\ | \qquad\qquad\qquad\quad // \\ CH_2—CH_2—C—OC_4H_9 \end{array}$$

The Reactions of Excess Hydrazoic Acid with Aldehydes and Ketones. The Formation of Tetrazoles

In the reactions discussed above, hydrazoic acid is used in equimolar quantity or in only slight excess. Even so, tetrazoles sometimes are ob-

[44] Schattner, thesis, Heidelberg, 1929.

[45] Ger. pat., 488,447 [*Frdl.*, **18**, 3048 (1933)]; U. S. pat., 1,889,323 [*C. A.*, **27**, 1361 (1933)].

tained as by-products.[3, 25, 43, 46] Thus, phenyltetrazole is a by-product of the reaction of benzaldehyde.[25]

$$C_6H_5CHO + 2HN_3 \rightarrow \begin{array}{c} C_6H_5C{=}N \\ \mid \quad\quad \mid \\ NH \quad N \\ \diagdown \quad \diagup\!\!\!\!\diagup \\ N \end{array}$$

Similarly tetrazoles are formed in small amounts when large cyclic ketones are treated with hydrazoic acid in equivalent amounts,[47] and several tetrazoles are formed when benzil is treated with 2 equivalents of hydrazoic acid.[39] If the substituted tetrazoles are desired as the main reaction products, an excess (2 molar equivalents or more) of hydrazoic acid is introduced. Acetone yields 1,5-dimethyltetrazole readily.[2, 48]

$$CH_3COCH_3 + 2HN_3 \rightarrow \begin{array}{c} CH_3C{=}N \\ \mid \quad\quad \mid \\ CH_3N \quad N \\ \diagdown \quad \diagup\!\!\!\!\diagup \\ N \end{array}$$

The behavior of benzophenone is exceptional; it does not yield 1,5-diphenyltetrazole but reacts with 3 moles of hydrazoic acid to form 5-phenylimino-1-phenyl-1,2-dihydrotetrazole.[2, 48]

$$C_6H_5COC_6H_5 + 3HN_3 \rightarrow \begin{array}{c} N \\ \diagup\!\!\!\!\diagup \quad \diagdown \\ N \quad\quad NH \\ \mid \quad\quad\quad \mid \\ C_6H_5N{=}C \text{———} NC_6H_5 \end{array}$$

Cyclic ketones react normally. The 1,5-cyclopentamethylenetetrazole obtained from cyclohexanone and hydrazoic acid is known commercially by the name of Metrazole or Cardiazole;[2, 48] it is a heart stimulant.

$$\begin{array}{c} CH_2 \\ \diagup \quad \diagdown \\ CH_2 \quad CO \\ \mid \quad\quad \mid \\ CH_2 \quad CH_2 \\ \diagdown \quad \diagup \\ CH_2 \end{array} + 2HN_3 \rightarrow \begin{array}{l} CH_2\text{—}CH_2\diagdown \\ \mid \qquad\qquad\quad C{=}N \\ CH_2 \qquad\qquad\; \mid \quad\;\; \mid \\ \mid \qquad\qquad\; \diagup N \quad N \\ CH_2\text{—}CH_2\diagup \quad \diagdown \;\diagup\!\!\!\!\diagup \\ \qquad\qquad\qquad\quad N \end{array}$$

Tetrazoles have been prepared from many other cyclic ketones such as polymethylene cycloketones,[25, 47, 49] camphor, and thujone.[50]

[46] v. Braun and Heymons, *Ber.*, **63**, 502 (1930).

[47] Ruzicka, Goldberg, and Hurbin, *Helv. Chim. Acta*, **16**, 1335 (1933).

[48] Ger. pat., 439,041 [*Frdl.*, **15**, 333 (1930)]; U. S. pat., 1,599,493 [*C. A.*, **20**, 3460 (1926)]

[49] Brit. pat., 555,140 [*C. A.*, **39**, 944 (1945)].

[50] Ger. pat., 606,615 [*Frdl.*, **21**, 675 (1936)]; U. S. pat., 2,029,799 [*C. A.*, **30**, 1950 (1936)]

The amides which are formed by the reaction of hydrazoic acid with ketones apparently are not intermediates in the formation of tetrazoles. It has been shown that ε-caprolactam, which is obtained from cyclohexanone and hydrazoic acid, does not react further with hydrazoic acid.[2] No tetrazoles are formed from N-benzoyl-N′-phenylurea, a fact which indicates that the tetrazoles formed from benzil and hydrazoic acid do not arise from further reaction of the major product.[39] Unlike most ketones, benzil does not give a higher yield of tetrazoles if an excess of hydrazoic acid is employed.[39]

The Reaction of Hydrazoic Acid with Quinones

The reaction of quinones with hydrazoic acid has been effected in the absence of strong mineral acid, and therefore such syntheses are not considered true Schmidt reactions.

Treatment of benzoquinone with a large excess of hydrazoic acid in benzene solution results in the formation of azidohydroquinone.[51]

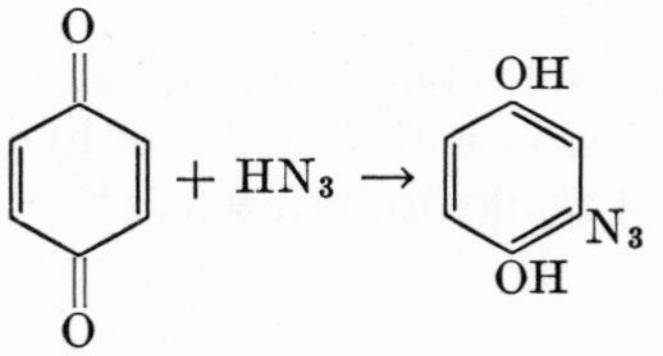

$$\text{benzoquinone} + HN_3 \rightarrow \text{azidohydroquinone (OH, OH, } N_3\text{)}$$

From 1,4- or 1,2-naphthoquinones, however, good yields of 2-amino-1,4-naphthoquinone and 4-amino-1,2-naphthoquinone, respectively, are obtained when glacial acetic acid serves as solvent and 1.7 equivalents of sodium azide is added.[52] 3-Bromo-1,2-naphthoquinone yields 3-bromo-

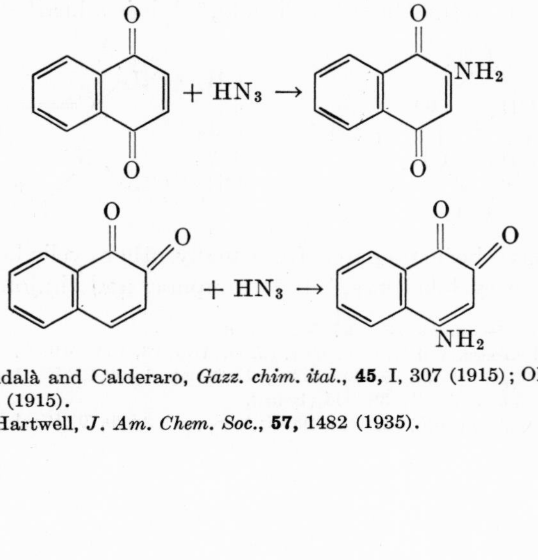

$$\text{1,4-naphthoquinone} + HN_3 \rightarrow \text{2-amino-1,4-naphthoquinone } (NH_2)$$

$$\text{1,2-naphthoquinone} + HN_3 \rightarrow \text{4-amino-1,2-naphthoquinone } (NH_2)$$

[51] Oliveri-Mandalà and Calderaro, *Gazz. chim. ital.*, **45**, I, 307 (1915); Oliveri-Mandalà, *ibid.*, **45**, II, 120 (1915).

[52] Fieser and Hartwell, *J. Am. Chem. Soc.*, **57**, 1482 (1935).

4-amino-1,2-naphthoquinone. However, certain substituents hinder the reaction. Neither 2-methyl-1,4-naphthoquinone nor 4-methyl-1,2-naphthoquinone reacts with hydrazoic acid.[52]

Phenanthrenequinone gives phenanthridone, retenequinone forms 1-methyl-7-isopropylphenanthridone, and chrysenequinone gives α-naphthophenanthridone.[53] No reaction occurs with acenaphthenequinone.

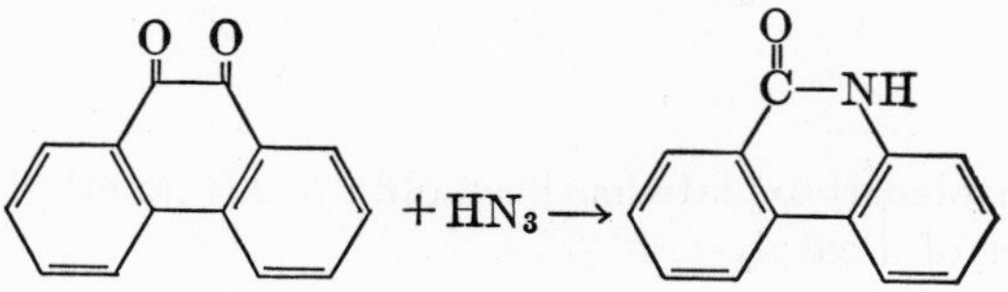

$$\text{Phenanthrenequinone} + HN_3 \rightarrow \text{Phenanthridone (C(=O)–NH)}$$

The Reactions of Hydrazoic Acid with Functional Groups Other than Carbonyl

Many functional groups besides the carbonyl group react with hydrazoic acid to give tetrazoles. In most of these reactions no catalyst is required. The tetrazoles thus obtained frequently are formed by rearrangement of intermediate azides. Since it may be desired to apply the Schmidt reaction to a molecule containing other functional groups or to a mixture of compounds, a few of the reactions leading to the formation of tetrazoles will be discussed briefly.

Nitriles. Nitriles usually do not react with hydrazoic acid unless concentrated sulfuric acid is present, in which case they yield tetrazoles.[54] The first step of the reaction may consist in the formation of carbodiimides, which are known to react with hydrazoic acid to form tetrazoles.[55, 56]

$$RCN + HN_3 \rightarrow HN{=}C{=}NR \qquad R = \text{aliphatic or aromatic}$$

$$HN{=}C{=}NR + HN_3 \rightarrow \begin{array}{c} H_2NC\!=\!=\!=\!N \\ | \qquad\quad | \\ RN \qquad N \\ \diagdown \quad /\!\!/ \\ N \end{array}$$

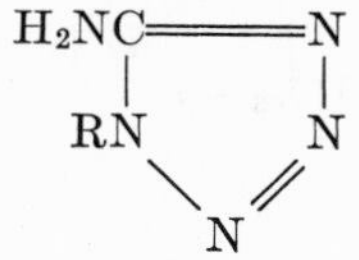

Several of these 5-amino-1-alkyltetrazoles have been prepared in satisfactory yields. If the reaction is carried out with a dinitrile, it is possible to obtain either the corresponding bistetrazole or the tetrazolenitrile, from which the tetrazolecarboxylic acid is readily accessible. Thus,

[53] Caronna, *Gazz. chim. ital.*, **71,** 481 (1941) [*C. A.*, **37,** 118 (1943)].

[54] v. Braun and Keller, *Ber.*, **65,** 1677 (1932).

[55] Oliveri-Mandalà, *Gazz. chim. ital.*, **52,** II, 139 (1922).

[56] Stollé, *Ber.*, **55,** 1289 (1922); Stollé and Henke-Stark, *J. prakt. Chem.*, (2), **124,** 261 (1930).

from octamethylene dicyanide, the mono- and bis-tetrazoles have been prepared.[54]

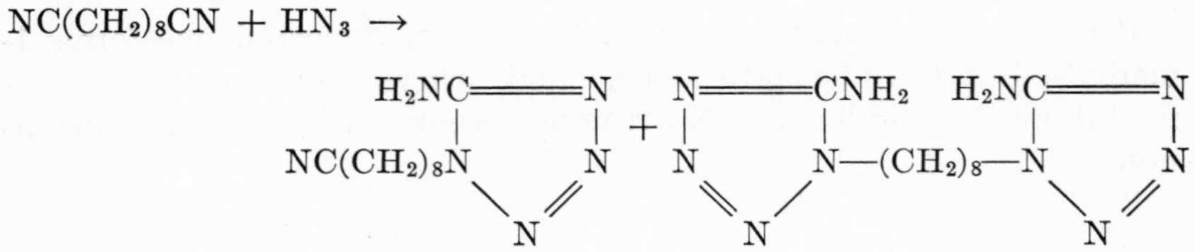

$NC(CH_2)_8CN + HN_3 \rightarrow$

```
     H2NC═════N    N═════CNH2  H2NC═════N
        |     |  +  |      |      |     |
NC(CH2)8N     N    N      N—(CH2)8—N    N
         \   //     \\   /          \  //
           N          N               N
```

Ethyl tetrazolecarboxylate has been obtained from ethyl cyanoformate in the absence of a catalyst.[57]

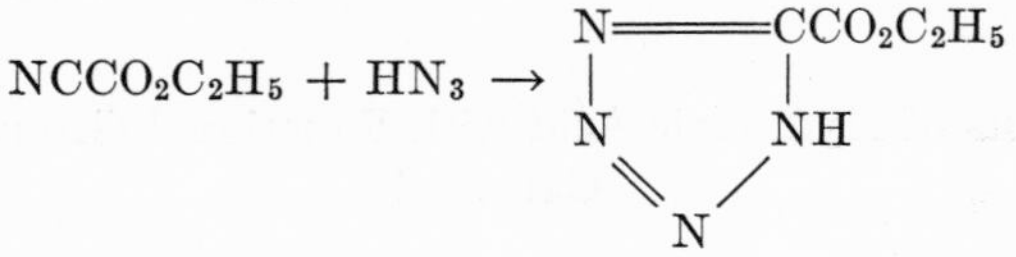

```
                      N═════CCO2C2H5
NCCO2C2H5 + HN3 →     |     |
                      N     NH
                       \\  /
                         N
```

Hydrocyanic Acid, Cyanamide, Cyanogen, and Isocyanides. From the reaction of hydrazoic acid with hydrocyanic acid an 80% yield of tetrazole is obtained; no catalyst is required.[58]

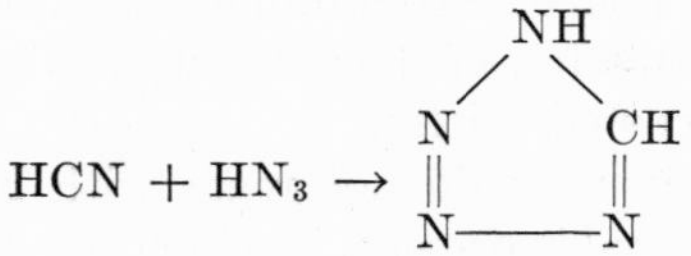

```
                 NH
                /  \
               N    CH
HCN + HN3 →    ‖    ‖
               N————N
```

Similarly tetrazole is obtained from cyanamide, 5-aminotetrazole from dicyanamide,[59] and 5-cyanotetrazole from cyanogen.[60]

Isocyanides yield substituted tetrazoles.[61]

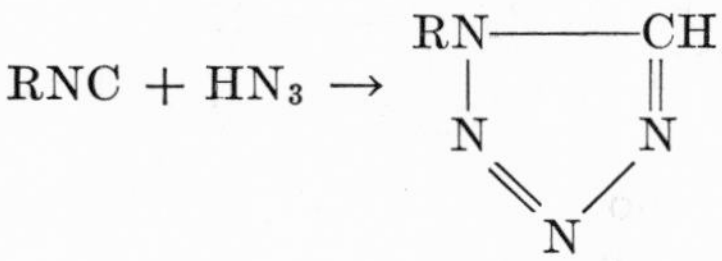

```
                RN————CH
RNC + HN3 →     |     ‖
                N     N
                 \\  /
                   N
```

Oximes, Amides, Amidoximes, Lactams, Hydroxamic Chlorides, Imide Chlorides, and Dichloroketones. The preparation of 1,5-pentamethylenetetrazole from cyclohexanoneoxime and sodium azide in the

[57] Oliveri-Mandalà, *Gazz. chim. ital.*, **41,** I, 59 (1911).

[58] Dimroth and Fester, *Ber.*, **43,** 2219 (1910).

[59] Stollé, *Ber.*, **62,** 1118 (1929).

[60] Oliveri-Mandalà and Passalacqua, *Gazz. chim. ital.*, **41,** II, 430 (1911).

[61] Oliveri-Mandalà and Alagna, *Gazz. chim. ital.*, **40,** II, 441 (1910); Oliveri-Mandalà, *Atti accad. Lincei*, **19,** I, 228 (1910) [*C. A.*, **4,** 2455 (1910)].

presence of fuming sulfuric acid or chlorosulfonic acid has been described.[62]

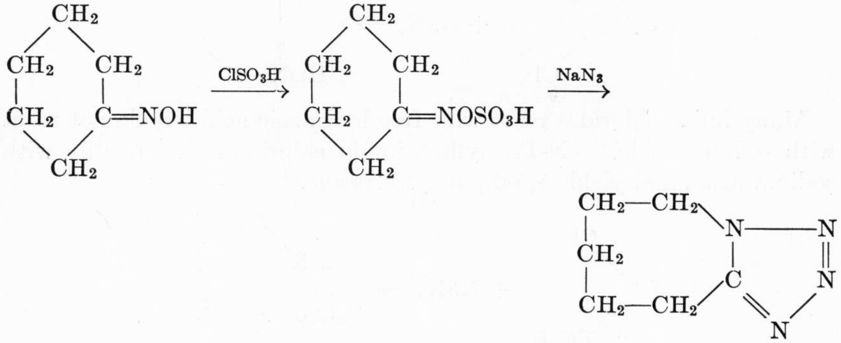

$$\underset{\text{(cyclohexanone oxime)}}{\text{CH}_2\text{—CH}_2\text{—CH}_2\text{—CH}_2\text{—CH}_2\text{—C=NOH (ring)}} \xrightarrow{\text{ClSO}_3\text{H}} \text{CH}_2\text{—CH}_2\text{—CH}_2\text{—CH}_2\text{—CH}_2\text{—C=NOSO}_3\text{H (ring)} \xrightarrow{\text{NaN}_3}$$

CH$_2$—CH$_2$—N——N

| | ‖

CH$_2$ C N

| ⟋ ⟍ ⟋

CH$_2$—CH$_2$ N

In the preparation of tetrazoles from oximes, monosubstituted amides, and amidoximes the use of acid chlorides such as thionyl chloride, benzenesulfonyl chloride, or phosphorus chlorides transforms the compounds into imide chlorides, which then yield tetrazoles upon treatment with sodium azide.[44, 62, 63]

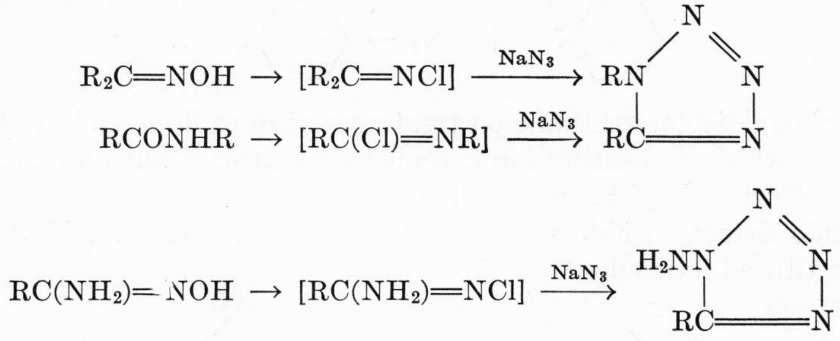

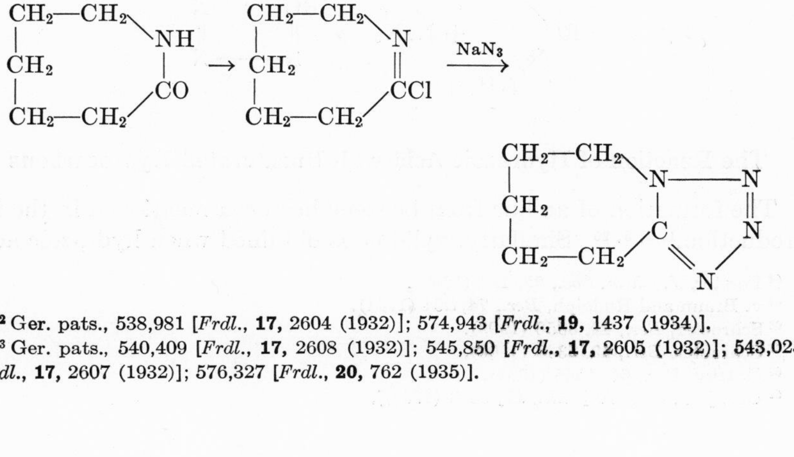

$$\text{R}_2\text{C=NOH} \rightarrow [\text{R}_2\text{C=NCl}] \xrightarrow{\text{NaN}_3} \text{RN—N=N—N=CR (tetrazole)}$$

$$\text{RCONHR} \rightarrow [\text{RC(Cl)=NR}] \xrightarrow{\text{NaN}_3} \text{RN—N=N—N=CR (tetrazole)}$$

$$\text{RC(NH}_2\text{)=NOH} \rightarrow [\text{RC(NH}_2\text{)=NCl}] \xrightarrow{\text{NaN}_3} \text{H}_2\text{NN—N=N—N=CR (tetrazole)}$$

$$\text{CH}_2\text{—CH}_2\text{—CH}_2\text{—CH}_2\text{—CH}_2\text{—CO—NH (ring)} \rightarrow \text{CH}_2\text{—CH}_2\text{—CH}_2\text{—CH}_2\text{—CH}_2\text{—CCl=N (ring)} \xrightarrow{\text{NaN}_3}$$

CH$_2$—CH$_2$—N——N

| | ‖

CH$_2$ C N

| ⟋ ⟍ ⟋

CH$_2$—CH$_2$ N

[62] Ger. pats., 538,981 [*Frdl.*, **17**, 2604 (1932)]; 574,943 [*Frdl.*, **19**, 1437 (1934)].

[63] Ger. pats., 540,409 [*Frdl.*, **17**, 2608 (1932)]; 545,850 [*Frdl.*, **17**, 2605 (1932)]; 543,025 [*Frdl.*, **17**, 2607 (1932)]; 576,327 [*Frdl.*, **20**, 762 (1935)].

Similarly tetrazoles are formed from hydroxamic chlorides.[64]

```
          NOH                    C6H5C=N
         //                       |     \
    C6H5C        + NaN3 →         |      N
         \                        |     //
          Cl                     HON—N
```

Many imide chlorides react with free hydrazoic acid but do not react with sodium azide.[65] N-Phenylbenzimido chloride reacts readily with sodium azide and yields 1,5-diphenyltetrazole.[66]

```
                                        N
          Cl                          /   \\
         /                           N      N
    C6H5C        + NaN3 →            ||     |
         \\                      C6H5C——————NC6H5
          NC6H5
```

2-Chloropyridine and 2-chloroquinoline, which may be regarded formally as imide chlorides, also yield benzotetrazole and naphthotetrazole respectively. No catalysts are needed for the imide chloride reactions.[65]

```
        Cl                          N—N
       /                          //   ||
   (pyridine)N   + HN3 →   (ring)N—————N
```

Diphenyldichloromethane on treatment with sodium azide yields the diazide, which on heating forms diphenyltetrazole [67] but on addition to 70% sulfuric acid yields 98% of benzanilide.[68]

Imido Esters. Imido esters react readily with sodium azide to form 5-substituted tetrazoles.[69]

```
                                    NH
        OR                        /    \
       /                        RC      N
    RC         + NaN3 →         ||      ||
       \\                       N———————N
        NH
```

The Reaction of Hydrazoic Acid with Unsaturated Hydrocarbons

The formation of aniline from benzene has been mentioned in the introduction.[1, 2, 3, 25] Similarly, xylidine is obtained when hydrazoic acid

[64] Forster, *J. Chem. Soc.*, **95,** 184 (1909).

[65] v. Braun and Rudolph, *Ber.*, **74,** 264 (1941).

[66] Schroeter, *Ber.*, **42,** 3356 (1909).

[67] Schroeter, *Ber.*, **42,** 2336 (1909).

[68] Gotzky, *Ber.*, **64,** 1555 (1931).

[69] Ger. pat., 521.870 [*Frdl.*, **17,** 2603 (1932)].

is decomposed by concentrated sulfuric acid in xylene solution.[3] These nuclear aminations do not proceed at temperatures essentially below 60–70°.[7] Small amounts of *o*- and *p*-toluidine have been obtained from toluene and hydrazoic acid with ultraviolet light or with aluminum chloride as catalyst.[8]

A very interesting reaction of hydrazoic acid with unsaturated aliphatic or cyclic compounds is referred to in a patent [7b] according to which aliphatic compounds form Schiff's bases in high yields. From amylene

$$RR'C{=}CHR'' + HN_3 \xrightarrow{H_2SO_4} RR'C{=}NCH_2R''$$

the products isolated after hydrolysis are acetone, methyl ethyl ketone, methylamine, and ethylamine. The formation of these products can be explained by hydrolysis of the two intermediate ketimines.

$$CH_3C(CH_3){=}CHCH_3 + HN_3 \rightarrow CH_3C(CH_3){=}NCH_2CH_3 \quad \text{and} \quad CH_3CH_2C(CH_3){=}NCH_3$$

Cyclic unsaturated compounds undergo ring enlargement.

$$\text{cyclopentene (}CH_2\text{—}CH_2\text{—}CH_2\text{—}CH{=}CH\text{, ring)} + HN_3 \rightarrow \text{ring } CH_2\text{—}CH{=}N\text{—}CH_2\text{—}CH_2\text{—}CH_2$$

For example, from camphene, a mixture of 50% of α- and 25% of β-N-dehydrocamphidine is claimed.

$$\text{camphene-type ring (}CH_3\text{—C bridgehead, }CH_2\text{—}CH_2\text{, }CH{=}CH\text{, }CH_3CCH_3\text{ bridge, CH)} + HN_3 \xrightarrow{H_2SO_4} \text{ring with }CH_2,\ CH{=}N,\ CH_2,\ CH_2 + \text{ring with }CH_2,\ CH_2\text{—}N{=}CH,\ CH_2$$

Compounds which contain tertiary hydroxyl groups or halogen atoms and therefore can form unsaturated hydrocarbons by dehydration or dehydrohalogenation also can react to yield Schiff's bases in high yields.

$$R_3CX + HN_3 \xrightarrow{H_2SO_4} R_2C{=}NR + HX \qquad X = OH \text{ or halogen}$$

[7b] Ger. pat., 583,565 [*Frdl.*, **20**, 947 (1935)].

From the reaction of *t*-butyl chloride with hydrazoic acid in the presence of concentrated sulfuric acid a yield of 70% of acetone and 80% of methylamine has been reported.

$$(CH_3)_3CCl + HN_3 \xrightarrow{H_2SO_4} (CH_3)_2C{=}NCH_3 \rightarrow CH_3COCH_3 + CH_3NH_2$$

Anethole dibromide yields α-bromopropionaldehyde and 75% of *p*-anisidine. There may be an analogy between this reaction and the formation

$$CH_3O\langle C_6H_4\rangle CHBrCHBrCH_3 + HN_3 \xrightarrow{H_2SO_4}$$

$$\left[CH_3O\langle C_6H_4\rangle N{=}CHCHBrCH_3\right] \rightarrow CH_3O\langle C_6H_4\rangle NH_2 + CH_3CHBrCHO$$

of aniline from cinnamic acid (p. 311), which could yield an intermediate of the structure $C_6H_5N{=}CHCH_2CO_2H$.

Benzohydrol is reported to yield 90% of benzalaniline.

$$C_6H_5CHOHC_6H_5 + HN_3 \xrightarrow{H_2SO_4} C_6H_5CH{=}NC_6H_5$$

Menthol reacts as follows.

$$\begin{array}{ccc} & CH_3 & \\ & | & \\ & CH & \\ / & & \backslash \\ CH_2 & & CH_2 \\ | & & | \\ CH_2 & & CHOH \\ \backslash & & / \\ & CH & \\ & | & \\ & CH(CH_3)_2 & \end{array} + HN_3 \xrightarrow{H_2SO_4}$$

$$\begin{array}{ccc} & CH_3 & \\ & | & \\ & CH & \\ / & & \backslash \\ CH_2 & & CH_2 \\ | & & | \\ | & & N \\ | & & \| \\ CH_2 & & CH \\ \backslash & & / \\ & CH & \\ & | & \\ & CH(CH_3)_2 & \\ & (15\%) & \end{array} + \begin{array}{ccc} & CH_3 & \\ & | & \\ & CH & \\ / & & \backslash \\ CH_2 & & CH_2 \\ | & & | \\ | & & CH_2 \\ | & & | \\ CH_2 & & N \\ \backslash & & /\!/ \\ & C & \\ & | & \\ & CH(CH_3)_2 & \end{array} \rightarrow \begin{array}{ccc} & CH_3 & \\ & | & \\ & CH & \\ / & & \backslash \\ CH_2 & & CH_2 \\ | & & | \\ | & & CH_2 \\ | & & | \\ CH_2 & & NH \\ \backslash & & / \\ & C & \\ & \| & \\ & C(CH_3)_2 & \\ & (50\%) & \end{array}$$

Borneol reacts in an analogous manner.

EXPERIMENTAL CONDITIONS

The Schmidt reaction can be carried out with a solution of hydrazoic acid in an appropriate organic solvent * or with sodium azide directly. The direct method has the advantage of eliminating one step and avoiding the isolation of the very poisonous hydrazoic acid. Most of the reactions reported, however, have been carried out with free hydrazoic acid, and when both methods have been reported on the same compound the yield was higher when free hydrazoic acid was used.[15] Other authors claim, however, that sodium azide may be used without detrimental effect to the yield,[12] and the claim seems to be corroborated by the increased use of sodium azide in recent investigations.[17, 22, 27–33, 71]

The Preparation of Hydrazoic Acid Solutions [10]

Since hydrazoic acid is very poisonous, all reactions involving it should be carried out under a good hood. If some hydrazoic acid has been inhaled accidentally, resulting in a feeling of pressure in the head, the drinking of a few cubic centimeters of 96% alcohol has been suggested to relieve these symptoms. Hydrazoic acid has a pungent odor.

In a large three-necked flask containing a dropping funnel, thermometer, efficient stirrer, and gas outlet tube, a paste is prepared from equal weights of technical sodium azide and warm water. To this paste, chloroform or benzene is added (about 40 cc. for each 6.5 g. of sodium azide used) and the mixture is cooled to 0°. While the mixture is stirred and cooled, concentrated sulfuric acid is added dropwise (1 mole of sulfuric acid for 2 moles of sodium azide). The temperature should not exceed 10°. After the addition of the calculated amount of acid, the mixture is cooled to 0° and the organic layer is decanted and dried over anhydrous sodium sulfate. The strength of the chloroform or benzene solution of hydrazoic acid can be determined by pipetting (*not using mouth suction*) a few cubic centimeters into a glass-stoppered bottle, shaking it with 30–50 cc. of distilled water, and titrating with a standard alkali solution. Usually the concentration of hydrazoic acid ranges from 4% to 10%.

* *Note added in proof.* Sanford, Blair, Arroya and Sherk [*J. Am. Chem. Soc.*, **67**, 1941 (1945)] have added dry gaseous hydrogen azide to ketones in benzene solution in the presence of sulfuric acid. The ketones used and the amides isolated were: $CH_3COCH_2CH_3$, $CH_3CONHC_2H_5$ (70%); $CH_3COCH_2CH(CH_3)_2$, $CH_3CONHCH_2CH(CH_3)_2$ (71%); $CH_3COC_6H_5$, $CH_3CONHC_6H_5$ (90%); $CH_3COC_6H_4CH_3$ (*p*), $CH_3CONHC_6H_4CH_3$ (*p*) (90%); $CH_3COC_6H_4OCH_3$ (*p*), $CH_3CONHC_6H_4OCH_3$ (*p*) (50%); $CH_3COC_{10}H_7$ (β), $CH_3CONHC_{10}H_7$ (β) (73%); $CH_3CH_2COC_6H_5$, $CH_3CH_2CONHC_6H_5$ (90%); $(C_6H_5)_2CO$ $C_6H_5CONHC_6H_5$ (80%); $C_6H_5CONHC_6H_4CH_3$ (*p*), $C_6H_5CONHC_6H_4CH_3$ (*p*) (82%).

[71] Arnold, *Ber.*, **76**, 777 (1943).

The Reaction of Hydrazoic Acid with Carbonyl Compounds

The Schmidt reaction with a carbonyl compound can be carried out in essentially three different ways:

1. Addition of hydrazoic acid. The organic acid or ketone is dissolved in at least twice its volume of concentrated sulfuric acid (plus chloroform or benzene in the case of a ketone). To the solution the hydrazoic acid solution is added with stirring. This method is preferable for the preparation of amines from acids.[10, 11, 13–16, 19, 24, 26, 38, 42, 72–74] The speed of the reaction can be observed by passing the escaping gases through a wash bottle. The gas stream should be lively but not violent. The amount of hydrazoic acid used is generally from 1 to 1.2 moles of hydrazoic acid for one carbonyl group. After all the acid has been added, stirring is continued until gas evolution has ceased.

2. Addition of concentrated sulfuric acid. To a stirred solution of the organic acid, ketone, or aldehyde in chloroform (or benzene) and hydrazoic acid (1 to 1.2 moles), concentrated sulfuric acid is added dropwise. This method avoids prolonged contact of the carbonyl compound with concentrated sulfuric acid. It is the only method that has been used for the reaction of aldehydes with hydrazoic acid.[2, 3, 11, 39, 42, 46]

3. Addition of the carbonyl compound and hydrazoic acid. A mixture of the carbonyl compound (1 mole) and the hydrazoic acid solution (1 to 1.2 moles) is added with stirring to concentrated sulfuric acid or to a concentrated sulfuric acid-chloroform mixture.[2, 3, 43]

The Generation of Hydrazoic Acid *in Situ*

To a stirred solution of the carbonyl compound in chloroform and concentrated sulfuric acid, sodium azide is added in small portions, until after addition of 1.0 to 1.2 moles of sodium azide no more gas is developed.[12, 15, 17, 22, 23, 27–33, 37, 71] It is possible that better yields might be achieved by an activation of technical sodium azide with hydrazine hydrate,[21] a process which is reported to give better results in the formation of isocyanates from acid halides and sodium azide.

Temperature

The Schmidt reaction with aldehydes and ketones always is carried out with cooling of the reaction mixture in an ice bath. The temperature

[72] v. Braun and Pinkernelle, *Ber.*, **67**, 1056 (1934).

[73] Cosciug, *Wien. Chem. Ztg.*, **46**, 145 (1943) [*C. A.*, **38**, 4575 (1944)].

[74] Jansen and Pope, *Proc. Roy. Soc. London*, **A154**, 53 (1936); *Chemistry & Industry*, **51**, 316 (1932).

range for the preparation of amines from acids is from 35° to 50° and in most cases is maintained between 40° and 45°. The reaction is exothermic, and the temperature can be controlled by the rate of addition of the hydrazoic acid solution. Only if the reaction is sluggish is a higher temperature of advantage. Glycine is obtained in only 29% yield from malonic acid at 40°, whereas the yield is 46% at 50°.[15] The yield of aniline from benzoic acid is 85% if the reaction is carried out at 40° and drops to 44% when boiling chloroform is used as a solvent.[11] However, the drop in yield with higher temperature may be due to loss of hydrazoic acid (b.p. 37°).

Solvents

In almost all preparations the hydrazoic acid is dissolved in chloroform or benzene. Since chloroform is completely inert towards hydrazoic acid it may be preferable, but under most conditions benzene is just as satisfactory. Trichloroethylene also has been used successfully as a solvent.[7] The addition of dioxane has been found to be of value in the preparation of *dl*-phenylalanine from benzylmalonic acid.[11] Ethyl ether is not a satisfactory solvent,[11] although its use has been mentioned in patents.[3]

Catalysts

Concentrated sulfuric acid in amounts of 2–4 cc. for 1 g. of carbonyl compound has been used most extensively as the catalyst for the Schmidt reaction. In dilute sulfuric acid the yield decreases sharply.[2, 11] The yield of aniline from benzoic acid drops from 85% to 15% if 75% sulfuric acid is used.[11] Other catalysts mentioned are hydrogen chloride;[15, 43] phosphorus trichloride, oxychloride, pentoxide, and pentachloride; thionyl chloride; ferric chloride, stannic chloride; sulfoacetic acid and other sulfonic acids;[25] phosphoric acid;[3] aluminum chloride;[25] and ultraviolet light.[8] There is no evidence that any of these catalysts is as good as concentrated sulfuric acid.

The Isolation of the Reaction Products

The amines are isolated either by liberation from the crystalline amine sulfate, or by steam distillation of the alkalized water extract of the reaction mixture, or by ether extraction of the alkaline solution. In the preparation of amino acids the isolation may be effected by forming an appropriate derivative such as a picrate or phosphotungstate.[15]

EXPERIMENTAL PROCEDURES

The Preparation of Amines and Derivatives of Amines

Heptadecylamine from Stearic Acid.[11] To a solution of 15 g. (0.53 mole) of purified stearic acid (m.p. 69.5°) in 500 cc. of benzene, 30 cc. of concentrated sulfuric acid is added and the mixture stirred vigorously at 40°. One and two-tenths moles of hydrazoic acid (52 cc. of a 5.3% solution in benzene) is then added slowly. After the reaction has ceased (about two hours), the acid layer is poured into water to precipitate the sulfate of heptadecylamine, which may be crystallized from ethanol as white plates that turn brown at 195° and decompose at 200°. The yield is 96%.

5-Ethoxy-1-(4-ethoxybutyl)-amylamine from 6-Ethoxy-2-(4-ethoxybutyl)-caproic Acid.[27] To a mixture of 6.3 g. (0.024 mole) of the acid, 41 cc. of concentrated sulfuric acid, and 80 cc. of chloroform is added with stirring at 50–55°, 1.82 g. (0.042 mole) of sodium azide in small portions. After all the azide has been added the mixture is heated for another thirty minutes at 50°, diluted with ice, and made alkaline. The reaction mixture is steam-distilled, hydrochloric acid is added to the distillate, and the solution is filtered. The free amine is liberated from its hydrochloride by the addition of alkali. The amine is taken up in ether, dried over potassium hydroxide, and distilled in vacuum (b.p. 162°/15 mm.). The yield is 4.7 g. or 84%.

Lactam of 16-Aminohexadecanoic Acid from Cyclohexadecanone.[43] To a stirred mixture of 50 cc. of concentrated sulfuric acid and 150 cc. of benzene, cooled in an ice bath, is added a solution of 15.3 g. (0.0643 mole) of cyclohexadecanone and 2.9 g. (0.0674 mole) of hydrazoic acid in 150 cc. of benzene. After fifteen minutes, ice is added to the reaction mixture, and the benzene layer is separated and washed with a dilute sodium hydroxide solution. The product obtained by concentration of the benzene layer can be purified by distillation (b.p. 171–178°/1 mm.), and crystallization of the distillate from acetone. The yield of pure lactam, melting at 125–126°, is 14 g. (86%).

Ethyl N-Methylacetimidate.[45] A mixture of 58 g. (1 mole) of acetone and 600 cc. of a benzene solution of hydrazoic acid containing 65 g. (1.5 moles) of hydrazoic acid is added dropwise with stirring to 250 cc. of ethanol previously saturated with hydrogen chloride; the temperature is kept below 25° by cooling, if necessary. When no more gas is evolved, the benzene and excess ethanol are evaporated; the residue consists of the very hygroscopic imido ester hydrochloride. The free base, liberated by treatment with strong alkali, is dissolved in ether. The ether solution is carefully dried and distilled. Ethyl N-methylacetimidate boiling at 99–100° is obtained in 50% yield.

The Preparation of Tetrazoles

1,5-Dimethyltetrazole.[48] To a mixture of 35 g. (0.814 mole) of hydrazoic acid dissolved in about 500 cc. of benzene and 50 cc. of concentrated sulfuric acid, 15.7 g. (0.27 mole) of acetone is added dropwise with stirring and cooling. Approximately 5 l. of nitrogen is evolved. The acid layer is then diluted with ice and neutralized with sodium carbonate, and ethanol is added to precipitate the sodium sulfate. After filtration, the solution is concentrated and the mercuric chloride complex of the reaction product is obtained by adding a cold saturated aqueous solution of mercuric chloride. The addition compound melts at 111°. The free 1,5-dimethyltetrazole is obtained by decomposing an aqueous solution of the addition product with hydrogen sulfide and evaporating the filtrate to dryness. The product is recrystallized from petroleum ether; it melts at 71°. The yield is about 80%.

1,5-Cyclohexamethylenetetrazole.[47] A solution of 12 g. (0.101 mole) of cycloheptanone and 11.5 g. (0.267 mole) of hydrazoic acid solution in 280 cc. of benzene is added during forty-five minutes with stirring and ice cooling to a mixture of 60 cc. of concentrated sulfuric acid and 100 cc. of benzene. The brownish green reaction mixture is diluted with ice and ice water. The benzene layer contains practically none of the reaction product. The sulfuric acid layer is made alkaline with sodium hydroxide and extracted exhaustively with ether. The crystalline product boils at 135–140°/0.1 mm. and melts after recrystallization from benzene at 66–68°.

1-*n*-Hexyl-5-aminotetrazole.[54] To a mixture of 11.1 g. (0.1 mole) enanthonitrile and a benzene solution containing 10.7 g. (0.25 mole) of hydrazoic acid, 44 g. of concentrated sulfuric acid is added dropwise with stirring at 35–40°. The temperature rises to about 45°. After cessation of the reaction, the benzene layer is separated and the sulfuric acid layer is diluted with ice. The addition of alkali precipitates a solid which contains some alkali sulfate. On recrystallization from ethanol, 1-*n*-hexyl-5-aminotetrazole melting at 162° is obtained in 60% yield.

TABLE OF COMPOUNDS PREPARED BY THE SCHMIDT REACTION

Parent Compound	Product	Yield	Reference
Acid, monobasic			
Caproic ($C_5H_{11}CO_2H$)	*n*-Pentylamine		9
Enanthic ($C_6H_{13}CO_2H$)	*n*-Hexylamine		9, 14
Caprylic ($C_7H_{15}CO_2H$)	*n*-Heptylamine	70–75%	9
Pelargonic ($C_8H_{17}CO_2H$)	*n*-Octylamine		9
Capric ($C_9H_{19}CO_2H$)	*n*-Nonylamine		9
Undecylic ($C_{10}H_{21}CO_2H$)	*n*-Decylamine	90%	9
Stearic ($C_{17}H_{35}CO_2H$)	*n*-Heptadecylamine	96%	11
Naphthenic ($C_6H_{11}CO_2H$ to $C_{11}H_{21}CO_2H$)	Amines ($C_6H_{11}NH_2$ to $C_{11}H_{21}NH_2$)	70–85%	10, 16 26
($C_{17}H_{33}CO_2H$)	$C_{17}H_{33}NH_2$	80%	14
Phenylacetic	Benzylamine	75, 92%	12, 13
Dibenzylacetic	*β,β'*-Diphenylisopropylamine	Over 70%	12
Dicyclopentylacetic	Dicyclopentylmethylamine	70%	18
α-Benzylpropionic	*β*-Phenylisopropylamine	73%	19
Podocarpic ($C_{17}H_{22}O_3$) *	$C_{16}H_{21}ONH_2$		11
CO_2H CH_2 CH_2 H C C C H CH_2 CH_2 CO_2H	H_2N CH_2 CH_2 H C C C H CH_2 CH_2 NH_2		
Spiroheptanedicarboxylic	Spiroheptanediamine	95%	74
β-Phenylpropionic	*β*-Phenethylamine	70%	12
β-(*p*-Methoxyphenyl)propionic	*β*-(*p*-Methoxyphenyl)ethylamine	55%	12
Cyclohexanecarboxylic	Cyclohexylamine	82%	12
β-(2,4-Dimethoxyphenyl)propionic	*β*-(2,4-Dimethoxyphenyl)ethylamine	Traces	12
β-(2,3,5-Trimethoxyphenyl)-propionic		0%	12
Cinnamic	Aniline Phenylacetaldehyde	32% 43%	12
Campholic	Camphelylamine	88%, 75%	10, 16
Fencholic	Fenchelylamine	91%	10, 16, 19
Dimethylcampholic	Dimethylcamphelylamine	75%	20
1-Phenylpiperidine-4-carboxylic	4-Amino-1-phenylpiperidine		22
5-Ethoxy-2-(3-ethoxypropyl)-valeric	4-Ethoxy-1-(3-ethoxypropyl)-butylamine	85% By titration	29

* For the structure of podocarpic acid, see formula VIII, p. 311.

Table of Compounds Prepared by the Schmidt Reaction—*Continued*

Parent Compound	Product	Yield	Reference
6-Ethoxy-2-(4-ethoxybutyl)-caproic	5-Ethoxy-1-(4-ethoxybutyl)-amylamine	84%	27
7-Ethoxy-2-(5-ethoxyamyl)-enanthic	6-Ethoxy-1-(5-ethoxyamyl)-hexylamine	78%	31
7-Ethoxy-2-(3-ethoxypropyl)-enanthic	6-Ethoxy-1-(3-ethoxypropyl)-hexylamine	78%	32
6-Ethoxy-3-(3-ethoxypropyl)-caproic	5-Ethoxy-2-(3-ethoxypropyl)-amylamine	85% By titration	30
Hexahydroindanyl-5-acetic	5-Aminomethylhexahydroindane	87%	71
5-Methyl-hexahydroindanyl-6-acetic	5-Methyl-6-hexahydroindanylmethylamine		71
4-Tetrahydropyrancarboxylic	4-Tetrahydropyranylamine	44%	28
4-Tetrahydropyranacetic	4-Tetrahydropyranmethylamine	52.5%	28
β-(4-Tetrahydropyranyl)-propionic	2-(4-Tetrahydropyranyl)-ethylamine	51.4%	28
α-(4-Tetrahydropyranyl)-propionic	1-(4-Tetrahydropyranyl)-ethylamine	66.5%	17
α-(4-Tetrahydropyranyl)-butyric	1-(4-Tetrahydropyranyl)-propylamine	68%	17
β-(4-Tetrahydropyranyl)-butyric	2-(4-Tetrahydropyranyl)-propylamine	74.5%	33
α-Methyl-α-(4-tetrahydropyranyl)-propionic	1-Methyl-1-(4-tetrahydropyranyl)-ethylamine	50%	17
β-(4-Tetrahydropyranyl)-valeric	2-(4-Tetrahydropyranyl)-butylamine	63%	33
Benzoic	Aniline	85%	7, 12, 13
Toluic	Toluidine *o*-	46%	11
	m-	24%	
	p-	70%	
Salicylic	*o*-Aminophenol	21%	12
3,4,5-Trimethoxybenzoic	3,4,5-Trimethoxyaniline	35%	12
m-Chlorobenzoic	*m*-Chloroaniline	75% *	7
m-Bromobenzoic	*m*-Bromoaniline	72% *	7
m-Iodobenzoic	*m*-Iodoaniline	62% *	7
m-Hydroxybenzoic	*m*-Aminophenol	80% *	7
m-Methoxybenzoic	*m*-Aminoanisole	77% *	7
m-Ethoxybenzoic	*m*-Aminophenetole	73% *	7

* Not corrected for the recovered acid.

TABLE OF COMPOUNDS PREPARED BY THE SCHMIDT REACTION—*Continued*

Parent Compound	Product	Yield	Reference
m-Cyanobenzoic	*m*-Aminobenzonitrile	59% *	7
m-Toluic	*m*-Toluidine	42% *	7
o-Methoxybenzoic	*o*-Aminoanisole	80% *	7
p-Methoxybenzoic	*p*-Aminoanisole	78% *	7
o-Nitrobenzoic	*o*-Nitroaniline	68%,* 83%	7, 12
p-Nitrobenzoic	*p*-Nitroaniline	41%,* 83%	7, 12
m-Nitrobenzoic	*m*-Nitroaniline	63%,* 83%	7, 12
Acid, dibasic			
Malonic	Glycine	29%	15
Benzylmalonic	*dl*-Phenylalanine	16%	11
Succinic	Ethylenediamine	8%	12
Adipic	Tetramethylenediamine	80%, 83%, 70%	12, 13, 72
Dodecamethylenedicarboxylic	Dodecamethylenediamine	90%	14
1,2,2-Trimethyl-1,3-cyclopentanedicarboxylic (camphoric)	1,3-Diamino-2,2,3-trimethylcyclopentane	75%	16
Cyclobutanedicarboxylic	1,2-Diaminocyclobutane	*cis* 35%, *trans* 55%	24
Homocamphoric	Homocamphoramine	84.6%	73
o-Phthalic	Anthranilic acid	79%	12
	o-Diaminobenzene	3%	
m-Phthalic	*m*-Aminobenzoic acid	57%	7
p-Phthalic	*p*-Aminobenzoic acid	79%	12
	p-Diaminobenzene	3%	
3-Nitrophthalic	3-Nitroisatoic acid		23
Glutamic	*d*-α,γ-Diaminobutyric acid	42%	15
Diphenic	Phenanthridone + 2,2′-diaminobiphenyl		23
Acid, amino			
α-Aminoadipic	*dl*-Ornithine	75%	15
α-Aminopimelic	*dl*-Lysine	74%	15
ϵ-Aminocaproic	Pentamethylenediamine	70%	13
γ-(*o*-Aminophenyl)-butyric	γ-(*o*-Aminophenyl)-propylamine	44%	42

* Not corrected for the recovered acid.

Table of Compounds Prepared by the Schmidt Reaction—*Continued*

Parent Compound	Product	Yield	Reference
Anhydride			
Acetic	Methylamine	85%	13
Phthalic	Isatoic anhydride		37
	Benzimidazolone		
	Anthranilic acid		
3-Nitrophthalic	3-Nitroisatoic acid		23
	5-Nitrophenylurea		
	2-Amino-3-nitrobenzoic acid		
Diphenic	Phenanthridone		23
Phenylglyoxylic	Oxanilide, benzoylphenylurea, and tetrazoles		40
Esters			
Ethyl benzoate	Aniline	24–30%	11, 13
Methyl benzoate	Aniline	26%	11
Acid chloride			
Benzoyl chloride	Aniline	80%	13
Aldehydes			
Acetaldehyde	Acetonitrile	64%	3
Benzaldehyde	Benzonitrile	70%	2, 3, 25
	Formanilide	13%	
m-Nitrobenzaldehyde	*m*-Nitroaniline	17%	2
	m-Nitrobenzonitrile	83%	
Ketones			
Acetone	Methylacetamide	Quantitative	2
Levulinic acid	β-Alanine	56%	38
	Succinic acid	10%	
Methyl levulinate	Methyl-β-aminopropionate	30%	38
Ethyl acetoacetate	Glycine	80–98%	2
Ethyl α-ethylacetoacetate	α-Aminobutyric acid	80–98%	2
Ethyl α-isopropylacetoacetate	Leucine	80–98%	2
Ethyl α-isoamylacetoacetate	α-Aminoisoamylacetic acid	80–98%	2
Ethyl α-benzylacetoacetate	β-Phenylalanine	80–98%	2
Ethyl α-dimethylacetoacetate	Ethyl-α-(N-acetyl)-aminoisobutyrate	—	25
Ethyl α-dibenzylacetoacetate	Dibenzylaminoacetic acid	80–98%	2
Diethyl acetylsuccinate	Aspartic acid	80–98%	2
Cyclopentanone	Piperidone	—	46
Cyclohexanone	ε-Caprolactam	70%	2, 3, 46
Cyclooctanone	8-Aminocaprylic acid lactam	70%	43
	Tetrazole	22%	
2-Methylcyclohexanone	6-Aminoenanthic acid lactam	45%	46

TABLE OF COMPOUNDS PREPARED BY THE SCHMIDT REACTION—*Continued*

Parent Compound	Product	Yield	Reference
Cyclohexadecanone	16-Aminohexadecanoic acid lactam	86%	43
α-Hydrindone	Dihydrocarbostyril	68%	42
α-Tetralone	Homodihydrocarbostyril	70%	42
Ethyl cyclopentanone-2-carboxylate	α-Aminoadipic acid and *dl*-ornithine	40% (ornithine)	15
Ethyl cyclohexanone-2-carboxylate	α-Aminopimelic acid and *dl*-lysine	60% (lysine)	15
Acetophenone	Acetanilide	77%	42
Benzophenone	Benzanilide	Quantitative	2, 3
Methyl β-phenylethyl ketone	N-(β-Phenylethyl) acetamide	62.5%	11
α-Benzyl-α-methylacetone	N-(β-Phenylisopropyl) acetamide	48%	11
Benzalacetone	N-Methyl cinnamamide	—	11
Benzil	N-Benzoyl-N′-phenylurea (and some oxanilide)	30–60%	39
Isatin or Acetylisatin	Anthranilamide	—	40
N-Ethylisatin	o-Ethylaminobenzamide	—	40

CHAPTER 9

THE CURTIUS REACTION

PETER A. S. SMITH

University of Michigan

CONTENTS

INTRODUCTION

The decomposition of acid azides to isocyanates and nitrogen is known as the Curtius rearrangement. The reaction is a preparative method

$$RCON_3 \rightarrow RN{=}C{=}O + N_2$$

for isocyanates and for compounds derivable from isocyanates, such as urethans, ureas, amides, and amines. When coupled with a hydrolytic step, the Curtius rearrangement becomes a practical procedure for replacing a carboxyl group by an amino group. The overall process of converting an acid through its azide to an amine is commonly referred to as the Curtius reaction.

$$RCO_2H \rightarrow RCON_3 \rightarrow RN{=}C{=}O \rightarrow RNH_2$$

Curtius, through his studies on diazo esters, discovered successively hydrazine, hydrazides, azides, and hydrazoic acid; in 1890 he encountered the rearrangement of acid azides, although he did not recognize its true nature at the time.[1, 2] Since then abundant investigations by Curtius and others have elucidated the reaction and demonstrated its generality.

Acid azides are commonly prepared by treating acid hydrazides in cold, aqueous solution with nitrous acid. The required hydrazides are prepared from esters by reaction with hydrazine. Acid azides can also be made by treatment of acid chlorides with sodium azide. In Curtius'

$$RCO_2CH_3 + NH_2NH_2 \rightarrow RCONHNH_2 + CH_3OH$$

$$RCONHNH_2 + HNO_2 \rightarrow RCON_3 + 2H_2O$$

$$RCOCl + NaN_3 \rightarrow RCON_3 + NaCl$$

numerous papers, the route to the azide through the hydrazide is the one described almost exclusively, although the acid chloride-sodium azide method was early known to him [3] and was used by others.[4, 5, 6] Naegeli and his students [7, 8, 9, 10] have demonstrated that the sodium azide method is satisfactory and often preferable; they have also reviewed critically the hydrazide method.

Azides can be rearranged in inert solvents like benzene and chloroform, from which the isocyanates can be isolated, or in the presence of reagents like alcohol or water which will react with the intermediate isocyanates to form urethans or ureas. Amines or their salts are obtained by hydrolysis of the isocyanates, urethans, or ureas.

$$RCON_3 \rightarrow RN{=}C{=}O \left\{ \begin{array}{l} \xrightarrow{C_2H_5OH} RNHCO_2C_2H_5 \\ \xrightarrow{\hspace{4em}} \\ \xrightarrow{H_2O} (RNH)_2CO \end{array} \right\} \xrightarrow[H^+ \text{ or } OH^-]{H_2O} RNH_2$$

[1] Curtius, *Ber.*, **23**, 3023 (1890).
[2] Curtius, *J. prakt. Chem.*, **50**, 275 (1894).
[3] Lindemann, *Helv. Chim. Acta*, **11**, 1027 (1928).
[4] Forster, *J. Chem. Soc.*, **95**, 184 (1909).
[5] Lindemann and Wessel, *Ber.*, **58**, 1221 (1925).
[6] Schroeter, *Ber.*, **42**, 2336 (1909).
[7] Naegeli, Grüntuch, and Lendorff, *Helv. Chim. Acta*, **12**, 227 (1929).
[8] Naegeli and Lendorff, *Helv. Chim. Acta*, **12**, 894 (1929).
[9] Naegeli and Lendorff, *Helv. Chim. Acta*, **15**, 49 (1932).
[10] Naegeli and Stefanovich, *Helv. Chim. Acta*, **11**, 609 (1928).

Other types of azides undergo analogous rearrangement.[11, 12, 13] Sulfonyl azides, however, do not rearrange.

The mechanism of the Curtius rearrangement is discussed in the chapter on the Hofmann reaction (p. 268).

SCOPE AND LIMITATIONS OF THE REACTION

The Curtius degradation has been carried out successfully on aliphatic, alicyclic, aromatic, and heterocyclic acids, on saturated and unsaturated acids, and on acids containing various functional groups. It may be expected to succeed for almost any carboxylic acid, and is, therefore, a general method for preparing isocyanates and the compounds obtainable from isocyanates, such as urethans, ureas, and amines. The reaction possesses the advantage of yielding primary amines which are scrupulously free of secondary and tertiary amines and in which the position of the amino group is usually unequivocal.

Effect of Structure and Substituents

The structure of the acid or the presence of substituents may affect certain steps in the Curtius reaction. Although it is usually a matter of choice whether the hydrazide method or the sodium azide method is employed for the preparation of a given azide, for certain azides one of the methods may fail completely or may be preferable because of the structure of the acid or the presence of certain groups in the molecule. As a rule the rearrangement of azides to isocyanates proceeds without difficulty. The product obtained by hydrolysis of the isocyanate is not always an amine; certain isocyanates yield aldehydes or ketones.

Saturated Monocarboxylic Acids. Azides of saturated acids can be prepared almost equally well by reaction of the hydrazides with nitrous acid or by reaction of the acid chlorides with sodium azide. The latter method is superior for very low-molecular-weight acids, whose hydrazides and azides are difficult to extract from water; by this method acetyl chloride is converted to methyl isocyanate through the azide in 60–72% yields.[14, 15] From lauroyl chloride, 86% of undecyl isocyanate is obtained by the sodium azide method.[16] The reaction of acid an-

[11] Curtius, Darmstaedter, Pringsheim, and Stangassinger, *J. prakt. Chem.*, **91**, 1 (1915).

[12] Franklin, *Chem. Revs.* **14**, 219 (1934).

[13] Porter, "Molecular Rearrangements," Chemical Catalog Co., 1928.

[14] Schroeter, *Ber.*, **42**, 3356 (1909).

[15] Slotta and Lorenz, *Ber.*, **58**, 1320 (1925).

[16] Allen and Bell, *Org. Syntheses*, **24**, 94 (1944).

hydrides with sodium azide has been reported; methyl isocyanate was obtained in 78% yield from acetic anhydride.[16a]

Low-molecular-weight esters react quite readily with hydrazine, but heavier ones must be coerced. Aromatic esters are less reactive than aliphatic esters toward hydrazine, and they and the more resistant aliphatic esters occasionally require prolonged heating with hydrazine at elevated temperatures in a sealed tube. Branching of the carbon chain *alpha* to the ester group retards hydrazide formation; in contrast with ethyl acetate, which reacts spontaneously with hydrazine at room temperature, ethyl pivalate (ethyl trimethylacetate) requires a temperature of 140°, and adamantane-1,3-dicarboxylic ester (I) failed to form a hydrazide under all conditions (unspecified) that were tried.[17]

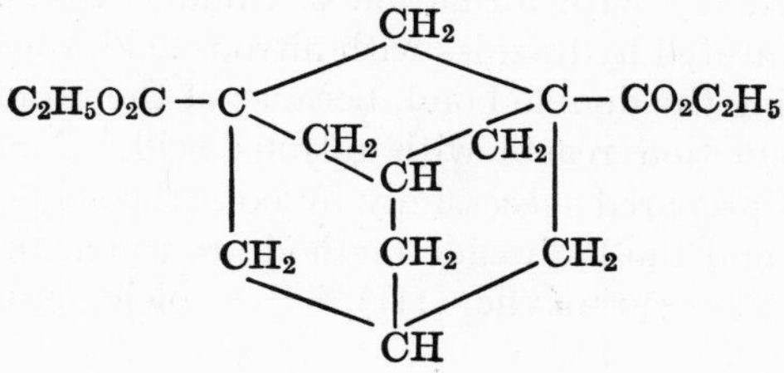

CH_2
$C_2H_5O_2C-C$ $C-CO_2C_2H_5$
CH_2 CH_2
CH
CH_2 CH_2 CH_2
CH

I

Simple saturated azides rearrange quantitatively to isocyanates as judged from the volume of nitrogen evolved. The actual yields of the isocyanates are slightly lower, particularly when the molecular weight is low, owing to volatilization with the nitrogen. This loss is eliminated when the rearrangement is carried out in alcohol, and excellent yields of urethans are obtained. Both the isocyanates and the urethans can be hydrolyzed smoothly to the amines.

Unsaturated Acids. The formation of olefinic acid azides by the sodium azide procedure appears to be limited only by the availability of the acid chloride. Examples of α,β-olefinic acid azides prepared by this method are crotonyl,[18] cinnamoyl,[18, 19] and methacrylyl [20] azides. The hydrazide route to the azide is sometimes complicated by side reactions. The esters of oleic acid and elaidic acid give the respective hydrazides in good yield under the usual conditions, but severe treatment causes reduction of the unsaturated hydrazides to stearoyl hydrazide.[21]

[16a] Colucci, *Can. J. Research*, **23**B, 111 (1945).
[17] Prelog and Seiwerth, *Ber.*, **74**, 1769 (1941).
[18] Jones and Mason, *J. Am. Chem. Soc.*, **49**, 2528 (1927).
[19] Forster, *J. Chem. Soc.*, **95**, 433 (1909).
[20] Coffman, U. S. pat. 2,335,012 [*C. A.*, **38**, 2772 (1944)].
[21] Van Alphen, *Rec. trav. chim.*, **44**, 1064 (1925).

Conversion of the hydrazides of α,β-olefinic acids to azides is frequently impossible owing to cyclization upon treatment with nitrous acid. Cinnamoyl hydrazide and nitrous acid, for example, yield 1-nitroso-5-phenyl-3-pyrazolidone.[22] Crotonyl hydrazide [23] and *m*-nitrocinnamoyl

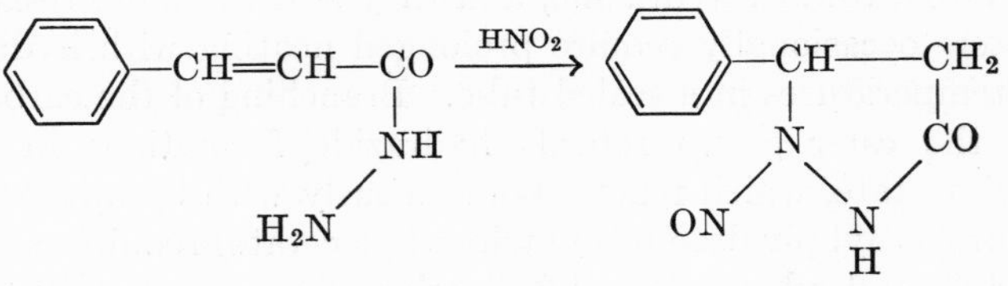

$$C_6H_5\text{—}CH{=}CH\text{—}CO\text{—}NH\text{—}NH_2 \xrightarrow{HNO_2} C_6H_5\text{—}CH\text{—}CH_2 \text{ (ring: }N(NO)\text{—}NH\text{—}CO\text{)}$$

hydrazide [24] behave analogously. Fumaryl hydrazide,[25] on the other hand, reacts normally with formation of fumaryl azide. In the reaction of the unsaturated hydrazides with nitrous acid, there is little likelihood of nitrosating the double bond, because of the rapidity with which the hydrazide function reacts with nitrous acid. Among the azides which have been prepared successfully by both the acid chloride-sodium azide procedure and the hydrazide method are the azides of chaulmoogric (II),[10] bornylenecarboxylic (III),[26, 27, 28] oleic, erucic, and undecenoic acids.[29]

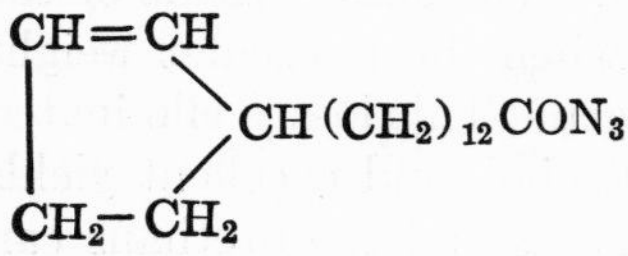

II: $CH{=}CH$ / $CH_2\text{—}CH_2$ ring with $CH(CH_2)_{12}CON_3$

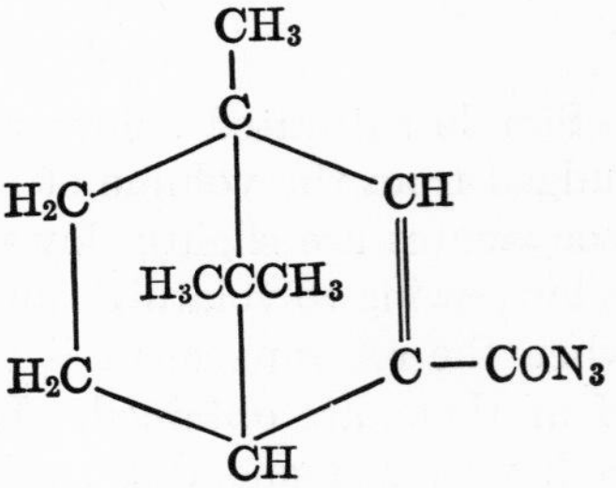

III: CH_3, C, H_2C, CH, H_3CCCH_3, H_2C, $C\text{—}CON_3$, CH

α,β-Olefinic azides rearrange to vinyl isocyanates; for example, methacrylyl azide yields α-methylvinyl isocyanate.[30] Certain vinyl isocyanates polymerize readily; the products of the rearrangement of the azide

[22] Muckermann, *Ber.*, **42**, 3449 (1909).
[23] von Braun, *Ber.*, **67**, 218 (1934).
[24] Curtius and Bleicher, *J. prakt. Chem.*, **107**, 86 (1924).
[25] Curtius and Radenhausen, *J. prakt. Chem.*, **52**, 433 (1895).
[26] Bredt and Hilbing, *Chem. Ztg.*, **35**, 765 (1911).
[27] Bredt, Perkin, Hilbing, Lankshear, and Regout, *J. prakt. Chem.*, **89**, 225 (1914).
[28] Bredt-Savelsberg and Bund, *J. prakt. Chem.*, **131**, 46 (1931).
[29] Oskerko, *Mem. Inst. Chem. Ukraine Acad. Sci.*, **2**, 69, 79, 293 (1935) [*C. A.*, **31**, 4644 (1937)].
[30] Coffman, U. S. pat. 2,335,012 [*C. A.*, **38**, 2772 (1944)].

formed from acrylyl chloride and sodium azide are polyvinyl isocyanate (30%) and only a little of the monomer.[31] Hydrolysis of the vinyl isocyanates or the related urethans and ureas yields aldehydes or ketones

$$RCH{=}CHCON_3 \rightarrow RCH{=}CHNCO \xrightarrow[H^+]{HOH} RCH_2CHO$$

rather than amines. Epicamphor (IV) is obtained in 93% yield [28] from bornylenecarbonyl chloride through the azide III.

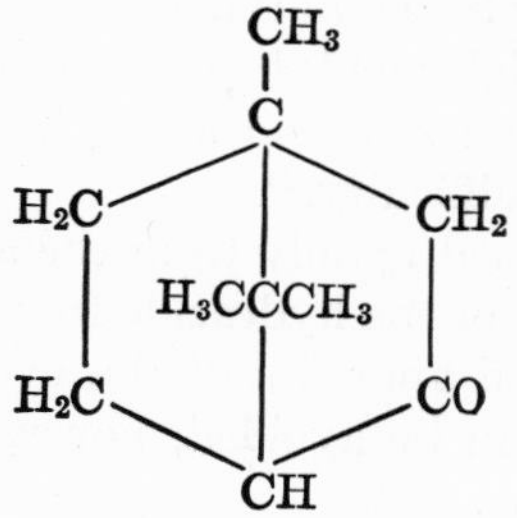

$$\begin{array}{ccc} & CH_3 & \\ & | & \\ & C & \\ H_2C & & CH_2 \\ | & H_3CCCH_3 & | \\ H_2C & & CO \\ & CH & \end{array}$$

IV

The esters of acetylenic acids, with the exception of α,β-unsaturated acids, can be converted to hydrazides. Ethyl stearolate [32] and ethyl undecynoate [33] readily give hydrazides, the latter in 80% yield. Esters of α,β-acetylenic acids react with hydrazine to form pyrazolones; for example, ethyl tetrolate gives 3-methyl-5-pyrazolone.[34]

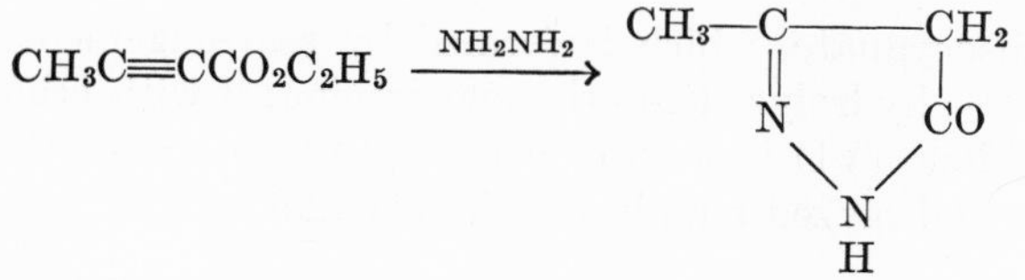

$$CH_3C{\equiv}CCO_2C_2H_5 \xrightarrow{NH_2NH_2} \begin{array}{ccc} CH_3{-}C & \text{———} & CH_2 \\ \| & & | \\ N & & CO \\ & \diagdown\;\diagup & \\ & N & \\ & H & \end{array}$$

In the single attempt to form an acetylenic azide, the sodium azide method failed with phenylpropiolyl chloride.[35]

Di- and Poly-carboxylic Acids. *Preparation of Diamines.* The presence of more than one carboxyl group does not interfere with the conversion of the acids to the amines. Adipyl hydrazide is formed from the

[31] Jones, Zomlefer, and Hawkins, *J. Org. Chem.*, **9**, 500 (1944).

[32] Oskerko, *J. Gen. Chem. U.S.S.R.*, **8**, 334 (1938); *Mem. Inst. Ukrain. Acad. Sci.*, **4**, 329 (1937) [*C. A.*, **32**, 5377 (1938)].

[33] Oskerko, *J. Gen. Chem. U.S.S.R.*, **7**, 595 (1937) [*C. A.*, **31**, 5761 (1937)].

[34] Oskerko, *J. Gen. Chem. U.S.S.R.*, **8**, 330 (1938); *Mem. Inst. Ukrain. Acad. Sci.*, **4**, 195 (1937) [*C. A.*, **32**, 3334 (1938)].

[35] Forster and Stötter, *J. Chem. Soc.*, **99**, 1337 (1911).

ester in 94% yield[36, 37] and smoothly gives putrescine hydrochloride

$$C_2H_5O_2C(CH_2)_4CO_2C_2H_5 \xrightarrow[\text{Reflux}]{NH_2NH_2} \underset{94\%}{H_2NNHOC(CH_2)_4CONHNH_2} \xrightarrow[0\text{–}5°]{HNO_2}$$

$$\underset{80\%}{N_3OC(CH_2)_4CON_3} \xrightarrow[\text{Reflux}]{C_2H_5OH} \underset{100\%}{C_2H_5O_2CNH(CH_2)_4NHCO_2C_2H_5} \xrightarrow[\text{Reflux}]{H_2O/HCl} \underset{90\%}{ClH_3N(CH_2)_4NH_3Cl}$$

in 72% yield.[37] Hexahydroterephthalic acid can be degraded to 1,4-diaminocyclohexane in high yield;[11] phthalic acid can be converted to *o*-phenylenediamine;[38] and trimesic acid yields 1,3,5-tris(carbethoxyamino) benzene without difficulty.[39]

Succinyl azide is obtained readily from the acid chloride and sodium azide.[40] The preparation of the hydrazide from the ester is complicated by the formation of small amounts of the cyclic secondary hydrazide (V); this side reaction can be avoided, however, by the choice of the proper reaction conditions.

$$\begin{matrix} CO_2C_2H_5 \\ H_2C \\ | \\ H_2C \\ CO_2C_2H_5 \end{matrix} \xrightarrow{NH_2NH_2} \begin{matrix} CONHNH_2 \\ H_2C \\ | \\ H_2C \\ CONHNH_2 \end{matrix} + \underset{\text{V}}{\begin{matrix} & CO & \\ H_2C & & NH \\ | & & | \\ H_2C & & NH \\ & CO & \end{matrix}}$$

Ethylene diisocyanate, which is formed by rearrangement of succinyl diazide, can be hydrolyzed to ethylenediamine;[41] with ethanol it gives an imidazolidone (VI) instead of a normal urethan, but the imidazolidone can be hydrolyzed readily to ethylenediamine.[9]

$$\begin{matrix} NCO \\ H_2C \\ | \\ H_2C \\ NCO \end{matrix} + C_2H_5OH \rightarrow \underset{\text{VI}}{\begin{matrix} & NCO_2C_2H_5 & \\ H_2C & & \\ | & & CO \\ H_2C & & \\ & NH & \end{matrix}}$$

[36] Curtius, Hallaway, and Heil, *J. prakt. Chem.*, **89**, 481 (1914).
[37] Unpublished observations of the author.
[38] Lindemann and Schultheis, *Ann.*, **464**, 237 (1928).
[39] Curtius, Bourcart, Heynemann, and Schmitz, *J. prakt. Chem.*, **91**, 39 (1915)
[40] Schroeter and Seidler, *J. prakt. Chem.*, **105**, 165 (1923).
[41] Curtius, *J. prakt. Chem.*, **52**, 210 (1895).

Phthalyl azide must be prepared from the acid chloride because the esters of phthalic acid on treatment with hydrazine form exclusively the secondary hydrazide.[41a]

$$C_6H_4(CO_2R)_2 + NH_2NH_2 \rightarrow C_6H_4\begin{matrix}CO—NH\\ | \\ CO—NH\end{matrix} + 2ROH$$

Preparation of Aldehydes and Ketones. Monosubstituted malonyl azides can be synthesized readily from the dihydrazides. Urethans of *gem*-diamines result when the azides are rearranged in alcohol; these urethans are hydrolyzed rapidly by mineral acids to aldehydes. Diethyl benzylmalonate can be converted to phenylacetaldehyde in about 70% yield by this procedure.[42]

$$C_6H_5CH_2CH(CO_2C_2H_5)_2 \xrightarrow[95\%]{} C_6H_5CH_2CH(CONHNH_2)_2 \rightarrow$$

$$C_6H_5CH_2CH(CON_3)_2 \xrightarrow[75\%]{} C_6H_5CH_2CH(NHCO_2C_2H_5)_2 \xrightarrow[98\%]{} C_6H_5CH_2CHO$$

This attractive method for preparing aldehydes has seen almost no application to synthesis.

The degradation of the azides of disubstituted malonic acids gives ketones, as illustrated by the conversion of butane-1,2,2-tricarbonyl hydrazide to 1-aminobutanone-2 in 70% yield.[43]

$$H_2NNHCO—CH_2C(CONHNH_2)_2CH_2CH_3 \rightarrow ClH_3N—CH_2C(=O)CH_2CH_3$$

The formation of hydrazides from the esters of disubstituted malonic esters becomes increasingly difficult with increase in the size of the substituents. Diethyl benzylmethylmalonate with excess hydrazine in

[41a] Curtius and Davidis, *J. prakt. Chem.*, **54**, 66 (1896).
[42] Curtius and Mott, *J. prakt. Chem.*, **94**, 323 (1916).
[43] Curtius and Gund, *J. prakt. Chem.*, **107**, 177 (1924).

boiling butanol yields 75% of the dihydrazide; diethyl dibenzylmalonate gives a poor yield, and diethyl bis(mesitylmethyl)malonate does not react with hydrazine.[44] The formation of substituted azides from malonyl chlorides and sodium azide has not been reported.

Stepwise Degradation to Amino Acids. There are several approaches to the transformation of a di- or poly-carboxylic acid to an amino acid. The most satisfactory procedure makes use of the ester acids and their salts. They react with hydrazine to form hydrazide acids, which may be degraded through the azide acids to amino acids. From substituted malonic esters α-amino acids are obtained. (For the preparation of α-amino acids from substituted cyanoacetic esters, see p. 359.) Thus, the potassium salt of the monoethyl ester of methylmalonic acid, which is prepared by half hydrolysis of the diethyl ester, gives alanine ethyl ester hydrochloride in 67% yield.[45] Many other amino acids have

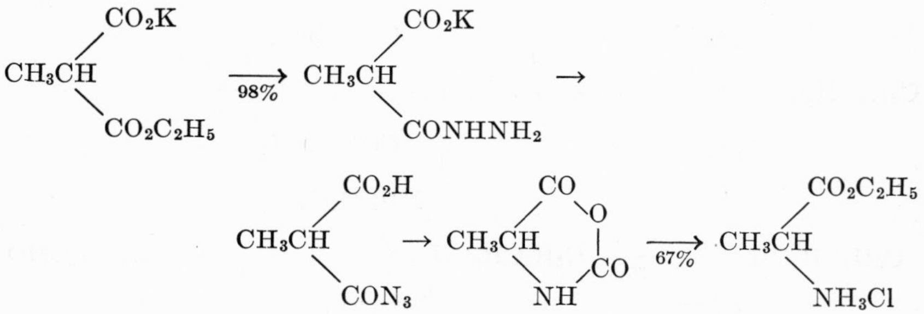

$$CH_3CH(CO_2K)(CO_2C_2H_5) \xrightarrow{98\%} CH_3CH(CO_2K)(CONHNH_2) \rightarrow$$

$$CH_3CH(CO_2H)(CON_3) \rightarrow CH_3CH\langle CO{-}O{-}CO{-}NH \rangle \xrightarrow{67\%} CH_3CH(CO_2C_2H_5)(NH_3Cl)$$

been prepared in this way; among them are β-phenylalanine (44% yield),[46] α-amino-*n*-butyric acid (41% yield),[46] α-amino-*n*-valeric acid (43% yield),[47] and 6-nitroanthranilic acid.[48] 2-Carboxy-3-nitrobenzazide when heated in ethanol is esterified (through intermediate formation of *o*-nitrophthalic anhydride), but when heated in dry chloroform rearranges to the isatoic anhydride.[48]

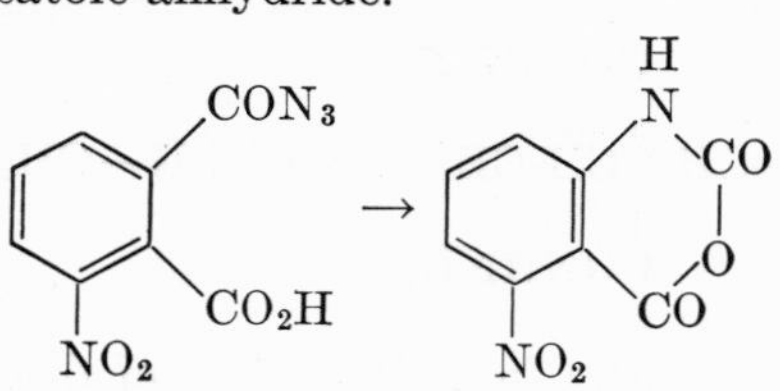

$$C_6H_3(CON_3)(CO_2H)(NO_2) \rightarrow C_6H_3(NH{-}CO{-}O{-}CO)(NO_2)$$

[44] P. A. S. Smith and L. E. Miller, unpublished results.

[45] Curtius and Sieber, *Ber.*, **54**, 1430 (1921).

[46] Curtius and Sieber, *Ber.*, **55**, 1543 (1922).

[47] Curtius, Hochschwender, Meier, Lehmann, Benckiser, Schenck, Wirbatz, Gaier, and Mühlhäusser, *J. prakt. Chem.*, **125**, 211 (1930).

[48] Curtius and Semper, *Ber.*, **46**, 1162 (1913).

The ester acids may also be converted to ester acid chlorides and then by reaction with sodium azide to ester azides. By these steps 3,4-dichloro-5-carbethoxypyrrole-2-carbonyl chloride [49] and sebacic ethyl ester chloride [50] have been converted to the corresponding ester azides, which were then rearranged; 1-carbethoxyheneicosane-21-carbonyl chloride has been converted to ω-aminobehenic acid in 66% yield.[51]

Cyclic anhydrides of certain dibasic acids can be converted directly to hydrazide acids for degradation to amino acids. Diphenic anhydride [52] and its 4-nitro derivative [53] react with hydrazine to form the corresponding hydrazide acids. Phthalic anhydride, on the other hand, gives only the secondary hydrazide.[54, 55] Succinic anhydride has not been tried, but succinimide gives succinamyl hydrazide.[56] Succinhydrazidic acid can be formed from succinic anhydride indirectly through ethyl hydrogen succinate or succinamic acid.[56] Succinimide-N-acetic ester and hydrazine give succinamyl hydrazide-N-acethydrazide (VII), which by reaction with nitrous acid followed by rearrangement and hydrolysis of the product yields β-alanine.[57]

$$\begin{array}{l} CH_2\text{—}CO \\ | \qquad\qquad \rangle NCH_2CO_2C_2H_5 \\ CH_2\text{—}CO \end{array} \rightarrow \begin{array}{l} CH_2CONHCH_2CONHNH_2 \\ | \\ CH_2CONHNH_2 \\ \qquad \text{VII} \end{array} \rightarrow \begin{array}{l} CH_2COO^- \\ | \\ CH_2NH_3^+ \end{array}$$

The esters of di- or poly-basic acids in which the groups are not structurally equivalent can usually be converted directly into ester hydrazides by reaction with hydrazine. Since the ester of an aromatic acid is much less reactive than the usual aliphatic ester, it is often possible to form the hydrazide from an aliphatic ester without affecting the aromatic ester group, when both types are present. This is illustrated by the conversion of *o*-carbethoxyphenoxyacetic ester with cold hydrazine to *o*-carbethoxyphenoxyacethydrazide; by refluxing with excess hydrazine the dihydrazide is formed in 95% yield.[58] N-(*o*-Carbomethoxyphenyl)-glycine ester behaves similarly, and many examples in the

[49] Fischer and Elhardt, *Z. physiol. Chem.*, **257**, 61 (1939).

[50] Flaschenträger and Halle, *Z. physiol. Chem.*, **192**, 253 (1930).

[51] Flaschenträger, Blechman, and Halle, *Z. physiol. Chem.*, **192**, 257 (1930).

[52] Labriola, *Anales asoc. quím. argentina*, **25**, 121 (1937) [*C. A.*, **32**, 4970 (1938)].

[53] Labriola and Felitte, *J. Org. Chem.*, **8**, 536 (1943).

[54] Curtius and Davidis, *J. prakt. Chem.*, **54**, 66 (1896).

[55] Gheorghiu, *Bull. soc. chim.*, [4] **47**, 630 (1930); Gheorghiu, *ibid.*, [4] **53**, 151 (1933) Diels, Alder, Friedrichsen, Klare, Winkler, and Schrum, *Ann.*, **505**, 103 (1933).

[56] Curtius, *J. prakt. Chem.*, **92**, 74 (1915).

[57] Curtius and Hechtenberg, *J. prakt. Chem.*, **105**, 289 (1923).

[58] Curtius, Moll, and Fingado, *J. prakt. Chem.*, **125**, 106 (1930).

pyrrole series have been described.[59, 60, 61, 62] The conversion of diesters of symmetrical dibasic acids to ester hydrazides has been successful only with certain compounds, such as the esters of terephthalic acid,[54] bisdiazoacetic acid,[63] and oxalic acid.[64]

Esters of certain polybasic acids upon treatment with a limited amount of hydrazine yield mixed primary-secondary hydrazides, often called hydrazi hydrazides, and thus some of the carboxyl groups are protected against degradation. Hemimellitic ester forms a hydrazi hydrazide (VIII), and a hydrazi azide, which on rearrangement and hydrolysis yields *o*-aminophthalhydrazide (IX).[39] 1-Phenylpropane-2,2,3-tricarboxylic ester has also been partially degraded through its hydrazi azide (X).[65]

$CONHNH_2$ / CO / NH / NH / CO — VIII

NH_2 / CO / NH / NH / CO — IX

$C_6H_5CH_2$—C(CO—NH)(CO—NH) / CH_2 / CON_3 — X

Attempts have been made to obtain hydrazide azides by causing dihydrazides to react with one molecule of nitrous acid. The resulting compounds are unstable, however, and generally undergo intramolecular acylation with elimination of hydrazoic acid and formation of cyclic or polymeric secondary hydrazides. Diphenic dihydrazide is an excep-

$R(CON_3)(CONHNH_2) \rightarrow R(CO-NH-NH-CO)$

tion, for the hydrazide azide (XI) can be isolated and by heating in ethanol is converted to phenanthridone (XII).[66] The formation of a

CO CO / H_2NNH N_3 — XI $\rightarrow$ C=N / HO — XII

[59] Fischer and Heidelmann, *Ann.*, **527**, 115 (1937).
[60] Fischer, Süs, and Weilguny, *Ann.*, **481**, 159 (1930).
[61] Fischer and Thurnher, *Z. physiol. Chem.*, **204**, 68 (1932).
[62] Fischer and Waibel, *Ann.*, **512**, 195 (1934).
[63] Curtius and Rimele, *Ber.*, **41**, 3108 (1908).
[64] Curtius and Hochschwender, *J. prakt. Chem.*, **91**, 415 (1915).
[65] Curtius and Sandhaas, *J. prakt. Chem.*, **125**, 90 (1930).
[66] Labriola, *J. Org. Chem.*, **5**, 329 (1940).

small amount of γ-amino-β-phenylbutyric acid from β-phenylglutaryl dihydrazide [67] and nitrous acid suggests that here, too, the hydrazide azide might be isolated.

Some diazides and presumably some polyazides can be caused to rearrange stepwise. Phthalyl diazide yields *o*-isocyanatobenzazide when heated in benzene and N-carbomethoxyanthranilic azide [38] when heated in methanol; the second azide group also rearranges on longer heating. Spontaneous half-rearrangement is exhibited by 1-*p*-xylyl-

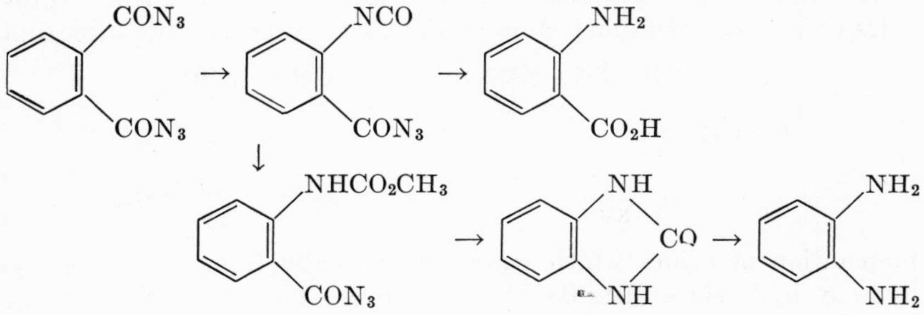

CON_3, CON_3 → NCO, CON_3 → NH_2, CO_2H

↓

$NHCO_2CH_3$, CON_3 → NH, CO, NH → NH_2, NH_2

1,2,3-triazole-4,5-dicarbonyl diazide; when the dihydrazide (XIII) is treated with aqueous nitrous acid, the isocyanate azide (XIV) is formed

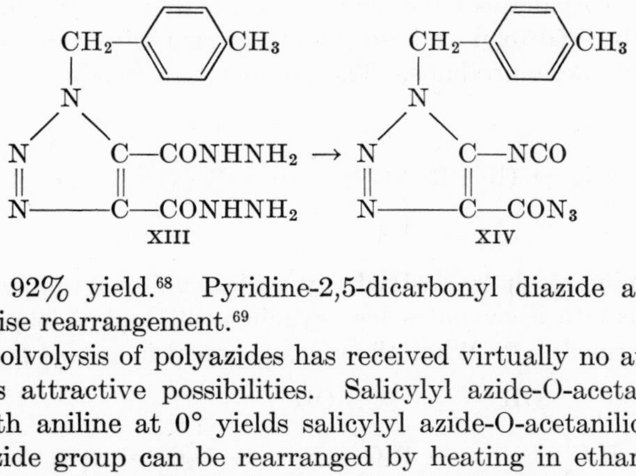

CH_2—C_6H_4—CH_3; N; N C—$CONHNH_2$; N—C—$CONHNH_2$ → CH_2—C_6H_4—CH_3; N; N C—NCO; N—C—CON_3

XIII XIV

in situ in 92% yield.[68] Pyridine-2,5-dicarbonyl diazide also undergoes stepwise rearrangement.[69]

Partial solvolysis of polyazides has received virtually no attention in spite of its attractive possibilities. Salicylyl azide-O-acetazide when treated with aniline at 0° yields salicylyl azide-O-acetanilide; the remaining azide group can be rearranged by heating in ethanol to give the urethan in 90% yield.[70] Succinazidylglycyl azide shows a similar behavior.[57]

Hydroxy Acids. Hydroxyl groups in an acid often complicate the conversion to an amino alcohol either by preventing the formation of

[67] Jackson and Kenner, *J. Chem. Soc.*, **1928**, 165.

[68] Bertho and Hölder, *J. prakt. Chem.*, **119**, 189 (1928).

[69] Meyer and Staffen, *Monatsh.*, **34**, 517 (1913).

[70] Curtius, Moll, and Fingado, *J. prakt. Chem.*, **125**, 106 (1930).

the azide or by causing the azide or the isocyanate to behave abnormally. Acylation or alkylation of the hydroxyl groups usually overcomes these difficulties.

Azides containing hydroxyl groups have been prepared by both the hydrazide and the sodium azide methods. The hydrazides of acids containing hydroxyl groups in the lactone-forming positions can usually be produced from the corresponding esters or the lactones, but on treatment with acid the hydrazides lose hydrazine and yield the lactones. This behavior has suggested that the compounds are not true hydrazides (XV) but hydrazino lactones (XVI).[71, 72] However, the successful

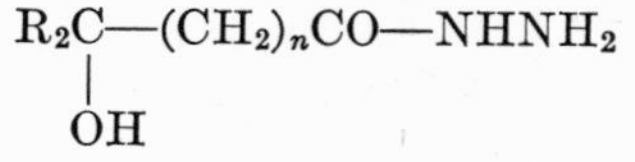

$$\underset{\text{XV}}{R_2C(OH)—(CH_2)_nCO—NHNH_2} \qquad \underset{\text{XVI}}{\begin{array}{l} R_2C—(CH_2)_n \\ \;|\qquad\quad | \\ O——C—OH \\ \qquad\quad | \\ \qquad NHNH_2 \end{array}}$$

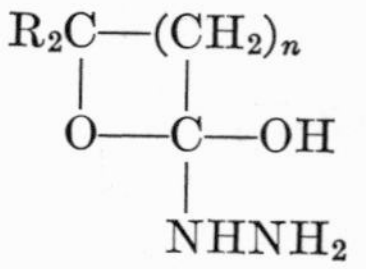

preparation of azides which rearrange normally from certain of the hydroxy hydrazides casts doubt on the cyclic formula.[38, 73] Lactones from acids containing secondary or tertiary hydroxyl groups show increased resistance to the action of hydrazine, and some such lactones cannot be made to react.[74]

Hydroxy isocyanates have never been isolated because of the interaction of the hydroxyl and isocyanate groups with the formation of cyclic or polymeric urethans. The products are usually readily hydro-

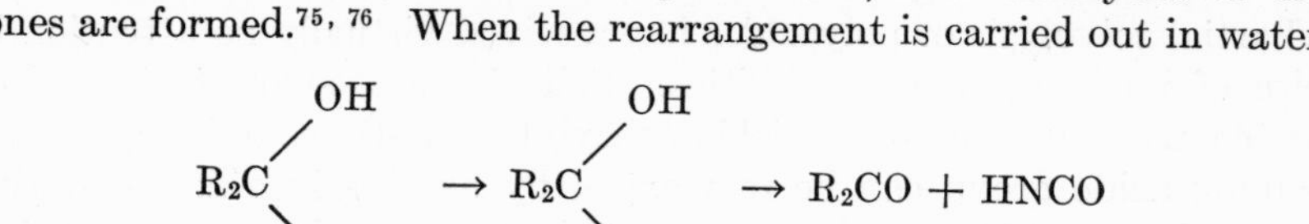

$$HO–R–CON_3 \rightarrow (HO–R–NCO) \rightarrow (–O–R–NHCO–)_x \text{ or } R\begin{array}{c} O \\ \diagup\;\diagdown \\ \\ \diagdown\;\diagup \\ NH \end{array}CO$$

lyzed to amino alcohols. α-Hydroxy azides exhibit a unique behavior; the intermediate isocyanates lose cyanic acid, and aldehydes or ketones are formed.[75, 76] When the rearrangement is carried out in water,

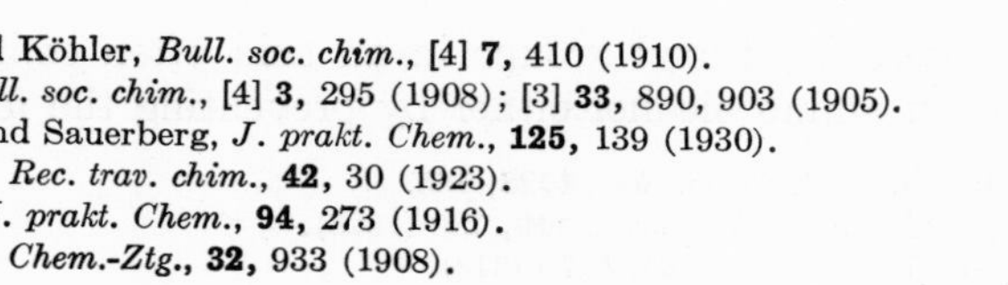

$$R_2C(OH)CON_3 \rightarrow R_2C(OH)NCO \rightarrow R_2CO + HNCO$$

[71] Blaise and Köhler, *Bull. soc. chim.*, [4] **7,** 410 (1910).

[72] Blanc, *Bull. soc. chim.*, [4] **3,** 295 (1908); [3] **33,** 890, 903 (1905).

[73] Curtius and Sauerberg, *J. prakt. Chem.*, **125,** 139 (1930).

[74] Teppema, *Rec. trav. chim.*, **42,** 30 (1923).

[75] Curtius, *J. prakt. Chem.*, **94,** 273 (1916).

[76] Schroeter, *Chem.-Ztg.*, **32,** 933 (1908).

the cyanic acid can be detected by reaction with semicarbazide to form insoluble hydrazodicarboxamide, $H_2NCONHNHCONH_2$.[77] This reaction can be used as a test for an α-hydroxy acid.[75, 78] Diphenylglycolyl azide yields benzophenone and phenylurea when it is heated in aniline.[79] The rearrangement of hydroxy azides in which the hydroxyl

$$(C_6H_5)_2C(OH)CON_3 \xrightarrow[\text{Heat}]{C_6H_5NH_2} (C_6H_5)_2CO + C_6H_5NHCONH_2$$

group is in a lactone-forming position succeeds only in certain instances, as in the conversion of *o*-hydroxymethylbenzazide to *o*-aminobenzyl alcohol or of the lactone of *o*-hydroxyphenylacetic acid to a derivative of *o*-hydroxybenzylamine.[38] Frequently the γ- and δ-hydroxy azides revert to the lactone through loss of hydrazoic acid; this reaction occurs less readily when a non-polar solvent is used in the rearrangement. (Cf. behavior of 2-carboxy-3-nitrobenzazide, p. 346.) Non-acylated

$$RCH(OH)CH_2CH_2CON_3 \rightarrow \underset{\text{(}\gamma\text{-lactone: } RCH-CH_2-CH_2-CO-O\text{)}}{RCH\!-\!CH_2\!-\!CH_2\!-\!CO\!-\!O} + HN_3$$

sugar acid azides always lose hydrazoic acid so readily that they cannot be isolated or degraded.[78]

The effect of alkylation or acylation of hydroxyl groups on the degradation of certain azides is illustrated in the following examples. The diazide of mucic acid,[79] prepared from the hydrazide, behaves like the azide of a typical α-hydroxy acid;[80] it loses cyanic acid after rearrangement and yields a mixture of tartaric dialdehyde and a double internal urethan. Tetraacetylmucyl diazide, however, when heated in an inert solvent forms the corresponding isocyanate (or a polymer thereof).[81] Acetone-quinide through its hydrazide and azide (XVII) yields 78% of 4,5-isopropylidenedioxy-3-hydroxycyclohexanone (XVIII), but its α-methyl ether forms the internal urethan (XIX) in 57% yield.[82] Tetra-

[77] Leboucq, *J. pharm. chim.*, **5**, 531 (1927).

[78] Weerman, *Rec. trav. chim.*, **37**, 52 (1917).

[79] Curtius, van der Laan, Aufhäuser, Goldberg, von Hofe, Ohlgart, Darapsky, and Sauvin, *J. prakt. Chem.*, **95**, 168 (1917).

[80] Jones and Powers, *J. Am. Chem. Soc.*, **46**, 2518 (1924).

[81] Diels and Löflund, *Ber.*, **47**, 2351 (1914).

[82] Fischer and Dangschat, *Ber.*, **65**, 1009 (1932).

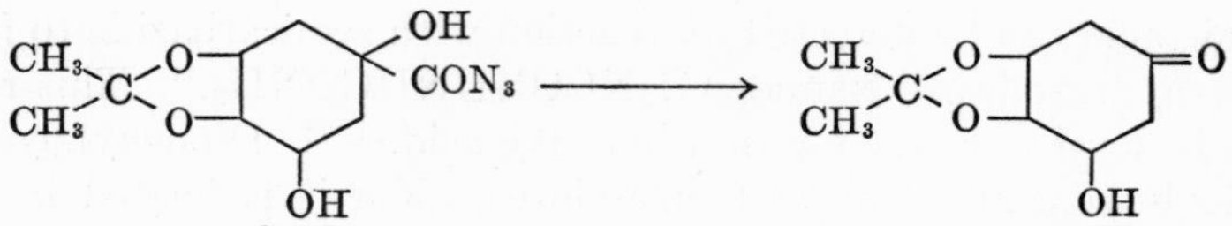

CH_3 C CH_3 O O OH CON_3 OH → CH_3 C CH_3 O O =O OH

XVII XVIII

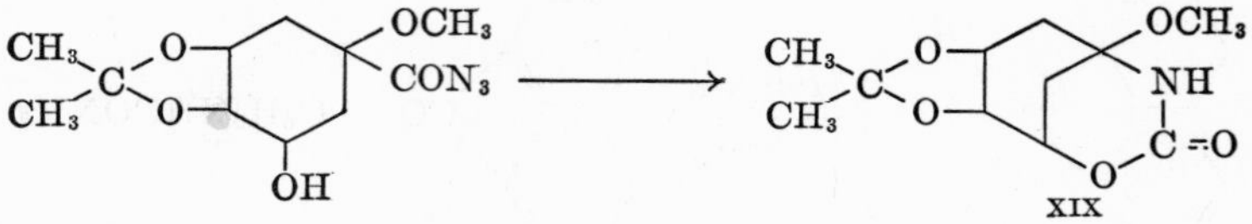

CH_3 C CH_3 O O OCH_3 CON_3 OH → CH_3 C CH_3 O O OCH_3 NH C=O O

XIX

acetylquinyl azide (XX), prepared from the acid chloride and sodium azide, when heated in toluene gives O,N-diacetyl-*p*-aminophenol (XXI) in 98% yield.[83]

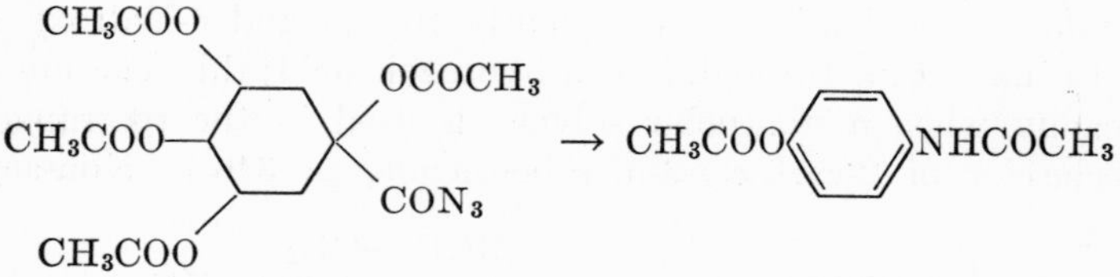

CH_3COO CH_3COO CH_3COO $OCOCH_3$ CON_3 → CH_3COO $NHCOCH_3$

XX XXI

Keto Acids. Keto acids have received little attention from the standpoint of the Curtius degradation. Some keto acids have been converted to amino ketones by the use of hydrazone hydrazides or oxime hydrazides as intermediates. These are treated with nitrous acid to give the keto azides or oxime azides, which rearrange normally in good yields.[62] Removal of the hydrazone group takes place simultaneously with the formation of the azide. (Even stable hydrazones can be cleaved by this means; thus the hydrazone and corresponding diphenylhydrazone of a ketone obtained from the degradation of vomicine react with nitrous acid with formation of the original ketone, nitrous oxide, and ammonia or diphenylamine.[84]) 2,4-Dimethyl-3-acetylpyrrole-5-carboxylic ester has thus been degraded to a derivative of the corresponding amine[62] in good yield. Methyl brucinonate has been converted through its oxime to a hydrazide and an azide, which has been rearranged.[85]

β-Keto esters react with hydrazine to form pyrazolones[86, 87] and consequently are not susceptible of Curtius degradation through the hydra-

[83] Fischer, *Ber.*, **54**, 775 (1921).
[84] Wieland and Horner, *Ann.*, **528**, 95 (1937).
[85] Leuchs and Gladkorn, *Ber.*, **56**, 1780 (1923).
[86] Curtius, *J. prakt. Chem.*, **50**, 508 (1894).
[87] von Rothenburg, *J. prakt. Chem.*, **51**, 43 (1895).

zides. The difficulty of obtaining β-keto acid chlorides has precluded the use of the sodium azide method. Blocking the β-keto group by oxime formation does not succeed since hydroxylamine is eliminated when such compounds are treated with hydrazine.

Amino Acids. Aliphatic primary amino acid azides have not been isolated, and in only a few instances have attempts been made to prepare them from the corresponding hydrazides. Nitrous acid attacks both the hydrazide and the primary amino group to yield mixtures of unidentified products.[88] When both the amino group and the carboxyl group are attached to an aromatic nucleus, the amino azide can be formed by the use of diazonium salts (p. 372). Diazonium salts react with *p*-aminobenzhydrazide to form *p*-aminobenzazide without affecting the amino group; the resulting azide can be rearranged and the product hydrolyzed to *p*-phenylenediamine.[88] Nitrous acid causes the

$$\text{ArCONHNH}_2 + \text{Ar}'\text{N}_2\text{Cl} \rightarrow \text{ArCON}_3 + \text{Ar}'\text{NH}_3\text{Cl}$$

replacement of the aromatic amino group by hydroxyl, yielding a hydroxy azide, from which an aminophenol is eventually obtained. By this means 3-nitro-5-aminophenol has been prepared from 3-nitro-5-aminobenzhydrazide.[89] If the amino group is *ortho* to a carboxyl group, cyclization to a triazine takes place when the hydrazide is treated with nitrous acid. Anthranilyl hydrazide (XXII) yields hydroxybenztriazine (XXIII),[90] and 2-amino-3-naphthoyl hydrazide yields a naphthotriazine.[90] 2,6-Diaminoisonicotinyl hydrazide is attacked first at the

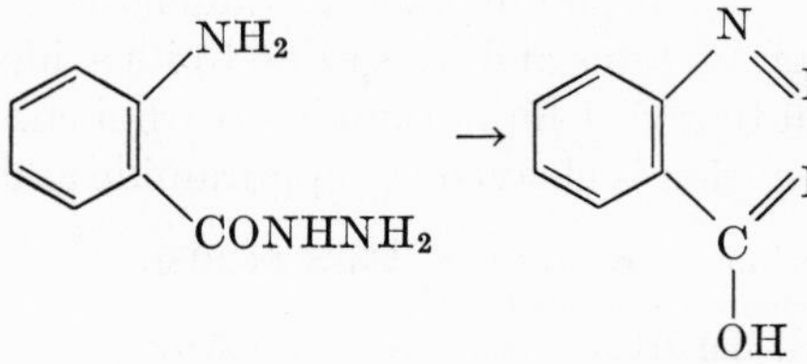

NH_2, $CONHNH_2$ (XXII) → N, N, N, C–OH (XXIII)

amino groups by nitrous acid and cannot be degraded to the triamine.[91a]

The preparation of secondary amino acyl azides has been very restricted in the aliphatic and benzene series. N-Phenylglycyl hydra-

[88] Curtius, Jansen, Colosser, Donselt, and Kyriacou, *J. prakt. Chem.*, **95**, 327 (1918).

[89] Curtius and Riedel, *J. prakt. Chem.*, **76**, 238 (1907).

[90] Fries, Walter, and Schilling, *Ann.*, **516**, 248 (1935).

[91a] Meyer and von Beck, *Monatsh.*, **36**, 731 (1915).

zide is converted by nitrous acid to N-phenyl-N-nitrosoglycyl azide.[25] Indefinite products are obtained from iminodiacethydrazide.[91b] In

$$C_6H_5NHCH_2CONHNH_2 + HNO_2 \rightarrow C_6H_5{-}N\begin{cases} CH_2CON_3 \\ NO \end{cases}$$

the pyrrole series, normal degradation is entirely successful; the pyrrole nitrogen does not become nitrosated.[59, 60, 92, 93, 94, 95] Although tertiary amino groups are also unaffected by nitrous acid, the usual procedure for isolating azides must be modified on account of the basicity of the molecule. In the aliphatic and benzene series no conclusive results have been reported,[88] but in heterocyclic compounds, where the tertiary amino group is a component of the nucleus, many successful degradations have been accomplished. 6-Methylnicotinic ester, for example, yields 63% of 2-methyl-5-aminopyridine.[96]

Acylated Amino Acids. The complications arising in the Curtius degradation of amino acids are eliminated to a large extent when the amino group is acylated. Many azides of acylated aliphatic α-amino acids have been synthesized, not for the purpose of rearranging them to diamines which can be hydrolyzed to aldehydes, but for use as acylating agents in place of the less tractable acid chlorides. Curtius and his students have explored this field extensively.[97–104]

Bergmann has employed the azides of acylated amino acids for the stepwise degradation of peptides, as illustrated by the conversion of hippurylalanine to hippuramide and acetaldehyde. Hippurylalanine is converted through its ester and hydrazide to its azide, which is heated with benzyl alcohol to give 1-hippuramido-1-carbobenzoxyaminoethane. This upon hydrogenation is cleaved to hippuramide and acetaldehyde.[105]

[91b] Curtius and Hofmann, *J. prakt. Chem.*, **96**, 202 (1918).

[92] Fischer and Endermann, *Ann.*, **531**, 245 (1937).

[93] Fischer, Guggemös, and Schafer, *Ann.*, **540**, 30 (1939).

[94] Fischer and Müller, *Z. physiol. Chem.*, **132**, 72 (1924).

[95] Piccinini and Salmoni, *Gazz. chim. ital.*, **32**, I, 246 (1902); *Atti accad. Lincei*, [5] **9**, I, 359

[96] Graf, *J. prakt. Chem.*, **133**, 19 (1932).

[97] Curtius and Curtius, *J. prakt. Chem.*, **70**, 158 (1904).

[98] Curtius and Gumlich, *J. prakt. Chem.*, **70**, 195 (1904).

[99] Curtius and Lambotte, *J. prakt. Chem.*, **70**, 109 (1904).

[100] Curtius, Laurent, Petridis, and Zimmerli, *J. prakt. Chem.*, **94**, 93 (1916).

[101] Curtius and Lenhard, *J. prakt. Chem.*, **70**, 230 (1904).

[102] Curtius and van der Linden, *J. prakt. Chem.*, **70**, 137 (1904).

[103] Curtius and Müller, *J. prakt. Chem.*, **70**, 223, (1904).

[104] Curtius and Wüstenfeld, *J. prakt. Chem.*, **70**, 73 (1904).

[105] Bergmann and Zervas, *J. Biol. Chem.*, **113**, 341 (1936); *Science*, **79**, 439 (1934).

$$C_6H_5CONHCH_2CONH{-}CH(CH_3)CON_3 \xrightarrow{C_6H_5CH_2OH}$$

$$C_6H_5CONHCH_2CONH{-}CH(CH_3)NHCO_2CH_2C_6H_5 \xrightarrow[H_2O]{H_2/Pd}$$

$$C_6H_5CONHCH_2CONH_2 + CH_3CHO + NH_3 + CO_2 + C_6H_5CH_3$$

Acylated aromatic amino acids can often be degraded successfully. 2-Acetamido-3-naphthoyl hydrazide gives the azide, which rearranges to N-acetylnaphthimidazolone.[91]

$$C_{10}H_6(NHCOCH_3)(CON_3) \rightarrow C_{10}H_6\langle N(COCH_3)\text{—}C{=}O\text{—}NH\rangle$$

Protection of amino groups from nitrous acid by acylation is not always successful, for deacylation may occur during treatment of the esters with hydrazine. Ethyl 2,6-dibenzamidoisonicotinate when treated with hydrazine gives 2,6-diaminoisonicotinyl hydrazide;[106] the ethyl ester of phthalylglycine is similarly cleaved to glycyl hydrazide and phthalhydrazide, a general reaction for phthalimides[107] (see p. 381).

Carbamic Acids. The esters of carbamic acid or substituted carbamic acids (urethans) do not react readily with hydrazine, but the corresponding carbamyl chlorides do. The semicarbazide or substituted semicarbazides that result yield carbamyl azides[108] with nitrous acid. Most carbamyl azides are prepared more conveniently from the carbamyl chlorides and sodium azide. Monosubstituted carbamyl azides can also be synthesized from isocyanates and hydrazoic acid.[109, 110, 111]

$$RNCO + HN_3 \rightarrow RNHCON_3$$

The azide of carbamic acid, NH_2CON_3, rearranges only with difficulty; among the products only a trace of a hydrazine compound was

[106] Meyer and von Beck, *Monatsh.*, **36**, 731 (1915).
[107] Ing and Manske, *J. Chem. Soc.*, **1926**, 2348.
[108] Thiele, *Ann.*, **283**, 37 (1894).
[109] Hantzsch and Vagt, *Ann.*, **314**, 339 (1901).
[110] Oliveri-Mandalá and Calderaro, *Gazz. chim. ital.*, **43**, I, 538 (1913).
[111] Oliveri-Mandalá and Noto, *Gazz. chim. ital.*, **43**, I, 514 (1913).

found.[112] The failure of monosubstituted carbamyl azides, $RNHCON_3$, to rearrange has been explained on the basis of an isourea structure, $RN{=}C(OH)N_3$,[112a] for the azide. Disubstituted carbamyl azides rearrange. The rearrangement is facilitated when one of the substituents is an aromatic group; usually cyclization to the aromatic ring follows the rearrangement. N-Ethyl-N-phenylcarbamyl azide when heated in boiling xylene gives 1-ethylindazolone (XXIV) in 68% yield.[113]

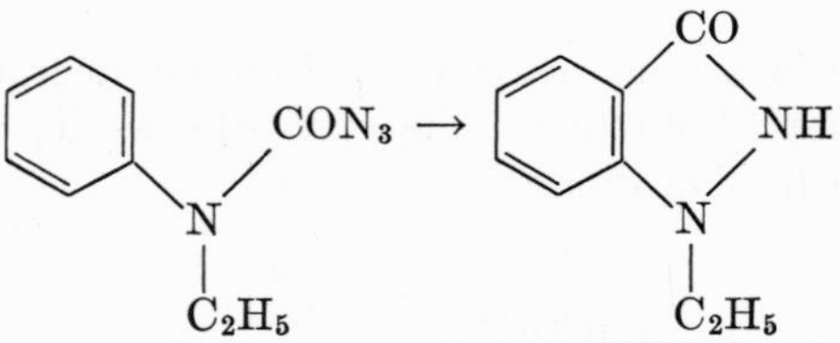

$$C_6H_5N(C_2H_5)CON_3 \rightarrow C_6H_4\begin{matrix}CO \\ N(C_2H_5)\end{matrix}\!\!>NH$$

XXIV

Halogenated Acids. Halogenated azides undergo rearrangement in the usual manner to isocyanates, from which halo amines are obtained by hydrolysis. If the halogen is in the α-position, the resulting halogenated isocyanate is hydrolyzed to an aldehyde or ketone. This reaction was adapted by von Braun to the structure proof of naphthenic acids.[23] Thus, dicyclopentylacetic acid is converted through the bromo acid chloride (XXV) to dicyclopentyl ketone in 60% yield.[23] Halogenated aromatic acid azides can be degraded without complication to the halogenated aromatic amines.

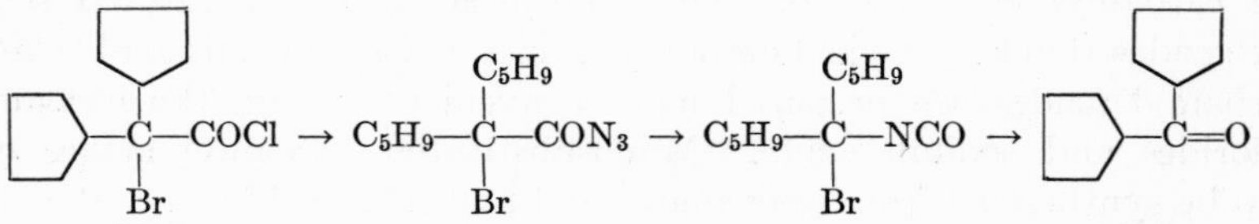

$$R_2C(Br)CON_3 \rightarrow R_2C(Br)NCO \rightarrow R_2CO + HBr + HNCO$$

$$(C_5H_9)_2C(Br)COCl \rightarrow C_5H_9{-}C(C_5H_9)(Br){-}CON_3 \rightarrow C_5H_9{-}C(C_5H_9)(Br){-}NCO \rightarrow (C_5H_9)_2C{=}O$$

XXV XXVI

The preparation of aliphatic halogenated acid azides is accomplished most advantageously from the acid chlorides and sodium azide. The course from the ester through the hydrazide is not applicable ordinarily

[112] Curtius and Schmidt, *J. prakt. Chem.*, **105**, 177 (1914).

[112a] Hurd and Spence, *J. Am. Chem. Soc.*, **49**, 266 (1927).

[113] Stollé, Nieland, and Merkle, *J. prakt. Chem.*, **116**, 192 (1927).

since the halogen atom is replaced by the hydrazino group. Special methods for synthesizing certain halogenated hydrazides are available. Halogens may be added to an olefinic hydrazide; δ-phenyl-α,β,γ,δ-tetrabromovaleryl hydrazide is prepared by addition of bromine to β-styrylacrylyl hydrazide.[114] Diazo hydrazides have been used with success for the preparation of several halogenated hydrazides; for example, diazoaceturic ester reacts with hydrazine to yield the hydrazide (XXVII, 82% yield), which reacts with dry hydrogen chloride to give chloroaceturyl hydrazide (XXVIII).[115] Iodoaceturyl and bromoaceturyl

$$\underset{\text{XXVII}}{N_2CHCONHCH_2CONHNH_2} \rightarrow \underset{\text{XXVIII}}{ClCH_2CONHCH_2CONHNH_3Cl} + N_2$$

hydrazides have been prepared similarly.[116] Direct bromination converts 2,4-dimethylpyrrole-5-carbonyl hydrazide to 2,4-dimethyl-3-bromopyrrole-5-carbonyl hydrazide.[60]

In the pyrrole series halogenated azides can be prepared by direct halogenation. 2,4-Dimethyl-3-ethylpyrrole-5-carbonyl azide has been brominated to 2-bromomethyl-3-ethyl-4-methylpyrrole-5-carbonyl azide;[60] and 2-methyl-3,4-diethylpyrrole-5-carbonyl azide (XXIX) has been chlorinated with sulfuryl chloride to 2-trichloromethyl-3,4-diethylpyrrole-5-carbonyl azide, which on treatment with methanol yields 3,4-diethyl-2-carbomethoxy-5-carbomethoxyaminopyrrole (XXX).[93] Dichlorination is also successful; 2,4-dimethyl-3-bromo-

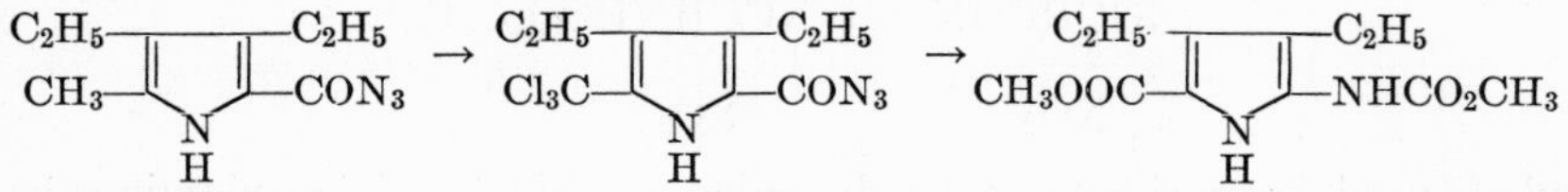

C₂H₅, C₂H₅ / CH₃—(pyrrole, N–H)—CON₃ (XXIX) → C₂H₅, C₂H₅ / Cl₃C—(pyrrole, N–H)—CON₃ → C₂H₅, C₂H₅ / CH₃OOC—(pyrrole, N–H)—NHCO₂CH₃ (XXX)

pyrrole-5-carbonyl azide yields 2-(dichloromethyl)-3-bromo-4-methylpyrrole-5-carbonyl azide (XXXI), which on mild alcoholysis gives 2-formyl-3-bromo-4-methylpyrrole-5-carbonyl azide (XXXII).[62]

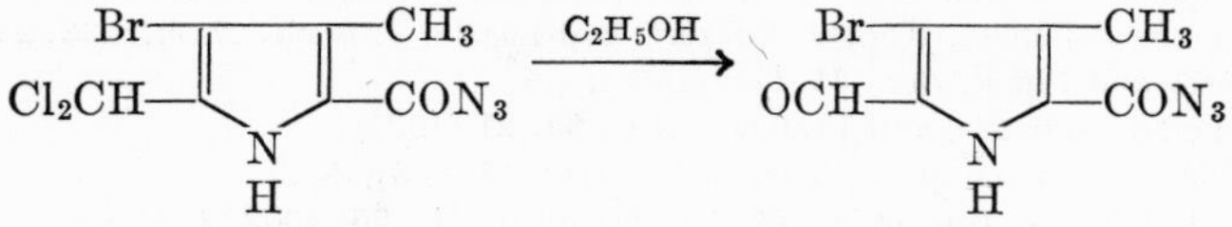

Br, CH₃ / Cl₂CH—(pyrrole, N–H)—CON₃ (XXXI) $\xrightarrow{C_2H_5OH}$ Br, CH₃ / OCH—(pyrrole, N–H)—CON₃ (XXXII)

Aromatic fluorine, chlorine, and bromine compounds are ordinarily unaffected by hydrazine, and many fluoro, chloro, and bromo benzhydrazides have been made by the hydrazide as well as by the sodium

[114] Riedel and Schulz, *Ann.*, **367**, 14 (1909).
[115] Curtius and Welde, *Ber.*, **43**, 862 (1910).
[116] Curtius and Callan, *Ber.*, **43**, 2457 (1910).

azide method. If the halogen is activated by *ortho* or *para* nitro groups, as in 3,5-dinitro-4-chlorobenzoic ester, treatment with hydrazine may cause its replacement.[117] Halogens in the α- and γ-positions of pyridine are reactive; ethyl 4,5-dichloronicotinate is converted by hydrazine to 4-hydrazino-5-chloronicotinyl hydrazide,[118] and 2,4-dihydroxy-6-chloronicotinamide to 2,4-dihydroxy-6-hydrazinonicotinyl hydrazide.[119] The halogens (even iodine) in the β-position of the pyridine ring are unaffected [120] by hydrazine.

Iodine in the benzene nucleus is sometimes removed by hydrazine through replacement or reduction; from ethyl 3-iodo-2-naphthoate and hydrazine, β-naphthoyl hydrazide is obtained.[121] Ethyl *p*-iodobenzoate yields *p*-iodobenzhydrazide,[122] but ethyl *o*-iodobenzoate yields the internal hydrazide of *o*-hydrazinobenzoic acid.[123]

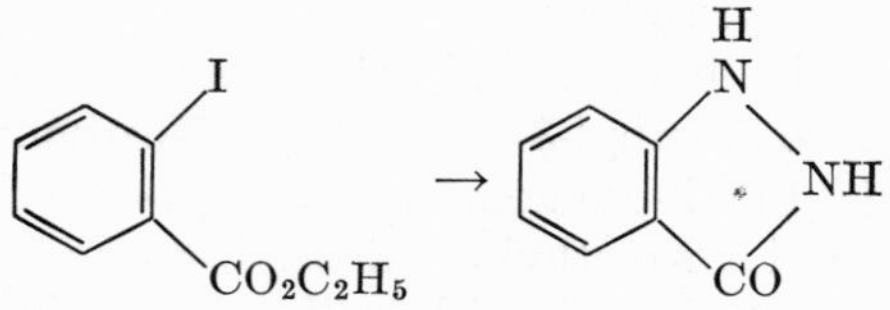

I

$CO_2C_2H_5$ $\rightarrow$

H

N

NH

CO

Nitro Groups. The Curtius degradation has been applied to only one nitro aliphatic azide; ethyl nitrocyanoacetate is converted through its hydrazide and azide to a urethan.[124] In the aromatic series, nitro-

$$\underset{\displaystyle NO_2}{NCCHCON_3} \rightarrow \underset{\displaystyle NO_2}{NCCHNHCO_2C_2H_5}$$

substituted benzazides can be degraded readily to nitroarylamines.[125] Many of the intermediate isocyanates have been isolated [126, 127, 128] and have proved to be useful reagents for characterizing amines and alcohols.[129, 130, 131]

[117] Müller, Zimmermann, Hoffmann, and Weisbrod, *J. prakt. Chem.*, **111**, 273 (1925).

[118] Graf, Lederer-Ponzer, Kopetz, Purkert, and László, *J. prakt. Chem.*, **138**, 244 (1933).

[119] Schroeter and Finck, *Ber.*, **71**, 680 (1938).

[120] Graf, Lederer-Ponzer, and Freiberg, *Ber.*, **64**, 21 (1931).

[121] Godstein and Cornamusaz, *Helv. Chim. Acta*, **15**, 935 (1932).

[122] Sah and Hsü, *Rec. trav. chim.*, **59**, 349 (1940) [*C. A.*, **35**, 4362 (1941)].

[123] Kahl, *Chem. Zentr.*, **1904** II, 1493.

[124] Darapsky and Hillers, *J. prakt. Chem.*, **92**, 297 (1925).

[125] Curtius, Struve, and Radenhausen, *J. prakt. Chem.*, **52**, 227 (1895).

[126] Naegeli and Tyabji, *Helv. Chim. Acta*, **16**, 349 (1933).

[127] Naegeli and Tyabji, *Helv. Chim. Acta*, **17**, 931 (1934).

[128] Schroeter, *Ber.*, **42**, 2336 (1909).

[129] Blanksma and Verberg, *Rec. trav. chim.*, **53**, 988 (1934).

[130] Meng and Sah, *J. Chinese Chem. Soc.*, **4**, 75 (1936).

[131] Sah and Ma, *J. Chinese Chem. Soc.*, **2**, 159 (1934).

The conversion of nitro aromatic acid chlorides to the azides with sodium azide is very generally applicable.[126, 127, 132, 133, 134] The adaptation of the hydrazide method sometimes involves complications due to the reducing action of hydrazine. *o*-, *m*-, and *p*-Nitrobenzhydrazide can be prepared from the esters in almost quantitative yields.[135, 136] 3,5-Dinitrobenzhydrazide is formed in satisfactory yield from the corresponding ester, but, if a large excess of hydrazine is employed and the reaction mixture is refluxed for twenty-four hours, 3-nitro-5-aminobenzhydrazide[89] results in 60% yield. Ethyl 2,4-dinitrobenzoate, on the other hand, yields only ethyl 2-nitro-4-aminobenzoate or ethyl 2-nitro-4-aminobenzhydrazide.[137] The half ester of *p*-nitrobenzylmalonic acid through its hydrazide yields *p*-nitrophenylalanine in normal fashion, but the diethyl ester of bis(*p*-nitrobenzyl)malonic acid gives only the cyclic secondary hydrazide of bis(*p*-aminobenzyl)malonic acid.[47]

Cyano Acids. Cyano azides rearrange to cyano isocyanates, which can be hydrolyzed to amino acids. Only α-cyano acids have been studied.

$$\underset{\displaystyle R}{\overset{}{NCCHCON_3}} \rightarrow NCCH(R)NCO \rightarrow {}^{-}OOCCH(R)NH_3^{+}$$

The availability of substituted cyanoacetic esters and the ease of conversion to cyanoacethydrazides and azides have made this method of preparing α-amino acids an attractive one. Leucine, α-amino-*n*-valeric acid, α-amino-γ,δ-dimethylvaleric acid,[138] valine, phenylalanine, tyrosine, and α-amino-δ-phenoxyvaleric acid[139] have been prepared by this general procedure though in yields not always high. (For the preparation of α-amino acids from substituted malonic esters, see p. 346.) In isolated instances hydrazine reacts with the cyano grouping to give resinous products,[139] amidrazones [$RC(NH_2){=}NNH_2$], or pyrazoles.[140] Cyanoacetyl chloride polymerizes readily[40] so that the reaction with sodium azide to form cyanoacetazide has not been applied.

Sulfonamide, Sulfide, and Other Sulfur-Containing Groups. The presence of sulfonamide and sulfide groups in an acid does not interfere with the conversion of the carboxyl group through the azide to an

132 Naegeli, Tyabji, and Conrad, *Helv. Chim. Acta*, **21**, 1127 (1938).
133 Lindemann and Pabst, *Ann.*, **462**, 29, 41 (1928).
134 Lindemann and Wessel, *Ber.*, **58**, 1221 (1925).
135 Curtius and Melsbach, *J. prakt. Chem.*, **81**, 523 (1910).
136 Curtius and Trachmann, *J. prakt. Chem.*, **51**, 165 (1895).
137 Curtius and Bollenbeck, *J. prakt. Chem.*, **76**, 281 (1907).
138 Darapsky, Decker, Steuernagel, and Schiedrum, *J. prakt. Chem.*, **146**, 250 (1936).
139 Gagnon, Gaudry, and King, *J. Chem. Soc.*, **1944**, 13.
140 von Rothenburg, *Ber.*, **27**, 685 (1894).

amino group. Mercapto acids have not been studied. *o*-Sulfonamidobenzhydrazide, from saccharin and hydrazine,[141] is converted quantitatively into the azide, which yields *o*-aminobenzenesulfonamide or its derivatives.[142] Similarly, the following have been degraded: 2-ethylmercapto-6-hydroxypyrimidine-5-acetic acid,[143] *o*-(α-thienylthio)benzoic acid,[144] several tetrahydrothiophenecarboxylic acids,[145, 146, 147] thiophenecarboxylic acids,[148, 149, 150] and thiazolecarboxylic acids.[151, 152, 153]

Azo, Diazo, and Azido Groups. Aliphatic diazo azides have never been synthesized. Diazo hydrazides, however, are quite readily prepared since hydrazine under mild conditions does not affect the diazo group in a diazo ester. Prolonged treatment with hydrazine may lead to a triazole or cause hydrolysis of the diazo group. Diazoacetylglycylglycine ester gives a hydrazide in 72% yield by gentle warming with hydrazine; by long heating with hydrazine in the presence of water, hydroxyaceturylglycyl hydrazide is formed, and by extensive heating with excess hydrazine the hydrazine salt of 5-hydroxytriazole-1-acetylglycyl hydrazide (XXXIII) is produced.[154] The diazo group in diazo

$$N_2CHCONHCH_2CONHCH_2CO_2R \begin{cases} \rightarrow HOCH_2CONHCH_2CONHCH_2CONHNH_2 \\ \rightarrow N_2CHCONHCH_2CONHCH_2CONHNH_2 \\ \rightarrow \text{HC=C—OH; N, N—}CH_2COCH_2CONHNH_2\text{; N (triazole ring)} \end{cases}$$

XXXIII

hydrazides has always been replaced by some other group such as halogen [115, 116] or acetoxy [154] before the degradation to azides and amines is continued. Diazoacetamide gives azidoacethydrazide on treatment with hydrazine.[155]

The presence of an aromatic azo group does not interfere with the

[141] Schrader, *J. prakt. Chem.*, **95**, 312 (1917).
[142] Schrader, *J. prakt. Chem.*, **95**, 392 (1917).
[143] Litzinger and Johnson, *J. Am. Chem. Soc.*, **58**, 1936 (1936).
[144] Steinkopf, Schmitt, and Fiedler, *Ann.*, **527**, 237 (1937).
[145] Brown and Kilmer, *J. Am. Chem. Soc.*, **65**, 1674 (1943).
[146] DuVigneaud, Hofmann, and Melville, *J. Am. Chem. Soc.*, **64**, 188 (1942).
[147] Kilmer, Armstrong, Brown, and DuVigneaud, *J. Biol. Chem.*, **145**, 495 (1942).
[148] Cheney and Piening, *J. Am. Chem. Soc.*, **66**, 1040 (1944).
[149] Curtius and Thyssen, *J. prakt. Chem.*, **65**, 1 (1902).
[150] Robinson and Todd, *J. Chem. Soc.*, **1939**, 1743.
[151] Cerecedo and Tolpin, *J. Am. Chem. Soc.*, **59**, 1660 (1937).
[152] Hinegardner and Johnson, *J. Am. Chem. Soc.*, **52**, 3724 (1930).
[153] Hinegardner and Johnson, *J. Am. Chem. Soc.*, **52**, 4139, 4141 (1930).
[154] Curtius and Callan, *Ber.*, **43**, 2447 (1910).
[155] Curtius, Darapsky, and Bockmühl, *Ber.*, **41**, 344 (1908).

degradation of the azide to an amine. *m*- [126] and *p*- [37] Phenylazobenzazide can be degraded to the corresponding isocyanates and amines in

$$C_6H_5N{=}N{-}C_6H_4{-}CON_3 \rightarrow C_6H_5N{=}N{-}C_6H_4{-}NCO$$

excellent yields. γ-Phenylazodipicolinazide gives a phenylazo diamine.[156] The preparation of azo azides is accomplished preferably

$$\text{4-}(N{=}NC_6H_5)\text{-2,6-}(N_3OC)_2C_5H_2N \rightarrow \text{4-}(N{=}NC_6H_5)\text{-2,6-}(H_2N)_2C_5H_2N$$

through the azo acid chloride and sodium azide. The hydrazide procedure may sometimes involve extra steps owing to the reducing action of hydrazine on the azo group; the azo ester is converted to a hydrazo hydrazide which must be reoxidized to the azo hydrazide before the azo azide is made.

The azido group is frequently unaffected during the conversion of the azide to an amine unless it is in the α-position. Ethyl β-azidopropionate reacts with hydrazine to give β-azidopropionhydrazide, which through the azide yields β-azidoethylamine.[157, 158] Ethyl γ-azidobutyrate, on the other hand, gives a mixture of products in this series of reactions.[157, 159] All the azido azides have characteristic explosive instability; the reaction of sodium azide with azidoacetyl chloride led to "some very alarming explosions."[160] If the azido group is in the α-position, it is lost in a manner similar to an α-halogen during hydrolysis of the isocyanate with formation of an aldehyde or ketone.

$$R_2C(CON_3)(N_3) \rightarrow R_2C(NCO)(N_3) \xrightarrow{H_2O} R_2C{=}O + HN_3 + CO_2 + NH_3$$

Heterocyclic Systems. The degradation of acids of several heterocyclic compounds has been mentioned in previous sections. In general almost every kind of heterocyclic carboxylic acid has been degraded successfully by the Curtius procedure, at least as far as the isocyanate

[156] Chichibabin and Ossetrowa, *J. Am. Chem. Soc.*, **56**, 1711 (1934).
[157] Curtius, *Ber.*, **45**, 1057 (1912).
[158] Curtius and Franzen, *Ber.*, **45**, 1037 (1912).
[159] Curtius and Giulini, *Ber.*, **45**, 1045 (1912).
[160] Forster and Müller, *J. Chem. Soc.*, **97**, 1056 (1910).

or urethan stage. The free amines in many instances are inherently unstable. Some molecules containing active methylene groups are nitrosated during the formation of the azide from the hydrazide. Pyrazolone-3-acetazide (XXXIV) yields 4-isonitrosopyrazolone-3-acetazide (XXXV).[161]

```
H2C———C—CH2CONHNH2        HON=C———C—CH2CON3
 |    ||              →        |    ||
O=C    N                     O=C    N
   \  /                         \  /
    N                            N
    H                            H
     XXXIV                        XXXV
```

Thiocarbamyl Azides, Imido Azides, and Hydroximido Azides. Thiosemicarbazides react with nitrous acid [162] and isothiocyanates react with hydrazoic acid [163] to yield azides of marked stability. For this

$$RNHCSNHNH_2 + HONO \rightarrow RNHCSN_3 \leftarrow RNCS + HN_3$$

reason they were postulated at first as thiatriazoles. The thiocarbamyl,[164] methylthiocarbamyl,[165] allylthiocarbamyl,[165] and phenylthiocarbamyl [162, 163] azides have been investigated. The thiocarbamyl azides lose nitrogen when heated with concentrated hydrochloric acid with formation of the hydrochlorides of bases which are probably isothiocyanoamines, RNHNCS; thiocarbamyl azide gives a crystalline hydrochloride, $N_2H_2CS \cdot HCl$. By the action of nitrous acid on amidrazones, high-melting, stable compounds are produced which appear to

```
      NH             [      NH ]          N—NH
R—C<          →      [ R—C<    ]  →  R—C<    |
      NHNH2          [      N3 ]          N=N
```

be tetrazoles.[166] Similarly, hydrazide oximes give hydroxytetrazoles.[166a]

```
      NOH
R—C<                                  OH
      NHNH2    \ HNO2                 |
                ↘                     N—N
                        R—C<          ||
                ↗                     N—N
      NOH      / NaN3
R—C<
      Cl
```

[161] Curtius and Kufferath, *J. prakt. Chem.*, **64**, 334 (1901).
[162] Freund and Hempel, *Ber.*, **28**, 74 (1895).
[163] Oliveri-Mandalá, *Gazz. chim. ital.*, **44**, I, 670 (1914).
[164] Freund and Schander, *Ber.*, **29**, 2500 (1896).
[165] Freund and Schwartz, *Ber.*, **29**, 2491 (1896).
[166] Pinner, *Ber.*, **30**, 1871 (1897).
[166a] Wieland, *Ber.*, **42**, 4199 (1909).

The same substances are formed by the reaction of hydroxamyl chlorides with sodium azide.[167]

Comparison of the Curtius, Hofmann, and Schmidt Reactions

The Curtius, Hofmann (see p. 267), and Schmidt (see p. 307) reactions are in that order decreasingly mild, decreasingly flexible, and increasingly expeditious. The last-named quality varies somewhat with the available starting material, whether the free acid or the ester. The Curtius reaction lends itself to the preparation of isocyanates, *sym*- and *as*-ureas, amides, urethans, and amines at will, and provides a wide choice of experimental conditions. For synthetic purposes the Hofmann reaction can be used only to prepare *sym*-ureas, urethans, and amines directly, and halting the reaction at a desired intermediate is often not possible. The variety of experimental conditions is narrower and more limited. The Schmidt reaction on carboxylic acids or derivatives has been applied as a preparative method only to the production of amines; although urethans and isocyanates have been prepared occasionally by this reaction, it can hardly be considered a preparative method for them. Amides can be prepared by the Schmidt reaction only from ketones. The choice of experimental conditions employable in the Schmidt reaction is narrow.

The Curtius and Schmidt reactions can be run in completely anhydroxylic environment, in the Schmidt reaction by use of such catalysts as stannic chloride instead of the customary sulfuric acid. All three reactions can be carried out under anhydrous conditions, but only in the Curtius and Hofmann reactions can an anhydrous alcohol be used as a solvent. Since the Curtius reaction is successful under conditions ranging from neutral to strongly acid, compounds may be degraded without exposure to strong acid or alkali. In the Hofmann reaction it is difficult to avoid a certain amount of exposure to strong alkali; in the Schmidt reaction all the required catalysts are strong acids in the Lewis sense and act as catalysts for a variety of other reactions.

Compounds very sensitive to oxidation may be attacked by the nitrous acid used for converting a hydrazide to an azide, but the sodium azide method is non-oxidizing. Although it is possible to avoid exposure to free halogens in the Hofmann reaction by using a previously prepared hypohalite solution, such solutions are themselves powerful oxidizing agents. The conditions of the Schmidt reaction are essentially non-oxidizing as far as organic compounds are concerned.

[167] Forster, *J. Chem. Soc.*, **95**, 433 (1909).

The classical Curtius degradation of the ester through the hydrazide, azide, and urethan to the amine is rather tedious when all the intermediates are isolated, and the yields are lowered by the concomitant mechanical losses. Even though in good practice these steps can be telescoped, the hydrazide modification of the Curtius reaction still is more laborious than the Hofmann and Schmidt reactions. The acid chloride-sodium azide method through the azide to the amine can be made as short as the Hofmann reaction, but it is still necessary to prepare the acid chloride, and the method cannot be condensed to the one step of the Schmidt reaction. The Hofmann reaction through the amide, N-haloamide, and urethan involves almost as many steps as the classical Curtius reaction, but these steps can nearly always be condensed into one operation, as compared with two for the usual procedure from the hydrazide by the Curtius method. The conservation of time by the Schmidt reaction is due chiefly to the fact that the reaction can be run directly on the free acid. This advantage disappears to a large extent when the ester or amide is the available starting material, for, although the Schmidt reaction can be run on these derivatives, it is not generally satisfactory, and the ester or amide must usually be hydrolyzed to the free acid before the Schmidt reaction can be successfully applied.

When esters of carboxylic acids are the compounds immediately at hand, the Curtius reaction is favored. Hydrazides can be made from esters more readily than can amides, and frequently more readily than the esters can be hydrolyzed. When amides are available, the Hofmann reaction is naturally the most convenient, although amides can be converted to hydrazides without difficulty if for other reasons the Curtius reaction is more suitable.

Syntheses in large quantities introduce two other factors. The cost-determining reagents, named in the order of decreasing cost, are hydrazine, sodium azide, and chlorine; therefore, the Hofmann reaction utilizing chlorine is the cheapest procedure. Since hydrazoic acid and many azides are poisonous as well as treacherously and violently explosive, it is not prudent to handle large quantities of hydrazoic acid or to *isolate* large amounts of azides of unproved stability. The Schmidt reaction, however, has been run with as much as 6 moles of hydrazoic acid at one time, and the Curtius reaction with as much as kilogram quantities. The acid chloride-sodium azide method may not be well adapted to large-scale work because of the difficulty of control. The Hofmann reaction has been used successfully on an industrial scale, and there appears to be no limit to the size of run that can be made.

The degradation of both carboxyl groups of malonic acids can be accomplished only by the Curtius reaction; the Hofmann and Schmidt reactions bring about the degradation of only one of the carboxyl groups. Succinic acids also are best degraded by the Curtius reaction for the same reason, although some diamine can be obtained by the Schmidt reaction.

Unsaturated acids are converted to amines most satisfactorily by the Curtius reaction (sodium azide method). The Hofmann reaction is applicable with certainty only to α,β-olefinic acid amides, since the olefin group in another position is likely to be halogenated by the reagent. The Schmidt reaction is applicable to all olefinic acids, although there is a possible danger of sulfonation at the site of unsaturation.

Keto acids are degraded best by the Hofmann reaction. The applicability of the Curtius reaction to keto-acids is limited; the Schmidt reaction occurs preferentially on the keto group rather than on the carboxyl group.

Acylated amino acids are degraded most satisfactorily by the Curtius method, but non-acylated amino acids must be degraded by the Hofmann method, which usually leaves the amino group unattacked. However, the Hofmann reaction is not suitable for degrading peptides because of the strongly hydrolytic conditions required, and the Curtius reaction is the preferred method. α-Amino acids are inert to the Schmidt reaction.

Aromatic acids containing active halogen are degraded by the Curtius reaction (sodium azide method); the Hofmann reaction is not applicable, and the Schmidt reaction has not been attempted. Aromatic acids with substituents like amino or methoxyl which cause the ring to be highly susceptible to halogenation or sulfonation must ordinarily be degraded by the Curtius reaction, although the Schmidt reaction might also be successful. 2-Hydroxy-3-naphthoic acid undergoes bromination in the ring when subjected to the Hofmann reaction, but the Curtius reaction through the hydrazide gives a cyclic urethan in 63% yield.[168]

The Curtius and Schmidt reactions are inapplicable to sugar acids. The Hofmann degradation has been applied successfully in this field.

The amides of carbamic acids (ureas) can be degraded to hydrazines by the Hofmann reaction; urea gives a good yield of hydrazine. The Curtius reaction succeeds only with disubstituted carbamic acids, and the Schmidt reaction has not been applied.

There are remarkably few amines for which yields are reported by the Curtius, Hofmann, and Schmidt reactions, and no significant conclusions can be drawn from the results that are available.

[168] Fries and Hass, *Ber.*, **58**, 2845 (1925).

RELATED REACTIONS

The Lossen Rearrangement. Alkali salts of hydroxamic acids and derivatives undergo rearrangement to isocyanates according to the following equation:

$$RCO—NK—OCOCH_3 \rightarrow RN{=}C{=}O + CH_3CO_2K$$

This reaction, known as the Lossen rearrangement, has seen but little synthetic application [27, 169, 170] and possesses no distinct advantages over the Curtius, Hofmann, and Schmidt reactions. It appears to be useful when hydroxamic acids result as primary products. The reaction has been reviewed recently.[171]

The Tiemann Reaction. Amidoximes undergo rearrangement to *as*-ureas when treated first with benzenesulfonyl chloride and then with water.[172, 173] This is the Tiemann reaction, which has so far been pri-

$$\underset{\text{NOH}}{\overset{\|}{\text{RCNH}_2}} \rightarrow RNHCONH_2$$

marily of theoretical interest. It might have application where the acid to be degraded is available only in the form of its nitrile, since nitriles can be converted readily to amidoximes by hydroxylamine.

Treatment of Silver Salts with Halogens. Silver salts of carboxylic acids lose carbon dioxide when treated with chlorine or bromine, and alkyl halides are produced in good yield.[174, 175] Although this reaction is not related to the Curtius reaction, it can be used to convert an acid to an amine when coupled with one of the many methods for replacing a halogen atom by an amino group.

SELECTION OF EXPERIMENTAL CONDITIONS

Preparation of Hydrazides

Hydrazides are prepared by much the same reactions as amides, with the significant difference that precautions must be taken to avoid the formation of secondary hydrazides, RCONHNHCOR, through acylation of the primary hydrazides, $RCONHNH_2$, initially formed.

[169] Thiele and coworkers, *Ann.*, **295**, 136, 167 (1897); *ibid.*, **309**, 189 (1899).

[170] Mohr, *J. prakt. Chem.*, **71**, 133 (1905); Bredt, Perkin, Hilbing, Lankshear, and Regout, *J. prakt. Chem.*, **89**, 225 (1914).

[171] Yale, *Chem. Revs.*, **33**, 209 (1943).

[172] Tiemann, *Ber.*, **24**, 4162 (1891).

[173] Pinnow, *Ber.*, **24**, 4167 (1891); **26**, 604 (1893).

[174] Prelog and Zelán, *Helv. Chim. Acta*, **27**, 535 (1944).

[175] Hunsdiecker and Hunsdiecker, *Ber.*, **75**, 291 (1942).

The usual procedure is to treat the methyl or ethyl ester of the acid with hydrazine. For most purposes the commercially available 85% aqueous hydrazine hydrate is preferable to anhydrous hydrazine and is generally employed. The formation of hydrazides from esters often proceeds spontaneously at room temperature with marked evolution of heat; if the reaction is not spontaneous, heating on a steam bath for periods varying from five minutes to several days commonly suffices to give excellent yields. Esters which react with great difficulty have been converted to hydrazides at elevated temperatures in a bomb,[62, 176] but there is some danger of decarboxylation under these conditions;[62] temperatures above 180° should be avoided. The hydrazides usually crystallize on cooling, and often during the heating, and frequently need only be collected and dried to be obtained analytically pure. Occasionally, small amounts of secondary hydrazide are formed. Since secondary hydrazides are insoluble in dilute acid, and much less soluble than the primary hydrazides in organic solvents, it is usually not difficult to remove them. The formation of secondary hydrazides can be kept to a minimum by dropping the ester into an excess of boiling hydrazine hydrate at such a rate that a second liquid phase never accumulates.[11, 177, 178] Hydrazides can also be purified by conversion to their crystalline isopropylidene derivatives by warming with acetone; the derivatives are then cleaved to the hydrazide hydrochlorides by treating their ethereal solutions with dry hydrogen chloride.[179] Only occasionally have hydrazides been purified by distillation.[176] The practice is to be avoided, since, at the high temperatures usually necessary for distillation, hydrazides frequently condense to form heterocyclic compounds.[180]

The use of a common solvent, such as ethanol, is indicated where the ester is markedly immiscible with hydrazine hydrate; it is frequently unnecessary to add sufficient solvent to bring about complete miscibility at the start. However, the presence of two immiscible phases *for an appreciable time* should be avoided as it favors the formation of secondary hydrazide and retards the reaction as well. Unreactive esters may be refluxed profitably with hydrazine in a higher-boiling alcohol, such as butyl or amyl alcohol.[37, 181, 182] The progress of hydrazide formation can often be followed by observing the rate of disappearance of

[176] Wieland, Hintermaier, and Dennstedt, *Ann.*, **452**, 1 (1927).
[177] Curtius and Dellschaft, *J. prakt. Chem.*, **64**, 419 (1901).
[178] Curtius and Hille, *J. prakt. Chem.*, **64**, 401 (1901).
[179] Curtius and Bockmuhl, *Ber.*, **45**, 1033 (1912).
[180] Wieland, "Die Hydrazine," Verlag Ferdinand Enke, Stuttgart, 1913.
[181] Schöpf, Perrey, and Jäck, *Ann.*, **497**, 49 (1932).
[182] Windaus and Raichle, *Ann.*, **537**, 157 (1939).

the ester layer. The more reactive anhydrous hydrazine is useful with inert esters and for preparing very hygroscopic hydrazides which are difficult to free from water.[46, *] On the other hand, anhydrous hydrazine, being a more vigorous reagent in every respect than the hydrate, is more likely to react with other functional groups in addition to the ester group.

The preparation of hydrazides from acid chlorides is an uncertain procedure which frequently gives rise to large quantities of secondary hydrazide.[118, 176] Indeed, the secondary hydrazide may be the only product if an unsuitable procedure is followed. The most successful method is to add slowly a chilled solution of the acid chloride in ether to a well-stirred, chilled alcoholic solution of hydrazine hydrate containing considerably more than the 2 moles theoretically required.[10] The product is usually separated from the hydrazine hydrochloride formed at the same time by extracting the latter with water. Where the ester is extremely unreactive, this may be the only practicable method for preparing the hydrazide.[183] On the other hand, if the acid chloride must be made, it is usually more expedient to convert it directly to the azide by reaction with sodium azide.

Amides can be converted to hydrazides by heating them with the theoretical amount or a slight excess of hydrazine hydrate, usually in the absence of a solvent. Since substituted amides, such as those occurring in peptide linkages, are more resistant than primary amides, peptide hydrazides can be prepared from peptide amides in good yield.[105] In general, amides appear to be more sluggish than esters in their reaction with hydrazine,[105] though a few amides, e.g., benzamide,[184] have been reported to react more smoothly. The reaction of hydrazine with amides has sometimes been used to cleave amide linkages occurring in natural products (ergotamine [185]).

Hydrazides have been prepared only infrequently by the more drastic procedure of fusing the hydrazine salts of acids. This process may give rise to secondary hydrazides in large amount. When applied to acetic,[186] propionic,[186] and citronellic acids,[187] among others, it gives good yields.

Anhydrides have been little used for the preparation of hydrazides. Most phthalic anhydride derivatives give only cyclic, secondary hydra-

* Cf. Cheney and Piening, *J. Am. Chem. Soc.*, **67**, 1040 (1945), for an alternative method in which water is removed by means of a Soxhlet apparatus charged with a drying agent.

183 Buning, *Rec. trav. chim.*, **40**, 327 (1921).

184 Curtius and Struve, *J. prakt. Chem.*, **50**, 295 (1894).

185 Stoll and Hofmann, *Helv. Chim. Acta*, **26**, 922, 944 (1943).

186 Curtius and Franzen, *Ber.*, **35**, 3240 (1902).

187 Sabetay, *Compt. rend.*, **190**, 1016 (1930).

zides (see p. 345), which are useless for the preparation of azides. Diphenic anhydride (see p. 347) and its 4-nitro derivative (see p. 347) yield the hydrazide acids. Isatoic anhydrides (XXXVI) appear to be excellent sources of hydrazides of certain amino acids.[90, 91] The reac-

$$\underset{\text{XXXVI}}{>C\left<\begin{matrix}\diagdown\!\diagup \\ C{-}CO \\ NH{-}CO\end{matrix}\right>O} + N_2H_4 \rightarrow\ >C\left<\begin{matrix}\diagdown\!\diagup \\ C{-}CO{-}NHNH_2 \\ NH_2\end{matrix}\right. + CO_2$$

tions of hydrazine with lactones, azlactones, anthranils, and similar compounds are not yet clearly defined. In some reactions true hydrazides have been obtained, which have been converted to the azides and rearranged;[38, 73] in others, products of uncertain structure are formed, isomeric with the normal hydrazide, or frequently both isomerides are obtained together.[188, 189] All such doubtful compounds are listed in the tables as hydrazides without regard to the original authors' opinions of their structure. Azides prepared from hydrazides derived from unsaturated azlactones readily lose hydrazoic acid to regenerate the azlactones.[190, 191]

Hydrazides can also be prepared by the Hofmann degradation of acylureas,[192] by the reaction of isocyanates with hydrazine,[193] and by the reduction of acylnitramides,[109, 193] but these methods are of no importance in connection with the Curtius reaction.

Preparation of Azides

From Hydrazides. All the techniques for converting hydrazides into azides are based on the reaction of the hydrazide with nitrous acid, with the exception of the rarely used diazonium method. The principal variables are: solvent, method of isolating the azide, *p*H, and the order of the addition of the reactants. The reaction is nearly always carried out at ice-bath temperatures.

The choice of method is governed by the following considerations: the solubility of the hydrazide and of the azide, the acidic or basic prop-

[188] Heller and Lauth, *Ber.*, **52**, 2295 (1919).

[189] Heller and Siller, *J. prakt. Chem.*, **116**, 9 (1927).

[190] Vanghelovici and Moise, *Soc. Chim. Romania Sect. Soc. romane Stiinte, Bul. Chim. pura apl.*, [2] **3A**, 85 (1941–1942) [*C. A.*, **38**, 5500 (1944)].

[191] Vanghelovici and Stefanescu, *Soc. Chim. Romania Sect. Soc. romane Stiinte, Bul Chim. pura apl.*, [2] **3A**, 159 (1941–1942) [*C. A.*, **38**, 5501 (1944)].

[192] Schestakov, *Ber.*, **45**, 3273 (1912); *J. Russ. Chem. Soc.*, **40**, 330 (1908).

[193] Backer, *Rec. trav. chim.*, **34**, 187 (1915).

erties of the molecule, the presence or absence of acid-sensitive groups, the explosiveness of the azide, the physical state of the azide, and the subsequent disposition of the azide.

The procedure to be followed in the absence of complicating factors, and thus the one most frequently used, is in outline as follows. The hydrazide, being basic, is dissolved in a slight excess of dilute aqueous hydrochloric acid, and the solution is chilled to 0–5° by means of an ice bath. The cold solution is covered with ether to extract the azide as soon as it is formed, and a concentrated aqueous solution of 1 mole of sodium nitrite is added with good mechanical stirring at such a rate that the temperature does not rise above 10°. Immediately upon completion of the addition, the ethereal azide layer is separated, washed with a little sodium bicarbonate solution, and dried. It is then heated with absolute alcohol, usually with simultaneous fractionation of the ether; the resulting urethan can be hydrolyzed to the amine when desired.

The only solvents which have seen appreciable use in the reaction of hydrazides with nitrous acid are water, alcohol, and acetic acid. Water is the solvent of choice when conditions permit. An alcohol is frequently chosen as the solvent when anhydrous conditions are desired; alkyl nitrites and dry hydrogen chloride are then generally used as the source of nitrous acid. The alcohol technique is indicated when the azide is difficult to extract from water or is easily hydrolyzed,[194, 195, 196] as when basic nitrogen groups are present in the molecule. It has also been employed for hydrazides that are not very soluble in aqueous acid.[197, 198] The azide is usually rearranged *in situ* by boiling the solution, although it can often be isolated by dilution with water.[198] The alkyl nitrite method has failed occasionally.[78, 120, 199] Aqueous sodium nitrite [200] and nitrogen trioxide [81] also have been used with alcohols as solvents.

Acetic acid, 50% to glacial, is a useful solvent for the conversion of high-molecular-weight hydrazides to azides. It is employed with [148, 183] or without [144, 152, 201, 202, 203, 204] the addition of a mole of mineral acid;

[194] Jensen and Howland, *J. Am. Chem. Soc.*, **48**, 1988 (1926).
[195] Windaus and Opitz, *Ber.*, **44**, 1721 (1911).
[196] Windaus and Vogt, *Ber.*, **40**, 3691 (1907).
[197] Pschorr, Einbeck, and Spangenberg, *Ber.*, **40**, 1998 (1907).
[198] Sharp, *J. Chem. Soc.*, **1936**, 1234.
[199] Kermack and Muir, *J. Chem. Soc.*, **1931**, 3089.
[200] Toschi, *Gazz. chim. ital.*, **44**, I, 443 (1914).
[201] Endermann and Fischer, *Ann.*, **538**, 172 (1939).
[202] Goldstein and Stern, *Helv. Chim. Acta*, **23**, 809, 818 (1940).
[203] Pschorr and Schröter, *Ber.*, **35**, 2726 (1902).
[204] Vollmann, Becker, Corell, and Streeck, *Ann.*, **531**, 44, 58, 137 (1937).

without the mineral acid the formation of some secondary hydrazide is more likely.[205] The customary technique consists in dissolving the hydrazide in glacial acetic acid, with heat if necessary, chilling rapidly so that the hydrazide will separate in finely divided form if it is insoluble in the cold solvent, and adding cracked ice and the required amount of aqueous sodium nitrite. Subsequent dilution with water causes the azide to separate, if it has not already done so. When a mineral acid is used in conjunction with acetic acid, a good procedure is to dissolve the hydrazide in a relatively small volume of glacial acetic acid. Subsequent dilution with even large quantities of dilute aqueous mineral acid frequently does not cause precipitation, but the azide separates at once when sodium nitrite is added. This technique is recommended also for hydrazides which, though soluble, dissolve only slowly in aqueous mineral acid. A mixture of benzene and acetic acid also has been found satisfactory as a reaction medium.[181, 206]

Acetone has been used as the solvent in the preparation of three azides from the hydrazides in the indoxazene series.[207] The advantage of acetone is not clear.

"Reverse addition," that is, addition of acid to a solution of the hydrazide and sodium nitrite, has found much application,[36, 349] particularly with acid-sensitive molecules.[82, 150, 208, 209] The reverse-addition technique is not recommended except where excess acid must be avoided, since a higher *p*H favors the formation of secondary hydrazides by the reaction [41, 205, 210, 211]

$$RCON_3 + RCONHNH_2 \rightarrow RCONHNHCOR + HN_3$$

Another disadvantage is the low solubility of most hydrazides in neutral or alkaline solutions. Cyclobutane-*gem*-dicarbonyl hydrazide unexpectedly gives a better yield of its diazide by the reverse-addition procedure.[210]

No simultaneous addition techniques have been reported. The closest approximation is the substitution of gaseous nitrogen trioxide for sodium nitrite and acid.[94, 177, 212, 213] This reagent has seen little use, probably because of its inconvenience and the difficulty in measuring the exact amount.

[205] Pschorr and Einbeck, *Ber.*, **38,** 2067 (1905).
[206] Schöpf, Jäck, and Perrey, *Ann.*, **497,** 59 (1932).
[207] Lindemann and Cissée, *J. prakt. Chem.*, **122,** 232 (1929).
[208] Curtius and Portner, *J. prakt. Chem.*, **58,** 190 (1898).
[209] Dimroth, *Ann.*, **364,** 210 (1908).
[210] Curtius and Grandel, *J. prakt. Chem.*, **94,** 339 (1916).
[211] Curtius, Schöfer, and Schwan, *J. prakt. Chem.*, **51,** 180 (1895).
[212] Curtius and Heidenreich, *J. prakt. Chem.*, **52,** 454 (1895).
[213] Curtius, Schätzlein, Wiengreen, and Krauth, *J. prakt. Chem.*, **89,** 508 (1914).

Hydrochloric acid is most commonly employed for the generation of nitrous acid from sodium nitrite, although sulfuric and nitric acids are equally satisfactory. The amount of acid employed varies from the stoichiometric to a large excess of concentrated acid, being governed by the solubility of the hydrazide and by the ease with which the secondary hydrazide forms. Acetic acid [214, 215, 216, 217] has been used frequently, especially with acid-sensitive molecules, but with greater likelihood of the formation of secondary hydrazide. Isoxazole-5-carbonyl hydrazide [218] and citraconyl hydrazide [218, 219] yield the secondary hydrazides in acetic acid, but the azides are formed in mineral acid. Hippurylaspartyl hydrazide,[97] glutaryl hydrazide,[220] and N-nitrosoiminodiacetyl hydrazide [221] show no apparent reaction when treated with sodium nitrite and acetic acid, but the addition of mineral acid causes the azides to precipitate.

Since the reaction of nitrous acid with hydrazides is rapid and exothermic, the reactants should be brought together no faster than the heat can be dissipated; a rise in temperature is likely to lower the yield by decomposition of nitrous acid or of the azide or of both. Slow addition provides time for the interaction of the azide with unchanged hydrazide to produce the secondary hydrazide; rapid addition lessens the extent of this side reaction.[181, 222] For effective cooling, ice is generally added directly to the reaction mixture; the addition of Dry Ice to the supernatant ether layer has been recommended as being even more efficient.[222]

The use of diazonium salts instead of nitrous acid to convert aromatic hydrazides to azides [88, 125] has received very little study, though it is a potentially applicable method for hydrazides carrying other functional groups which might be attacked by nitrous acid. For example, *p*-phenylenediamine has been obtained in this way from *p*-aminobenzhydrazide (see p. 353). The cold, aqueous solution of 1 equivalent of diazonium salt is added to a cold solution of the hydrazide containing excess acid. If precipitation of the azide does not begin at once, the addition of sodium acetate usually initiates it. Under special conditions, the intermediate diazo hydrazides, RCONHNHN=NAr, can be isolated and

[214] Blomquist and Stevenson, *J. Am. Chem. Soc.*, **56**, 146 (1934).

[215] Curtius and Leimbach, *J. prakt. Chem.*, **65**, 20 (1902).

[216] Manske and Robinson, *J. Chem. Soc.*, **1927**, 240.

[217] Miki and Robinson, *J. Chem. Soc.*, **1933**, 1467.

[218] Freri, *Atti accad. Lincei*, **22**, II, 264 (1935) [*C. A.*, **30**, 6374 (1936)].

[219] Freri, *Gazz. chim. ital.* **66**, 23 (1936) [*C. A.*, **30**, 6387 (1936)].

[220] Curtius and Clemm, *J. prakt. Chem.*, **62**, 189 (1900).

[221] Curtius, Darapsky, and Müller, *Ber.*, **41**, 356 (1908).

[222] Weissberger and Porter, *J. Am. Chem. Soc.*, **65**, 62 (1943).

can subsequently be caused to decompose into the azide and amine.[223, 224] The diazo hydrazides obtained from aliphatic hydrazides decompose, however, into the acid amide and aryl azide, and diazonium salts therefore cannot be employed to prepare aliphatic acid azides.

Isolation of Azides. When the reaction of the hydrazide with nitrous acid is carried out in aqueous solution, the azide is usually extracted as fast as it is formed, usually with ether, but sometimes with other solvents such as chloroform [63, 82] and carbon tetrachloride.[225] Azides containing a high proportion of azide nitrogen (*ca.* 25%) should be handled only in solution, since the pure azides are likely to be dangerously explosive. High-molecular-weight azides are usually innocuous crystalline solids and can be isolated as such. Since azides which are prepared in acetic acid as the solvent are usually of high molecular weight, they are best precipitated by dilution with water. Azides prepared in alcohol are not usually isolated.

From Acid Chlorides and Sodium Azide. The reaction between an acid chloride and sodium azide can be carried out under anhydrous conditions according to procedures described by Schroeter,[14] Forster,[167] and Naegeli,[10] or with aqueous sodium azide according to Lindemann.[226] The dry method is the only practical one for highly reactive chlorides, such as acetyl chloride, or for the preparation and rearrangement of very unstable azides. It provides a means of carrying out the reaction sequence $RCO_2H \rightarrow RCOCl \rightarrow RCON_3 \rightarrow RNCO \rightarrow RNH_2$ in the same reaction vessel as one multiple step. On the other hand, it is not a reliable method, for many acid chlorides are inert to dry sodium azide. The reaction is sometimes difficult to control, since the heating required for the formation of the azide may also cause rearrangement; the two exothermic reactions occurring simultaneously sometimes get out of control, particularly when large amounts are being handled (see p. 364). The use of aqueous sodium azide requires the isolation of the azide as an extra operation, but the reaction is more reliable, easier to control, and usually much faster. A small reduction in yield may sometimes be expected.

In the dry method, the acid chloride dissolved in an inert solvent is stirred and/or heated with powdered sodium azide (ammonium azide has also been used [91]). Part or all of the azide may be converted to the isocyanate at the same time, a step that is completed by refluxing. The isocyanate may then be isolated as such by distillation or concentration, or it may be converted to the urea, urethan, or amine by the appropriate method.

[223] Curtius, *Ber.*, **26**, 1263 (1893).
[224] Dimroth and Montmollin, *Ber.*, **43**, 2904 (1910).
[225] Curtius and Ulmer, *J. prakt. Chem.*, **125**, 54 (1930).
[226] Lindemann and Schultheis, *Ann.*, **451**, 241 (1927).

The dry method owes its unreliability in part to the insolubility of inorganic azides in organic solvents. Individual lots of sodium azide vary greatly in their reactivity, and the reactivity of a given lot varies with age.[10, 28] Sodium azide prepared according to Thiele [227] from hydrazine and ethyl nitrite appears to give better results [7] than the commercial product, which is prepared from sodamide and nitrous oxide. It is uncertain whether the variable activity is due to a surface condition or to the presence or absence of some trace of impurity. The Nelles procedure [228] for activating commercial sodium azide by trituration with hydrazine followed by precipitation with acetone gives a product apparently as active as Thiele's. Nevertheless many chlorides, particularly those of heterocyclic acids, cannot be made to react satisfactorily with dry sodium azide even of the activated variety.[120, 126, 144, 229]

Benzene,[7, 230] toluene,[231] xylene,[230] nitrobenzene,[144] pyridine,[23] amyl ether,[14] ethyl ether,[10, 18, 160] *o*-nitrotoluene,[160] bromobenzene,[160] and acetic acid [9, 129] have been used as solvents in the dry method. Ethyl ether is not to be generally recommended because its boiling point is below the decomposition temperature of many azides; Naegeli records an explosion traceable to an accumulation of azide when using this solvent.[7] If the isocyanate is to be distilled, the boiling point of the solvent should not be too close to that of the isocyanate.

In the wet method, a concentrated aqueous solution (*ca.* 25%) of sodium azide is stirred into a solution of the acid chloride in an organic solvent miscible with water. The kind of sodium azide is immaterial. The reaction mixture is usually kept at or below room temperature. The organic solvents that have been used are acetone,[132, 133, 233, 234] methanol,[132] ethanol,[113, 235] dioxane,[132, 234] and acetic acid,[5, 226] of which acetone appears to be the most generally satisfactory. Acetic acid is not the best choice for either the wet or dry method, since it may react with the acid chloride to form the free acid and acetyl chloride, with consequent loss in yield and contamination of the product.[9] The azide is precipitated completely by further dilution with water. Some azides have been prepared in the absence of any solvent except the water for the sodium azide; [16] this procedure is practicable only when both the

[227] Thiele, *Ber.*, **41**, 2681 (1908).
[228] Nelles, *Ber.*, **65**, 1345 (1932).
[229] Spoerri and Erickson, *J. Am. Chem. Soc.*, **60**, 400 (1938).
[230] Komppa and Beckmann, *Ann.*, **512**, 172 (1934).
[231] Grewe, *Ber.*, **76**, 1076 (1943).
[232] Hofmann and Bridgewater, *J. Am. Chem. Soc.*, **67**, 738 (1945).
[233] Powell, *J. Am. Chem. Soc.*, **51**, 2436 (1929).
[234] Ruschig, *Med. & Chem.*, **4**, 327 (1942) [*C. A.*, **38**, 4954 (1944)].
[235] Stollé, *Ber.* **57**, 1063 (1925).

acid chloride and azide are liquids, and it is not to be generally recommended. A two-phase system consisting of the ethereal acid chloride and aqueous sodium azide has been used sometimes.[232]

Other Methods of Preparing Azides. Ketenes [110] and isocyanates [111] react with hydrazoic acid to produce azides, but these methods are of no importance for a Curtius degradation.

Rearrangement of Azides

The readiness with which azides rearrange varies from rapid, spontaneous reaction at room temperature [183] to complete inertness.[236] The vast majority of azides rearrange at a convenient rate somewhere in the temperature range 20–150°, and their rearrangement is usually brought about by refluxing in a solvent boiling in the neighborhood of 80°. Experience has shown that an hour at this temperature is frequently sufficient for the reaction, but some azides require a longer time or a higher temperature. Many aromatic azides are rearranged most conveniently at the temperature of boiling toluene, and some of the more recalcitrant carbamyl azides must be boiled in xylene or decalin. Some danger attends the use of a solvent boiling too high, however, because the rearrangement is exothermic and its rate has a high temperature coefficient. The heat of rearrangement is often sufficient to raise the temperature of the reaction mixture to a point where the rearrangement gets violently out of control, unless this rise is curtailed by the boiling of the solvent. A recommended procedure for dealing with a new azide is to start with a solvent boiling at about 80°; if the rearrangement appears to be too slow at this temperature, a higher-boiling solvent is added and the original low-boiling solvent is distilled. Alternatively, a relatively large volume of solvent can be taken in order to distribute and absorb the heat of the rearrangement. The choice of a solvent boiling far above the optimum rearrangement temperature is often unavoidable, for it may be desired to fractionate the resulting isocyanate from the solvent, or, in the dry sodium azide method, a higher temperature may be necessary for the formation of the azide. The reaction may then need to be moderated by application of an ice bath, a stream of water, or a wet rag to the reaction vessel at appropriate intervals.

It should be obvious from the foregoing remarks that the rearrangement of azides in the complete absence of a solvent is highly hazardous; however, it has sometimes been accomplished successfully.[237] Catalysts

[236] Bertho, *J. prakt. Chem.*, **120**, 89 (1928).

[237] Bühler and Fierz-David, *Helv. Chim. Acta*, **26**, 2123 (1943).

have not been studied, but ultrasonic waves have been found to speed up the rearrangement markedly.[238, 239] The rearrangement of azides is unimolecular, and the rate appears to be independent of the nature of the solvent.

The progress of the rearrangement is indicated by the rate of evolution of nitrogen and can be followed by watching the formation of bubbles in the hot liquid, by gauging the flow of gas through an attached mercury trap, or more elegantly by collecting the evolved nitrogen in a calibrated azotometer.[7] Undecomposed azides can be detected by hydrolysis with aqueous alkali,* followed by mild acidification of the aqueous extract with nitric acid and precipitation of white, very insoluble silver azide (explosive when dry!) with silver nitrate.

Preparation of Isocyanates. Isocyanates are prepared by rearranging azides in inert solvents such as ethers, chloroform, benzene and its homologs, malonic ester, and ligroin. If the isocyanate is to be isolated, the solvent is removed by distillation, or, if the isocyanate is the lower boiling, it is distilled directly. In this operation, a safety shield is advisable to guard against a possible explosion of yet undecomposed azide. Isocyanates can be converted to *sym*-ureas by reaction with water, to urethans by reaction with alcohols, to *as*-ureas by reaction with amines, or to acylamines by reaction with anhydrous acids or acid anhydrides, or they can be hydrolyzed directly to amines. Acylamines can also be obtained from isocyanates by reaction with Grignard reagents.[214, 240, 241]

$$\mathrm{RN{=}C{=}O} + \mathrm{R'MgBr} \rightarrow \mathrm{RN{=}\underset{\substack{|\\ \mathrm{OMgBr}}}{C}{-}R'} \xrightarrow[\mathrm{H_2O}]{\mathrm{H^+}} \mathrm{RNHCOR'}$$

One occasionally encounters isocyanates that polymerize more or less readily to isocyanurates, which are sometimes extremely difficult to hydrolyze and are recognizable by their inertness and insolubility. Examples are *m*-nitrophenyl [126] and benzyl [242] isocyanates. Such isocyanates should be submitted to further reaction before polymerization sets in.

Preparation of Ureas. *sym*-Ureas are best prepared from azides by heating in a moist inert solvent, like acetone,[126] benzene, chloroform, or ether; aqueous alcohols usually give rise to a mixture of the urea and

* Acid azides in general hydrolyze about as readily as acid anhydrides.

[238] Barrett and Porter, *J. Am. Chem. Soc.*, **63**, 3434 (1941).

[239] Porter and Young, *J. Am. Chem. Soc.*, **60**, 1497 (1938).

[240] Burtner, *J. Am. Chem. Soc.*, **56**, 666 (1934).

[241] Singleton and Edwards, *J. Am. Chem. Soc.*, **60**, 540 (1938).

[242] Letts, *Ber.*, **5**, 91 (1872).

the urethan. The formation of *sym*-ureas from the isocyanates can be formulated as follows:

$$RNCO + H_2O \rightarrow CO_2 + RNH_2$$

$$RNH_2 + RNCO \rightarrow RNHCONHR$$

Azides can also be converted to *sym*-ureas by merely heating them with water. This is a dangerous procedure, since the water-insoluble azides sometimes detonate under such treatment.[126] A possible side reaction when azides are heated with water alone is hydrolysis to the acid with loss of hydrogen azide; [243, 244] further loss may occur by complete hydrolysis of some of the isocyanate to the amine.[243, 244] These losses are minimized under the previously mentioned conditions.[126]

as-Ureas are obtained best by heating the azide in an inert solvent and treating the resulting isocyanate with the desired amine.[18, 131] They also result from heating the azide with the amine directly in an inert solvent,[130] but this technique not infrequently gives rise to an amide by direct reaction of the amine with the azide without rearrangement.

Preparation of Urethans. Urethans are prepared by refluxing azides in absolute alcohols. When the azide is originally prepared in ethereal solution, the solution is dried, a large excess of absolute alcohol is added, and most of the ether is removed by distillation. The urethans are isolated by evaporation or distillation of the excess solvent. Urethans from higher alcohols, such as benzyl alcohol and cholesterol, are usually prepared from a small excess of the alcohol in toluene or xylene.

Although the ethyl urethans have been the ones most commonly prepared from azides, almost any urethan can be prepared with the appropriate alcohol. Rearrangement in methanol usually succeeds as well as in ethanol, but occasionally, because the decomposition temperature of the azide may be above the boiling point of methanol, the azide is recovered unchanged or is converted to the methyl ester.[89]

$$RCON_3 + CH_3OH \rightarrow RCO_2CH_3 + HN_3$$

Preparation of Acylamines. Heating azides with anhydrous organic acids usually gives rise to acylamines, along with more or less of the *sym*-urea. This reaction proceeds through mixed anhydrides of the

$$RCON_3 + R'CO_2H \rightarrow RNHCOR' + CO_2 + N_2$$

type RNHCOOCOR',[245] which either may lose carbon dioxide on heat-

[243] Curtius, *J. prakt. Chem.*, **52,** 243 (1895).

[244] Curtius, *J. prakt. Chem.*, **87,** 513 (1913).

[245] Naegeli and Tyabji, *Helv. Chim. Acta,* **18,** 142 (1935).

ing to form the acylamine or may disproportionate into symmetrical anhydrides, one of which then decomposes to the *sym*-urea.[127, 245]

$$\text{RNHCOOCOR}' \begin{cases} \nearrow \text{RNHCOR}' + \text{CO}_2 \\ \searrow \text{RNHCOOCONHR} + \text{R}'\text{COOCOR}' \end{cases}$$

$$\downarrow$$

$$\text{RNHCONHR} + \text{CO}_2$$

The predominating reaction is determined by the structure of the acid and azide concerned and by the temperature at which the reaction is carried out. Aromatic azides (through their isocyanates) give largely *sym*-ureas and anhydrides, whereas aliphatic azides give mostly acylamines (60–80% yield).[127, 245, 246, 247] The structure of the acid has little effect except as it influences the *p*K of the carboxyl group; stronger acids, such as cyanoacetic and trichloroacetic, give almost entirely acylamine, even with aromatic isocyanates.[127] Room temperature favors the formation of the acylamine, whereas higher temperatures favor the disproportionation reaction.[127] It appears preferable to rearrange the azide in an inert solvent first, and then to treat the isocyanate formed with the anhydrous acid.

A number of azides have been converted to the corresponding acetyl amines by heating them in an excess of acetic anhydride, with or without the addition of a catalytic amount of sulfuric acid.[129, 180, 202, 204, 248, 249] Diacetyl amines appear to be intermediates, but they are usually hydrolyzed to the monoacetyl amines during the isolation procedure.[202] Acetic anhydride is a useful alternative reagent when glacial acetic acid gives largely the *sym*-urea.

Preparation of Amines. Of the many ways of converting azides to amines, the direct hydrolysis of the intermediate isocyanates would appear to be the most efficient, since the reaction is much more rapid than the hydrolysis of either urethans or ureas. Nevertheless, this route to the amine has seen relatively little use, partly because isocyanates are converted by water quite easily to *sym*-ureas. It is wise not to risk valuable compounds, available in small amount only, with this method. No one method for converting azides to amines can be said to be the best, and the method must be chosen with due regard for the chemistry of the other functional groups in the molecule.

Isocyanates are converted expeditiously to amine hydrochlorides by warming them with concentrated hydrochloric acid; the most con-

[246] Schöpf and Salzer, *Ann.*, **544**, 1 (1940).

[247] Stevenson and Johnson, *J. Am. Chem. Soc.*, **59**, 2525 (1937).

[248] Goldstein and Viaud, *Helv. Chim. Acta*, **27**, 883 (1944).

[249] Lindemann and Cissée, *Ann*, **469**, 44 (1929).

venient technique consists in adding a severalfold excess of acid to a warm solution of the isocyanate in the solvent in which it has been obtained from the azide.[7, 250] The evolution of carbon dioxide usually commences at once and may even become violent; a reflux condenser is therefore advisable with volatile isocyanates. Removal of solvents and excess acid by distillation leaves the amine hydrochloride. Small amounts of the *sym*-urea, which can be removed by filtration, occasionally accompany the amine; the use of hydrochloric acid previously saturated with hydrogen chloride at 0° aids in avoiding the formation of the urea.[7]

Isocyanates are also hydrolyzable by heating with aqueous or alcoholic alkali,[23, 126, 251, 252] a procedure of value with acid-sensitive molecules. The initial product of such treatment is sometimes the alkali carbamate, $RNHCOO^{-}M^{+}$, which usually remains dissolved. On acidification the carbamic acids decarboxylate spontaneously to amines.[253] The alkaline hydrolysis of an isocyanato group attached to an asymmetric carbon atom may lead to racemization, but with acid hydrolysis the activity is preserved.[254]

Distillation from slaked lime has been used to hydrolyze refractory isocyanates to amines,[7, 255] as well as to hydrolyze urethans and ureas. The isocyanate is mixed with an excess of slaked lime in a retort, and the amine is distilled under atmospheric pressure (a fore-run of solvent may be collected). The method is not satisfactory for low-molecular-weight compounds on account of the volatility but is of advantage where milder methods fail. The yields are commonly of the order of 50–70%.

In a less reliable method of converting azides to amines the azide is heated directly with acidulated water. *sym*-Ureas frequently accompany the amines,[5, 126] if, indeed, they are not formed exclusively.[5, 202, 248, 249] Hydrolysis of the azide to the acid and hydrogen azide occasionally occurs.[202, 256] Strong acetic acid, in which azides are frequently soluble, is a useful reagent.[3, 93, 120, 207, 257] Partially diluted acetic acid (3 : 1 to 1 : 1) appears to produce less *sym*-urea than does glacial acetic acid. On the other hand, the formation of *sym*-urea is more likely to occur with acetic acid than with a stronger acid, such as sulfuric acid.[5, 127, 249] Rearrangement of azides in concentrated sulfuric

[250] Naegeli, Grüntuch, and Lendorff, *Helv. Chim. Acta*, **12**, 234 (1929).

[251] Bell, *Chemistry & Industry*, **1933**, 584; *J. Chem. Soc.*, **1934**, 835.

[252] John and Lukas, *J. prakt. Chem.*, **130**, 332 (1931).

[253] Meyer and Topsch, *Monatsh.*, **35**, 189 (1914).

[254] Kenyon and Young, *J. Chem. Soc.*, **1941**, 263.

[255] Naegeli and Vogt-Markus, *Helv. Chim. Acta*, **15**, 60 (1932).

[256] Goldstein and Studer, *Helv. Chim. Acta*, **17**, 1485 (1934).

[257] Graf, *J. prakt. Chem.*, **133**, 36 (1932).

acid approximates closely the conditions of the Schmidt reaction, and amines are accordingly obtained; [121, 129] but there is some question regarding the advisability of introducing azides indiscriminately into such a reagent.[5, 126, 129]

Urethans, being usually stable, purifiable, and crystalline, are convenient stopping points in the conversion of azides to amines. Although they are more difficultly hydrolyzed than isocyanates, they are more easily handled. The common procedure is to heat them with concentrated hydrochloric acid, either under reflux or in a sealed tube at elevated temperatures. The reflux method is often slow, requiring several hours to several days; the sealed-tube method is inconvenient, particularly with large amounts. Hydrochloric acid hydrolysis has the advantage that all reagents can be removed by distillation and the amine hydrochloride isolated without ever making the solution alkaline. The addition of alcohol or acetic acid occasionally facilitates the hydrolysis of urethans.

Alkaline hydrolysis of urethans has been conducted in aqueous [120, 168, 209, 258] and in alcoholic [106, 150, 259, 260] solution, and with either alkali metal hydroxides or barium [146, 150] hydroxide. With barium hydroxide, the progress of the reaction can be followed conveniently by watching the precipitation of barium carbonate. The alcoholic medium appears to give a cleaner reaction. The common procedure consists in refluxing the urethan for several hours with an excess of the alkaline reagent, usually in about 20–40% concentration, although the alkali can be more dilute. Metal carbamates occasionally result initially just as in the alkaline hydrolysis of isocyanates. Hydrolysis of urethans by distillation from slaked lime often succeeds where other methods fail; it cannot be used with low-molecular-weight urethans because of their volatility.[10, 261, 262] A few urethans have been heated with ammonia in a bomb tube to bring about cleavage to amines.[197, 203, 205] The principal advantage is the mildness of the reagent.

Benzyl urethans can be converted to amines by mild hydrogenation. The benzyl group is removed as toluene, and the carbamic acid which results decarboxylates to the amine. This method, originated by

$$RNHCO_2CH_2C_6H_5 \xrightarrow[Pd]{H_2} RNH_2 + CO_2 + C_6H_5CH_3$$

[258] Fischer and Dangschat, *Helv. Chim. Acta*, **17**, 1200 (1934).

[259] Jambuserwala, Holt, and Mason, *J. Chem. Soc.*, **1931**, 373.

[260] Mayer and Sieglitz, *Ber.*, **55**, 1835 (1922).

[261] Vanghelovici, *Bul. Soc. Chim. Romania*, **20A**, 231 (1938) [*C. A.*, **34**, 4073 (1940)].

[262] Windaus and Dalmer, *Ber.*, **53**, 2304 (1920).

Hans Fischer and his students,[62] has been adapted to the stepwise degradation of peptides.[105] The advantage of this method is that the conditions can be made almost completely non-hydrolytic. Benzyl urethans also appear to be more readily hydrolyzed by conventional methods than methyl and ethyl urethans.[262a, 262b]

Another essentially non-hydrolytic method for cleaving urethans and ureas has been developed by Ing and Manske.[107, 263] The carboalkoxy group of the urethan is first replaced by the phthalyl group, usually in excellent yields, by fusion with phthalic anhydride. The resulting

$$RNHCO_2C_2H_5 + C_6H_4(CO)_2O \rightarrow C_6H_4(CO)_2NR + CO_2 + C_2H_5OH$$

phthalimides are readily split into amines and *sec*-phthalhydrazide by warming with alcoholic hydrazine. The phthalhydrazide is easily re-

$$C_6H_4(CO)_2NR + NH_2NH_2 \rightarrow RNH_2 + C_6H_4(CO)_2(NH)_2$$

moved by virtue of its sparing solubility in most solvents. Occasionally the reaction halts with the formation of an addition compound between hydrazine and the phthalimide, which, however, can be decomposed to the amine hydrochloride and phthalhydrazide by the addition of dilute hydrochloric acid. This method, being quick and moderately convenient, is receiving wider application.[152, 153, 217, 264]

EXPERIMENTAL PROCEDURES

Reagents

Note on the Handling of Hydrazine. Hydrazine, alone or in solution, attacks rubber and cork rapidly. Apparatus should have ground-glass connections, if possible. Hydrazine does not cause such joints to "freeze."

Anhydrous Hydrazine. The best procedure for preparing anhydrous hydrazine is distillation of hydrazine hydrate from solid potassium

[262a] Jensen and Hansen, *Dansk. Tids. Farm.*, **17**, 189 (1943) [*C. A.*, **39**, 2058 (1945)].

[262b] Barkdoll and Ross, *J. Am. Chem. Soc.*, **66**, 951 (1944).

[263] Manske, *J. Am. Chem. Soc.*, **51**, 1202 (1929).

[264] Manske, *Can. J. Research*, **4**, 591 (1931) [*C. A.*, **25**, 4880 (1931)].

hydroxide.[265] Excellent directions for this method have been published in *Organic Syntheses*.[265a] Ground-glass apparatus is preferable to the corks covered with tin foil specified in these directions. Since hydrazine has been known to decompose with violence during distillation, distillation should be carried out behind a safety screen.

Activation of Sodium Azide. (A) (Modified [37] procedure of Nelles.[228]) Twenty grams of pure sodium azide is moistened with 0.5–1.0 cc. of 85% hydrazine hydrate and ground in a mortar until homogeneous. After standing for twelve hours the material is dissolved in the minimum amount of hot water (*ca.* 40 cc.) in a 2-l. beaker. About 0.5–1.0 l. of cold acetone is added, and the mixture is allowed to stand for about an hour. The precipitated sodium azide is collected, washed with acetone, and dried in air. The resulting cake is crushed in a mortar and dried for a short time in vacuum; yield, 12–17 g. Sodium azide thus activated begins to lose its activity after a day, but the activity can be regenerated at any time by dissolving the sodium azide in water and reprecipitating with acetone.

(*B*) Improved directions for the preparation of active sodium azide from hydrazine and ethyl nitrite according to Thiele [227] have been published by Naegeli and Vogt-Markus,[255] and by Newman.[455]

Hydrazide Method

Ester to Amine via Urethan

Benzylamine from Ethyl Phenylacetate. (Method of Curtius and Boetzelen [266] with modifications.[37]) Ethyl phenylacetate (16.4 g., 0.1 mole), 85% hydrazine hydrate (7.5 cc., 0.1 mole), and absolute ethanol (10 cc.) are refluxed for six hours. The phenylacethydrazide which crystallizes from the cooled mixture is collected and washed with a little cold ether; yield, 12–15 g. (80–100%); m.p. 110–112°. A solution of 15 g. (0.1 mole) of the hydrazide in 150 cc. of ice water containing 17 cc. of 6 *N* hydrochloric acid is placed in an ice-salt bath, 100 cc. of ether is added, and a solution of 7.5 g. of sodium nitrite in 15–20 cc. of water is then added at a moderate rate, while the reaction mixture is stirred rapidly. If necessary, cracked ice is added directly to the reaction mixture in order to keep the temperature below 10°. The ether layer is separated, and the aqueous layer is extracted with 50-cc. portions of fresh ether. The combined ethereal extracts are washed with a little sodium bicarbonate solution, then with water, and finally dried

[265] Raschig, *Ber.*, **43**, 1927 (1910).

[265a] Smith and Howard, *Org. Syntheses*, **24**, 53 (1944).

[266] Curtius and Boetzelen, *J. prakt. Chem.*, **64**, 314 (1901).

for five minutes over calcium chloride. The ethereal solution of the azide is decanted from the drying agent into a flask containing 40 cc. of absolute ethanol, and the ether is distilled through a short column until the residual volume is about 50 cc. The full heat of a steam bath is then applied to complete the decomposition of the azide and to remove the excess ethanol. The residue of ethyl N-benzyl urethan, which sets to a cake on cooling, weighs 11–13 g. (60–70%). The entire quantity is refluxed with 20 cc. of concentrated hydrochloric acid and 10 cc. of glacial acetic acid until the oily layer has disappeared (twelve to thirty-six hours). The mixture is then distilled nearly to dryness from a steam bath under reduced pressure (water pump). The solid residue is dissolved in 50 cc. of warm water, and the solution is filtered from any insoluble matter. Distillation of the filtrate to dryness and recrystallization of the residue from hot absolute ethanol give 7–8 g. (*ca.* 80%) of benzylamine hydrochloride; m.p., *ca.* 250°.

An alternative procedure is to add the dried ethereal solution of the azide to 50 cc. of dry benzene, remove the ether by distillation, and then continue as described in the dry sodium azide procedure (p. 387)

Preparation of an Acylamine

N-(β-3,4-Dibenzyloxyphenylethyl)-homopiperonylamide.[206, 246] A mixture of 30 g. of β-3,4-dibenzyloxyphenylpropionic ester, 32 g. of hydrazine hydrate, and 16 cc. of amyl alcohol is refluxed for five hours. The crystalline hydrazide, which separates on cooling, is washed with water and ether; yield, 82%; m.p. 138°.

A solution of 5.64 g. of the hydrazide in a mixture of 20 cc. each of glacial acetic acid and benzene is chilled to −5°. To it is then added all at once a chilled solution of 1.5 g. of sodium nitrite in 5 cc. of water with shaking. After the solution has stood for thirty minutes in the ice bath, 125 cc. of benzene is added and the entire solution is poured carefully into 650 cc. of well-cooled 1.5 *N* sodium carbonate solution. The benzene layer is separated, and the aqueous phase is extracted with benzene. The combined extracts are dried first over sodium sulfate, then over calcium chloride, and are finally distilled at normal pressure to a volume of about 50 cc. After the solution has been refluxed for two hours to complete rearrangement of the azide, a solution of 3.3 g. of homopiperonylic acid in a little dry benzene is added, and the refluxing is continued for ten hours with protection from moisture. The resulting solution is extracted with sodium carbonate solution and then evaporated to give the crystalline amide; yield, 74%; m.p. 119–121° after two recrystallizations from benzene.

Preparation of an Aldehyde

Phenylacetaldehyde from Benzylmalonic Ester.[42] A mixture of 100 g. of ethyl benzylmalonate, 50 g. of hydrazine hydrate, and 10 cc. of absolute ethanol is refluxed for six hours on a steam bath. The dihydrazide is filtered from the cooled mixture and washed with a little ethanol and ether; after drying on a clay plate and then in vacuum, the crude product weighs 91–91.5 g. (*ca.* 100%) and melts at 164°. A solution of 11.1 g. of this dihydrazide in a cold solution of 9.8 g. of concentrated sulfuric acid in 44 cc. of water is covered with 50 cc. of ether and cooled to −5° in an ice-salt bath. A solution of 10.35 g. of sodium nitrite in 21 cc. of water is added slowly with stirring, the ether layer is then separated, and the aqueous phase is extracted once with ether. After the combined ethereal extracts have been dried for one hour over sodium sulfate at 0°, 100 cc. of absolute ethanol is added, and the mixture is refluxed for three hours; during this time most of the ether is allowed to escape. The resulting solution of the *gem*-diurethan is concentrated to a syrup and allowed to crystallize in vacuum over sulfuric acid; yield, 10.5 g. (75%); m.p. 166°. (If the next step is to be performed immediately, the crystallization is unnecessary.)

A mixture of 4.2 g. of the urethan and 50 g. of 2% sulfuric acid is steam-distilled, the distillate is extracted with ether, and the extracts are dried over sodium sulfate. Distillation gives 1 g. (56%) of phenylacetaldehyde; b.p. 81–82°/12 mm. If the aldehyde is isolated from the steam distillate as the crystalline benzoylhydrazone by treatment with benzhydrazide, the yield is increased to 98%.

Preparation of an α-Amino Acid from a Malonic Ester

β-Phenylalanine from Benzylmalonic Ester.[46] A filtered solution of 46 g. of pure potassium hydroxide in 800 cc. of absolute ethanol is added to a solution of 200 g. of ethyl benzylmalonate in 100 cc. of absolute ethanol. After one day the mixture is freed from solvents by distillation and dried in vacuum over sulfuric acid. The resulting cake is rubbed in a mortar with absolute ethanol, filtered, and dried; the weight of potassium ethyl benzylmalonate is 176 g. (84.6%).

A mixture of 100 g. of the above salt and 20 g. of anhydrous hydrazine in 75 cc. of absolute ethanol is refluxed for one and one-half hours and then cooled in a vacuum desiccator over sulfuric acid to remove part of the ethanol and excess hydrazine. The product is rubbed with fresh absolute ethanol, filtered, and washed with absolute ether. The weight of potassium benzylmalonhydrazidate is 93.2 g. (98.5%).

A solution of 10 g. of the hydrazidate in 200 cc. of water is combined with a solution of 2.8 g. of sodium nitrite in 25 cc. of water. While the solution is stirred with 200 cc. of ether, a solution of 8 g. of concentrated hydrochloric acid in 25 cc. of water is added slowly at room temperature. The ether layer, containing most of the benzylmalonazidic acid, is removed, and the aqueous layer is extracted twice with ether. The combined extracts are washed with a little cold water and dried overnight with sodium sulfate. The ether is then distilled by gentle heating; the residue begins to foam on further heating, and then becomes semisolid. The resulting isatoic anhydride is cooled, filtered, and washed with ether; yield, 3.4 g. (44%); m.p. 127–128°. A mixture of 5 g. of the anhydride and 25 cc. of concentrated hydrochloric acid is evaporated on a steam bath to incipient crystallization, and the solution is cooled. The crystals of β-phenylalanine hydrochloride are filtered, washed with a little ice-cold concentrated hydrochloric acid, and dried in vacuum over potassium hydroxide; yield, 5.2 g. (nearly 100%), m.p. 234–235°, dec. The filtrate from the isatoic anhydride yields some additional β-phenylalanine on treatment with hydrochloric acid.

PREPARATION OF AN α-AMINO ACID FROM A CYANOACETIC ESTER

Glycine from Cyanoacetic Ester.[267] A solution of 10 cc. of ethyl cyanoacetate and 12 cc. of hydrazine hydrate (14.2 cc. of 85% hydrazine hydrate) in 50 cc. of absolute ethanol is refluxed for one hour. The solvents are then removed by distillation, and 25 cc. of ether is added to the syrupy residue. The resulting crystals of cyanoacethydrazide are recrystallized from absolute ethanol; yield, 9 g. (100%); m.p. 110–112°.

A chilled solution of 4.5 cc. of concentrated hydrochloric acid in 20 cc. of water is added to a chilled solution of 5 g. of the hydrazide in 10 cc. of water, and the solution is covered with 25 cc. of ether. The mixture is cooled to 0° in an ice bath, and a solution of 3.45 g. of sodium nitrite in 10 cc. of water is added slowly with stirring. The ether layer is separated, and the aqueous phase is extracted twice with 10-cc. portions of ether. After short drying over magnesium sulfate, the combined ethereal extracts are added to 50 cc. of absolute ethanol, the ether is largely removed by distillation through a short column, and the solution is refluxed until nitrogen evolution ceases. After concentration to about 15 cc., 50 cc. of 95% ethanol is added and then a saturated solution of 32 g. of barium hydroxide octahydrate in boiling water. The solution is refluxed for four hours on a sand bath, cooled, and treated with

[267] Sah, *J. Chinese Chem. Soc.*, **4**, 198 (1936).

5.56 cc. of concentrated sulfuric acid in 20 cc. of water. The mixture is again brought to the boiling point, cooled, and filtered. The filtrate is tested for excess of either barium or sulfate ions, and the excess is removed by careful addition of the indicated reagent and filtration. The filtrate is concentrated to a volume of 5 cc., and the glycine is precipitated by the addition of 5 cc. of absolute ethanol; yield, 2.05 g. (54%).

Reverse-Addition Procedure

1,4-Diaminocyclohexane from Hexahydroterephthalic Acid.[11] A mixture of 20 g. of dimethyl *trans*-hexahydroterephthalate, 20 g. of hydrazine hydrate (23.5 g. of 85%), and 20 cc. of absolute ethanol is refluxed on a steam bath for two hours; crystals appear in a few minutes. The mixture is cooled and filtered, and the dihydrazide is washed with ethanol and with ether; weight, 18.8 g. (94%). A solution of 5 g. of the dihydrazide in 800 cc. of warm water is poured into a solution of 5 g. of sodium nitrite in 3 l. of water, the solution is cooled to 5°, and 7 cc. of glacial acetic acid is added with stirring. One or two grams of sodium nitrite is then added, and the precipitated azide is removed after forty-five minutes and washed with water. After drying for four hours in vacuum in an ice chest, the azide weighs 4.8 g. (86%).

A solution of 5 g. of the azide in 200 cc. of absolute ethanol is refluxed for two hours, filtered, and concentrated in vacuum. On cooling, 5.2–5.5 g. (90–95%) of the urethan crystallizes; m.p. 236°. A mixture of 4.8 g. of the urethan and 50 cc. of concentrated hydrochloric acid is heated for seven hours at 120° in a sealed tube (or for twenty-four hours under reflux) and then evaporated to dryness. The resulting 1,4-diaminocyclohexane dihydrochloride weighs 3.3–3.4 g. (95–98%).

Use of Amyl Nitrite

4-Hydroxy-2-methylpyrimidine-5-methylamine.[267a] A mixture of 100 g. of 4-hydroxy-2-methylpyrimidine-5-acetic ester and 135 cc. of 50% hydrazine hydrate is heated on a steam bath for two hours, during which time the ester dissolves and the hydrazide separates. The hydrazide is filtered from the cooled solution and recrystallized from ethanol; m.p. 246°; yield, 80–85%.

To a suspension of 20 g. of the hydrazide in 300 cc. of absolute ethanol containing 6 g. of hydrogen chloride is added 19.3 g. of amyl nitrite; the mixture is then warmed to 50–60° and kept there until nitrogen evolution ceases (about one hour). During this heating the hydrazide slowly

[267a] Todd, Bergel, Fraenkel-Conrat, and Jacob, *J. Chem. Soc.*, **1936**, 1601.

dissolves and the jellylike urethan hydrochloride separates. Ether is added to the cooled solution to complete the separation of the urethan hydrochloride, which is filtered and dried in a desiccator; m.p. 209°; yield, 98%.

A mixture of 5 g. of the urethan hydrochloride and 50 cc. of concentrated hydrochloric acid is heated for two hours at 100° in a sealed tube. The resulting clear solution is evaporated to a small volume in vacuum. The addition of ether causes the amine hydrochloride to crystallize; yield, 100%; m.p. 278–282° after recrystallization from absolute ethanol.

Sodium Azide Method

Dry Procedure

Acid Chloride to Amine via Isocyanate. *Benzylamine Hydrochloride from Phenylacetyl Chloride.*[37] A suspension of 6 g. of freshly activated sodium azide * (p. 382) in 100 cc. of dry benzene containing 13 g. of phenylacetyl chloride is refluxed for twenty hours on a steam bath while protected from moisture by a calcium chloride tube. The cooled suspension is then filtered with suction directly into a 300-cc. round-bottomed flask; a little benzene is used to rinse the flask and is poured through the filter. Fifty cubic centimeters of concentrated hydrochloric acid is added all at once to the filtrate, and the mixture is refluxed on a steam bath for two and one-half hours; during this time the crystals which at first form in the benzene layer entirely disappear. The cooled layers are separated, and the benzene layer is washed with a little water. Evaporation or distillation to dryness of the combined aqueous phases leaves 11.3 g. (94%) of benzylamine hydrochloride; m.p. 255–257°.

Wet Procedure

Acid Chloride to Isocyanate and Amine. *m-Isocyanatoazobenzene and m-Aminoazobenzene from Azobenzene-m-carbonyl Chloride.* (Method of Naegeli and Tyabji [126] with modifications.[37]) A solution of 0.7 g. of sodium azide in 2 cc. of water is added to a chilled solution of 2.45 g. of azobenzene-*m*-carbonyl chloride in acetone (25 cc.) with swirling and cooling in an ice bath. The resulting suspension is diluted after about fifteen minutes with about 50 cc. of water to complete the separation of the azide, and the azide is filtered, washed with a little water, pressed as dry as possible, and dried in vacuum; m.p. 76–77°; weight, 2.2 g. (*ca.* 90%). The dried azide in 5 cc. of dry benzene is heated under

* If unactivated sodium azide (Eastman Kodak Company) is used, 10.4 g. (85%) of benzylamine hydrochloride is obtained.

reflux in an oil bath at 90–100° until the nitrogen evolution ceases (one to four hours). Distillation of the benzene in vacuum leaves about 2 g. (nearly theoretical yield) of crystalline *m*-isocyanatoazobenzene; m.p. 45–46°. (If boiling toluene or xylene is substituted for benzene, the rearrangement is completed in a few minutes, but the subsequent removal of the solvent is more tedious.) If the amine is desired, the solution of the isocyanate is warmed with about 10 cc. of 50% aqueous potassium hydroxide; *m*-aminoazobenzene (m.p. 67°) is rapidly formed and is obtained in about the theoretical yield by distillation of the organic solvent. The corresponding *p*-carbonyl chloride can be degraded similarly in almost identical yield.[37]

Undecyl Isocyanate from Lauroyl Chloride. Excellent directions for this preparation are given in *Organic Syntheses*.[16]

SURVEY OF THE CURTIUS REACTION

The following table is intended to include all examples of the Curtius reaction, partial or complete, published before May, 1945; nevertheless, there are probably some omissions. It is unnecessary to emphasize that the recorded yields are not necessarily the maximum and that the conditions are not always the optimum.

Nomenclature. The names by which the compounds are listed in the table are those which emphasize the parent acid, in order to facilitate ready location. Thus "benzoic ester" is used instead of "ethyl benzoate." Ethyl esters are referred to simply as "ester"; all other esters are specifically designated. Cyclic anhydrides, lactones, and azlactones are listed under the parent acid rather than under heterocyclic compounds.

Yields, References, and Symbols. The presence of a reference number in parentheses indicates that the compound was isolated in the yield given or in an unreported yield, indicated by a dash. The procedure employed is shown by a symbol (Sd, Ua, etc.) in parentheses.

The yield of any compound is based on the preceding intermediate appearing on the same line, except that the yield of urethan is based on the azide or preceding intermediate and not on the isocyanate. In the amine column, the symbols indicate the compound (or its precursor if it was not isolated) on which the yield is based. It will be noted that the overall yield from starting material to product cannot always be calculated, because of the failure of the investigator to report the yields in all steps.

(Sd) or (Sw) alone, without a yield and reference number, indicates that the azide was not isolated but was made by the method expressed by the symbol and was used further. For these entries the yield of a compound immediately following the azide is based on the acid chloride and not on the azide.

In the isocyanate column are reported all other compounds isomeric with the isocyanate which are formed under the same conditions, such as internal urethans, isatoic anhydrides, and isocyanurates. Where these occur, the entry is starred (*); stars are also used in the urethan column to indicate that the products are *sym*-ureas. No distinction is made among urethans derived from different alcohols; nearly all, however, are ethyl urethans.

A number of hydrazides and azides are listed in the column headed "Starting Material." This is done when the structure of the precursor does not supply the identity of the hydrazide or azide obtained from it; the precursor is then identified in a footnote.

The following symbols indicate the various procedures which were employed; if no symbol occurs in the azide column, the azide was prepared by the action of nitrous acid on the hydrazide. Most of the symbols correspond to the initial letters of the compound and procedure involved.

Sd = **s**odium azide (**d**ry method).
Sw = **s**odium azide (**w**et method).
Ua = **u**rethan or urea, **a**cid hydrolysis.
Ub = **u**rethan or urea, **b**asic hydrolysis.
Ia = **i**socyanate, **a**cid hydrolysis.
Ib = **i**socyanate, **b**asic hydrolysis.
L = **l**ime distillation of urethan or urea.
P = **p**hthalimide prepared from urethan or urea and cleaved by hydrazine.
C = **c**arbobenzoxyl group (of benzylurethan) removed by hydrogenation.
X = azide prepared by other methods.
Z = amine or acylamine prepared by other methods.

INDEX TO TABLE

Aliphatic Acid Derivatives

Carbamic Acid Derivatives

Alicyclic Acid Derivatives

Arylaliphatic Acid Derivatives

Aromatic Acid Derivatives

Heterocyclic Acid Derivatives *

* The ring systems listed here include their hydrogenated derivatives.

COMPOUNDS SUBJECTED TO THE CURTIUS REACTION

Aliphatic Acid Derivatives

Starting Material	Hydrazide	Azide	Isocyanate	Urethan	Amine, etc.
Formic ester	— (211)				
Acetic ester	— (211, 268, 269)			— (179)	
Acetic acid	95% (186)				
Acetyl chloride		(Sd)			65% (Ia), 63% (Z) (7)
		(Sd)	72% (14), 62% (15)		
Acetic anhydride		(Sd)	78% (16*a*)		
Ketene		(X) Yields N-methylcarbamyl azide			
Propionic ester	80% (178)			44% (178)	Good (Ua) (178)
Propionic acid	92% (186)				
Propionyl chloride		(Sd)	50% (37)		
Butyric ester	80% (270)				
Isobutyric ester	99% (271), — (272)		56% (271)	Quant. (271) *	
Isovaleric ester	Good (178), — 273)	Good (178)		Good (178)	Good (Ua) (178)
Pivalic ester	— (176)	65% (237)	94% (237)	— (237)	— (237)
Pivalyl chloride	0% (176)	Poor (Sd) (237)			
γ-Methylvaleric ester	Quantitative (271)		50% (271)	— (271) *	Quant. (Ua) (271)
n-Heptanoyl chloride		(Sd)			71% (Ia) (228)
Isoamylacetic ester	Quantitative (271)			55% (271)	95% (Ua), 73% (L) (271)
α-Ethyl-γ-methylvaleric ester	76% (271)			30% (271) *	Quant. (Ua) (271)

α-Isobutyl-α-amylacetic ester	77% (271)		54% (271)	Quant. (271) *	93% (Ua) (271)
Lauric ester	89% (213)			— (213)	— (Ua, L) (213)
Lauroyl chloride		(Sw) (Sd)	86% (16)		80% (Ia), 76% (Z), 71% (L) (7), 67% (Z) (9)
Palmitic ester	93% (177)	87% (177)		— (177)	— (Ua, L) (177)
Palmitoyl chloride		(Sd)			96% (Ia), 80% (L), 82% (Z) (7)
Stearoyl chloride		(Sd)			94% (Ia), 81% (Z), 75% (L) (7)
Chloroacetic ester	0% (116)				
Chloroacetyl chloride		(Sd)	66% (14)		
Chloroacetyl bromide		(Sd)	— (111)		
Trichloroacetic ester	0% (274)				
Trichloroacetyl chloride	0% (274)	0% (Sd) (274, 228)			
Bromoacetyl bromide		(Sd)	— (111)		
α-Bromocaprylyl chloride		(Sd)			30% (Ib) (23) Enanthal
α-Bromodibutylacetyl chloride		(Sd)			77% (Ib) (23) Dibutyl ketone
Ethoxyacetic ester	82% (79)	— (79)		— (79)	— (Ua) (79) Formaldehyde
n-Propoxyacetic ester	88% (79)	— (79)		— (79)	— (Ua) (79) Formaldehyde
Isoamyloxyacetic ester	81% (79)	— (79)		— (79)	— (Ua) (79) Formaldehyde
Benzyloxyacetic ester	— (275)				

References 268–454 appear on pp. 446–449.

COMPOUNDS SUBJECTED TO THE CURTIUS REACTION—*Continued*

ALIPHATIC ACID DERIVATIVES—*Continued*

Starting Material	Hydrazide	Azide	Isocyanate	Urethan	Amine, etc.
γ-Phenoxybutyric ester	83% (263)			62% (263) *	— (P) (263)
Glycolic ester	97% (157)	57% (157), — (41)		— (41, 157)	
Lactic acid	— (186)				
Lactic ester	94% (79)	Poor (79)		— (79) Acetaldehyde	
Hydracrylic ester	— (79)	0% (79)			
γ-Valerolactone	— (276, 277)				
δ-Valerolactone	60% (278)	0% (278)			
α-Methylbutyrolactone	— (72)				
α-Methyl-γ-valerolactone	— (277, 279)				
β-Methyl-γ-valerolactone	— (276, 277)				
(α- or β-) Isopropyl butyrolactone	— (72)				
α-Methyl-γ-caprolactone	— (277, 279)				
ε-Octanolactone	— (71)				
β-Isopropyl-δ-valerolactone	— (72)				
γ-Nonanolactone	— (71)				
α-Methyl-γ-nonanolactone	— (276, 277)				
α-Methyl-δ-nonanolactone	— (276, 277)				
d-Gluconolactone	— (78)				
l-Arabinolactone	— (78)				
l-Mannonolactone	Quantitative (78)				
Metasaccharinic lactone	— (78)				
Other sugar acid lactones	— (280, 281)				

THE CURTIUS REACTION 395

Hippurylglycolic ester	Yields hippuryl hydrazide and glycolyl hydrazide (275)				
Levulinic ester	— (86)				
Glycine ester	— (282)	0% (282)			
N-Phenylglycine ester	— (25)	Yields N-nitroso-N-phenylglycine azide (25)			
Aceturic ester	— (25, 100)	— (25), 0% (100)			
Chloroaceturyl hydrazide	(116) †	57% (116)		37% (116)	
Bromoaceturyl hydrazide	(116) †	66% (116)		74% (116)	
Iodoaceturyl hydrazide	(116) †	18% (116)		94% (116)	
Acetoxyaceturyl hydrazide	(154) †				
Phenylureidoaceturic ester	96% (101)	86% (101)		— (101)	
Diazoaceturic ester	82% (115)				
Isopropylureidoacetic ester	99% (271)	— (271)			
N-(4-Methylamyl)-ureido-acetic ester	— (271)	— (271)			
Phenylureidoacetic ester	70% (101)	92% (101)		— (101)	
Benzamidomethylureido-acetic ester	— (100)	— (100)			
Hippuric ester	— (243, 283)	90% (243)	94% (244) *	— (284)	
Hippuramide	— (243)				
p-Bromohippuric ester	91% (285)	89% (285)	— (285) *	75% (285), 76% (244) *	
m-Nitrohippuric ester	85% (285)	49% (285)	— (285) *	— (285)	
p-Nitrohippuric ester	89% (100)	— (100)			

References 268–454 appear on pp. 446–449.

† Prepared from diazoaceturyl hydrazide.

COMPOUNDS SUBJECTED TO THE CURTIUS REACTION—*Continued*

ALIPHATIC ACID DERIVATIVES—*Continued*

Starting Material	Hydrazide	Azide	Isocyanate	Urethan	Amine, etc.
Phthalylglycine ester	(25) *sec*-Phthalhydrazide and glycyl hydrazide				
Carbobenzoxy-*d*-alanylglycine ester	78% (454)	Good (454)			
Carbobenzoxy-*l*-alanylglycine ester	— (454)	— (454)			
Chloroaceturylglycyl hydrazide	(116) †				
Hydroxyaceturylglycyl hydrazide	(154) †				
Phenylureidoaceturylglycine ester	86% (101)	90% (101)		— (101)	
Diazoaceturylglycine ester	72% (154)				
Hippurylglycine ester	85% (104), — (283)	— (104)	85% (100)*	— (100, 104)	— (104) Formaldehyde
p-Nitrohippurylglycine ester	89% (100)	— (100)			
Benzoylalanylglycine ester	95% (102)	24% (102)			
Hippurylglycylglycine ester	70% (104), — (283)	— (104)			
Benzoyl-*tris* (glycyl)-glycine ester	90% (104)	50% (104)			
Benzoyl-*tetrakis* (glycyl)-glycine ester	70% (282)	0% (282)			
N,N-Dimethylalanine ester	— (88)	— (88)			— (Z) (88) Acetaldehyde
N,N-Dimethyl-β-alanine ester	— (88)	0% (88)			
Benzoylalanine ester	96% (102)	60% (102)		— (102)	

Carbobenzoxyglycyl-*l*-alanine ester	87% (105)	46% (105)			
Hippurylalanine ester	85% (99)	80% (99)		— (99)	
Hippuryl-*l*-alanine amide	75% (105)	87% (105)		13% (105)	— (C) (105) Acetaldehyde
Benzoylalanylalanine ester	— (102)	— (102)			
Hippurylalanylalanine ester	75% (99)	70% (99)		— (99)	
β-Hippuramidobutyric ester	80% (98)	— (98)		— (98)	50% (Ua) (98)
β-Hippuramidobutyryl-β-aminobutyric ester	— (98)	— (98)			
γ-Hippuramidobutyric ester	— (103)				
α-Benzamidoisobutyryl chloride	— (188)				
α-Benzamidoisobutyric azlactone	— (188)				
N-Benzoylleucine methyl ester	88% (105)			32% (105)	82% (C) (105)
Carbobenzoxyglycyl-*l*-alanyl-*l*-leucine ester	60% (105)	57% (105)			
Hippuryl-*l*-alanyl-*l*-leucine amide	43% (105)			43% (105)	72% (C) (105) Isovaleraldehyde
Diazoacetic ester	0% (155)				
Diazoacetamide	Yields triazoacethydrazide, *q.v.* (155)				
Triazoacetic ester	46% (179), — (155)	— (179, 155)		— (157)	
Triazoacetyl chloride		(Sd)	— (160)		
α-Triazopropionic ester	82% (158)			52% (158)	
β-Triazopropionic ester	71% (158)	— (158)		— (158)	Quantitative (Ub) (157)
γ-Triazobutyric ester	Good (159)	— (159)		— (159)	64% (Ub) (157)

References 268–454 appear on pp. 446–449. † Prepared from diazoaceturylglycyl hydrazide.

COMPOUNDS SUBJECTED TO THE CURTIUS REACTION—*Continued*

ALIPHATIC ACID DERIVATIVES—*Continued*

Starting Material	Hydrazide	Azide	Isocyanate	Urethan	Amine, etc.
Malonic ester	Quantitative (286), Good (211), — (47, 287, 288, 289), 26% (47) Ester hydrazide	— (41)		— (41)	— (Ua) (41)
Ethyl potassium malonate	98% (45)	— (47)	4% (47) *		
Bromomalonic ester	Yields hydrazinomalonyl hydrazide (288)				
Methylmalonic ester	59% (290), — (286, 288)	— (290)		— (290)	— (Ua) (290) Acetaldehyde
Ethyl potassium methylmalonate	Quantitative (45) Monohydrazide			— (47)	— (Ua) (47) 67% (Ia) (45) alanine methyl ester
Dimethylmalonic ester	Poor (290)	— (290)		— (290)	— (Ua) (290) Acetone
Ethylmalonic ester	85% (291), — (288, 292)	40% (291)			70% (Ua) (291) Propionaldehyde
Ethyl potassium ethylmalonate	Quantitative (46)		41% (46) *	51% (46)	Quantitative (Ia), 67% (Ua) (46)
n-Propylmalonic ester	96% (47), 61% (288)		94% (47)	26% (47)	46% (Ua) (47) Butyraldehyde
Ethyl potassium *n*-propylmalonate	96% (47)				43% (Ia) (47) α-Aminovaleric acid
Isopropylmalonic ester	77% (288)				

Ethyl hydrogen isopropylmalonate	Quantitative (293)				
	Monohydrazide				
Ethyl potassium isopropylmalonate	98% (47)			37% (47)	90% (Ua) (47) Valine
Potassium isopropylmalonamate	21% (47)	— (47)		— (47) *	
	Dihydrazide				
n-Butylmalonic ester	73% (288)				
Ethyl potassium isobutylmalonate	85% (47)				68% (Ia) (47) α-Amino acid
Potassium isobutylmalonamate	0% (47)				
Isoamylmalonic ester	Quantitative (290)	Poor (290)		— (290)	— (Ua) (290) Isobutylacetaldehyde
Ethyl potassium isoamylmalonate	— (47)				63% (Ia) (47) α-Amino acid
Potassium isoamylmalonamate	— (47)				81% (Ua) (47) α-Amino acid
β-Hydroxyethylmalonic ester lactone	Ester hydrazide — (73)				
	Dihydrazide 81% (73)	Lactone azide — (73)		— (73)	
γ-Chloro-β-hydroxypropylmalonic ester lactone	— (294) Ester hydrazide				
Cyanoacetic ester	Quantitative (124, 140, 267)	— (124, 222)		— (124)	38% (Ua) (124), 54% (Ub) (267) † Glycine
Isonitrosocyanoacetic ester	60% (124)	79% (124)		— (124)	— (Ua) (124) Oxalic acid
Nitrocyanoacetic methyl ester	48% (124)	62% (124)		— (124)	0% (Ua) (124)
n-Propylcyanoacetic ester					31% (Ua) (138) α-Amino acid

References 268–454 appear on pp. 446–449

† Yield based on the hydrazide.

COMPOUNDS SUBJECTED TO THE CURTIUS REACTION—*Continued*

Aliphatic Acid Derivatives—*Continued*

Starting Material	Hydrazide	Azide	Isocyanate	Urethan	Amine, etc.
Isopropylcyanoacetic ester					60% (Ua) (139) Valine
γ-Phenoxypropylcyanoacetic ester				38% (139)	40% (Ua) (139) α-Amino acid
Isobutylcyanoacetic ester				54% (138)	51% (Ua) (138) Leucine
Isoamylcyanoacetic ester	84% (138)	— (138)		— (138)	26% (Ua) (138) α-Amino acid
Carbonic ester	70% (295)	— (295)			
Chloroformic methyl ester		— (Sd) (212)			
Oxalic ester	66% (64)			23% (64)	
	Monohydrazide 61% (296), — (211, 297)	— (298), 0% (211)		0% (298)	
	Dihydrazide				
Oxamic ester	— (299)	28% (64)		65% (64)	
N-Phenyloxamic ester	— (300)				
N-Benzyloxamic ester	— (301)	— (301)		— (301)	
Oxalylglycolic ester	Yields oxalyl hydrazide and glycolyl hydrazide (275)				
Succinic ester	— (211, 286, 287, 297)	— (41), 0% (211)	65% (57)	— (41, 57)	— (Ua) (41) 3% (Ua) (57)
Succinyl chloride		(Sd)			75% (Ia), — (Z) (9)
		(Sd)	— (40)	— (40)	

Ethyl hydrogen succinate	— (56)	15% (56)			
Succinamic acid	— (56)			7% (56)	0% (Ua) (56)
Succinylglycolic ester	Quantitative (275) of succinyl hydrazide and glycolyl hydrazide				
Glutaric ester	94% (220), 19% (56)	— (220)		— (220)	— (Ua) (220)
Adipic ester	94% (37), 90% (11)	61% (11)	— (302)	84% (11), 84% (37)	83% (Ua) (11), 90% (Ua) (37), 72% (Ia) (37)
Adipyl chloride		(Sd)			68% (Ia) (9)
Ethylsuccinic ester	69% (303)		— (303)	29% (303)	— (Ua, Ia) (303)
Pimelic ester	60% (11)			43% (11)	— (Ua) (11)
Suberic ester	80% (11), — (304)	— (11, 304)		— (11, 304)	97% (Ua) (11), — (304)
Sebacic ester	78% (305)	91% (305)	— (302)	99% (305)	Quantitative (Ua) (305), — (P) (263)
Sebacic ester chloride		(Sd)	94% (50)		76% (Ia) (50)
Sebacyl chloride		(Sd)			81% (Ia), 52% (L), 73% (Z) (9)
Heptane-1,7-dicarbonyl azide			— (302)		
1-Carbethoxyheneicosane-21-carbonyl chloride		(Sd)			66% (Ia) (51)
Perhydronorbixin chloride		(Sd)			50% (Ia) (8)
2-Methyltridecane-1,13-dicarbonyl chloride	— (306)				
Bromosuccinic ester	0% (115)				
Malic ester	Quantitative (79), — (297)	— (79)		— (79)	— (Ua) (79) Aminoacetaldehyde
Tartaric methyl ester	— (307)	63% (79)		10% (79) Glyoxal	

References 268–454 appear on pp. 446–449.

COMPOUNDS SUBJECTED TO THE CURTIUS REACTION—*Continued*

ALIPHATIC ACID DERIVATIVES—*Continued*

Starting Material	Hydrazide	Azide	Isocyanate	Urethan	Amine, etc.
Tartaric ester	99% (79)				
Shellolic ester	— (308)	0% (308)			
Mucic ester	98% (79)	72% (79)	70% (79) * + 33% tartraldehyde		
Tetraacetylmucyl chloride	77% (81)	47% (X) (81) 58% (Sw) (81)	Good (81) *		
Oxalacetic ester	0% (87) †				
Iminodiacetic ester	84% (309)	Poor (309)			
N-Nitrosoiminodiacetic ester	— (221)	99% (309), — (221)		91% (309)	— (Ua) (98) Diazacyclobutane-1,3-dicarboxylic ester
Succinyl glycine	— (57), 0% (25)				
Phenylsuccinylglycine ester	— (303)	75% (303)		36% (303)	
Dibenzoylcystine ester	— (88)	— (88)		— (88)	— (Ua) (88) Aldehyde
Dihippurylcystine methyl ester	— (88)	— (88)		— (88)	— (Ua) (88) Aldehyde
Aspartic ester	— (88)			Poor (88) Aminoacetaldehyde	
Asparagine	— (88) Monohydrazide	— (88)			

N,N-Dimethylaspartic ester	— (88)			Poor (88) Aminoacetaldehyde	
Hippurylaspartic ester	90% (97)	50% (97)		— (97)	— (Ua) (97) Aminoacetaldehyde
Benzoylaminomethylureidosuccinic ester	87% (100)	87% (100)	— (100) *	— (100)	
p-Bromobenzoylaminomethylureidosuccinic ester	— (100)	— (100)			
Glutaramyl chloride N-acetic ester	— (310) Dihydrazide			48% (310)	16% (Ua) (310) γ-Aminobutyric ester·HCl
Benzoylglutamic methyl ester	80% (105)	64% (105)		25% (105)	61% (C) (105)
Hippuryl-*l*-alanyl-*l*-leucyl-*l*-glutamic methyl ester	97% (105)	70% (105)		52% (105)	50% (C) (105)
Hydrazodioxalic ester	Quantitative (64)	— (64)		Poor (64)	— (Ua) (64)
Triazosuccinic ester	— (311)	42% (311)			
Cyanosuccinic ester	Good (37)				
α,β-Dicyanopropionic ester	0% (139)				
Tricarballylic ester	— (312)	— (312)		— (312)	— (Ua) (312)
sym-Ethanetetracarboxylic ester	97% (313)	— 25% (313)		— (312) Glyoxal	
	— (313) Mixed *pri-sec*-hydrazide	— (313) Ethanetricarbonyl azide			
Butane-1,2,2-tricarboxylic ester	92% (43)			78% (43)	90% (Ua) (43) 1-Amino-2-butanone
α-Cyanoadipic ester	— (139)	0% (139)			
α-Cyanopimelic ester	— (139)	0% (139)			
Pentane-1,1,5,5-tetracarboxylic ester	60% (210)	Quantitative (210)			— (Ua) (210) Dialdehyde

References 268–454 appear on pp. 446–449.

† Some pyrazolone-3-carbonyl hydrazide is formed.

COMPOUNDS SUBJECTED TO THE CURTIUS REACTION—*Continued*

ALIPHATIC ACID DERIVATIVES—*Continued*

Starting Material	Hydrazide	Azide	Isocyanate	Urethan	Amine, etc.
Citric ester	Quantitative (297), 91% (296), — (79, 287, 289)	64% (79)			— (Ua) (79) Diaminoacetone
	— (79) Mixed *pri-sec*-hydrazide	— (79)		0% (79)	
Amine-N,N,N-triacetic ester, $N(CH_2CO_2C_2H_5)_3$	— (309)	— (309)			
Hippurylaspartylaspartic ester	89% (97)	— (97) Mixed *sec*-hydrazide azide			
Benzamidomethylureido-ethylenedicarbamylaspartic ester	— (100)	— (100)			
Hippurylaspartylaspartyl-hydrazidiaspartic ester	— (97)				
Acrylyl chloride		(Sd)	5% (31) + 30% polymer		
Methacrylyl chloride		(Sd)	— (20)		
Crotonic ester	88% (22) (314)	0% (22, 314)			
Crotonyl chloride		47% (Sd) (18)		43% (18) *	
Isocrotonyl chloride		— (Sd) (18)		Poor (18) *	
d-Citronellic acid	— (187)				
Undecenoic methyl ester	— (29)	— (29)	— (29)	— (29)	
Undecenoyl chloride		— (S) (29)			

Oleic methyl ester	— (29)	— (29)	— (29)	-- (29)	
Oleyl chloride		— (S) (29)			
Oleic acid?	— (21) Stearoyl hydrazide				
Elaidic acid?	— (21) Stearoyl hydrazide				
Erucic methyl ester	— (29)	— (29)	— (29)	-- (29)	
Erucyl chloride		— (S) (29)			
β-Chloroisocrotonic ester	0% (219) Yields 5-methylpyrazolone				
Fumaric methyl ester	— (25)	— (25)		-- (25)	
Citraconic methyl ester	Good (219)	Good (219), — (218)			
Itaconic methyl ester	— (219)	— (219)			
Mesaconic methyl ester	— (219)	— (219)			
Dicarbethoxyglutaconic ester	— (315) Yields malonyl hydrazide				
Tetrolic ester	0% (34) Yields 3-methylpyrazolone-5				
ω-Undecynoic ester	— (33, 316)				
Stearolic ester	— (32)				
Acetylenedicarboxylic ester	— (87, 161) Yields pyrazolone-3-carboxylic ester or hydrazide, *q.v.*				

References 268–454 appear on pp. 446–449.

COMPOUNDS SUBJECTED TO THE CURTIUS REACTION—*Continued*

Carbamic Acid Derivatives

Starting Material	Hydrazide	Azide	Isocyanate	Urethan	Amine, etc.
Semicarbazide		— (212, 109)	— (112) Hydrazodicarbonamide		
Cyanic acid		— (X) (109)			
Methyl isocyanate		— (X) (110)			
Dimethylcarbamyl chloride	— (317)	80% (Sd) (318)			Poor (Ia) (318)
Diethylcarbamic ester	0% (319)				
Diethylcarbamyl chloride		0% (Sd) (319)			
Diisobutylcarbamyl chloride		80% (Sd) (318)	? (318)		
Diisoamylcarbamyl chloride		68% (Sd) (318)	? (318)		
Chloromethyl isocyanate		— (X) (111)			
Benzohydryl isocyanate		— (X) (110)			
Phenylcarbamic ester	— (298)	— (268, 298)		0% (268, 298)	
Phenylurea	90% (101)	— (101)			
N-Methyl-N-phenylcarbamyl chloride		64% (Sd) (113)	— (113) An indazolone		
N-Ethyl-N-phenylcarbamyl chloride		60% (Sd) (113)	68% (113) An indazolone		
N-Methyl-N-*o*-tolylcarbamyl chloride		Quantitative (Sd) (113)	12% (113) + 31% of indazolone		
N-Ethyl-N-*o*-tolylcarbamyl chloride		— (Sd) (113)	28% (113)		

N-Ethyl-N-*p*-tolylcarbamyl chloride		97% (318)	— (318) An indazolone		
N-Phenyl-N-benzylcarbamyl chloride		Quantitative (Sd) (318)	99% (318) An indazolone		
Diphenylcarbamyl chloride	 — (379)	— (Sw) (235) — (200)	89% (235) An indazolone		
Di-*p*-tolylcarbamyl chloride		98% (Sd) (318)	11% (318) + 37% of indazolone		
N-Ethyl-N-α-naphthylcarbamyl chloride		80% (Sd) (318)	50% (318) An indazolone		
N-Phenyl-N-α-naphthylcarbamyl chloride		Quantitative (Sd) (318)	58% (318) An indazolone		
N-Phenyl-N-β-naphthylcarbamyl chloride		97% (Sd) (318)	96% (318) An indazolone		
N,N-Di-β-naphthylcarbamyl chloride		77% (Sd) (318)	94% (318) An indazolone		
Thiocarbamyl hydrazide		62% (164)	— (164)		
Methyl isothiocyanate	— (165)	— (165)	— (165)		
Ethyl isothiocyanate	— (165)	73% (165)			
Allyl isothiocyanate	— (165)	66% (165)	— (165)		
Phenyl isothiocyanate	— (162)	Good (162), — (163)	— (163)		
p-Tolyl isothiocyanate		— (X) (163)	— (163)		
Hydrazinedicarboxylic ester	57% (320)	— (320, 321)	0% (321)	0% (321)	
α-Phenyl-β-benzalcarbazyl chloride		94% (Sd) (318)	0% (322)		
α-Phenyl-β-*o*-chlorobenzalcarbazyl chloride		99% (Sd) (318)	0% (322)		

References 268–454 appear on pp. 446–449.

COMPOUNDS SUBJECTED TO THE CURTIUS REACTION—*Continued*

ALICYCLIC ACID DERIVATIVES

Starting Material	Hydrazide	Azide	Isocyanate	Urethan	Amine, etc.
Cyclobutane-1,1-dicarboxylic ester	58% (210)				26% (Ua) (210) Cyclobutanone
cis-Cyclobutane-1,2-dicarboxylic ester	80% (323)			55% (323)	Quantitative (Ub) (323)
trans-Cyclobutane-1,2-dicarboxylic ester	Quantitative (323)			60% (323)	Quantitative (Ub) (323)
cis-Cyclopentane-1,3-dicarboxylic methyl ester	84% (324)			— (324)	— (Ua) (324)
Dicyclopentylacetyl chloride		(Sd)			35% (Ia) (23)
α-Bromocyclopentylacetyl chloride		(Sd)			30% (Ib) (23) Aldehyde
α-Bromodicyclopentylacetyl chloride		(Sd)			60% (Ib) (23) Ketone
Dihydrohydnocarpic acid		(Sd)			76% (Ia), 43% (Z), — (L) (255)
Dihydrochaulmoogric acid		(Sd)			43% (Z), — (Ia, L) (255)
cis-Cyclohexane-1,3-dicarboxylic methyl ester	93% (325)			62% (325)	Quantitative (Ua) (325)
trans-Cyclohexane-1,3-dicarboxylic methyl ester	— (325)			79% (325)	Quantitative (Ua) (325)
trans-Cyclohexane-1,4-dicarboxylic methyl ester	94% (11)	86% (11)		95% (11)	97% (Ua) (11)

1-Bromocyclohexanecarbonyl chloride		(Sd)			57% (Ib) (23) Cyclohexanone
Tetraacetylquinyl chloride		39% (Sw) (83)	97% (83) * *p*-Acetoxyacetanilide		
4,5-Isopropylidenequinic lactone	80% (82)		78% (82) * Ketone		
1-O-Methyl-4,5-isopropylidenequinic lactone	75% (82)		57% (82) *		
Dihydroshikimic methyl ester	85% (258)		72% (258) *		
Decalin-*x*-carboxylic methyl ester	— (29)	— (29)	— (29)		
Decalin-*x*-carbonyl chloride		— (S) (29)			
2,5-Endomethylenecyclohexanecarbonyl chloride		(Sd)	Quant. (230)		99% (Ia) (230)
exo-2,5-Endomethylenecyclohexanecarbonyl chloride		(Sd)			Quantitative (Ia) (326)
endo-2,5-Endomethylenecyclohexanecarbonyl chloride		(Sd)			Quantitative (Ia) (326)
trans-3,6-Endomethylenecyclohexane-1,2-dicarbonyl chloride	— (326)	— (326) (Sd)			— (Ua?) (326) — (Ia) (326)
2,5-Endomethylenecyclohexane-1-acetyl chloride		(Sd)			— (Ia) (327)
Adamantane-1,3-dicarboxylic methyl ester	0% (17)				
13-Methyl-*asym*-octahydrophenanthrene-9-carbonyl chloride		(Sd)			68% (Ia) (231)

References 268–454 appear on pp. 446–449.

COMPOUNDS SUBJECTED TO THE CURTIUS REACTION—*Continued*

ALICYCLIC ACID DERIVATIVES—*Continued*

Starting Material	Hydrazide	Azide	Isocyanate	Urethan	Amine, etc.
13,14-Trimethyleneoctahydrophenanthrene-9-carbonyl chloride		(Sd)			— (Ia) (231)
9-Methyl-9,10-dihydrophenanthrene-10-carboxylic methyl ester	— (330)				— (Ua) (330) 9-Methylphenanthrene
3-Methoxy-9,10-dihydrophenanthrene-9-carboxylic methyl ester	— (331)	— (331)		— (331)	— (Ua) (331) 3-Methoxyphenanthrene
3,4-Methylenedioxy-9,10-dihydrophenanthrene-9-carboxylic methyl ester	— (331)	— (331)		— (331) *	
Desoxycholic ester	— (261)	— (261)		— (261)	— (L) (261)
Cholanic ester	— (328)	— (328)		— (328)	— (?) (328)
Cholic ester	— (329)	— (329)			
Hydnocarpic acid		(Sd)			70% (Ia), 54% (Z), — (L) (255)
Chaulmoogric ester	80% (10)			50% (10)	26% (Ua) (10)
Chaulmoogryl chloride		(Sd)		90% (10)	
Chaulmoogric acid		(Sd)			78% (Ia), 45% (Z, L) (255)
Bornylene-3-carboxylic ester	0% (27)				

Bornylene-3-carbonyl chloride	94% (27), — (26)	(Sd)			86% (Ua) (27), — (26) 93% (Ia) (28) Epicamphor
Acetoxy-*bisnor*-cholenyl chloride		— (Sw) (234)	— (234)		— (Ia) (234)
Arylaliphatic Acid Derivatives					
Phenylacetic ester	Quantitative (266)	Good (266)		Good (266)	83% (Ua) (266)
Phenylacetyl chloride		(Sd)			95% (Ia) (37)
(+)-α-Phenylpropionic acid		(Sd)			68% (Ia) (254), 35% (Ia) (341)
p-Chlorophenylacetic ester	80% (213)	— (213)		— (213)	Quantitative (Ua) (213)
p-Nitrophenylacetic ester	Quantitative (213)	Quantitative (213)		— (213)	91% (Ua) (213)
2,4-Dinitrophenylacetic ester	— (332)				
3,4-Dimethoxyphenylacetic ester	— (333)				
o-Hydroxyphenylacetic lactone	— (349, 350)	— (38), 0% (350)	— (38) *		— (Ib) (38)
Mandelic ester	97% (351)	— (351)		— (351) Benzaldehyde	
β-Phenylpropionic ester	97% (334), — (335)	Quantitative (334), — (335)		— (334, 335)	91% (Ua) (334), — Ua) (335)
β-Phenylpropionyl chloride		(Sd)	— (35)		
β-Phenylisobutyryl chloride		— (Sd) (342)		97% (343) *	
d-β-Phenylisobutyryl chloride		97% (Sd) (342)	— (342)		96% (Ia) (342)

References 268–454 appear on pp. 446–449.

COMPOUNDS SUBJECTED TO THE CURTIUS REACTION—*Continued*

Arylaliphatic Acid Derivatives—*Continued*

Starting Material	Hydrazide	Azide	Isocyanate	Urethan	Amine, etc.
β-Bromo-β-phenylpropionic acid	— (336) Yields β-phenylhydracryl-yl hydrazide				
β-Methoxy-β-phenylpropionic methyl ester	53% (337)	95% (337)		60% (337)	55% (Ua) (337)
β-*o*-Methoxyphenylpropionic methyl ester	Quantitative (205)			— (205)	— (Z) (205)
β-*p*-Methoxyphenylpropionic methyl ester	93% (338)	Good (338)		Good (338)	94% (Ua) (338)
β-*m*-Benzyloxyphenylpropionic ester	95% (181)	90% (181)			— (Z) (181)
β-3,4-Dimethoxyphenylpropionic methyl ester	Quantitative (453)	— (453) †			
β-3,4-Dimethoxyphenylpropionic ester	95% (181)	90% (181)			— (Z) (181)
β-3-Benzyloxy-4-methoxyphenylpropionic ester	Quantitative (181)				
β-3,4-Dibenzyloxyphenylpropionic ester	82% (206), — (179)	— (246)	— (246)		74% (Z) (246), — (Z) (206)
β-2,3,4-Trimethoxyphenylpropionic ester	— (339)			— (339)	— (Ua) (339) Trihydroxyphenylethylamine
β-2,4,5-Trimethoxyphenylpropionic methyl ester	— (338)			59% (338)	68% (Ua) (338)

β-3,4,5-Trimethoxyphenylpropionic methyl ester			98% (340)	48% (340) ‡	
β-Hydroxy-β-phenylpropionic ester	60% (336), — (352)	— (336, 352)	Quant. (6),* — (76, 352) *		
β-*o*-Hydroxyphenylpropionic lactone	— (205)			8% (205) *	65% (Ua) (205)
β-Phenylisocaprolactone	— (76)	— (76)	0% (76)		
β-Piperonylhydracrylyl hydrazide			76% (352) *		— (Ia) (352)
α-Benzamido-β-phenylpropionic methyl ester	94% (105)			63% (105)	65% (C) (105)
α-Hippurylamino-β-phenylpropionic ester	— (103)	— (103)			
dl-Tyrosine ester	94% (88)	0% (88)			
l-Tyrosine ester	— (88)	0% (88)			
N-Benzoyltyrosine ester	— (88)	— (88)		— (88)	
β-1-Naphthylpropionic acid	90% (260)			51% (260)	Quantitative (Ub) (260)
β-2-Naphthylpropionic ester	88% (344)			— (344)	— (Ub) (344)
β-2-(9,10-Dihydrophenanthryl)-propionic methyl ester	85% (345)				75% (Ub) (345)
β-2-Phenanthrylpropionic ester	— (346)			Poor (346)	
β-3-Phenanthrylpropionic ester	— (346)			Poor (346)	
β-7-(2-Methoxy-9,10-dihydrophenanthryl)-propionic methyl ester	90% (345)				59% (Ub) (345)

References 268–454 appear on pp. 446–449.

† Converted to corydaldine in "poor" yield.

‡ Yield based on isocyanate.

COMPOUNDS SUBJECTED TO THE CURTIUS REACTION—*Continued*

Arylaliphatic Acid Derivatives—*Continued*

Starting Material	Hydrazide	Azide	Isocyanate	Urethan	Amine, etc.
α-Bromo-δ-phenylvaleryl chloride		(Sd)			59% (Ib) (23) Aldehyde
α,β,γ,δ-Tetrabromo-δ-phenylvaleryl hydrazide	(114) †				
Diphenylketene		— (X) (110) Diphenylmethylcarbamyl azide			
Dibenzylacetyl chloride		90% (Sw) (233)	— (233)	— (233)	
Triphenylacetyl chloride	41% (176)				
Diphenylglycolic lactone	63% (79)	— (79)		— (79) Benzophenone	
o-Hydroxydiphenylacetic lactone	— (278)	— (278)	0% (278)	Poor (278)	— (Ub) (278)
p-Hydroxydiphenylacetic ester	Quantitative (353)			— (353)	— (Ib) (353)
Desylglyoxalic ester	Yields diphenylpyrazolonecarboxylic ester (354)				
Cinnamic ester	54% (22, 314)	— 0% (22, 314)			
Cinnamoyl chloride		12% (Sd) (18), — (Sd) (167)	72% (18), — (167)	— (167)	
		(Sd)	77% (228)	98% (18) *	
Allocinnamoyl chloride		(Sd)		9% (18) *	

m-Nitrocinnamic ester	82% (24)	76% (348)		69% (348)	Poor (Ua) (348) Aldehyde
β-Styrylacrylic ester	— (114)				
Phenylpropiolyl chloride		0% (Sd) (35)			
Benzalaceturic azlactone	77% (188)				
Benzalhippuric azlactone	75% (188), — (191)				
Benzalhippuric methyl ester	— (191)	— (191)		0% (191)	
p-Methylbenzalhippuric azlactone	— (191)				
p-Methylbenzalhippuric methyl ester	— (191)	— (191)		0% (191)	
o-Nitrobenzalhippuric azlactone	— (191)	— (191)		0% (191)	
m-Nitrobenzalhippuric azlactone	— (191)				
m-Nitrobenzalhippuric methyl ester	— (191)	— (191)		0% (191)	
p-Nitrobenzalhippuric azlactone	— (191)	— (191)		0% (191)	
p-Nitrobenzalhippuric methyl ester	— (191)				
p-Methoxybenzalhippuric azlactone	— (190)				
p-Methoxybenzalhippuric methyl ester	— (190)	— (190)		0% (190)	
Benzylmalonic ester	96% (42), — (288)			75% (42)	98% (Ua) (42) Phenylacetaldehyde
Ethyl potassium benzylmalonate	99% (46)			72% (46)	57% (Ua) (46) Phenylalanine

References 268–454 appear on pp. 446–449.

† Prepared from β-styrylacrylyl hydrazide.

COMPOUNDS SUBJECTED TO THE CURTIUS REACTION—*Continued*

ARYLALIPHATIC ACID DERIVATIVES—*Continued*

Starting Material	Hydrazide	Azide	Isocyanate	Urethan	Amine, etc.
Benzylcyanoacetic ester	85% (139)				50% (Ua) (194) Phenylalanine
Ethyl potassium *p*-nitrobenzylmalonate	77% (47)	Quantitative (47)			— (Ia) (47) Amino acid
p-Methoxybenzylcyanoacetic ester	95% (139)				30% (Ua) (139) Amino acid
Phenylsuccinic ester	96% (303)		(303)		36% (Ua) (303)
m-Xylene-α-malonic ester	88% (347)	— (347)		— (347)	— (Ua) (347) Aldehyde
Ethyl potassium *m*-xylene-α-malonate	99% (47)		61% (47) *		88% (Ia) (47) Amino acid
Benzylsuccinyl hydrazide	— (65) †	— (65)			
β-Phenylglutaric ester	— (67)			98% (67)	43% (Ua) (67)
β-Phenylglutaryl chloride		(Sd)			48% (Ia) (228)
β-*p*-Methoxyphenylglutaric ester	— (67)			— (67)	— (Ua) (67) *p*-Hydroxydiamine
2,3-Dimethoxyphenylglutaric ester	— (67)			— (67)	— (Ua) (67) dihydroxydiamine
Benzylmethylmalonic ester	73% (44), Poor (290)				20% (Ua) (44) Phenylacetone
β-Phenylethylmethylmalonic ester	60% (44)				47% (Ua) (44) Benzylacetone
2,4,6-Trimethylbenzylmalonic ester	Good (44)				*ca.* 25% (Ua) (44) Aldehyde

bis(2,4,6-Trimethylbenzyl)-malonic ester	0% (44)				
bis(*p*-Nitrobenzyl)-malonic ester	0% (47)				
1-Phenylpropane-2,2,3-tricarboxylic ester	67% (65) Mixed *pri-sec*-hydrazide	90% (65)	— (65) *	— (65)	
Aromatic Acid Derivatives					
Benzoic acid	— (186)				
Benzoyl chloride	Quantitative (10), — (184)	57% (Sw) (238), Quantitative (233)		— (238) *	
		(Sd)	— (14, 352)		
		(Sd)			69% (Ia) (228)
Benzoic ester	90% (184), 75% (355), — (269)	79% (355), — (284)	93% (352), 87% (6), 73% (355)	— (284), — (41, 239, 244, 268) *	— (Ua) (284) 98% (Ua) (41)
Benzamide	Good (184)	— (78) Phenylcarbamylbenzhydrazide			
o-Toluic ester	81% (356)				
m-Toluic ester	Quantitative (356)				
p-Toluyl azide	— (186)				
p-Toluyl chloride		— (Sw) (132)	— (132)		
p-Toluic ester	Quantitative (356)				

References 268–454 appear on pp. 446–449.

† Prepared from 1-phenylpropane-2,2,3-tricarboxylic ester.

COMPOUNDS SUBJECTED TO THE CURTIUS REACTION—*Continued*

AROMATIC ACID DERIVATIVES—*Continued*

Starting Material	Hydrazide	Azide	Isocyanate	Urethan	Amine, etc.
Phthalyl chloride	0% (54)	— (Sw) (357) Isatoyl diazide		70% (357)	50% (Ub) (357) *o*-Phenyleneurea
		— (Sw) (38)	— (38) *o*-Isocyanatobenzazide		
Phthalic ester	0% (54, 287)		— (38) Diisocyanate		
Isophthalyl chloride	— (54)				
Isophthalic ester	70% (54), — (287)	Good (54)	— (358)	— (54)	— (Ua) (54)
Terephthalic ester	— (54) Ester hydrazide	— (54) Ester azide			
Hemimellitic ester	Quantitative (39) Mixed *pri-sec*-hydrazide	— (39)		40% (39) *	54% (Ua) (39) *o*-Aminophthalhydrazide
Trimesic ester	— (39)	— (39)		— (39)	— (Ua) (39) 3,5-Dicarbethoxyaminoaniline and phloroglucinol
o-Fluorobenzamide	80% (359)	— (359)		— (359) *	— (U) (359)
m-Chlorobenzoic ester	97% (360), — (361)	Quantitative (360), — (362)		— (360)	— (Ua) (360)
p-Chlorobenzoic ester	— (123)	— (363)			
o-Bromobenzoic ester	— (125, 364)				
m-Bromobenzoyl chloride		(Sd)			90% (Ib) (126)
m-Bromobenzoic ester	98% (208), 90% (365)	Quantitative (208), 95% (366)			92% (Ua) (208)

p-Bromobenzoic acid	— (186)				
p-Bromobenzoic ester	93% (123), — (208), 89% (367)	90% (368), — (208)		— (208), — (368) *	72% (Ua) (208)
2,6-Dibromobenzoyl chloride	— (183)				— (Ua) (183)
2,6-Dibromobenzoic ester	0% (183)				
2,6-Dibromo-4-methylbenzoyl chloride	— (183)				— (Ua) (183)
2,6-Dibromo-4-methylbenzoic ester	0% (183)				
2,4,6-Tribromobenzoyl chloride	— (183)				— (Ua) (183)
2,4,6-Tribromobenzoic ester	0% (183)				
o-Iodobenzoic ester	0% (123)				
p-Iodobenzoic ester	90% (359)	— (370)		— (370)	
o-Nitrobenzoyl chloride		— (Sw) (132)	— (132)		
o-Nitrobenzoic ester	Quantitative (136), 96% (371), — (135)	94% (371), — (125, 284)	Quantitative (6)	— (284, 371)	— (Ua) (284)
m-Nitrobenzoyl chloride		Quant. (Sw) (126)	Quant. (126)		
m-Nitrobenzoic ester	Quantitative (135), — (136)	90% (130), — (125, 284, 372)	Quant. (358), — (372)	— (125, 284)	— (Ua) (125, 284)
p-Nitrobenzoyl chloride		— (Sw) (126)	— (126)		94% (Ib) (126)
p-Nitrobenzoic ester	Quant. (136), 88% (373), — (135)	85% (374), — (125, 284)	90% (371)	Quant. (374), — (125, 284)	— (Ua) (125, 284)
2-Nitro-6-carbomethoxybenzoic acid	— (48) Hydrazide acid	— (48)	— (48) *		— (I) (48)
2,4-Dinitrobenzoyl chloride		91% (Sw) (132)	82% (132)	— (132)	
2,4-Dinitrobenzoic ester	Yields 2-nitro-4-aminobenzoic ester (137)				

References 268–454 appear on pp. 446–449.

COMPOUNDS SUBJECTED TO THE CURTIUS REACTION—*Continued*

AROMATIC ACID DERIVATIVES—*Continued*

Starting Material	Hydrazide	Azide	Isocyanate	Urethan	Amine, etc.
3,5-Dinitrobenzoyl chloride		— (Sw) (129), — (Sd) (126)	— (126)		— (Z) (129) 97% (Ia) (126)
3,5-Dinitrobenzoic ester	69% (89), 64% (131)	99% (131), — (89)	— (131)	Quantitative (89)	— (Ua) (89)
3,5-Dinitro-4-methylbenzoic methyl ester	70% (375)	90% (375)		— (375)	
2,4,6-Trinitrobenzoyl chloride		82% (Sw) (132), 40% (Sw) (376)	— (132, 376)	— (132)	
2-Chloro-3,5-dinitrobenzoyl chloride		— (Sw) (129)		— (129)	— (Z) (129)
4-Chloro-3,5-dinitrobenzoyl chloride	0% (5)	— (Sw) (5, 129)		— (129)	— (Z) (5)
2-Chloro-4-methyl-3,5-dinitrobenzoyl chloride		— (Sw) (133)			— (Z) (133)
2-Bromo-3,5-dinitrobenzoyl chloride		— (Sw) (129)		— (129)	— (Z) (129)
4-Bromo-3,5-dinitrobenzoyl chloride		— (Sw) (129)		— (129)	— (Z) (129)
2-Bromo-4-methyl-3,5-dinitrobenzoyl chloride		— (Sw) (133)		— (133)	— (Z) (133)
o-Methoxybenzazide			— (358)		
m-Methoxybenzoyl chloride		— (Sw) (132)	— (132)	— (132) *	
Anisoyl chloride	— (377)	— (Sw) (132)	— (132)	— (132)	
Anisic ester	95% (378), 75% (135)	95% (378), 75% (379), — (140)	80% (379)	85% (378),* — (140)	

p-Ethoxybenzoic ester	95% (378), 89% (225)	95% (378)	81% (225)	85% (378) * Quant. (225)	— (Ua) (225) *p*-Aminophenol
Veratric methyl ester	93% (279)	74% (379)	Quant. (379)	— (379)	
3,5-Dimethoxybenzoic methyl ester	50% (380)	84% (380)		— (380)	
3,4,5-Trimethoxybenzoic methyl ester	— (332)				
3,4,5-Trimethoxybenzoic ester	— (381)	— (381)			
Hemipinic α-monomethyl ester	33% (382) (Dihydrazide, 3%) (382) Hydrazide acid				
Hemipinic β-monomethyl ester	26% (382) Dihydrazide				
o-Carbethoxyphenoxyacetic ester	95% (58) Dihydrazide	— (58)		— (58)	0% (Ua) (58)
	— (58) *o*-Carbethoxyhydrazide	— (58)	— (58)	— (58)	0% (Ua) (58)
O-(N-Phenylcarbamylmethyl)-salicylyl azide		(58) †		90% (58)	— (Ua) (58) Benzomorpholone
O-Acetylsalicylyl chloride		— (Sw) (226)	— (226)	— (226)	
O-Acetyl-3,5-dibromosalicylyl chloride		96% (Sw) (226)	— (226)	— (226)	— (Ua, Z) (226)
Salicylic ester	86% (383), 73% (135), — (123, 125)	78% (383), — (125)	— (358) *	— (125) *	
Salicylic methyl ester	— (125)				
m-Hydroxybenzoic ester	— (125)	— (125)	— (358) *	— (125) *	

References 268–454 appear on pp. 446–449.
† Prepared from the preceding diazide.

COMPOUNDS SUBJECTED TO THE CURTIUS REACTION—*Continued*

Aromatic Acid Derivatives—*Continued*

Starting Material	Hydrazide	Azide	Isocyanate	Urethan	Amine, etc.
p-Hydroxybenzoic ester	— (125)	Quantitative (125)	— (358) *	— (125) *	
2-Hydroxy-3,5-dibromobenzoyl chloride		— (Sw) (226)	— (226) *		
3-Nitro-5-hydroxybenzazide		(89) †		— (89)	— (Ub) (89)
Gallic ester	— (123)				
Phthalide	— (38, 287, 350)	— (38), 0% (350)	— (38) *		— (Ib) (38)
α-Methylphthalide	0% (384)				
α,α-Dimethylphthalide	0% (384)				
α-Ethylphthalide	0% (384)				
α,α-Diethylphthalide	0% (384)				
α-Phenylphthalide	0% (384)				
α,α-Diphenylphthalide	0% (384)				
5-Nitrophthalide	— (287, 384)				
5-Nitro-α-methylphthalide	— (384)				
5-Nitro-α,α-dimethylphthalide	0% (384)				
5-Nitro-α-ethylphthalide	0% (384)				
5-Nitro-α,α-diethylphthalide	0% (384)				
5-Chlorophthalide	— (384)				
5-Bromophthalide	— (384)				
5-Chloro-α-methylphthalide	— (384)				
5-Bromo-α-methylphthalide	— (384)				
5-Chloro-α-ethylphthalide	0% (384)				

5-Bromo-α-ethylphthalide	0% (384)				
5,6-Dimethoxyphthalide	— (287)				
3-Nitro-5,6-dimethoxyphthalide	Yields 3-nitro-5-methoxy-6-hydrazinophthalide (287)				
Anthranilic ester	80% (135)	65% (189), 0% (90)			
Isatoic acid	75% (90) Anthranilyl hydrazide				
Isatoyl diazide		— (357) ‡		60% (357)	0% (Ub) (357)
N-Acetylanthranilic ester	0% (385, 386)				
N-Acetylanthranilic amide	0% (385)				
N-Acetylanthranilic azlactone	— (385)	— (385)			
N-Oxalylanthranilic azlactone	— (385)				
N-Malonylanthranilic azlactone	— (385)				
N-Anthranilylanthranilic azlactone	— (188)				
N′-Acetyl-N-anthranilylanthranilic azlactone	82% (188)				
m-Aminobenzoic ester	— (125)	— (125)			
p-Aminobenzoic ester	Good (88)	80% (189), — (125)	— (125) *		— (Ia) (125)
N-Methylanthranilic methyl ester	70% (386)				

References 268–454 appear on pp. 446–449.
† Prepared from 3-nitro-5-aminobenzhydrazide.
‡ Prepared from phthalyl chloride.

COMPOUNDS SUBJECTED TO THE CURTIUS REACTION—*Continued*

AROMATIC ACID DERIVATIVES—*Continued*

Starting Material	Hydrazide	Azide	Isocyanate	Urethan	Amine, etc.
N-Methyl-N-acetylanthranilyl hydrazide	(386) †				
o-Carbethoxyphenylglycine	90% (58)	80% (58)		— (58)	0% (Ua) (58)
ester	— (58) *o*-Carbethoxy hydrazide	— (58)		— (58)	0% (Ua) (58)
N-(N′-Phenylcarbamylmethyl)-anthranilyl azide		(58) ‡		— (58) *	
N,N-Dimethylanthranilic methyl ester	— (88)	— (88)		— (88)	
5-Nitroisatoic acid	— (387)	— (387)		— (137)	— (Ub) (137)
2-Nitro-4-aminobenzoic ester	70% (137)	— (137)			
3,Nitro-5-aminobenzhydrazide	(89) §	— (89) 3-Nitro-5-hydroxybenzazide			
3,5-Dinitro-4-anilinobenzoyl chloride		— (Sw) (5)		-- (5) *	
5-Aminophthalide	— (287, 384)				
3-Amino-5,6-dimethoxyphthalide	— (287)				
5-Amino-*α*-methylphthalide	0% (384)				
5-Amino-*α*,*α*-dimethylphthalide	0% (384)				
5-Amino-4,6-dibromo-*α*,*α*-dimethylphthalide	0% (384)				

5-Amino-α,α-diethylphthalide	0% (384)				
5-Amino-4,6-dibromo-α,α-diethylphthalide	0% (384)				
Azobenzene-*m*-carbonyl chloride		90% (Sw) (126)			Quantitative (Ib) (126)
Azobenzene-*p*-carbonyl chloride		Good (Sw) (37)	Good (37)	Good (37)	
o-Sulfamylbenzoic ester	85% (141)	Quantitative (141)	57% (142) *	— (142)	
Saccharin	20% (141) *o*-Sulfamylbenzhydrazide				
Biphenyl-*p*-carbonyl chloride	0% (176)				
Biphenyl-*p*-carboxylic ester	90% (176)				
d and *l*-6-Nitro-2-methylbiphenyl-2′-carbonyl chloride		(Sd)			— (Ib) (251)
Diphenic anhydride	— (52) Diphenic hydrazidic acid	— (66)		— (66) Phenanthridone	
Diphenic ester	55% (66), — (52)	— (66) — (66, 388) Hydrazide azide		— (66) — (66, 388) Phenanthridone	— (Ub) (66), — (Ia, Ub) (388)
l and *dl*-6,6′-Dimethylbiphenyl-2,2′-dicarbonyl chloride		(Sd)			— (Ib) (251)
4-Nitrodiphenic methyl ester	45% (53), — (388)				
4-Nitrodiphenic anhydride	90% (53) Hydrazidic acid	— (53)		— (53) 7-Nitrophenanthridone	
6-Nitrodiphenic methyl ester	85% (388)				

References 268–454 appear on pp. 446–449.
† Prepared from N-methylanthranilyl hydrazide.
‡ Prepared from the preceding diazide.
§ Prepared from 3,5-dinitrobenzoic ester.

COMPOUNDS SUBJECTED TO THE CURTIUS REACTION—*Continued*

AROMATIC ACID DERIVATIVES—*Continued*

Starting Material	Hydrazide	Azide	Isocyanate	Urethan	Amine, etc.
1-2,2′-Dimethoxy-6,6′-dicarbomethoxybiphenyl	— (389)				
α-Naphthoyl chloride (?)	— (377)				
β-Naphthoic ester	75% (365)	94% (390), — (256)		Quant. (390), — (256)	
β-Naphthoic methyl ester	90% (121)				
β-Naphthoyl chloride	— (121)				
4-Methyl-1-naphthoic ester	— (260)			— (260)	— (Ub) (260)
2-Methyl-1-naphthoic ester	0% (260)				
2-Methyl-1-naphthoyl chloride	— (260)			— (260)	— (Ub) (260)
5,8-Dichloro-2-naphthoic methyl ester	85% (248)	98% (248)		80% (248)	— (Z) (248)
5-Bromo-2-naphthoic methyl ester	Quantitative (202)	Quantitative (202)		— (202)	— (Z) (202)
5,8-Dibromo-2-naphthoic ester	Quantitative (202)	Quantitative (202)	— (202)	85% (202)	90% (Z) (202)
3-Iodo-2-naphthoyl chloride	55% (121)	85% (121)		— (121)	85% (Z) (121)
3-Iodo-2-naphthoic ester	Yields β-naphthoyl hydrazide (121)				
3-Methoxy-2-naphthoic methyl ester	94% (259)			72% (259)	93% (Ub), 85% (L) (259), Quant. (Ua) (259) Hydroxy amine
3-Hydroxy-2-naphthoic ester	— (391)	70% (168)	90% (168) *	85% (168)	70% (Ua), 65% (Ib) (168)
3-Amino-2-naphthoic ester	— (91)				

3-Carboxyamino-2-naphthoic anhydride	— (91)	0% (91)			
3-Acetylamino-2-naphthoic azlactone	88% (91)	— (91)	— (91) *		
3-Phenanthroic methyl ester	77% (37)				
9-Phenanthroic ester	90% (203)	Quantitative (203)		80% (203)	— (Ua) (203) 9-Phenanthrol 80% (Z) (203)
3-Methoxy-6-phenanthroic ester	83% (392)			40% (392)	— (Z) (392)
3-Methoxy-9-phenanthroic ester	98% (392)			88% (392)	— (Z) (392)
3-Methoxy-9-phenanthroic ester	— (392)			90% (392)	65% (Z) (392)
3,4-Dimethoxy-8-phenanthroic acid?	— (197)			80% (197)	90% (Z) (197)
3,4-Dimethoxy-9-phenanthroic ester	81% (393)	Good (393)		80% (393)	— (Ub) (393)
2,3,4,5-Tetramethoxy-9-phenanthroic methyl ester	— (332)				
2,3,4,6-Tetramethoxy-9-phenanthroic methyl ester	— (332)				
2,3,4,6-Tetramethoxy-9-phenanthroic ester	76% (198)	77% (198)		82% (198)	95% (Ub) (198)
2,3,4,7-Tetramethoxy-9-phenanthroic methyl ester	— (332)				
Fluoranthene-4-carboxylic ester	— (394)	— (394)		— (394)	— (Ua) (394)
Fluoranthene-12-carboxylic ester	— (394)	Quantitative (394)		95% (394)	Quantitative (Ua) (394)
Pyrene-4-carbonyl chloride	93% (204)				68% (Z) (204)

References 268–454 appear on pp. 446–449.

COMPOUNDS SUBJECTED TO THE CURTIUS REACTION—*Continued*

Aromatic Acid Derivatives—*Continued*

Starting Material	Hydrazide	Azide	Isocyanate	Urethan	Amine, etc.
Pyrene-3,8-dicarbonyl chloride	— (204)				(Z) (204)
Pyrene-3,10-dicarbonyl chloride	— (204)				— (Z) (204)
3,4-Benzpyrene-10-carboxylic methyl ester	— (182)	— (182)			— (Z) (182)
Heterocyclic Acid Derivatives					
Ethyleneimine-2,3-dicarboxylic anhydride (?)	40% (395) Monohydrazide	75% (395)		0% (395)	
N-Carbamylethyleneimine-2,3-dicarboxylic ester (?)	— (395)	— (395)			
Succinimide-N-acetic ester	Yields succinhydrazidylglycyl hydrazide (57)				
2,4-Dimethylpyrrole-5-acetic ester	Quantitative (62)				
2,4-Dimethylpyrrole-3-β-propionic methyl ester	— (60)	0% (60)			
2-Phenylpyrrole-5-β-propionic ester	80% (150), — (396)			— (150)	Poor (Ub) (150)
1-Methyl-2-phenylpyrrole-5-β-propionic methyl ester	84% (397)	85% (397)			57% (Ub) (398)

1,5-Diphenylpyrrole-2-β-propionic ester	97% (397), — (452)	92% (397)			59% (Ub) (398)
2,4-Dimethyl-5-carbethoxypyrrole-3-β-propionic acid	67% (399) Dihydrazide				
2,4-Dimethyl-5-carbethoxypyrrole-3-β-propionic methyl ester	Quantitative (60) Monohydrazide	— (60)	— (60) *	— (60)	— (Ua) (60)
2,4-Dimethyl-3-(β-methylmalonic ester)-pyrrole-5-carboxylic ester	90% (61) Aliphatic dihydrazide	70% (61)		72% (61)	
2,4-Dimethyl-3-(β-cyano-β-carbethoxyethyl)-pyrrole-5-carboxylic ester	90% (61) Aliphatic monohydrazide	150% (61)		72% (61)	
5-Carbethoxypyrrole-3-β-acrylic ester		33% (60) Aliphatic monoazide		Poor (60)	
2,4-Dimethyl-5-carbethoxypyrrole-3-β-acrylic methyl ester	35% (59) Aliphatic monohydrazide	63% (59)		38% (59)	
2,4-Dimethyl-5-carbethoxypyrrole-3-β-acrylic acid	— (60) Hydrazide acid	— (60)			
2-Chloromethyl-4-methyl-5-carbethoxypyrrole-3-acrylyl azide		(59) †			
2-p-Anisylpyrrole-5-β-propionic ester	Quantitative (150)	0% (150)			
2-Methoxymethyl-4-methyl-5-carbethoxypyrrole-3-acrylyl azide		(59) ‡			

References 268–454 appear on pp. 446–449.

† Prepared from the 2-methyl azide.

‡ Prepared from the 2-chloromethyl azide.

COMPOUNDS SUBJECTED TO THE CURTIUS REACTION—*Continued*

HETEROCYCLIC ACID DERIVATIVES—*Continued*

Starting Material	Hydrazide	Azide	Isocyanate	Urethan	Amine, etc.
3-Methyl-4-hydroxypyrrole-4-β-propionic methyl ester	72% (400)	80% (400)		— (400)	
4-Methyl-5-hydroxypyrrole-3-β-propionic methyl ester	93% (400)	80% (400)		— (400)	
Pyrrole-2-carboxylic methyl ester	Quantitative (95)	61% (95)		— (95)	— (Ua), 0% (Ub) (95)
2,4-Dimethylpyrrole-3-carboxylic ester	— (60)	0% (60)			
2,4-Dimethylpyrrole-5-carboxylic ester	98% (60)	Quantitative (60), — (62)		— (60) *	16% (Z) (60)
2,3,4-Trimethylpyrrole-5-carboxylic ester	86% (49)	55% (49)		42% (49) *	
2,3,5-Trimethylpyrrole-4-carboxylic ester	Poor (399)	87% (399)			
2,4-Dimethyl-3-ethylpyrrole-5-carboxylic ester	97% (60)	84% (60)		46% (60),* — (399) *	— (Z) (93)
2,3-Dimethyl-4-ethylpyrrole-5-carboxylic ester	87% (201)	— (201)			
2-Methyl-3,4-diethylpyrrole-1-carboxylic ester	Yields 2-methyl-3,4-diethylpyrrole-5-carbonyl hydrazide (93)				
2-Methyl-3,4-diethylpyrrole-5-carboxylic ester	80% (93)	81% (93)		Quant. (93),* — (49) *	— (Z), 0% (C) (93)

2,4-Dimethyl-3-vinylpyrrole-5-carboxylic ester	Yields 2,4-dimethylpyrrole-5-carbonyl hydrazide (60)				
2,4-Dimethylpyrrole-3,5-dicarboxylic ester	Quantitative (62), — (60), 0% (94)	82% (62)		Quant. (62)	
	— (62) 5-Monohydrazide	Quantitative (62)			
2,4-Dimethylpyrrole-3-carboxylic ester-5-carboxylic acid	0% (62)				
2,4-Dimethylpyrrole-3-carboxylic acid-5-carboxylic ester	Yields 2,4-dimethylpyrrole-5-carbonyl hydrazide (62)				
2,4-Dimethyl-3-cyanopyrrole-5-carboxylic ester	86% (49)	52% (49)		59% (49)	
2-Carbethoxy-3-ethyl-4-methylpyrrole-5-carbonyl azide		(201) †		— (201)	
2-Methyl-4-ethylpyrrole-2,5-dicarboxylic ester	Quantitative (92)	Good (92)	— (201) *	0% (92)	— (Z), 0% (Ia) (201)
2,4-Dimethyl-3-bromopyrrole-5-carbonyl azide		(62) ‡			
2-Carbomethoxy-3-bromo-4-methylpyrrole-5-carbonyl azide		(62) §		66% (62) *	94% (62)
2-Formyl-3-bromo-4-methylpyrrole-5-carbonyl azide		(62) ||		93% (62)	

References 268–454 appear on pp. 446–449.

† Prepared from the 2-methyl azide.
‡ Prepared from the 3-acetyl azide.
§ Prepared from the 2-trichloromethyl azide.
|| Prepared from the 2-dichloromethyl azide.

COMPOUNDS SUBJECTED TO THE CURTIUS REACTION—*Continued*

Heterocyclic Acid Derivatives—*Continued*

Starting Material	Hydrazide	Azide	Isocyanate	Urethan	Amine, etc.
2-Chloromethyl-3,4-dimethylpyrrole-5-carbonyl azide		(49) †			
2-Chloromethyl-3-ethyl-4-methylpyrrole-5-carbonyl azide		(60) †			
2-Bromomethyl-4-methylpyrrole-5-carbonyl hydrazide		— (60) ‡			
2-Bromomethyl-3-ethyl-4-methylpyrrole-5-carbonyl azide		(60) §			
2-Dichloromethyl-3,4-dimethylpyrrole-5-carbonyl azide		(49) §			
2-Dichloromethyl-3-ethyl-4-methylpyrrole-5-carbonyl azide		(60) §			
2-Dichloromethyl-3,4-diethylpyrrole-5-carbonyl azide		(93) §			
3,4-Dichloropyrrole-2,5-dicarboxylic acid	Quantitative (49)	52% (49)			
3,4-Dichloropyrrole-2-carbonyl chloride-5-carboxylic ester	94% (49) Monohydrazide	44% (49), 72% (Sw) (49)		57% (49)	

2-Dichloromethyl-3-bromo-4-methylpyrrole-5-carbonyl azide		(62) §			
2-Trichloromethyl-3-bromo-4-methylpyrrole-5-carbonyl-azide		(62) ‖			
2-Methoxymethyl-3-ethyl-4-methylpyrrole-5-carbonyl azide		(60) ¶			
2-Methoxymethyl-3,4-diethylpyrrole-5-carbonyl azide		(93) ¶			
2-Hydroxy-5-methylpyrrole-4-carboxylic ester	55% (94)	41% (94)		— (94)	0% (Ub) (94)
2-Hydroxy-3,5-dimethylpyrrole-4-carboxylic ester	67% (94)	81% (94)		— (94)	0% (Ub) (94)
2,4-Dimethyl-3-formylpyrrole-5-carbonyl azide		(60, 62) ††		Quant. (62)	58% (C), 0% (Ua) (62)
2-Formyl-3-ethyl-4-methylpyrrole-5-carbonyl azide		(60, 399) ‡‡		58% (399), — (201)	
2-Formyl-3-methyl-4-ethylpyrrole-5-carbonyl azide		(201) ‡‡		79% (201)	
2-Formyl-3,4-diethylpyrrole-5-carbonyl azide		(93) ‡‡		72% (93)	

References 268–454 appear on pp. 446–449.

† Prepared from the 2-methyl azide.

‡ Prepared from the 2-methyl hydrazide.

§ Prepared from the 2-methyl azide.

‖ Prepared from the 2-methyl azide.

¶ Prepared from the 2-chloromethyl azide.

†† Prepared from 2,4-dimethylpyrrole-5-carbonyl azide.

‡‡ Prepared from the 2-dichloromethyl azide.

COMPOUNDS SUBJECTED TO THE CURTIUS REACTION—*Continued*

HETEROCYCLIC ACID DERIVATIVES—*Continued*

Starting Material	Hydrazide	Azide	Isocyanate	Urethan	Amine, etc.
2,4-Dimethyl-3-acetylpyrrole-5-carboxylic ester	80% (62) Hydrazide hydrazone	81% (62) Ketone azide	— (62) *	Quant. (62) *	— (C) (62)
2,4-Dimethyl-5-carbethoxypyrrole-3-ethanoneoxalic ester	0% (94)				
4,4′-Dimethyl-3,3′-diethyl-5,5′-dicarbethoxypyrromethene	— (60)				
3,3′,5,5′-Tetramethyl-4,4′-di-β-propionic ester pyrromethene	— (60)				
4,4′-Dimethyl-3,3′-di-β-methylmalonic ester-5,5′-dicarbethoxypyrromethene	89% (61)	— (61)		— (61)	
Iso-uroporphyrin octamethyl ester	88% (61)	75% (61)			
6-Bromopyrroporphyrin ester	Quantitative (401)				
Indole-3-β-propionic ester	Quantitative (216)	— (216)	77% (216),* — (264) *	— (264)	— (P) (263, 264)
Indole-2-carboxylic methyl ester	— (95)	— (95)		— (95)	0% (Ua, Ub) (95)
5,7-Dinitroindole-2-carboxylic methyl ester	80% (402)	Quantitative (402)		63% (402)	

O-Ethyldinitrostrycholcarboxylic ester	Quantitative (403)	— (403)		48% (403)	
Dinitrostrychnic ester	— (404)	— (404)		— (404)	
Dinitroisostrychnic ester	— (404)				
3,5,7-Trinitroindole-2-carboxylic methyl ester	— (402)	— (402)		— (402)	
Carbazole-9-acetic ester	— (405)	— (405)		— (405)	
Dihydrobrucininic ester	95% (85)	68% (85)		43% (85) Isobrucinolone	
Brucinonic oxime methyl ester	88% (406)	— (406)		— (406)	
Tetrahydrofuran-2-β-propionic ester	— (262)	— (262)		— (262)	— (L) (262)
Tetrahydrofuran-2-ω-pentanol-3,4-dicarboxylic ester	— (407)			— (407)	— (Ub) (407)
Furan-2-β-propionic ester	— (262)			— (262)	— (L) (262)
2-Phenylfuran-5-β-propionic ester	Quantitative (150)			90% (150)	60% (Ub) (150)
2-p-Anisylfuran-5-β-propionic ester	— (150)			— (150)	Poor (Ub) (150)
3,4-Dicarbomethoxyfuran-2-acetic methyl ester	— (408)				
2-Furoyl chloride		92% (Sw) (241) (Sd)	75% (247), 73% (241) Poor (214)		89% (Z) (241)
2-Furoic ester	— (215, 409, 410)	66% (410), — (215, 409)		Quant. (409), Poor (215), — (410)	0% (Ua, Ub) (215, 409), 0% (L) (410)
3-Furoic ester	75% (240)	— (240)	— (240)		

References 268–454 appear on pp. 446–449.

COMPOUNDS SUBJECTED TO THE CURTIUS REACTION—*Continued*

HETEROCYCLIC ACID DERIVATIVES—*Continued*

Starting Material	Hydrazide	Azide	Isocyanate	Urethan	Amine, etc.
5-Methyl-2-furoyl chloride		(Sd)	35% (214)		
5-Methyl-2-furoic ester	— (214)	— (215)		— (214)	
2-Methyl-3-furoic ester	93% (247), 91% (240), — (214)	95% (247), — (214, 240)	— (214, 240, 247)	— (214, 247)	73% (Z) (247), — (240)
2,4-Dimethyl-3-furoic ester	— (214)	— (214)	— (214)	— (214)	
2,5-Dimethyl-3-furoic ester	95% (247), — (214)	96% (247), — (214)	— (214)	— (214)	80% (Z) (247)
Furan-3,4-dicarbonyl chloride		Quant. (Sw) (411)		Good (411)	
2-Methylfuran-3,4-dicarboxylic ester	0% (232)				
2-Methylfuran-3,4-dicarbonyl chloride		(Sw)		77% (232)	
2-(ω-Acetoxyamyl)furan-3,4-dicarbonyl chloride		(Sw)	57% (232)		
Furan-2-ω-valeryl piperidide-3,4-dicarbonyl chloride		(Sw)		46% (232)	
5-Bromo-2-furoic ester	— (214)	— (214)	— (214)	— (214)	
3,4-Dihydroxyfuran-2,5-dicarboxylic methyl ester	91% (412)	60% (412)	— (412) *	Poor (412)	
Benzodihydrofuran-2-carboxylic ester	Good (413)	75% (413)		88% (413)	0% (Ua, Ub) (413)
Benzofuran-2-carboxylic ester	— (414)	— (414)	Quant. (358)	— (414)	0% (Ua, Ub) (414)

Tetrahydrodibenzofuran-3-γ-*n*-butyric ester	— (415)			— (415)	— (Ub) (415)
Dibenzofuran-3-γ-*n*-butyric ester	— (415)			66% (415)	77% (Ub) (415)
Dibenzofuran-3-γ-(γ-oxobutyric acid)	0% (415) Yields a pyrazone				
cis-Tetrahydrothiophene-2,5-dicarboxylic ester	23% (145)			53% (145)	0% (Ua) (145)
Tetrahydrothiophene-3,4-dicarboxylic ester	11% (147)			88% (147)	58% (Ua) (147)
2-Phenylthiophene-5-β-propionic methyl ester	Quantitative (150)			— (150)	60% (Ub) (150)
2-*p*-Anisylthiophene-5-β-propionic methyl ester	Quantitative (150)			80% (150)	60% (Ub) (150)
o-(α-Thienylthio)-benzoyl chloride	65% (144)	— (144) (Sd)	77% (144), 5% (144)		
Thiophene-2-carboxylic ester	91% (149)	93% (149)		60% (149)	0% (Ua) (149)
3-Benzamido-4-carbethoxythiophene-2-ω-valeryl azide	91% (148) Monohydrazide	93% (148)		95% (148)	58% (U) (148)
Biotin ester	— (146)	— (146)		— (146)	— (Ub) (146) Triamine
Pyrazolinedicarboxylic ester	86% (416)				
Pyrazoline-3,4,5-tricarboxylic ester	— (39) — (39) Mixed *pri-sec*-hydrazide	— (39) — (39)		— (39)	0% (Ua) (39)
Pyrazole-3-carboxylic ester (?)	— (415*a*)	— (415*a*)		— (415*a*)	— (Ua, Ub) (415*a*)
Pyrazole-3,5-dicarboxylic ester (?)	— (415*a*)	— (415*a*)		— (415*a*)	— (Ub) (415*a*)

References 268–454 appear on pp. 446–449.

COMPOUNDS SUBJECTED TO THE CURTIUS REACTION—*Continued*

Heterocyclic Acid Derivatives—*Continued*

Starting Material	Hydrazide	Azide	Isocyanate	Urethan	Amine, etc.
Pyrazole-3,4,5-tricarboxylic ester	— (39) — (39) Mixed *pri-sec*-hydrazide	— (39) 67% (39)		— (39) 77% (39)	0% (Ua) (39) 0% (Ua) (39)
4-Isonitrosopyrazolone-3-carboxylic ester	— (87) Hydrazone hydrazide				
Imidazole-5-acetic ester	80% (195)				35% (Ua) (195)
Imidazole-4-β-propionic ester	— (196)				55% (Ua) (196)
Imidazole-4-carboxylic ester	Quantitative (417)	Quantitative (417)		50% (417)	
Imidazolone-4,5-dicarbonyl hydrazide	(395) †				
Isoxazole-5-carboxamide	84% (418)	49% (418)		53% (418)	0% (Ua) (418)
5-Methylisoxazole-3-carboxylic methyl ester	80% (418)	Quantitative (418)		83% (418)	65% (Ua) (418) 2-Benzoyl-5-methylisoxazolone-3
4-Methylthiazole-5-acetic ester	81% (151)				
bis (2-Phenylthiazolyl-4-methyl) acetic ester	75% (152)	80% (152)		70% (152)	60% (P) (152)
2-Phenylthiazole-4-β-propionic ester	80% (152)	90% (152)	85% (152) *	66% (F) (152)	
2-*p*-Anisylthiazole-4-β-propionic ester	95% (153)	94% (153)		97% (153) *	68% (P) (153)
2-(3,4-Dimethoxyphenyl)-thiazole-4-β-propionic ester	94% (153)	90% (153)		90% (153) *	38% (P) (153)

2,4-Dimethylthiazole-5-carboxylic ester	84% (418*a*)			60% (418*a*)	32% (Ua) (418*a*)
1-Benzyl-4,5-dihydrotriazole-4,5-dicarboxylic ester	73% (301)	— (301)			
4,5-Dicarbethoxy-4,5-dihydro-triazole-1-acetic ester	62% (419)				
4-Hydroxytriazole-3-acethydrazide	— (115) ‡				
5-Hydroxytriazole-1-aceturyl hydrazide	(154) §				
1-Phenyltriazole-5-carboxylic ester	— (209)	— (209)		Quant. (209)	— (Ub), 0% (Ua) (209)
2-Phenyltriazole-4,5-dicarboxylic methyl ester	60% (416)				
1-Benzyltriazole-4,5-dicarboxylic ester	— (301)	— (301)			
1-*p*-Methylbenzyltriazole-4,5-dicarboxylic methyl ester	80% (68)	92% (68) Azide isocyanate		21% (68) Azide *sym*-urea	
Triazole-1,4,5-tricarboxylic methyl ester	90% (419)				
4,5-Dicarbomethoxytriazole-1-acetic methyl ester	92% (419)				
4,5-Dicarbamyltriazole-1-acetic methyl ester	— (419)				
4,5-Dicarbomethoxytriazole-1-α-propionic methyl ester	— (419)				

References 268–454 appear on pp. 446–449.

† Prepared from N-carbamylethyleneimine-2,3-dicarboxylic ester.

‡ Prepared from diazoaceturic ester.

§ Prepared from diazoaceturylglycine ester.

COMPOUNDS SUBJECTED TO THE CURTIUS REACTION—*Continued*

HETEROCYCLIC ACID DERIVATIVES—*Continued*

Starting Material	Hydrazide	Azide	Isocyanate	Urethan	Amine, etc.
4,5-Dicarbomethoxytriazole-1-β-propionic methyl ester	— (419)	— (419)			
Picolinic ester	Quantitative (420)			36% (420)	— (Ua) (420)
Nicotinic ester	Quantitative (421)	— (421)		— (421)	— (Ua) (421)
Nicotinamide	53% (422)	— (422)			
Isonicotinic ester	— (420)	Poor (420)			
6-Methylnicotinic ester	97% (96)	70% (96)			93% (Ub) (96), 21% (Z) (96)
4-Chloropicolinic methyl ester	89% (120)				99% (Z) (120), — (Ua, Ub) (120)
4-Chloropicolinyl chloride		0% (Sd) (120)			
2,6-Dichloroisonicotinic methyl ester	— (106)	— (106)		— (106)	91% (Ub) (106)
4,6-Dichloropicolinic methyl ester	— (257)	— (257)		— (257)	— (Z) (257), — (Ua) (257) 4-Chloro-6-iodo-2-aminopyridine
5,6-Dichloronicotinic ester	— (118), 5-Chloro-6-hydrazinonicotinyl hydrazide				
5-Bromonicotinic methyl ester	— (118)	— (118)		— (118)	— (Ub) (118)
5-Bromonicotinyl chloride	0% (118)				
4-Iodopicolinic methyl ester	— (120)	— (120)		— (120)	— (Ua, Z) (120)

2,4-Dihydroxy-6-chloronicotinamide	— (119), 2,4-Dihydroxy-6-hydrazinonicotinyl hydrazide				
2,6-Diaminoisonicotinic methyl ester	— (106)	0% (106)			
2,6-Dibenzamidoisonicotinic methyl ester	— (106), 2,5-Diaminoisonicotinyl hydrazide				
2-Hydrazino-6-chloroisonicotinyl hydrazide	— (106) †				
2,4-Dihydroxy-6-hydrazinonicotinyl hydrazide	— (119) ‡				
Quinolinic methyl ester	— (420)				
Quinolinic anhydride	0% (55)				
Pyridine-2,4-dicarboxylic methyl ester	— (253)	— (253)		— (253)	70% (Ub) (253)
Pyridine-2,5-dicarboxylic methyl ester	— (69)	— (69)		— (69) Also azide urethan	— (Ua) (69)
Pyridine-2,6-dicarboxylic methyl ester	— (420)	— (420)		— (420)	Good (Ub) (420), Poor (Ua) (420)
Cinchomeronic methyl ester	— (253), — (55, 420) Monohydrazide	— (253)		— (253)	— (Ub) (253)
2,6-Dimethylpyridine-3,5-dicarboxylic ester	85% (423)	84% (423)			48% (Ua) (423)

References 268–454 appear on pp. 446–449.

† Prepared from 2,6-dichloroisonicotinic methyl ester.

‡ Prepared from 2,4-dihydroxy-6-chloronicotinamide.

COMPOUNDS SUBJECTED TO THE CURTIUS REACTION—*Continued*

Heterocyclic Acid Derivatives—*Continued*

Starting Material	Hydrazide	Azide	Isocyanate	Urethan	Amine, etc.
4-Phenylazopyridine-2,6-dicarboxylic methyl ester	93% (156)	— (156)		57% (156)	93% (Ub) (156)
β-2-Quinolylpropionic ester	Quantitative (199)	0% (199)			
2-Phenylquinoline-4-β-propionic methyl ester	97% (427)			82% (427)	90% (Ua) (427)
6,7-Dimethoxyquinaldine-4-β-propionic methyl ester	88% (217)	82% (217)		76% (217) (428)	80% (Ua), — (F) (217)
Cinchoninic ester	86% (424)	— (425)		92% (425)	91% (U) (425)
Quinaldine-3-carboxylic ester	— (426)	— (426)		— (426)	
2-Phenylcinchoninic ester	99% (429)	88% (429)	91% (429)	94% (429)	Quantitative (Ua), — (Ib) (429)
2-Phenylcinchoninyl chloride	94% (430)				
2-Phenylcinchoninyl chloride hydrochloride	— (431)				
2-*p*-Tolylcinchoninic ester	97% (432)	95% (432)	93% (432)	84% (432)	Quantitative (Ua), 78% (Ib) (432)
2-Phenyl-3-methylcinchoninic ester	0% (433)				
2-Phenyl-3-methylcinchoninyl chloride	97% (433)	94% (433)		96% (433) *	
2-Phenyl-6-methylcinchoninic ester	Quantitative (434)	94% (434)	Quant. (434)	66% (434)	Quantitative (Ua), 56% (Ia) (434)

2-Phenyl-8-methylcinchoninic ester	— (434)	94% (434)	— (434)	— (434)	77% (Ua) (434)
2-Chlorocinchoninic ester	— (424) 2-Hydrazinocinchoninyl hydrazide				
2-*p*-Bromophenylcinchoninic ester	— (435)	— (435)		— (435)	— (Ua) (435)
2-Phenyl-6-bromocinchoninic ester	— (435)	— (435)		— (435)	— (Ua) (435)
6-Methoxycinchoninic ester	98% (436)	94% (436)	95% (436)	Quant. (436)	74% (Ua), 0% (Ib) (436)
6-Methoxyquinoline-8-carboxylic ester	— (437)	— (437)		— (437)	— (L) (437)
6-Ethoxyquinoline-8-carbonyl azide					— (Z) (438)
2-Phenyl-6-methoxycinchoninic ester	87% (439)	Quantitative (439)	99% (439)	74% (439)	Quantitative (Ua), 96% (Ib) (439)
2-Phenyl-6-ethoxycinchoninic ester	Quantitative (252)	93% (252)	99% (252)	57% (252)	92% (Ib), 84% (Ua) (252)
6-Hydroxycinchoninic ester	97% (440)	83% (440)	Quant. (440) *	86% (440)	86% (Ua), 78% (Ib) (440)
2-Phenyl-6-hydroxycinchoninic ester	99% (441)	— (441)		85% (441)	96% (Ua) (441)
2-Hydrazinocinchoninyl hydrazide	— (424) †				
Acridine-9-propionic ester	— (194)			— (194)	— (Ua) (194)
Acridine-10-butadiene-$\alpha,\beta,\gamma,\delta$-tetracarboxylic methyl ester	— (442)				

References 268–454 appear on pp. 446–449.

† Prepared from 2-chlorocinchoninic ester.

COMPOUNDS SUBJECTED TO THE CURTIUS REACTION—*Continued*

HETEROCYCLIC ACID DERIVATIVES—*Continued*

Starting Material	Hydrazide	Azide	Isocyanate	Urethan	Amine, etc.
Acridine-9-carboxylic ester	— (443)	— (443)			
3,4-Dihydro-1,2-naphthacridine-14-carbonyl chloride	91% (444)		85% (444)	63% (444)	Quant. (Ua), 56% (Ib) (444)
Benzo[*f*]quinoline-1-carboxylic methyl ester	23% (445)	Quantitative (445)			78% (Z) (445)
5,6-Dihydro-5,6-dichlorobenzo[*f*]quinoline-5-carboxylic methyl ester	82% (445) Preceding hydrazide				
Lysergic amides (e.g., ergotamine)	70% (185)	Good (185)			
Dihydrolysergic amides	— (446)				
Chitenin ester	92% (447)			95% (447)	
Pyrazine-2,5-dicarbonyl chloride		0% (Sd) (229)			
Pyrazine-2,5-dicarboxylic methyl ester	97% (229)	90% (229)	79% (229)	84% (229)	— (Ua, Ub, Ia), 0% (Ib) (229)
4,5-Benzpyrazine-3-carboxylic ester	80% (448)	— (448)		60% (448)	75% (Ua) (448)
Uracil-5-acetic ester	97% (143)	— (143)	91% (143)	Good (143)	— (Ua) (143)

2-Methyl-4-hydroxypyrimidine-5-acetic ester	85% (449)			98% (449)	Quantitative (Ua) (449)
2-Ethylmercapto-6-hydroxypyrimidine-5-acetic ester	96% (143)	57% (143)	Quant. (143) *	84% (143)	— (Ua) (143) Uracil-5-methylamine
Quinoxaline-2-pyruvic ester	72% (450) Hydrazone hydrazide				
Quinoxaline-3-carboxylic ester	— (451)				
Dihydrotetrazine-3,6-dicarboxylic ester	99% (63) Monohydrazide	27% (63) Tetrazinedicarbonyl ester azide, *q.v.*			
	— (63) Dihydrazide	— (63)			
Tetrazine-3,6-dicarbonyl ester azide		See preceding compound		— (63)	0% (Ua) (63)
Indoxazene-3-carbonyl chloride		— (Sw) (3)			— (Z) (3) (207)
Indoxazene-3-carboxylic ester	— (207)	— (207)			
6-Chloroindoxazene-3-carboxylic ester	— (207)	— (207)			— (Z) (207)
6-Nitroindoxazene-3-carboxylic methyl ester	— (249)	— (249)			— (Z) (249)
6-Acetamidoindoxazene-3-carboxylic ester	— (207)	— (207)		— (207)	— (Z) (207)

References 268–454 appear on pp. 446–449.

REFERENCES FOR TABLE

[268] Curtius and Hofmann, *J. prakt. Chem.*, **53**, 513 (1896)
[269] Stollé, *J. prakt. Chem.*, **69**, 145 (1904).
[270] Stollé and Zinsser, *J. prakt. Chem.*, **69**, 486 (1904).
[271] Curtius, Sieber, Nadenheim, Hambsch, and Ritter, *J. prakt. Chem.*, **125**, 152 (1930)
[272] Stollé and Gutmann, *J. prakt. Chem.*, **69**, 497 (1904).
[273] Stollé and Hille, *J. prakt. Chem.*, **69**, 481 (1904).
[274] Spiegel and Spiegel, *Ber.*, **40**, 1733 (1907).
[275] Curtius and Schwan, *J. prakt. Chem.*, **51**, 353 (1895).
[276] Blaise and Luttringer, *Bull. soc. chim.*, [3] **33**, 1095 (1905).
[277] Blaise and Luttringer, *Compt. rend.*, **140**, 790 (1905).
[278] Darapsky, Berger, and Neuhaus, *J. prakt. Chem.*, **147**, 145 (1936)
[279] Blaise and Luttringer, *Bull. soc. chim.*, [3] **33**, 816 (1905).
[280] van Marle, *Rec. trav. chim.*, **39**, 549 (1920).
[281] Kiliani, *Ber.*, **55**, 2817 (1922); **58**, 2361 (1925).
[282] Curtius and Levy, *J. prakt. Chem.*, **70**, 89 (1904)
[283] Curtius, *Ber.*, **35**, 3226 (1902).
[284] Curtius, *Ber.*, **27**, 778 (1894).
[285] Curtius, Hallaway, and Heil, *J. prakt. Chem.*, **89**, 481 (1914).
[286] Bülow and Weidlich, *Ber.*, **39**, 3372 (1906).
[287] Blanksma and Bakels, *Rec. trav. chim.*, **58**, 497 (1939).
[288] Blanksma and de Graf, *Rec. trav. chim.*, **57**, 3 (1938); thesis, Leiden, 1930 [*C A.*, **24**, 5723 (1930)].
[289] Turner and Hartman, *J. Am. Chem. Soc.*, **47**, 2044 (1925).
[290] Curtius and Cäsar, *J. prakt. Chem.*, **94**, 299 (1916).
[291] Curtius and Rechnitz, *J. prakt. Chem.*, **94**, 309 (1916).
[292] Bülow and Bozenhardt, *Ber.*, **42**, 4801 (1909).
[293] Fischer and Brauns, *Ber.*, **47**, 3181 (1914).
[294] Traube and Lehmann, *Ber.*, **34**, 1975 (1901).
[295] Kesting, *Ber.*, **57**, 1321 (1924).
[296] Franzen and Schmitt, *Ber.*, **58**, 222 (1925).
[297] Franzen and Ostertag, *Z. physiol. Chem.*, **119**, 150 (1922).
[298] Curtius and Burkhardt, *J. prakt. Chem.*, **58**, 205 (1898).
[299] Kerp and Unger, *Ber.*, **30**, 585 (1897).
[300] Sah and Han, *Science Repts. Natl. Tsing Hua Univ.*, A**3**, 469 (1936) [*C. A.*, **31**, 3825 (1937)].
[301] Curtius and Raschig, *J. prakt. Chem.*, **125**, 466 (1930).
[302] Dickey and Straley, U. S. pat., 2,360,210 (to Eastman Kodak Company); [*C. A.*, **39**, 946 (1945)].
[303] Curtius, von Brüning, and Derlon, *J. prakt. Chem.*, **125**, 63 (1930).
[304] Curtius and Clemm, *Ber.*, **29**, 1166 (1896).
[305] Curtius and Steller, *J. prakt. Chem.*, **62**, 212 (1900).
[306] Ruzicka and Stoll, *Helv. Chim. Acta*, **10**, 691 (1927).
[307] Frankland and Slator, *J. Chem. Soc.*, **83**, 1363 (1903).
[308] Nagel and Mertens, *Ber.*, **72**, 985 (1939).
[309] Curtius and Hoffmann, *J. prakt. Chem.*, **96**, 202 (1918).
[310] Curtius and Hechtenberg, *J. prakt. Chem.*, **105**, 319 (1923).
[311] Curtius and Hartmann, *Ber.*, **45**, 1050 (1912).
[312] Curtius and Hesse, *J. prakt. Chem.*, **62**, 232 (1900).
[313] Curtius and Thiemann, *J. prakt. Chem.*, **94**, 364 (1916).
[314] Muckerman, *J. prakt. Chem.*, **83**, 513 (1911).
[315] Ruhemann, *Ber.*, **27**, 1661 (1894).
[316] Oskerko, *Mem. Inst. Ukrain. Acad. Sci.*, **3**, 577 (1936) [*C. A.*, **31**, 7844 (1937)].
[317] Vogelesang, *Rec. trav. chim.*, **62**, 5 (1943) [*C. A.*, **39**, 1393 (1945)].

[318] Stollé, Nieland, and Merkle, *J. prakt. Chem.*, **117**, 185 (1927).
[319] Hurd and Spence, *J. Am. Chem. Soc.*, **49**, 266 (1927).
[320] Stollé, *Ber.*, **43**, 2468 (1910).
[321] Stollé and Krauch, *Ber.*, **47**, 728 (1914).
[322] Stollé and Merkle, *J. prakt. Chem.*, **119**, 275 (1928).
[323] Buchman, Reims, Skei, and Schlatter, *J. Am. Chem. Soc.*, **64**, 2696 (1942).
[324] Diels, Blom, and Koll, *Ann.*, **443**, 246, 257 (1925).
[325] Skita and Rössler, *Ber.*, **72**, 461 (1939).
[326] Alder, Stein, Rolland, and Schulze, *Ann.*, **514**, 211 (1934).
[327] Alder and Windemuth, *Ber.*, **71**, 1956 (1938).
[328] Vanghelovici, *Bul. Soc. Chim. România*, **19A**, 35 (1937) [*C. A.*, **33**, 639 (1939)].
[329] Bondi and Müller, *Z. physiol. Chem.*, **47**, 499 (1906).
[330] Windaus, Schramme, and Jensen, *Ber.*, **57**, 1875 (1924).
[331] Windaus and Eickel, *Ber.*, **57**, 1871 (1924).
[332] Cook, Graham, Cohen, Lapsley, and Lawrence, *J. Chem. Soc.*, **1944**, 322.
[333] Aggarwal, Khera, and Rây, *J. Chem. Soc.*, **1930**, 2354.
[334] Curtius and Jordan, *J. prakt. Chem.*, **64**, 297 (1901).
[335] Sah and Kao, *Science Repts. Natl. Tsing Hua Univ.*, A**3**, 525 (1936) [*C. A.*, **31**, 3889 (1937)].
[336] Darapsky, *J. prakt. Chem.*, **96**, 321 (1917).
[337] Sah and Tseu, *J. Chinese Chem. Soc.*, **5**, 134 (1937).
[338] Jansen, *Rec. trav. chim.*, **50**, 291 (1931).
[339] Barger and Ewins, *J. Chem. Soc.*, **97**, 2253 (1910).
[340] Manske and Holmes, *J. Am. Chem. Soc.*, **67**, 95 (1945).
[341] Bernstein and Whitmore, *J. Am. Chem. Soc.*, **61**, 1324 (1939).
[342] Jones and Wallis, *J. Am. Chem. Soc.*, **48**, 169 (1926).
[343] Wallis, *J. Am. Chem. Soc.*, **51**, 2982 (1929).
[344] Mayer and Schnecko, *Ber.*, **56**, 1408 (1923).
[345] Stuart and Mosettig, *J. Am. Chem. Soc.*, **62**, 1110 (1940).
[346] van de Kamp, Burger, and Mosettig, *J. Am. Chem. Soc.*, **60**, 1321 (1938).
[347] Curtius and Marangolo, *J. prakt. Chem.*, **94**, 331 (1916).
[348] Curtius and Kenngott, *J. prakt. Chem.*, **107**, 99 (1924).
[349] Stoermer, *Ann.*, **313**, 86 (1900).
[350] Wedel, *Ber.*, **33**, 766 (1900).
[351] Curtius and Müller, *Ber.*, **34**, 2794 (1901).
[352] Schroeter, *Frdl.*, **10**, 1309 (1910–12).
[353] Darapsky and Berger, *J. prakt. Chem.*, **147**, 161 (1936).
[354] Borsche and Hahn, *Ann.*, **537**, 236 (1939).
[355] Kindlmann, *Oesterr. Chem. Ztg.*, **42**, 15 (1939) [*C. A.*, **33**, 6275 (1939)].
[356] Stollé and Stevens, *J. prakt. Chem.*, **69**, 366 (1904).
[357] Darapsky and Gaudian, *J. prakt. Chem.*, **147**, 43 (1936).
[358] Stoermer, *Ber.*, **42**, 3133 (1909).
[359] Schiemann and Baumgarten, *Ber.*, **70**, 1416 (1937).
[360] Curtius and Foerster, *J. prakt. Chem.*, **64**, 324 (1901).
[361] Sah and Wu, *Science Repts. Natl. Tsing Hua Univ.*, A**3**, 443 (1936) [*C. A.*, **30**, 8148 (1936)].
[362] Sah and Wu, *J. Chinese Chem. Soc.*, **4**, 513 (1936) [*C. A.*, **31**, 3891 (1937)].
[363] Kao, Fang, and Sah, *J. Chinese Chem. Soc.*, **3**, 137 (1935) [*C. A.*, **29**, 6172 (1935)].
[364] Kao, *Science Repts. Natl. Tsing Hua Univ.*, A**3**, 555 (1936) [*C. A.*, **31**, 3825 (1937)].
[365] Chen and Sah, *J. Chinese Chem. Soc.*, **4**, 62 (1936); Kao, Tao, Kao, and Sah, *ibid.*, **4**, 69 (1936) [*C. A.*, **30**, 8074 (1936)].
[366] Sah and Chang, *Rec. trav. chim.*, **58**, 8 (1939).
[367] Wang, Kao, Kao, and Sah, *Science Repts. Natl. Tsing Hua Univ.*, A**3**, 279 (1935) [*C. A.*, **30**, 2875 (1936)].
[368] Sah, Kao, and Wang, *J. Chinese Chem. Soc.*, **4**, 193 (1936).
[369] Sah and Hsü, *Rec. trav. chim.*, **59**, 349 (1940).

[370] Sah and Young, *Rec. trav. chim.*, **59,** 357, 364 (1940) [*C. A.*, **35,** 4363 (1941)].
[371] Sah, *Rec. trav. chim.*, **59,** 231, 248 (1940).
[372] Sah and Woo, *Rec. trav. chim.*, **58,** 1013 (1939).
[373] Chen, *J. Chinese Chem. Soc.*, **3,** 251 (1935).
[374] Sah and Chiao, *Rec. trav. chim.*, **58,** 595 (1939).
[375] Sah, *Rec. trav. chim.*, **58,** 582 (1939).
[376] Vasilevskii, Bloshtein, and Kustrya, *J. Gen. Chem.* (*U.S.S.R.*), **5,** 1652 (1935) [*C. A.*, **30,** 3416 (1936)].
[377] Stollé and Bambach, *J. prakt. Chem.*, **74,** 13 (1906).
[378] Sah and Chang, *Ber.*, **69,** 2762 (1936).
[379] Brunner and Wöhrl, *Monatsh.*, **63,** 374 (1933).
[380] Seka and Fuchs, *Monatsh.*, **57,** 63 (1931).
[381] Pepe, *J. prakt. Chem.*, **126,** 241 (1930).
[382] Wegscheider and Rušnov, *Monatsh.*, **24,** 378 (1903).
[383] Bondi, *Z. physiol. Chem.*, **52,** 170 (1907).
[384] Teppema, *Rec. trav. chim.*, **42,** 30 (1923).
[385] Heller, *Ber.*, **48,** 1183 (1915).
[386] Heller, Göring, Kloss, and Köhler, *J. prakt. Chem.*, **111,** 36 (1925).
[387] Kratz, *J. prakt. Chem.*, **53,** 210 (1896).
[388] Labriola and Felitte, *Anales asoc. quím. argentina*, **32,** 57 (1944) [*C. A.*, **39,** 1405 (1945)].
[389] Hsing and Adams, *J. Am. Chem. Soc.*, **58,** 587 (1936).
[390] Sah, *J. Chinese Chem. Soc.*, **5,** 100 (1937) [*C. A.*, **31,** 4655 (1937)].
[391] Franzen and Eichler, *J. prakt. Chem.*, **78,** 164 (1908).
[392] Burger and Mosettig, *J. Am. Chem. Soc.*, **56,** 1745 (1934).
[393] Knorr and Hörlein, *Ber.*, **40,** 2040 (1907).
[394] von Braun, Manz, and Kratz, *Ann.*, **496,** 170 (1932).
[395] Curtius and Dörr, *J. prakt. Chem.*, **125,** 425 (1930).
[396] Blicke, Warzynski, Faust, and Gearien, *J. Am. Chem. Soc.*, **66,** 1675 (1944).
[397] Blicke, Faust, Warzynski, and Gearien, *J. Am. Chem. Soc.*, **67,** 205 (1945).
[398] Blicke, Gearien, Warzynski, and Faust, *J. Am. Chem. Soc.*, **67,** 240 (1945).
[399] Metzger and Fischer, *Ann.*, **527,** 1 (1937).
[400] Fischer and Plieninger, *Z. physiol. Chem.*, **274,** 231 (1942) [*C. A.*, **38,** 1231 (1944)].
[401] Fischer and Dietl, *Ann.*, **547,** 86 (1941).
[402] Menon and Robinson, *J. Chem. Soc.*, **1931,** 773.
[403] Menon, Perkin, and Robinson, *J. Chem. Soc.*, **1930,** 830.
[404] Siddiqui, *Proc. Indian Acad. Sci.*, **11A,** 268 (1940) [*C. A.*, **34,** 6295 (1940)].
[405] Seka, *Ber.*, **57,** 1527 (1924).
[406] Leuchs and Gladkorn, *Ber.*, **56,** 1780 (1923).
[407] Hofmann, *J. Am. Chem. Soc.*, **66,** 157 (1944).
[408] Archer and Pratt, *J. Am. Chem. Soc.*, **66,** 1656 (1944).
[409] Freundler, *Bull. soc. chim.*, [3] **17,** 419 (1897).
[410] Marquis, *Ann. chim.*, [8] **4,** 196, 283 (1905).
[411] Stork, *J. Am. Chem. Soc.*, **67,** 884 (1945).
[412] Darapsky and Stauber, *J. prakt. Chem.*, **146,** 209 (1936).
[413] Stoermer and König, *Ber.*, **39,** 492 (1906).
[414] Stoermer and Calov, *Ber.*, **34,** 770 (1901).
[415] Mayer and Krieger, *Ber.*, **55,** 1659 (1922).
[415a] Knorr, *Ber.*, **37,** 3520 (1904).
[416] Seka and Preissecker, *Monatsh.*, **57,** 71 (1931).
[417] Balaban, *J. Chem. Soc.*, **1930,** 268.
[418] Freri, *Gazz. chim. ital.*, **62,** 459 (1932) [*C. A.*, **26,** 5952 (1932)].
[418a] Jensen and Hansen, *Dansk. Tids. Farm.*, **17,** 189 (1943) [*C. A.*, **39,** 2058 (1945)].
[419] Curtius and Klavehn, *J. prakt. Chem.*, **125,** 498 (1930).
[420] Meyer and Mally, *Monatsh.*, **33,** 393 (1912).
[421] Curtius and Mohr, *Ber.*, **31,** 2494 (1898).

[422] Fox and Field, *J. Biol. Chem.*, **147,** 651 (1943).
[423] Mohr, *Ber.*, **33,** 1114 (1900).
[424] Thielepape, *Ber.*, **55,** 127 (1922).
[425] Bydówna, *Roczniki Chem.*, **12,** 89 (1932) [*C. A.*, **27,** 298 (1933)].
[426] Borsche, Doeller, and Wagner-Roemmich, *Ber.*, **76,** 1099 (1943) [*C. A.*, **38,** 4947 (1944)].
[427] John and Grossmann, *Ber.*, **58,** 2799 (1925).
[428] Robinson and Tomlinson, *J. Chem. Soc.*, **1934,** 1524.
[429] John, Grossmann, and Fischl, *Ber.*, **59,** 1447 (1926).
[430] John and Ottawa, *J. prakt. Chem.*, **133,** 13 (1932).
[431] Hübner, *Ber.*, **39,** 982 (1906).
[432] John, *J. prakt. Chem.*, **131,** 314 (1931).
[433] John and Ottawa, *J. prakt. Chem.*, **131,** 301 (1931).
[434] John and Schmit, *J. prakt. Chem.*, **132,** 15 (1932).
[435] Feist and Kuklinski, *Arch. Pharm.*, **274,** 244 (1936) [*C. A.*, **30,** 4863 (1936)].
[436] John and Andraschko, *J. prakt. Chem.*, **128,** 180 (1930).
[437] I. G. Farbenindustrie, Ger. pat., 492,250 [*Frdl.* **16,** 2682 (1931)].
[438] I. G. Farbenindustrie, Swiss pat., 148,955 [*Chem. Zentr.*, **1932** I, 2239].
[439] John and Lukas, *J. prakt. Chem.*, **130,** 314 (1931).
[440] John and Andraschko, *J. prakt. Chem.*, **128,** 201 (1930).
[441] John and Lukas, *J. prakt. Chem.*, **130,** 304 (1931).
[442] Diels and Thiele, *Ann.*, **543,** 79 (1939).
[443] Eisleb, *Med. u. Chem. Abhandl. med.-chem. Forschungsstätten I. G. Farbenind.*, **3,** 41 (1936) [*C. A.*, **31,** 5804 (1937)].
[444] John and Schmit, *J. prakt. Chem.*, **133,** 187 (1932).
[445] Barnum and Hamilton, *J. Am. Chem. Soc.*, **64,** 540 (1942).
[446] Sandoz Ltd., Belg. pat., 445,225 (1942) [*C. A.*, **39,** 532 (1945)].
[447] John and Andraschko, *J. prakt. Chem.*, **128,** 223 (1930).
[448] Darapsky and Heinrichs, *J. prakt. Chem.*, **146,** 307 (1936).
[449] Todd, Bergel, Fraenkel-Conrat, and Jacob, *J. Chem. Soc.*, **1936,** 1601.
[450] Borsche and Doeller, *Ann.*, **537,** 44 (1939).
[451] Piutti and Marini, *Gazz. chim. ital.*, **66,** 270 (1936).
[452] Holdsworth and Lions, *J. Proc. Roy. Soc. N. S. Wales*, **70,** 431 (1937) [*C. A.*, **31,** 6653 (1937)].
[453] Mohunta and Rây, *J. Chem. Soc.*, **1934,** 1263.
[454] Bergmann and Fruton, *J. Biol. Chem.*, **117,** 189 (1937).
[455] Newman, *J. Am. Chem. Soc.*, **57,** 732 (1935).

INDEX

Numbers in bold-face type refer to experimental procedures

Middlesex Community College Library
Middletown, CT 06457
A2100 043408 7